ATOMIC MASSES OF THE ELEMENTS

Name	Symbol	Atomic Number	Atomic Mass[a]	Name	Symbol	Atomic Number	Atomic Mass[a]
Actinium	Ac	89	(227)	Neodymium	Nd	60	144.2
Aluminum	Al	13	26.98	Neon	Ne	10	20.18
Americium	Am	95	(243)	Neptunium	Np	93	(237)
Antimony	Sb	51	121.8	Nickel	Ni	28	58.69
Argon	Ar	18	39.95	Niobium	Nb	41	92.91
Arsenic	As	33	74.92	Nitrogen	N	7	14.01
Astatine	At	85	(210)	Nobelium		102	(259)
Barium	Ba	56	137.3	Osmium		76	190.2
Berkelium	Bk	97	(247)			8	16.00
Beryllium	Be	4	9.012			5	106.4
Bismuth	Bi	83	209.0				30.97
Bohrium	Bh	107	(264)			78	195.1
Boron	B	5	10.81			94	(244)
Bromine	Br	35	79.90	P	Po	84	(209)
Cadmium	Cd	48	112.4	Po...m	K	19	39.10
Calcium	Ca	20	40.08	Praseodymium	Pr	59	140.9
Californium	Cf	98	(251)	Promethium	Pm	61	(145)
Carbon	C	6	12.01	Protactinium	Pa	91	231.0
Cerium	Ce	58	140.1	Radium	Ra	88	(226)
Cesium	Cs	55	132.9	Radon	Rn	86	(222)
Chlorine	Cl	17	35.45	Rhenium	Re	75	186.2
Chromium	Cr	24	52.00	Rhodium	Rh	45	102.9
Cobalt	Co	27	58.93	Roentgenium	Rg	111	(272)
Copper	Cu	29	63.55	Rubidium	Rb	37	85.47
Curium	Cm	96	(247)	Ruthenium	Ru	44	101.1
Darmstadtium	Ds	110	(271)	Rutherfordium	Rf	104	(261)
Dubnium	Db	105	(262)	Samarium	Sm	62	150.4
Dysprosium	Dy	66	162.5	Scandium	Sc	21	44.96
Einsteinium	Es	99	(252)	Seaborgium	Sg	106	(266)
Erbium	Er	68	167.3	Selenium	Se	34	78.96
Europium	Eu	63	152.0	Silicon	Si	14	28.09
Fermium	Fm	100	(257)	Silver	Ag	47	107.9
Fluorine	F	9	19.00	Sodium	Na	11	22.99
Francium	Fr	87	(223)	Strontium	Sr	38	87.62
Gadolinium	Gd	64	157.3	Sulfur	S	16	32.07
Gallium	Ga	31	69.72	Tantalum	Ta	73	180.9
Germanium	Ge	32	72.64	Technetium	Tc	43	(98)
Gold	Au	79	197.0	Tellurium	Te	52	127.6
Hafnium	Hf	72	178.5	Terbium	Tb	65	158.9
Hassium	Hs	108	(269)	Thallium	Tl	81	204.4
Helium	He	2	4.003	Thorium	Th	90	232.0
Holmium	Ho	67	164.9	Thulium	Tm	69	168.9
Hydrogen	H	1	1.008	Tin	Sn	50	118.7
Indium	In	49	114.8	Titanium	Ti	22	47.87
Iodine	I	53	126.9	Tungsten	W	74	183.8
Iridium	Ir	77	192.2	Uranium	U	92	238.0
Iron	Fe	26	55.85	Vanadium	V	23	50.94
Krypton	Kr	36	83.80	Xenon	Xe	54	131.3
Lanthanum	La	57	138.9	Ytterbium	Yb	70	173.0
Lawrencium	Lr	103	(260)	Yttrium	Y	39	88.91
Lead	Pb	82	207.2	Zinc	Zn	30	65.41
Lithium	Li	3	6.941	Zirconium	Zr	40	91.22
Lutetium	Lu	71	175.0	—	—	112	(285)
Magnesium	Mg	12	24.31	—	—	113	(284)
Manganese	Mn	25	54.94	—	—	114	(289)
Meitnerium	Mt	109	(268)	—	—	115	(288)
Mendelevium	Md	101	(258)	—	—	116	(292)
Mercury	Hg	80	200.6	—	—	118	(293)
Molybdenum	Mo	42	95.94				

[a]Values in parentheses are the mass number of the most stable isotope.

Improve Your Understanding!

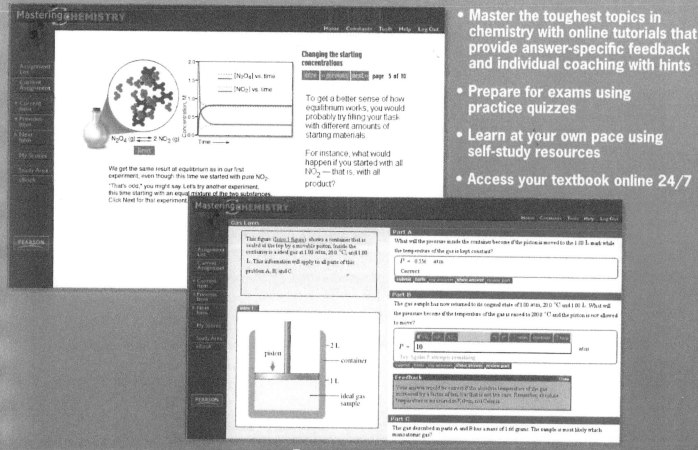

GENERAL, ORGANIC, AND BIOLOGICAL
CHEMISTRY

Structures of Life
Volume 1
KAREN C. TIMBERLAKE

GEORGIA PERIMETER COLLEGE EDITION
CHEM 1151

Taken from:
General, Organic, and Biological Chemistry: Structures of Life, Third Edition
by Karen C. Timberlake

Custom Publishing

New York Boston San Francisco
London Toronto Sydney Tokyo Singapore Madrid
Mexico City Munich Paris Cape Town Hong Kong Montreal

Cover credit: Courtesy of Photodisc/Getty Images.

Taken from:

General, Organic, and Biological Chemistry: Structures of Life, Third Edition
by Karen C. Timberlake
Copyright © 2010 by Pearson Education, Inc.
Published by Prentice Hall
A Pearson Education Company
Upper Saddle River, New Jersey 07458

This special edition published in cooperation with Pearson Custom Publishing.

Printed in the United States of America

10 9 8 7

2009180021

DM

Pearson
Custom Publishing
is a division of

www.pearsonhighered.com

ISBN 10: 0-558-33160-2
ISBN 13: 978-0-558-33160-3

BRIEF CONTENTS

CONTENTS

3

Atoms and Elements   95

4

Nuclear Chemistry   138

5

Compounds and Their Bonds   168

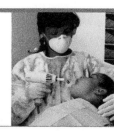

6

Chemical Reactions and Quantities   210

7

Gases   261

8

Solutions   295

9
Chemical
Equilibrium   336

10
Acids
and Bases   371

APPLICATIONS AND ACTIVITIES

ENVIRONMENTAL NOTE

GREEN CHEMISTRY NOTE

GUIDE TO PROBLEM SOLVING

ABOUT THE AUTHOR

Karen Timberlake is Professor Emerita of chemistry at Los Angeles Valley College, where she taught chemistry for allied health and preparatory chemistry for 36 years. She received her bachelor's degree in chemistry from the University of Washington and her master's degree in biochemistry from the University of California at Los Angeles.

Professor Timberlake has been writing chemistry textbooks for 33 years. During that time, her name has become associated with the strategic use of pedagogical tools that promote student success in chemistry and the application of chemistry to real-life situations. More than one million students have learned chemistry using texts, laboratory manuals, and study guides written by Karen Timberlake. In addition to *General, Organic, and Biological Chemistry: Structures of Life*, third edition, she is also the author of *Basic Chemistry*, second edition, and *Chemistry: An Introduction to General, Organic, and Biological Chemistry*, tenth edition with the accompanying *Study Guide, Selected Solutions Manual, Laboratory Manual*, and *Essential Laboratory Manual*.

Professor Timberlake belongs to numerous science and educational organizations including the American Chemical Society (ACS) and the National Science Teachers Association (NSTA). She was the Western Regional Winner of Excellence in College Chemistry Teaching Award given by Chemical Manufacturers Association. In 2004, she received the McGuffey Award in Physical Sciences from the Text and Academic Authors Association for her textbook *Chemistry: An Introduction to General, Organic, and Biological Chemistry*, eighth edition, which has demonstrated excellence over time. In 2006, she received the Textbook Excellence Award for the first edition of *Basic Chemistry*. She has participated in education grants for science teaching including the Los Angeles Collaborative for Teaching Excellence (LACTE) and a Title III grant at her college. She speaks at conferences and educational meetings on the use of student-centered teaching methods in chemistry to promote learning success of students.

Her husband, Bill, is also a chemistry professor and has contributed to writing this text. He taught preparatory and organic chemistry at Los Angeles Harbor College for 36 years. When the professors Timberlake are not writing textbooks, they relax by hiking, traveling, trying new restaurants, cooking, and playing tennis.

PREFACE

To the Student

Welcome to the third edition of *General, Organic, and Biological Chemistry: Structures of Life.* This chemistry text was written and designed to help you prepare for a career in a health-related profession, such as nursing, dietetics, respiratory therapy, and environmental and agricultural science. My main objective in writing this text is to make the study of chemistry an engaging and positive experience for you by relating the structure and behavior of matter to its functions in health and life. This new edition introduces rich problem-solving strategies, including new concept checks, more problem-solving guides, conceptual and challenge problems, and new sets of combined problems.

It is also my goal to help you become a critical thinker by connecting the scientific concepts with current issues concerning health and the environment. Thus, I have utilized materials that

- motivate you to learn and enjoy chemistry;
- relate chemistry to careers that interest you;
- develop problem-solving skills that lead to your success in your chemistry course; and
- promote learning and your success in your chosen career.

I hope that this textbook helps you discover exciting new ideas and gives you a rewarding experience as you develop an understanding and appreciation of the role of chemistry in your life.

Features of this Text

You may wonder why your career path includes a class in chemistry. A common view is that chemistry is just a lot of facts to be memorized. To change this perception, I have included many features to help you learn about chemistry in your life and career choice and to give you the skills to learn chemistry successfully. These features include connections to health, the environment, and green chemistry, visual guides to problem solving, and in-chapter problem sets to work immediately that reinforce the learning of new concepts. A successful learning program in this text provides you with many learning tools, which are discussed here.

Career Focus and Real-World Applications

This Text Was Designed to Help Students Attain Their Career Goals

Chapter Opening Interviews with Scientists and Health Care Professionals Each chapter begins with an interview with a professional in a career such as nursing, forensic anthropology, nuclear medicine, dentistry, and oceanography. These professionals discuss the importance of chemistry in their careers.

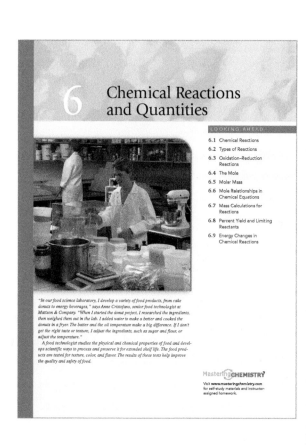

CAREER FOCUS

Occupational Therapist

"Occupational therapists teach children and adults the skills they need for the job of living," says occupational therapist Leslie Wakasa. "When working with the pediatric population, we are crucial in educating children with disabilities, their families, caregivers, and school staff in ways to help them be as independent as they can be in all aspects of their daily lives. It's rewarding when you can show children how to feed themselves, which is a huge self-esteem issue for them. The opportunity to help people become more independent is very rewarding."

A combination of technology and occupational therapy helps children who are nonverbal to communicate and interact with their environment. By leaning on a red switch, Alex is learning to use a computer.

Career Focus   Within the chapters are additional interviews with allied health professionals using chemistry.

On the Web   The **MasteringChemistry Study Area** features in-depth resources for each of the health professions featured in the book and takes students through interactive case studies.

Students Will Learn Chemistry Using Real-World Examples

NEW Green Chemistry Notes   The new **Green Chemistry Notes** highlight the practical applications of chemistry that are beneficial to human health and the environment. The new green chemistry approach that chemists, engineers, scientists, health professionals, and researchers are taking focuses on practices and products that are "benign by design" and that provide sustainability.

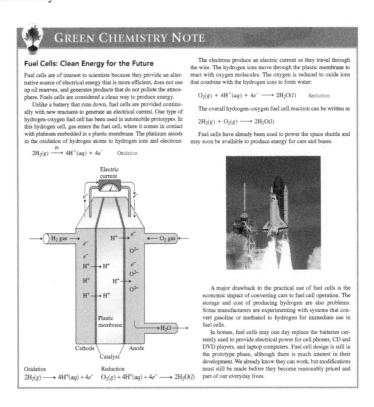

GREEN CHEMISTRY NOTE

Fuel Cells: Clean Energy for the Future

Fuel cells are of interest to scientists because they provide an alternative source of electrical energy that is more efficient, does not use up oil reserves, and generates products that do not pollute the atmosphere. Fuels cells are considered a clean way to produce energy.

Unlike a battery that runs down, fuel cells are provided continually with new reactants to generate an electrical current. One type of hydrogen–oxygen fuel cell has been used in automobile prototypes. In this hydrogen cell, gas enters the fuel cell, where it comes in contact with platinum embedded in a plastic membrane. The platinum assists in the oxidation of hydrogen atoms to hydrogen ions and electrons:

$$2H_2(g) \xrightarrow{Pt} 4H^+(aq) + 4e^- \quad \text{Oxidation}$$

The electrons produce an electric current as they travel through the wire. The hydrogen ions move through the plastic membrane to react with oxygen molecules. The oxygen is reduced to oxide ions that combine with the hydrogen ions to form water:

$$O_2(g) + 4H^+(aq) + 4e^- \longrightarrow 2H_2O(l) \quad \text{Reduction}$$

The overall hydrogen–oxygen fuel cell reaction can be written as

$$2H_2(g) + O_2(g) \longrightarrow 2H_2O(l)$$

Fuel cells have already been used to power the space shuttle and may soon be available to produce energy for cars and buses.

A major drawback to the practical use of fuel cells is the economic impact of converting cars to fuel cell operation. The storage and cost of producing hydrogen are also problems. Some manufacturers are experimenting with systems that convert gasoline or methanol to hydrogen for immediate use in fuel cells.

In homes, fuel cells may one day replace the batteries currently used to provide electrical power for cell phones, CD and DVD players, and laptop computers. Fuel cell design is still in the prototype phase, although there is much interest in their development. We already know they can work, but modifications must still be made before they become reasonably priced and part of our everyday lives.

Oxidation $\quad$ Reduction
$$2H_2(g) \longrightarrow 4H^+(aq) + 4e^- \quad O_2(g) + 4H^+(aq) + 4e^- \longrightarrow 2H_2O(l)$$

ENVIRONMENTAL NOTE

Plastics

Terephthalic acid (an acid with two carboxyl groups) is produced in large quantities for the manufacture of polyesters such as Dacron and plastics.

When terephthalic acid reacts with ethylene glycol, ester bonds can form on both ends of the molecules, allowing many molecules to combine until they have formed a long polymer known as a *polyester*:

A section of the polyester Dacron

Dacron polyester is used to make permanent press fabrics, carpets, and clothes. In medicine, artificial blood vessels and valves are made of Dacron, which is biologically inert and does not clot the blood. The polyester can also be made as a film called Mylar and as a plastic known as PETE (polyethyleneterephthalate). PETE is used for plastic soft drink bottles as well as for containers of salad dressings, shampoos, and dishwashing liquids.

Today PETE (recycling symbol "1") is the most widely recycled of all the plastics. In 1992, there were 365 million pounds (166 million kilograms) of PETE recycled. After it is separated from other plastics, PETE can be changed into other useful items, including polyester fabric for T-shirts and coats, fill for sleeping bags, doormats, and containers for tennis balls.

Environmental Notes   **Environmental Notes** throughout the text relate chemistry to real-life topics in science and medicine that are interesting and motivating and support the role of chemistry in the real world. They delve into issues such as global warming, biodiesel fuels, radon, acid rain, pheromones, ozone depletion, and toxicity of mercury.

HEALTH NOTE

Hot Packs and Cold Packs

In a hospital, at a first-aid station, or at an athletic event, an instant *cold pack* may be used to reduce swelling from an injury, remove heat from inflammation, or decrease capillary size to lessen the effect of hemorrhaging. Inside the plastic container of a cold pack, there is a compartment containing solid ammonium nitrate (NH_4NO_3) that is separated from a compartment containing water. The pack is activated when it is hit or squeezed hard enough to break the walls between the compartments and cause the ammonium nitrate to mix with the water (shown as H_2O over the reaction arrow). In an endothermic process, each gram of NH_4NO_3 that dissolves absorbs 79 cal of heat from the water. The temperature drops and the pack becomes cold and ready to use.

Endothermic Reaction in a Cold Pack

$$6.2 \text{ kcal} + NH_4NO_3(s) \xrightarrow{H_2O} NH_4NO_3(aq)$$

Hot packs are used to relax muscles, lessen aches and cramps, and increase circulation by expanding capillary size. Constructed in the same way as cold packs, a hot pack may contain the salt $CaCl_2$. The dissolving of the salt in water is exothermic and releases 160 cal per gram of salt. The temperature rises and the pack becomes hot and ready to use.

Exothermic Reaction in a Hot Pack

$$CaCl_2(s) \xrightarrow{H_2O} CaCl_2(aq) + 18 \text{ kcal}$$

Health Notes   The many **Health Notes** in each chapter apply chemical concepts to relevant topics of health and medicine. These topics include weight loss and weight gain, artificial fats, sweeteners, anabolic steroids, alcohol, genetic diseases, viruses, and cancer.

EXPLORE YOUR WORLD

Using Gumdrops and Toothpicks to Model Chiral Objects

Part 1: Achiral Objects

Obtain some toothpicks and several orange, yellow, green, purple, and black gumdrops. Place four toothpicks into the black gumdrop, making the ends of toothpicks form a tetrahedron. Attach gumdrops to the toothpicks: two orange, one green, and one yellow.

Using another black gumdrop, make a second model that is the mirror image of the original model. Now rotate one of the models, and try to superimpose it on the other model. Are the models superimposable? If achiral objects have superimposable mirror images, are these models chiral or achiral?

Part 2: Chiral Objects

Using one of the original models, replace one orange gumdrop with a purple gumdrop. Now there are four different colors of gumdrops attached to the black gumdrop. Make its mirror image by replacing one orange gumdrop with a purple one. Now rotate one of the models, and try to superimpose it on the other model. Are the models superimposable? If chiral objects have nonsuperimposable mirror images, are these models chiral or achiral?

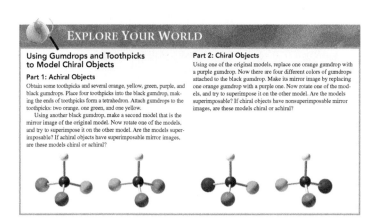

Explore Your World   **Explore Your World** contains hands-on activities that use everyday materials to encourage students to actively explore selected chemistry topics, either individually or in group-learning environments. Each activity is followed by questions to encourage critical thinking.

Student-Friendly Approach

Keeping Students Engaged Is the Ultimate Goal

Student-Friendly Writing Style   To enhance student understanding, I try to use an accessible writing style, based on a carefully paced and simple development of chemical ideas, suited to the background of allied health students. All terms are precisely defined, and clear goals are set for each section of the text. Clear analogies help students visualize and understand key chemical concepts.

Learning Goals   At the beginning of each section, a **Learning Goal** clearly identifies the key concept of the section, providing a roadmap for studying. All information contained in that section relates back to the Learning Goal. The Learning Goals for each section are also repeated in the Chapter Review so students can make sure they have mastered the key concepts.

NEW Concept Checks   The many **Concept Checks** throughout each chapter allow students to check their understanding of new concepts. The many new Concept Checks give students an opportunity to focus on their understanding of newly introduced chemical terms and ideas.

Concept Maps   Each chapter ends with a **Concept Map** that reviews the key concepts of each chapter and how they fit together.

6.1 Chemical Reactions

As we discussed in Chapter 2, a *chemical change* occurs when a substance is converted into one or more new substances. For example, when silver tarnishes, the shiny silver metal (Ag) reacts with sulfur (S) to become the dull, black substance we call *tarnish* (Ag_2S). (See Figure 6.1.)

LEARNING GOAL
Write a balanced chemical equation from the formulas of the reactants and products for a chemical reaction.

CONCEPT CHECK 6.4

■ Moles and Particles

Explain why 0.20 mole of aluminum is a small number, but the number of atoms in 0.20 mole is a large number: 1.2×10^{23} atoms of aluminum.

ANSWER
The term *mole* is used as a collection term that represents 6.02×10^{23} particles. Because atoms are submicroscopic particles, a large number of atoms are in 1 mole of aluminum.

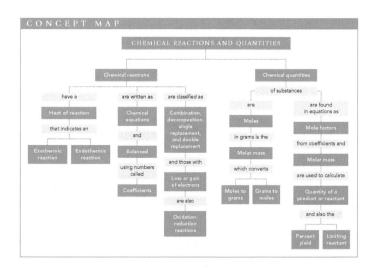

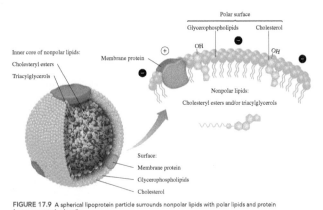

FIGURE 17.9 A spherical lipoprotein particle surrounds nonpolar lipids with polar lipids and protein for transport to body cells.
Q Why are the polar components on the surface of a lipoprotein particle and the nonpolar components at the center?

Clear Illustrations Help Students Visualize Chemistry

The **art program** is not only beautifully rendered, but pedagogically effective as well.

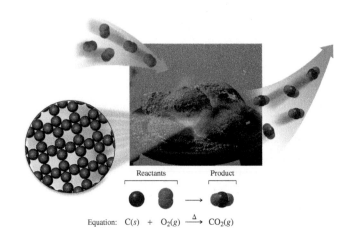

Equation: $C(s) + O_2(g) \xrightarrow{\Delta} CO_2(g)$

Macro-to-Micro Art

Macro-to-Micro Art   **Macro-to-micro art** portrays the atomic structure of recognizable objects, putting chemistry in context and connecting the atomic world to the macroscopic world. A question with each figure challenges students to think critically about photos and illustrations. Many new photos expand visual connections.

Problem Solving

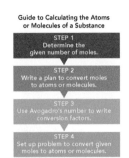

Guide to Calculating the Atoms or Molecules of a Substance

STEP 1
Determine the given number of moles.

STEP 2
Write a plan to convert moles to atoms or molecules.

STEP 3
Use Avogadro's number to write conversion factors.

STEP 4
Set up problem to convert given moles to atoms or molecules.

Many Tools Show Students How to Solve Problems

A Visual Guide to Problem Solving   As part of a comprehensive learning program, the **Guides to Problem Solving** (GPS) illustrate the steps students need to solve problems. I clearly understand the learning challenges facing students in this course, so I walk students through the problem-solving process step by step. For each type of problem, I use a unique, color-coded flow chart that is coordinated with parallel worked examples as a visual guide for each problem-solving strategy.

Sample Problems with Study Checks   Numerous **Sample Problems** appear throughout the text to demonstrate the application of each new concept. The worked-out solutions give step-by-step explanations, provide a problem-solving model, and illustrate required calculations. Each Sample Problem is followed by a **Study Check** question that allows students to test their understanding of the problem-solving strategy.

Integrated Questions and Problems   **Questions and Problems** at the end of each section encourage students to apply concepts and begin problem solving after each section. **Paired Problems** of each even-numbered problem with a matching odd-numbered problem guide students through solving problems. **Answers** to odd-numbered problems are given at the end of each chapter.

End-of-Chapter Questions and Problems   **Understanding the Concepts** questions encourage students to think about the concepts they have learned. **Additional Questions and Problems** integrate the topics from the entire chapter to promote understanding and critical thinking. **Challenge Questions** are designed for group work in cooperative learning environments.

SAMPLE PROBLEM   6.5

■ **Calculating the Atoms of an Element**

How many carbon atoms are present in 1.50 moles of aspirin, $C_9H_8O_4$?

SOLUTION

STEP 1   **Given** 1.50 moles of $C_9H_8O_4$ **Need** carbon atoms

STEP 2   **Plan**

Moles of $C_9H_8O_4$ Subscript   moles of C atoms   Avogadro's number   C atoms

STEP 3   **Equalities/Conversion Factors**

1 mole of $C_9H_8O_4$ = 9 moles of C atoms

$$\dfrac{9 \text{ moles C}}{1 \text{ mole } C_9H_8O_4} \quad \text{and} \quad \dfrac{1 \text{ mole } C_9H_8O_4}{9 \text{ moles C}}$$

1 mole of C atoms = 6.02×10^{23} C atoms

$$\dfrac{1 \text{ mole C atoms}}{6.02 \times 10^{23} \text{ C atoms}} \quad \text{and} \quad \dfrac{6.02 \times 10^{23} \text{ C atoms}}{1 \text{ mole C atoms}}$$

STEP 4   **Set Up Problem**   The conversion factors of the subscript and Avogadro's number can be combined to calculate the number of atoms of C from moles of $C_9H_8O_4$.

$$1.50 \text{ moles } C_9H_8O_4 \times \dfrac{9 \text{ moles C}}{1 \text{ mole } C_9H_8O_4} \times \dfrac{6.02 \times 10^{23} \text{ C atoms}}{1 \text{ mole C atoms}} = 8.13 \times 10^{24} \text{ C atoms}$$

STUDY CHECK

How many moles of aspirin, $C_9H_8O_4$, contain 0.480 mole of O atoms?

NEW Combining Ideas Problem Sets   This **new feature** appears after every 2–4 chapters as a set of integrated problems designed to test students' cumulative understanding of the previous chapters.

The Most Advanced Chemistry Homework and Tutorial System

www.masteringchemistry.com

MasteringChemistry™ is the most advanced chemistry homework and tutorial system available. This online homework and tutoring system uses the Socratic Method to coach students through problem-solving techniques, offering hints and simpler questions on request. It tutors students individually with feedback specific to their errors. MasteringChemistry helps students learn, not just practice. (See the MasteringChemistry insert at the front of the book.)

Instructional Package

General, Organic, and Biological Chemistry: Structures of Life, third edition, is the nucleus of an integrated teaching and learning package of support material for both students and professors.

For Students

Study Guide   for *General, Organic, and Biological Chemistry*, third edition, by Karen Timberlake, is keyed to the learning goals in the text and designed to promote active learning through a variety of exercises with answers as well as practice tests. (ISBN 0321587553)

Selected Solutions Manual   for *General, Organic, and Biological Chemistry*, third edition, by Karen Timberlake, contains the complete solutions to the odd-numbered problems. (ISBN 0321616634)

Laboratory Manual for General, Organic, and Biological Chemistry   by Karen Timberlake. This best-selling lab manual coordinates 42 experiments with the topics in *General, Organic, and Biological Chemistry*, third edition; uses new terms during the lab; and explores chemical concepts. Laboratory investigations develop skills of manipulating equipment, reporting data, solving problems, making calculations, and drawing conclusions. (ISBN 0805349049)

Essential Laboratory Manual   by Karen Timberlake. This manual contains 25 experiments for the standard course sequence of topics in *General, Organic, and Biological Chemistry*, third edition. (ISBN 0805330232)

For Instructors

Instructor Resource Center on CD/DVD   This CD/DVD includes all the art and tables from the book in JPG format for use in classroom projection or creating study materials and tests. In addition, the instructor can access the PowerPoint™ lecture outlines, featuring over 2000 slides. Also available on the discs are downloadable files of the *Instructor Manual*, a set of "clicker questions" suitable for use with classroom-response systems, and the test bank. (ISBN 0321587561)

Transparency Pack   Contains 300 full-color transparency acetates. (ISBN 032158757X)

Instructor Solutions Manual   Prepared by Kathy Thrush Shaginaw and Karen Timberlake, this manual highlights chapter topics and includes suggestions for the laboratory. Contains complete solution setups and answers to all problems in the text. (ISBN 0321587596)

Printed Test Bank   Prepared by Kathy Thrush Shaginaw, Lynn Carlson, and Bill Timberlake, this test bank contains over 2000 questions in multiple-choice, matching, true-false, and short-answer format. (ISBN 0321587588)

Online Instructor Manual for Laboratory Manual   Contains answers to report pages for the Laboratory Manual and Essential Laboratory Manual. (ISBN 0321499670)

Course Management: Blackboard and WebCT   course management systems provide powerful course management capability. All of the content available in the Mastering-Chemistry Study Area is also available in **WebCT** and **Blackboard**. Pearson Prentice Hall offers content cartridges for these text-specific Classroom Management Systems. Visit **http://www.pearsonhighered.com** or contact your Prentice Hall sales representative for details.

Also visit the Prentice Hall catalog page for Timberlake's *General, Organic, and Biological Chemistry*, third edition, at **www.pearsonhighered.com** to download available instructor supplements.

New to This Edition

New features have been added throughout this third edition, including the following:

- A new Prologue introduces chemistry, the scientific method, and a study plan for learning chemistry.
- New Concept Checks with Answers build conceptual understanding.
- More Guides to Problem Solving (GPS) illustrate step-by-step problem-solving strategies.
- New Green Chemistry Notes include "Biodiesel as an Alternative Fuel," "Greenhouse Gases," and "Energy-Saving Light Bulbs."
- New Health Note "Brachytherapy" has been added.
- New Career interviews include Geologist and Conservator of Photographs.
- New molecular models in problem sets improve visual understanding of chemical reactions.
- New photos and updated diagrams improve clarity and provide visual connections to real life.
- New units of measurement include parts per million (ppm) and parts per billion (ppb).
- New Sample Problems and Study Checks model problem-solving strategies.
- New Understanding the Concepts problems add more visual examples to conceptual learning.
- New inter-chapter Combining Ideas problem sets provide problems with greater depth using concepts from several chapters.

Chapter Organization

Throughout this text, the structures of compounds and organic and biochemical molecules are related to their function. The discussion of bonding and shapes of molecules in Chapter 5 provides a foundation for understanding the structure of organic and biochemical molecules. The topic of stereochemistry and chiral organic molecules in Chapter 14 is revisited as an important concept in the understanding of structures of carbohydrates, amino acids, and chiral drugs.

The structures of molecules are related to their physical and chemical properties such as solubility in water, density, and boiling point. The structural levels of proteins are related to their function, while chemical processes that denature proteins emphasize the importance of structure to activity. Throughout the text, the atomic structure of matter is highlighted by macro-to-micro art that relates the atomic level to the macroscopic structures of real-life materials. In this way, the chemical concepts and structures of molecules are continuously related to the behavior and function of biomolecules in the body.

In each textbook I write, I consider it essential to relate every chemical concept to real-life issues of health and environment. In this text, I have added the theme of Structures of Life. All the material usually found in appendices has been integrated with the appropriate chapter material so that there are no longer any appendices at the end of the book. Because a course of chemistry for allied health may be taught in different time frames, it may be difficult to cover all the chapters in this text. However, each chapter is a complete package, which allows some chapters to be skipped or the order of presentation to be changed.

Prologue

The **Prologue**, a new feature, introduces students to the concepts of chemicals and chemistry, discusses the scientific method, and asks students to develop a study plan for learning chemistry. A *Health Note*, "Early Chemists: The Alchemists," was added.

Chapters 1 and 2

Chapter 1, "Measurements," looks at measurement and the need to understand numerical structures of the metric system in the sciences. The section on *Scientific Notation* is now a separate section. Items added include *peta* prefix to Metric and SI Prefixes, and parts per million (ppm) and parts per billion (ppb) to percentage conversion factors.

- A new feature called *Green Chemistry Note* discusses "Toxicology and Risk-Benefit Assessment."
- *Health Note*, "Bone Density," has been rewritten to discuss changes in bone density with age.
- New *Guides to Problem Solving*, "Calculating Density" and "Using Density," use color blocks as visual guides in the step-by-step solution pathway.
- The discussion of "Temperature" has been moved to Chapter 2.

Chapter 2, "Energy and Matter," now combines temperature, physical and chemical changes, energy, and matter into a single chapter that discusses energy and heat, nutritional energy values, temperature conversions, states of matter, and energy involved in changes of state. New energy problems use the SI unit of the joule (J).

- *Green Chemistry Note* updates the content of "Carbon Dioxide and Global Warming."
- New macro-to-micro art emphasizes the atomic level for changes of state.
- Many *Sample Problems* were reworked to utilize the Guide to Problem Solving strategy.

- New to this edition is an inter-chapter problem set, *Combining Ideas from Chapters 1 and 2.*

Chapters 3 and 4

Chapter 3, "Atoms and Elements," looks at elements, atoms, subatomic particles, and atomic mass. *The Periodic Table* emphasizes the numbering of groups from 1–18. Elements with atomic numbers 116 and 118 were added.

- New items include a discussion of the discovery of electrons by J. J. Thomson using the cathode ray tube. The calculation of the average atomic mass of an element uses percent abundance and isotope mass.
- Section 3.8, *Periodic Trends*, discusses periodic properties of elements including valence electrons, atomic size, and ionization energy.
- A new *Green Chemistry Note*, "Energy-Saving Lightbulbs," has been added.

Chapter 4, "Nuclear Chemistry," extends the concepts of subatomic particles, atomic number, and atomic mass to a discussion of radioisotopes including the positron. Nuclear equations are written and balanced for both naturally occurring and artificially produced radioactivity. The topic of biological effects of radiation is now part of the chapter content.

- Tables of radioisotopes were expanded.
- New *Health Note*, "Brachytherapy," was added.
- Update on "Radon in Our Homes."
- The half-lives of radioisotopes are discussed, and the amount of time for a sample to decay is calculated.
- Radioisotopes that are important in the field of nuclear medicine are emphasized.

Chapters 5 and 6

Chapter 5, "Compounds and Their Bonds," describes how atoms form ionic and covalent bonds in compounds. Chemical formulas are written, and ionic compounds—including those with polyatomic ions—and covalent compounds are named. An introduction to the three-dimensional shape of molecules provides a basis for the shape of organic and biochemical compounds. The discussion of polyatomic ions, which includes more polyatomic ions, follows the formation of ionic compounds. The concept of resonance is discussed for the electron-dot formulas for compounds with multiple bonds.

- New items include a discussion on the sizes of ions compared to the sizes of their corresponding atoms.
- New questions use the electron-dot formulas or electron configurations to determine chemical formulas and names. Electronegativity leads to a discussion of the polarity of bonds and molecules.
- The section *Attractive Forces in Compounds* now appears in Chapter 5.

Chapter 6, "Chemical Reactions and Quantities," includes the quantitative aspects of reactions such as the mole and molar mass (which are used in calculations of the number of particles in a quantity) and mass calculations in reactions. Equations for chemical reactions are balanced and organized into combination, decomposition, single replacement, and double replacement reactions.

- Section 6.3, *Oxidation–Reduction Reactions*, was rewritten to include oxidation–reduction in biological systems.
- A new *Green Chemistry Note*, "Fuel Cells: Clean Energy for the Future," has been added.
- Mole and mass relationships among the reactants and products are examined along with calculations of percent yield and limiting reactants.
- The material on limiting reactants has been expanded to give more examples.
- Section 6.9, *Energy Changes in Chemical Reactions*, is now included with Chapter 6.
- New to this edition is an inter-chapter problem set, *Combining Ideas from Chapters 3 to 6*.

Chapters 7 and 8

Chapter 7, "Gases," discusses the properties of a gas and calculates changes in gases using the gas laws.

- New art was added on gas pressure at different altitudes.
- The chapter includes calculations of the amount of a gas required or produced in a chemical reaction.
- New items include predicting changes in gas variables, a *Guide to Problem Solving*, "Using Molar Volume," and a *Summary* of Gas Laws.
- A new *Green Chemistry Note*, "Greenhouse Gases," on the types and sources of greenhouse gases has been added.

Chapter 8, "Solutions," describes solutions, electrolytes, saturation and solubility, concentrations, osmosis, and dialysis. The volumes and molarities of solutions are used to calculate product quantities in chemical reactions.

- The topics of dilution and titration were updated and new problems on concentrations and dilution were added.
- New items include Table 8.3, *Possible Combinations of Solutes and Solvents*, and Section 8.6, *Physical Properties of Solutions*, which discusses the impact of solution particles on the lowering of freezing points and the elevation of boiling points.
- The material on electrolytes and nonelectrolytes, saturation, and osmosis has been rewritten and new questions added.

Chapters 9 and 10

Chapter 9, "Chemical Equilibrium," looks at the rates of reactions and the equilibrium condition when forward and reverse

rates for a reaction become equal. Equilibrium expressions for reactions are written and equilibrium constants are calculated. Le Châtelier's principle is used to evaluate the impact on concentrations when a stress is placed on the system.

- A new Section 9.6, *Equilibrium in Saturated Solutions*, and a new Guide to Problem Solving, "Guide to Calculating K_{sp}," have been added.

Chapter 10, "Acids and Bases," discusses acids and bases and their strengths; conjugate acid–base pairs; pH; and buffers. Section 10.1, *Acids and Bases*, now includes Brønsted–Lowry Acids and Bases.

- The acids HCN, $HClO$, and $HClO_4$ have been added to Table 10.1, *Naming Common Acids*.
- A *Green Chemistry Note*, "Acid Rain," updates the topic of acid rain.
- New problems related to acid rain have been added. Acid–base titration uses the neutralization reaction between an acid and a base to calculate quantities of an acid in a sample.
- The chapter includes discussions of strengths of acids and bases, their dissociation constants, acid–base properties of salt solutions, and buffers.
- New to this edition is an inter-chapter problem set, *Combining Ideas from Chapters 7 to 10*.

Chapter 11, 12, and 13

Chapter 11, "Introduction to Organic Chemistry: Alkanes," discusses the structure, nomenclature, and reactions of alkanes. Guides to Problem Solving (GPS) clarify the rules for nomenclature. An overview of functional groups and isomers describes the structure of organic chemistry and forms a basis for understanding the biomolecules of living systems.

- The subsection *Halogenation of Alkanes (Substitution)* was deleted.
- The *Health Note* "Toxicity of Carbon Monoxide" describes the products of incomplete combustion and their toxicity.
- A new *Career Focus*, "Geologist," has been added.

Chapter 12, "Alkenes, Alkynes, and Aromatic Compounds," discusses alkenes and alkynes, cis–trans isomers, addition reactions, polymers of alkenes used in everyday items, and aromatic compounds.

- Section 12.2, *Cis–Trans Isomers*, has been rewritten for clarity.
- An *Explore Your World* feature, "Modeling Cis–Trans Isomers," now asks students to model cis and trans isomers using gumdrops and toothpicks.
- The discussion of addition reactions hydrogenation, halogenation, hydrohalogenation, and hydration illustrates reactions important in biological systems.
- The *Career Focus* "Laboratory Technologist" is now included in this chapter.

Chapter 13, "Alcohols, Phenols, Ethers, and Thiols," discusses structures, names, properties, and reactions of alcohols, phenols, thiols, and ethers.

- The *Health Note* "Some Important Alcohols and Phenols" now includes a discussion of bisphenol A (BPA).
- Section 13.3, *Physical Properties of Alcohols, Phenols, and Ethers*, was rewritten for clarity.
- The *Health Note* "Oxidation of Methanol" is now titled "Methanol Poisoning."
- The *Health Note* "Oxidation of Alcohol in the Body" has been updated to include current methods of determining blood alcohol.

Chapters 14 and 15

Chapter 14, "Aldehydes, Ketones, and Chiral Molecules," discusses the nomenclature and structures of aldehydes and ketones.

- The subsection *Some Important Aldehydes and Ketones* is now a *Health Note*.
- Section 14.5, *Chiral Molecules*, uses simple compounds to introduce chiral molecules and chirality early in the text in preparation for the next chapter.
- An *Explore Your World* feature, "Using Gumdrops and Toothpicks to Model Chiral Objects," constructs chiral and achiral molecules by using gumdrops and toothpicks.

Chapter 15, "Carbohydrates," applies the organic chemistry of alcohols, aldehydes, and ketones to biomolecules, which relates the study of chemistry to health and medicine.

- Section 15.2 is now *Fischer Projections of Monosaccharides*, and Section 15.3 is *Haworth Structures of Monosaccharides*.
- New art includes Fischer projections for all the carbohydrate structures.
- The section *Haworth Structures of Monosaccharides* is rewritten to provide clearer instructions for drawing the closed ring structures.
- The *Health Notes* "How Sweet Is My Sweetener?" and "Blood Types and Carbohydrates" have been updated with recently developed sweeteners and information on blood types.
- New to this edition is an inter-chapter problem set, *Combining Ideas from Chapters 11 to 15*.

Chapters 16, 17, and 18

Chapter 16, "Carboxylic Acids and Esters," discusses two organic families that are important in biochemical systems.

- In this new edition, there is more emphasis on the use of Le Châtelier's principle to explain direction of reactions such as esterification and acid hydrolysis of esters.

Chapter 17, "Lipids," contains the functional groups of alcohols, aldehydes, and ketones in larger molecules such as triacylglycerols, glycerophospholipids, and steroids.

- Table 17.1, *Structures and Melting Points of Common Fatty Acids*, now includes arachidonic acid. The differences in the structures of prostaglandins E and F are now explained. Structures for fatty acids now include the line-bond formula. *Health Notes* of interest to students include olestra, trans fatty acids, and lipoproteins.
- A new *Green Chemistry Note*, "Biodiesel as an Alternative Fuel," has been added.
- Section 17.6, *Sphingolipids*, has been rewritten to clarify the structural differences between a sphingomyelin, ceramide, glycosphingolipid, and ganglioside. The role of lipids and cholesterol in cell membranes is discussed along with lipids that function as bile salts and steroid hormones.

Chapter 18, "Amines and Amides," emphasizes the nitrogen atom in their functional groups and their names.

- New *Guides to Problem Solving* now include steps for naming amines and amides. *Health Notes* include amines and amides in health and medicine, as well as alkaloids, which are naturally occurring amines in plants.

Chapters 19, 20, and 21

Chapter 19, "Amino Acids and Proteins," connects the functional groups of amines and amides to their related biomolecules. The classification of amino acids has been rewritten to include their ionized structures.

- Table 19.2, *The 20 Amino Acids (Ionized) in Proteins*, compares the form of amino acids above, below, and at the isoelectric point (pI). The importance of the structure of proteins from primary to quaternary is related to the shapes and activity of proteins.

Chapter 20, "Enzymes and Vitamins," relates the importance of the three-dimensional shape of proteins to their function as enzymes. Table 20.1, *Classification of Enzymes*, was simplified. The students learn that the shape of an enzyme is a factor in enzyme regulation and how end products might change the shape of an enzyme to increase or decrease the rate of an enzyme-catalyzed reaction. We also see that proteins change shape and lose function when subjected to pH changes and high temperatures. The important role of water-soluble vitamins as coenzymes is related to enzyme function.

- New to this edition is an inter-chapter problem set, *Combining Ideas from Chapters 16 to 20*.

Chapter 21, "Nucleic Acids and Protein Synthesis," describes the nucleic acids and their importance as biomolecules that store and direct information for cellular components, growth, and reproduction. The role of complementary base pairing is highlighted in both DNA replication and the formation of mRNA during protein synthesis. Discussions include the genetic code, its relationship to the order of amino acids in a protein, and how mutations can occur when the nucleotide sequence is altered.

- The *Explore Your World* feature "A Model for DNA Replication and Mutation" is expanded to include formation of mRNA and dipeptide formation.
- The preparation and uses of recombinant DNA in forensic science and the discussion of the Human Genome Project have been updated.
- The role of DNA or RNA in viruses that utilize host cells to replicate is discussed.

Chapters 22, 23, and 24

Chapter 22, "Metabolic Pathways for Carbohydrates," describes the stages of metabolism and the digestion of carbohydrates, our most important fuel. The breakdown of glucose to pyruvate is described using the glycolytic pathway, which is followed under aerobic conditions by the decarboxylation of pyruvate to acetyl CoA. The synthesis of glycogen and the synthesis of glucose from noncarbohydrate sources are discussed.

Chapter 23, "Metabolic Pathways and Energy Production," looks at the entry of acetyl CoA into the citric acid cycle and the production of reduced coenzymes for the electron transport system and oxidative phosphorylation.

- The discussion of the reactions of the citric acid cycle has been expanded and now includes the enzymes that catalyze the reactions.
- Details on the structure and function of ATP synthase are included.

Chapter 24, "Metabolic Pathways for Lipids and Amino Acids," discusses the digestion of lipids and proteins and the metabolic pathways that convert fatty acids and amino acids into energy. Discussions include the conversion of excess carbohydrates to triacylglycerols in adipose tissue and how the intermediates of the citric acid cycle are converted to nonessential amino acids.

- The *Explore Your World* feature "Fat Storage and Blubber" has been updated and expanded to give clear instructions for the procedures.
- Finally, the relationships between the catabolic and anabolic pathways in metabolism are summarized.
- New to this edition is an inter-chapter problem set, *Combining Ideas from Chapters 21 to 24.*

ACKNOWLEDGMENTS

The preparation of a new edition is a continuous effort of many people. As in my work on other textbooks, I am thankful for the support, encouragement, and dedication of many people who put in hours of tireless effort to produce a high-quality book that provides an outstanding learning package. The editorial team at Pearson Publishing has done an exceptional job. I want to thank Nicole Folchetti, editor in chief, and acquisitions editor, Dawn Giovanniello, who supported my vision of this third edition and the addition of new *Concept Checks*, *Green Chemistry Notes*, *Combining Ideas*, problem sets, and an updated art program. I much appreciate all the wonderful work of Jessica Neumann, assistant editor, who was like an angel encouraging me at each step while skillfully coordinating reviews, art, website materials, and all the things it takes to make a book come together. I am grateful to Ray Mullaney, editor in chief of science book development, and Karen Nein, developmental editor, for their watchful eyes during the writing and development of this new edition. I appreciate the work of Beth Sweeten, project manager, and Lynn Lustberg of Macmillan Publishing Solutions, who brilliantly coordinated all phases of the manuscript to the final pages of a beautiful book. Thanks to Kathy Thrush Shaginaw, manuscript reviewer, and Richard Camp, copy editor, who precisely reviewed and edited the initial and final manuscripts to make sure the words and problems were correct to help students learn chemistry.

I am especially proud of the art program in this text, which lends beauty and understanding to chemistry. I would like to thank Suzanne Behnke, art director and book designer, and Travis Amos, photo editor, whose creative ideas provided the outstanding design for the cover and pages of the book. Eric Schrader, photo researcher, was invaluable in researching and selecting vivid photos for the text so that students can see the beauty of chemistry. Thanks also to *Bio-Rad Laboratories* for their courtesy and use of *KnowItAll ChemWindows Edition* drawing software that helped me produce chemical structures for the manuscript. The macro-to-micro illustrations designed by Production Solutions and Precision Graphics give students visual impressions of the atomic and molecular organization of everyday things and are a fantastic learning tool. I want to thank Michael Rossa for the hours of proofreading all the pages. I also appreciate all the hard work in the field put in by the marketing team and Elizabeth Averbeck, marketing manager.

This text also reflects the contributions of many professors who took the time to review and edit the manuscript and provide outstanding comments, help, and suggestions. A special thanks to Kathy Thrush Shaginaw, Mark Quirie, and Timothy Kreider for their outstanding accuracy reviews of the entire manuscript. Their keen eyes and thoughtful comments were extremely helpful in the development of this text.

I am extremely grateful to an incredible group of peers for their careful assessment of all the new ideas for the text; for their suggested additions, corrections, changes, and deletions; and for providing an incredible amount of feedback about improvements for the book. In addition, I appreciate the time scientists took to let us take photos and discuss their work with them. I admire and appreciate every one of you.

If you would like to share your experience with chemistry or have questions and comments about this text, I would appreciate hearing from you.

Karen Timberlake
E-mail: khemist@aol.com

REVIEWERS

Chemistry in Our Lives

San Francisco Museum of Art

"As a conservator of photographic materials, it is essential to have an understanding of the chemical reactions of many different photographic processes," says Theresa Andrews, Conservator of Photographs at the San Francisco Museum of Modern Art. "For example, the creation of the latent image in many photographs is based upon the light sensitivity of silver halides. Photolytic silver 'prints out' when exposed to a light source such as the sun and filamentary silver 'develops out' when an exposed photographic paper is placed in a bath with reducing agents. Photolytic silver particles are much smaller than filamentary silver particles making them more vulnerable to abrasion and image loss. This knowledge is critical when making recommendations for light levels and for the protection of photographs when they are on exhibition. Conservation treatments require informed decisions based on the reactivity of the materials within the photograph and also the compatibility of materials that might be required for repair or preservation of the photograph."

Visit **www.masteringchemistry.com**
for self-study materials and instructor-
assigned homework.

What are some questions in science you have been curious about? Perhaps you are interested in how smog is formed, what causes ozone depletion, how nails form rust, or how aspirin relieves a headache. Just like you, chemists are curious about the world we live in.

- How does car exhaust produce the smog that hangs over our cities? One component of car exhaust is nitrogen oxide (NO), which forms in car engines where high temperatures convert nitrogen gas (N_2) and oxygen gas (O_2) to NO. In chemistry, these reactions are written in the form of equations such as $N_2(g) + O_2(g) \longrightarrow 2NO(g)$. The reaction of NO with oxygen in the air produces NO_2, which gives smog its characteristic reddish-brown color.

- Why has the ozone layer been depleted in certain parts of the atmosphere? During the 1970s, scientists discovered that substances called *chlorofluorocarbons* (CFCs) were associated with the depletion of ozone (O_3) over Antarctica. As CFCs are broken down by ultraviolet (UV) light, chlorine (Cl) is released and acts rapidly with ozone in the atmosphere to form chlorine oxide gas (ClO) and oxygen: $Cl(g) + O_3(g) \longrightarrow ClO(g) + O_2(g)$. This reaction causes the breakdown of ozone molecules and the destruction of the ozone layer.

- Why does an iron nail rust when exposed to air and rain? When solid iron (Fe) in a nail reacts with oxygen gas in the air, the oxidation of iron forms rust (Fe_2O_3): $4Fe(s) + 3O_2(g) \longrightarrow 2Fe_2O_3(s)$.

- Why does aspirin relieve a headache? When a part of the body is injured, substances called *prostaglandins* are produced that cause inflammation and pain. Aspirin acts to block the production of prostaglandins, thereby reducing inflammation, pain, and fever.

Chemists perform many different kinds of research. Some design new fuels and more efficient ways to use them. Researchers in the medical field look for evidence that will help them understand and design new treatments for diabetes, genetic defects, cancer, AIDS, and other diseases. For the chemist in the laboratory, the physician in the dialysis unit, or the agricultural scientist, chemistry plays a central role in providing understanding, assessing solutions, and making important decisions.

P.1 Chemistry and Chemicals

LEARNING GOAL

Define the term *chemistry* and identify substances as chemicals.

Chemistry is the study of the composition, structure, properties, and reactions of matter. *Matter* is another word for all the substances that make up our world. Perhaps you imagine that chemistry is done only in a laboratory by a chemist wearing a lab coat and goggles. Actually, chemistry happens all around you every day and has a big impact on everything you use and do. You are doing chemistry when you cook food, add chlorine to a swimming pool, or start your car. A chemical reaction takes place when a nail rusts or an antacid tablet fizzes when dropped into water. Plants grow because chemical reactions convert carbon dioxide, water, and energy to carbohydrates and oxygen. Chemical reactions take place when you digest food and break it down into substances that you need for energy and health.

All the things you see around you are composed of one or more chemicals. A **chemical** is a substance that always has the same composition and properties wherever it is found. When a chemical undergoes a *chemical change*, a new substance with a new composition and properties is formed. Chemical changes take place in chemistry laboratories, manufacturing plants, and pharmaceutical labs as well as every day in nature and in our bodies. Often, the terms *chemical* and *substance* are used interchangeably to describe a specific type of matter.

TABLE P.1 Chemicals Commonly Used in Toothpaste

Chemical	Function
Calcium carbonate	Acts as an abrasive to remove plaque
Sorbitol	Prevents loss of water and hardening of toothpaste
Carrageenan (seaweed extract)	Keeps toothpaste from hardening or separating
Glycerin	Makes toothpaste foam in the mouth
Sodium lauryl sulfate	Acts as a detergent used to loosen plaque
Titanium dioxide	Makes toothpaste base white and opaque
Triclosan	Inhibits bacteria that cause plaque and gum disease
Sodium fluorophosphate	Prevents formation of cavities by strengthening tooth enamel with fluoride
Methyl salicylate	Gives a pleasant flavor of wintergreen

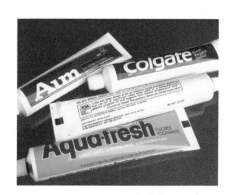

Each day you use products containing substances that were developed and prepared by chemists. Soaps and shampoos contain chemicals that combine with oils on your skin and scalp. When you shower in the morning, these oils are removed by rinsing with water. When you brush your teeth, the chemicals in toothpaste clean your teeth, prevent plaque formation, and prevent tooth decay. Some chemicals commonly contained in toothpaste are listed in Table P.1.

In cosmetics and lotions, chemicals are used to moisturize the skin, fight bacteria, prevent deterioration of the product, and thicken the product. Your clothes may be made of natural materials such as cotton, or synthetic substances such as nylon or polyester. Perhaps you wear a ring or watch made of gold, silver, or platinum. Your breakfast cereal is probably fortified with iron, calcium, and phosphorus, while the milk you drink is enriched with vitamins A and D. Antioxidants are chemicals added to your cereal to prevent it from spoiling. Some of the chemicals you may encounter when you cook in the kitchen are shown in Figure P.1.

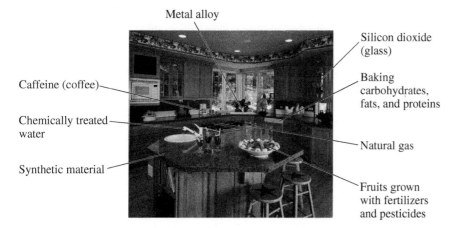

Metal alloy

Silicon dioxide (glass)

Baking carbohydrates, fats, and proteins

Caffeine (coffee)

Chemically treated water

Natural gas

Synthetic material

Fruits grown with fertilizers and pesticides

FIGURE P.1 Many of the items found in a kitchen are obtained using chemical reactions.

Q What are some other chemicals found in a kitchen?

CONCEPT CHECK P.1

■ Chemicals

Why is copper wire an example of a chemical, while sunlight is not?

ANSWER

Copper wire is a substance that has the same composition and properties wherever it is found. Sunlight is not a substance and does not contain matter.

SAMPLE PROBLEM   P.1

■ Everyday Chemicals

Identify the chemical described by each of the following statements:

a. Aluminum is used to make cans.
b. Salt (sodium chloride) is used as a preservative.
c. Sugar (sucrose) is used as a sweetener.

SOLUTION

a. aluminum   **b.** salt (sodium chloride)   **c.** sugar (sucrose)

STUDY CHECK

Which of the following are chemicals?

a. iron   **b.** tin   **c.** a low temperature   **d.** water

The answers for all Study Checks are included at the end of each chapter.

QUESTIONS AND PROBLEMS

Chemistry and Chemicals

The answers for all the magenta, odd-numbered Questions and Problems are included at the end of each chapter. Checking your answers will let you know if you understand the material.

P.1 Obtain a vitamin bottle and observe the list of ingredients. List four. Which ones are chemicals?

P.2 Obtain a box of breakfast cereal and observe the list of ingredients. List four. Which ones are chemicals?

P.3 A "chemical-free" shampoo includes the following ingredients: water, cocomide, glycerin, and citric acid. Is the shampoo "chemical-free"?

P.4 A "chemical-free" sunscreen includes the following ingredients: titanium dioxide, vitamin E, and vitamin C. Is the sunscreen "chemical-free"?

P.5 Pesticides are chemicals. Give one advantage and one disadvantage of using pesticides.

P.6 Sugar is a chemical. Give one advantage and one disadvantage of eating sugar.

P.2 Scientific Method: Thinking Like a Scientist

When you were very young, you explored the things around you by touching and tasting. When you grew a little older, you asked questions about the world in which you live. What is lightning? Where does a rainbow come from? Why is water blue? As an adult, you may have wondered how antibiotics work or why vitamins are important to your health. Each day you ask questions and seek answers as you organize and make sense of the world around you.

When the late Nobel Laureate Linus Pauling described his student life in Oregon, he recalled that he read many books on chemistry, mineralogy, and physics. "I mulled over the properties of materials: why are some substances colored and others not, why are some minerals or inorganic compounds hard and others soft?" He said, "I was building up this tremendous background of empirical knowledge and at the same time asking a great number of questions." Linus Pauling won two Nobel Prizes: the first, in 1954, was in chemistry for his work on the structure of proteins; the second, in 1962, was the Peace Prize.

Scientific Method

Although the process of trying to understand nature is unique to each scientist, a set of general principles called the **scientific method** helps to describe how a scientist thinks.

1. **Observations.** The first step in the scientific method is to observe, describe, and measure an event in nature. Observations based on measurements are called *data*.

2. **Hypothesis.** After sufficient data are collected, a *hypothesis* is proposed that states a possible interpretation of the observations. The hypothesis must be stated in a way that it can be tested by experiments.

3. **Experiments.** Experiments are tests that determine the validity of the hypothesis. Often many experiments are performed, and a large amount of data is collected. If the results of the experiments are different than those predicted by the hypothesis, then a new or modified hypothesis is proposed, and new experiments are performed.

4. **Theory.** When many scientists repeat the experiments with consistent results that confirm the hypothesis, the hypothesis becomes a *theory*. Each theory, however,

continues to be tested and, based on new data, sometimes needs to be modified or even replaced. Then a new hypothesis is proposed, and the process of experimentation takes place once again.

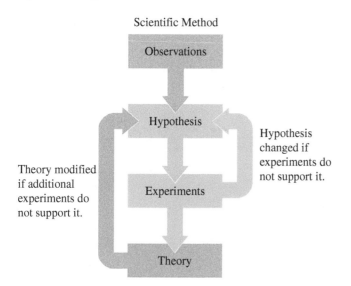

Scientific Method

Using the Scientific Method in Everyday Life

You may be surprised to realize that you use the scientific method in your everyday life. Suppose you visit a friend in her home. Soon after you arrive, your eyes start to itch and you begin to sneeze. Then you observe that your friend has a new cat. Perhaps you ask yourself why you are sneezing and form the hypothesis that you are allergic to cats. To test your hypothesis, you leave your friend's home. If the sneezing stops, perhaps your hypothesis is correct. You test your hypothesis further by visiting another friend who also has a cat. If you start to sneeze again, then your experimental results support your hypothesis that you are allergic to cats. However, if you continue sneezing after you leave your friend's home, your hypothesis is not supported. Now you need to form a new hypothesis, which could be that you have a cold.

 TUTORIAL
Scientific Method

CONCEPT CHECK P.2

■ Scientific Method

Label each of the following as an observation, hypothesis, or experiment:

a. Drinking coffee at night keeps me awake.
b. When I drink coffee only in the morning, I can sleep at night.
c. I will try drinking coffee only in the morning.

ANSWER
a. An observation describes what happens when I drink coffee.
b. An observation describes what happens if I drink coffee only in the morning.
c. Changing the time for drinking coffee is an experiment.

SAMPLE PROBLEM   P.2

■ Scientific Method

Identify each of the following statements as an observation or a hypothesis:

a. A silver tray turns a dull gray color when left uncovered.
b. It is warmer in summer than in winter in the northern hemisphere.
c. Ice cubes float in water because they are less dense.

SOLUTION

a. observation   **b.** observation   **c.** hypothesis

STUDY CHECK

The following statements are found in a student's notebook. Identify each of the following as observation (O), hypothesis (H), or experiment (E):

a. "Today, I planted two tomato seedlings in the garden. I put two more tomato seedlings in a closet. I will give all the plants the same amount of water and fertilizer."

b. "After 50 days, the tomato plants in the garden are 3 feet high with green leaves. The plants in the closet are 8 inches tall and yellow."

c. "Tomato plants need sunlight to grow."

HEALTH NOTE

Early Chemists: The Alchemists

For many centuries, chemists have studied changes in matter. From the time of the Greeks to about the sixteenth century, alchemists, early chemists who studied matter, described matter in terms of four components of nature: earth, air, fire, and water. These components had the qualities of hot, cold, damp, or dry. By the eighth century, alchemists believed that they could rearrange these qualities to change metals such as copper and lead into gold and silver. They searched for an unknown substance called a *philosopher's stone* that they thought would turn metals into gold as well as prolong youth and postpone death. Although these efforts failed, the alchemists did provide information on the processes and chemical reactions involved in the extraction of metals from ores. The alchemists also designed some of the first laboratory equipment and developed early laboratory procedures. These early efforts were some of the first observations and experiments using the scientific method.

The alchemist Paracelsus (1493–1541) thought that alchemy should be about preparing new medicines, not about producing gold. Using observation and experiments, he viewed the body as a series of chemical processes that could be unbalanced by certain chemical compounds and rebalanced by using minerals and medicines. For example, he determined that inhaled dust, not underground spirits, caused the lung diseases of miners. He also thought that goiter was a problem caused by contaminated drinking water, and he treated syphilis with compounds of mercury. His opinion of medicines was that the right dose makes the difference between a poison and a cure. Today this idea is part of the risk analysis of medicines. Paracelsus changed alchemy in ways that helped to establish modern medicine and chemistry.

Science and Technology

When scientific information is applied to industrial and commercial uses, it is called *technology*. Such uses have made the chemical industry one of the largest industries in the United States. Every year, technology provides new materials or procedures that produce more energy, cure diseases, improve crops, and produce new kinds of synthetic materials. Table P.2 lists some of the important scientific discoveries, laws, theories, and technological innovations that have been made over the past 300 years.

TABLE P.2 Some Important Scientific Discoveries, Laws, Theories, and Technological Innovations

Discovery, Law, Theory, or Innovation	Date	Name	Country
Law of gravity	1687	Isaac Newton	England
Oxygen	1774	Joseph Priestley	England
Electric battery	1800	Alessandro Volta	Italy
Atomic theory	1803	John Dalton	England
Anesthesia, ether	1842	Crawford Long	United States
Nitroglycerin	1847	Ascanio Sobrero	Italy
Germ theory	1865	Louis Pasteur	France
Antiseptic surgery	1865	Joseph Lister	England
Discovery of nucleic acids	1869	Friedrich Miescher	Switzerland
Radioactivity	1896	Henri Becquerel	France
Discovery of radium	1898	Marie and Pierre Curie	France
Quantum theory	1900	Max Planck	Germany
Theory of relativity	1905	Albert Einstein	Germany
Identification of components of RNA and DNA	1909	Phoebus Theodore Levene	United States
Insulin	1922	Frederick Banting, Charles Best, John Macleod	Canada
Penicillin	1928	Alexander Fleming	England
Nylon	1937	Wallace Carothers	United States
Discovery of DNA as genetic material	1944	Oswald Avery	United States
Synthetic production of transuranium elements	1944	Glenn Seaborg, Arthur Wahl, Joseph Kennedy, Albert Ghiorso	United States
Determination of DNA structure	1953	Francis Crick, Rosalind Franklin, James Watson	England
Polio vaccine	1954	Jonas Salk	United States
	1957	Albert Sabin	United States
Laser	1958	Charles Townes	United States
	1960	Theodore Maiman	United States
Cellular phones	1973	Martin Cooper	United States
MRI (magnetic resonance imaging)	1980	Paul Lauterbur	United States
Prozac	1988	Ray Fuller	United States
HIV protease inhibitor	1995	Joseph Martin, Sally Redshaw	United States

Not all scientific discoveries, however, have been positive. The production of some substances has contributed to the development of hazardous conditions in our environment. We have become concerned about the energy requirements of new products and how some materials may cause changes in our oceans and atmosphere. We want to know if the new materials can be recycled, how they are broken down, and whether there are alternate and safer processes. The ways in which we continue to utilize scientific research will strongly affect our planet and its communities in the future. These decisions can best be made if every citizen has an understanding of science.

ENVIRONMENTAL NOTE

DDT: Good Pesticide, Bad Pesticide

DDT (dichlorodiphenyltrichloroethane) was once one of the most commonly used pesticides. Although DDT was first made in 1874, it was not used as an insecticide until 1939. Before DDT was widely used, insect-borne diseases such as malaria and typhus were rampant in many parts of the world. Paul Müller, who discovered that DDT was an effective pesticide, was recognized for saving many lives and received the Nobel Prize for medicine and physiology in 1948. At that time, DDT was considered the ideal pesticide because it was toxic to many insects, had a low toxicity to humans and animals, and was inexpensive to prepare.

In the United States, DDT was used extensively on home gardens as well as on farm crops, particularly cotton and soybeans. Because of its stable chemical structure, DDT did not break down quickly in the environment, which meant that it did not have to be reapplied frequently. At first, everyone was pleased with DDT—crop yields increased and diseases such as malaria and typhus were under control.

However, during the early 1950s, problems attributed to DDT began to arise. Insects were becoming more resistant to the pesticide. At the same time, the public was increasingly concerned about the long-term impact of a substance that could remain in the environment for many years. The metabolic systems of humans and animals cannot break down DDT, which is soluble in fats but not in water and is stored in the fatty tissues of the body. Although the concentrations of DDT applied to crops were extremely low, the concentrations of DDT found in fish and the birds that ate the fish were as much as

10 million times greater. Although the affected birds did not die immediately, the DDT in their bodies reduced the amount of calcium in their eggshells. As a result, the incubating eggs cracked open early, causing many offspring to die. Because of this difficulty with reproduction, the populations of birds such as bald eagles and brown pelicans dropped significantly.

By 1972, DDT was banned in the United States. The Environmental Protection Agency (EPA) reported that by 1978 DDT levels were reduced by 90% in fish in Lake Michigan. Today, new types of pesticides that are more water soluble and do not persist in the environment have replaced long-lasting pesticides such as DDT. However, these new pesticides are much more toxic to humans.

QUESTIONS AND PROBLEMS

Scientific Method: Thinking like a Scientist

P.7 Identify each of the following statements as an observation (O), a hypothesis (H), an experiment (E), or a theory (T): At a popular restaurant, where Chang is the head chef, the following occur:
  a. Chang determines that sales of the chef's salad have dropped.
  b. Chang decides that the chef's salad needs a new dressing.
  c. In a taste test, four bowls of lettuce are prepared with four new dressings: sesame seed, oil and vinegar, blue cheese, and anchovies.
  d. The tasters rate the dressing with sesame seeds the best.
  e. After two weeks, Chang notes that the orders for the chef's salad with the new sesame dressing have doubled.
  f. Chang decides that the sesame dressing improved the sales of the chef's salad because the sesame dressing improved the taste of the salad.

P.8 Identify each of the following statements as an observation (O), a hypothesis (H), an experiment (E), or a theory (T): Lucia wants to develop a process for dyeing shirts so that the color will not fade when the shirt is washed. She proceeds with the following activities:
  a. Lucia notices that the dye in a design on T-shirts fades when the shirt is washed.
  b. Lucia decides that the dye needs something to help it set in the T-shirt fabric.
  c. She places a spot of dye on each of four T-shirts and then places each one separately in water, salt water, vinegar, and baking soda and water.
  d. After 1 hour, all the T-shirts are removed and washed with a detergent.
  e. Lucia notices that the dye has faded on the T-shirts soaked in water, salt water, and baking soda, while the dye did not fade in the T-shirts soaked in vinegar.
  f. Lucia thinks that the vinegar binds with the dye so it does not fade when the shirt is washed.

P.3 A Study Plan for Learning Chemistry

Here you are taking chemistry, perhaps for the first time. Whatever your reasons are for choosing to study chemistry, you can look forward to learning many new and exciting ideas.

LEARNING GOAL

Develop a study plan for learning chemistry.

Features in This Text Help You Study Chemistry

This text has been designed with a variety of study aids to complement different learning styles. On the inside of the front cover is a periodic table of the elements that provides information about the elements. On the inside of the back cover are tables that summarize useful information needed throughout the study of chemistry. Each chapter begins with *Looking Ahead*, which outlines the topics in the chapter. A *Learning Goal* at the beginning of each section previews the concepts you are to learn. A comprehensive *Glossary/Index* is included at the end of the text.

Before you begin to read a chapter, obtain an overview of the topics by reviewing the list of topics in *Looking Ahead*. As you prepare to read a section of the chapter, look at the section title and turn it into a question. For example, for Section P.1, "Chemistry and Chemicals," you could write a question that asks "What is chemistry?" or "What are chemicals?" When you are ready to read that section, review the *Learning Goal*, which tells you what you need to accomplish. As you read, try to answer the question you wrote. Throughout the chapter, you will find *Concept Checks* that will help you understand key ideas. When you come to a *Sample Problem*, take the time to work it through, and try the associated *Study Check*. Then, check your answer at the end of the chapter. If your answer does not match, you may need to study the section again. When you finish each section, immediately work through the *Questions and Problems* for practice.

Throughout the chapters, boxes titled *Health Notes*, *Green Chemistry Notes*, and *Environmental Notes* connect the chemical concepts you are studying to real-life situations. Many of the figures and diagrams throughout the text use macro-to-micro illustrations to depict the atomic level of organization of ordinary objects. These visual models illustrate the concepts described in the text and allow you to "see" the world in a microscopic way.

At the end of each chapter, you will find several study aids that complete the chapter. *Chapter Reviews* and *Concept Maps* at the end of each chapter give a summary and show the connections between important concepts. The *Key Terms* are boldfaced in the text and listed again at the end of the chapter. *Understanding the Concepts* is a set of questions that use art and structures to help you visualize concepts. *Additional Questions and Problems* and *Challenge Problems* provide more problems to test your understanding of the topics in the chapter. Answers to all the *Study Checks* and *Answers to Selected Questions and Problems* are provided at the end of the chapter.

Using Active Learning to Learn Chemistry

A student who is an active learner continually interacts with the chemical ideas while reading the text and attending lectures. Let's see how this is done.

As you read and practice solving problems, you remain actively involved in studying, which enhances the learning process. In this way, you learn small bits of information at a time and establish the necessary foundation for understanding the next section. You may also note questions you have about the reading to discuss with your professor and laboratory instructor. Table P.3 summarizes these steps for active learning. The time you spend in lecture can also be useful as a learning time. By keeping track of the class schedule and reading the assigned material before lecture, you become aware of the new terms and concepts you need to learn. Some questions that occur during your reading may be answered during the lecture. If not, you can ask for further clarification from your professor.

TABLE P.3 Steps in Active Learning

1. Read the set of *Looking Ahead* topics and *Learning Goals* for an overview of the material.
2. Form a question from the title of the section you are going to read.
3. Read the section looking for answers to your question.
4. Self-test by working *Concept Checks*, *Sample Problems*, and *Study Checks* within each section.
5. Complete the *Questions and Problems* that follow each section and check the magenta odd-numbered answers.
6. Proceed to the next section and repeat the above steps.

Many students think that studying with a group can be beneficial to learning. In a group, students motivate each other to study, fill in gaps, and correct misunderstandings by teaching and learning together. Studying alone does not allow the process of peer correction that takes place when you work with a group of students in your class. In a group, you can cover the ideas more thoroughly as you discuss the reading and problem solving with other students. Waiting to study until the night before an exam does not give you time to understand concepts and practice problem solving. You may ignore or avoid ideas that turn out to be important on test day.

Thinking Scientifically About Your Study Plan

As you embark on your journey into the world of chemistry, think about your approach to studying and learning chemistry. You might consider some of the ideas in the following list. Check those ideas that will help you learn chemistry successfully. Commit to them now. Your success depends on you.

My study of chemistry will include the following:

_____ Reviewing the *Learning Goals*

_____ Keeping a problem notebook

_____ Reading the text as an active learner

_____ Self-testing by working the chapter problems and checking solutions in the text

_____ Reading the chapter before lecture

_____ Being an active learner in lecture

_____ Going to lecture

_____ Organizing a study group

_____ Seeing the professor during office hours

_____ Attending review sessions

_____ Organizing my own review sessions

_____ Studying a little bit as often as I can

CONCEPT CHECK P.3

■ **A Study Plan for Chemistry**

What are some advantages to studying in a group?

ANSWER

In a group, students motivate and support each other, fill in gaps, and correct misunderstandings. Ideas are discussed while reading and problem solving together.

SAMPLE PROBLEM   P.3

■ **A Study Plan for Learning Chemistry**

Which of the following activities would you include in a study plan for successfully learning chemistry?

a. skipping a lecture
b. forming a study group
c. keeping a problem notebook
d. waiting to study until the night before the exam
e. becoming an active learner

SOLUTION

Your success in chemistry can be helped if you include the following in your study plan:

b. forming a study group
c. keeping a problem notebook
e. becoming an active learner

STUDY CHECK

Which of the following would help you learn chemistry?

a. skipping review sessions
b. working assigned problems
c. attending the professor's office hours
d. staying up all night before an exam
e. reading the assignment before a lecture

QUESTIONS AND PROBLEMS

A Study Plan for Studying Chemistry

P.9 A student in your class asks you for advice on learning chemistry. Which of the following might you suggest?
   a. Form a study group.
   b. Skip a lecture.
   c. Visit the professor during office hours.
   d. Wait until the night before an exam to study.
   e. Become an active learner.

P.10 A student in your class asks you for advice on learning chemistry. Which of the following might you suggest?
   a. Do the assigned problems.
   b. Don't read the book; it's never on the test.
   c. Attend review sessions.
   d. Read the assignment before lecture.
   e. Keep a problem notebook.

CONCEPT MAP

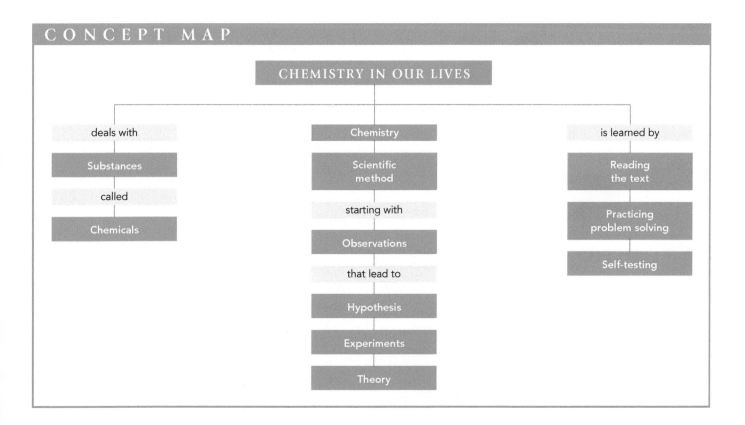

CHAPTER REVIEW

P.1 Chemistry and Chemicals
LEARNING GOAL: *Define the term* chemistry, *and identify substances as chemicals.*
Chemistry is the study of the composition of substances and the way in which they interact with other substances. A chemical is any substance used in or produced by a chemical process.

P.2 Scientific Method: Thinking like a Scientist
LEARNING GOAL: *Describe the activities that are part of the scientific method.*
The scientific method is a process of explaining natural phenomena beginning with observations, a hypothesis, and experiments, which may lead to a theory when experimental results support the hypothesis. Technology involves the application of scientific information to industrial and commercial uses.

P.3 A Study Plan for Learning Chemistry
LEARNING GOAL: *Develop a study plan for learning chemistry.*
A study plan for learning chemistry utilizes the visual features in the text and develops an active learning approach to study. By using the *Learning Goals* and *Concept Checks* in the chapter and working the *Sample Problems* and *Study Checks* and the problems at the end of each section, the student can successfully learn the concepts of chemistry.

 # KEY TERMS

chemical A substance that has the same composition and properties wherever it is found.
chemistry A science that studies the composition of substances and the way they interact with other substances.
experiment A procedure that tests the validity of a hypothesis.
hypothesis An unverified explanation of a natural phenomenon.
observation Information determined by noting and recording a natural phenomenon.

scientific method The process of making observations, proposing a hypothesis, testing the hypothesis, and developing a theory that explains a natural event.
theory An explanation of an observation that has been validated by experiments that support a hypothesis.

UNDERSTANDING THE CONCEPTS

P.11 According to Sherlock Holmes, "One must follow the rules of scientific inquiry, gathering, observing, and testing data, then formulating, modifying, and rejecting hypotheses, until only one remains." Did Sherlock use the scientific method? Why or why not?

P.12 In "A Scandal in Bohemia," Sherlock Holmes receives a mysterious note. He states, "I have no data yet. It is a capital mistake to theorize before one has data. Insensibly one begins to twist facts to suit theories instead of theories to suit facts." What do you think Sherlock meant?

P.13 Select the correct phrase(s) to complete the following statement: If experimental results do not support your hypothesis, you should
   a. pretend that the experimental results do support your hypothesis.
   b. write another hypothesis.
   c. do more experiments.

P.14 Select the correct phrase(s) to complete the following statement: A hypothesis becomes a theory when
   a. one experiment proves the hypothesis.
   b. many experiments by many scientists validate the hypothesis.
   c. you decide to call it a theory.

ADDITIONAL QUESTIONS AND PROBLEMS

For instructor-assigned homework, go to ***www.masteringchemistry.com***.

P.15 Why does the scientific method include a hypothesis?

P.16 Why is experimentation an important part of the scientific method?

P.17 Classify each of the following statements as either an observation or a hypothesis:
   a. Aluminum melts at 660 °C.
   b. Dinosaurs became extinct when a large meteorite struck Earth and caused a huge dust cloud that severely decreased the amount of light reaching Earth.
   c. The 100-yard dash was run in 9.8 seconds.

P.18 Classify each of the following statements as either an observation or a hypothesis:
   a. Analysis of 10 ceramic dishes showed that four dishes contained lead levels that exceeded federal safety standards.
   b. Marble statues undergo corrosion in acid rain.
   c. Statues corrode in acid rain because the acidity is sufficient to dissolve calcium carbonate, the major substance of marble.

CHALLENGE QUESTIONS

P.19 Classify each of the following statements as an observation, hypothesis, or experiment:
  a. The bicycle tire is flat.
  b. If I add air to the bicycle tire, it will expand to the proper size.
  c. When I added air to the bicycle tire, it was still flat.
  d. The bicycle tire must have a leak in it.

P.20 Classify each of the following statements as an observation, hypothesis, or experiment:
  a. A big log in the fire does not burn well.
  b. If I chop the log into small pieces, it will burn better.
  c. The smaller pieces of wood burn brighter and make a hotter fire.
  d. The small wood pieces burn faster than burning the big log.

ANSWERS

ANSWERS TO STUDY CHECKS

P.1 **a.**, **b.**, and **d.**

P.2 **a.** E **b.** O **c.** H

P.3 **b.**, **c.**, and **e.**

ANSWERS TO SELECTED QUESTIONS AND PROBLEMS

P.1 Many chemicals are listed on a vitamin bottle such as vitamin A, vitamin B_3, vitamin B_{12}, folic acid, etc.

P.3 No. All of the ingredients listed are chemicals.

P.5 One advantage of a pesticide is that it gets rid of insects that bite humans or animals or damage crops. One disadvantage is that a pesticide can destroy beneficial insects or be retained in a crop that is eventually eaten by animals or humans.

P.7 **a.** O **b.** H **c.** E **d.** O **e.** O **f.** T

P.9 **a.**, **c.**, and **e.**

P.11 Yes. Sherlock's investigation includes making observations (gathering data), formulating a hypothesis, testing the hypothesis, and modifying it until one of the hypotheses is validated.

P.13 **b.** and **c.**

P.15 A hypothesis, which is a possible explanation for an observation, can be tested with experiments.

P.17 **a.** observation **b.** hypothesis **c.** observation

P.19 **a.** observation **b.** hypothesis **c.** experiment **d.** hypothesis

1

Measurements

"I use measurement in just about every part of my nursing practice," says registered nurse Vicki Miller. "When I receive a doctor's order for a medication, I have to verify that order. Then I draw a carefully measured volume from an IV or a vial to create that particular dose. Some dosage orders are specific to the size of the patient. I measure the patient's weight and calculate the dosage required for the weight of that patient."

Nurses use measurement each time they determine a patient's temperature, height, weight, or blood pressure. Measurement is used to obtain the correct amounts for injections and medications and to determine the volumes of fluid intake and output. For each measurement, the amounts and units are recorded in the patient's records.

Mastering**CHEMISTRY**™

Visit **www.masteringchemistry.com** for self-study materials and instructor-assigned homework.

C hemistry and measurement are an important part of our everyday lives. Levels of toxic materials in the air, soil, and water are discussed in our newspapers. We read about radon in our homes, holes in the ozone layer, trans fatty acids, global warming, and DNA analysis. Understanding chemistry and measurement helps us make proper choices about our world.

Think about your day; you probably made some measurements. Perhaps you checked your weight by stepping on a scale. If you did not feel well, you may have taken your temperature. To make some soup, you added 2 cups of water to a package of mix. If you stopped at the gas station, you watched the gas pump measure the number of gallons of gasoline you put in the car.

Measurement is an essential part of health careers such as nursing, dental hygiene, respiratory therapy, nutrition, and veterinary technology. The temperature, height, and weight of a patient are measured in degrees Celsius, meters, and kilograms, respectively. Samples of blood and urine are collected and sent to a laboratory where glucose, pH, urea, and protein are measured by the lab technicians.

By learning about measurement, you will develop skills for solving problems and how to work with numbers in chemistry. If you intend to go into a health career, an understanding and assessment of measurements will be an important part of your evaluation of a patient's health.

1.1 | Units of Measurement

Scientists and health professionals throughout the world use the **metric system**. It is also the common measuring system in all but a few countries. In 1960, scientists adopted a modification of the metric system called the *International System of Units*, Système International (**SI**), to provide additional uniformity for units used in the sciences. In this text, we will use metric units and introduce some of the SI units.

LEARNING GOAL

Write the names and abbreviations for the units used in measurements of length, volume, time, and mass.

Length

The metric and SI unit of length is the **meter** (**m**). A meter is 39.4 inches (in.), which makes it slightly longer than a yard (yd). The **centimeter** (**cm**) is a smaller unit of length that is commonly used in chemistry and is about as wide as your little finger. For comparison, there are 2.54 cm in 1 inch (in.). (See Figure 1.1.)

$$1\text{ m} = 100\text{ cm}$$
$$1\text{ m} = 39.4\text{ in.}$$
$$2.54\text{ cm} = 1\text{ in.}$$

FIGURE 1.1 Length in the metric and SI systems is based on the meter, which is slightly longer than a yard.

Q How many centimeters are in a length of one inch?

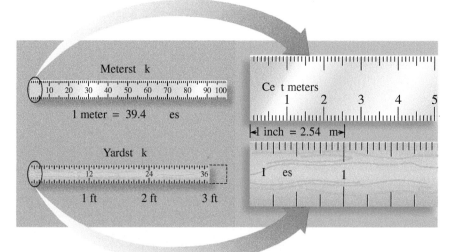

FIGURE 1.2 Volume is the space occupied by a substance. In the metric system, volume is based on the liter, which is slightly larger than a quart.

Q How many milliliters are in 1 quart?

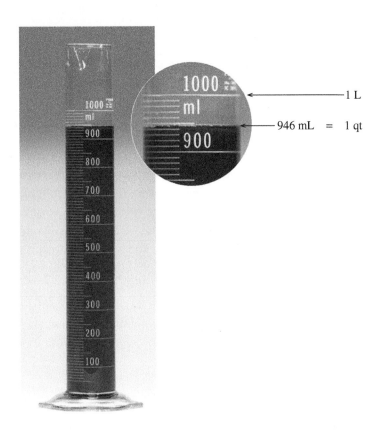

1 L

946 mL = 1 qt

Volume

Volume is the amount of space a substance occupies. A **liter (L)**, which is slightly larger than a quart (qt), is commonly used to measure volume. The **milliliter (mL)** is more convenient for measuring smaller volumes of fluids in hospitals and laboratories. The SI unit of volume is the cubic meter (m^3), a unit that is too large for practical use in the laboratory or hospital. A comparison of metric and U.S. units for volume appears in Figure 1.2.

$$1 \text{ L} = 1000 \text{ mL}$$
$$1 \text{ L} = 1.06 \text{ qt}$$
$$946 \text{ mL} = 1 \text{ qt}$$
$$1000 \text{ L} = 1 \text{ m}^3$$

Mass

The **mass** of an object is a measure of the quantity of material it contains. In the metric system, the unit for mass is the **gram (g)**. The SI unit of mass, the **kilogram (kg)**, is used for larger masses such as body weight. It takes 2.20 pounds (lb) to make 1 kg, and 454 g are needed to equal 1 pound.

$$1 \text{ kg} = 1000 \text{ g}$$
$$1 \text{ kg} = 2.20 \text{ lb}$$
$$454 \text{ g} = 1 \text{ lb}$$

FIGURE 1.3 On an electronic balance, mass is shown in grams as a digital readout.

Q How many grams are in 1 pound of candy?

You may be more familiar with the term *weight* than with mass. Weight is a measure of the gravitational pull on an object. On Earth, an astronaut with a mass of 75.0 kg has a weight of 165 lb. On the moon where the gravitational pull is one-sixth that of Earth, the astronaut has a weight of 27.5 lb. However, the mass of the astronaut is the same as on Earth, 75.0 kg. Scientists measure mass rather than weight because mass does not depend on gravity.

In a chemistry laboratory, a balance is used to measure the mass of a substance, as shown in Figure 1.3.

Temperature

You use a thermometer to see how hot something is, how cold it is outside, or perhaps to determine if you have a fever. (See Figure 1.4.) **Temperature** tells us how hot or cold an object is. A typical laboratory thermometer consists of a glass bulb containing a liquid that expands as the temperature increases. On the **Celsius (°C) temperature scale**, water freezes at 0 °C and boils at 100 °C, while on the Fahrenheit (°F) scale, water freezes at 32 °F and boils at 212 °F. In the SI system, temperature is measured using the **Kelvin (K) temperature scale**, on which the lowest temperature possible is assigned a value of 0 K. Note that the units on the Kelvin scale are called *kelvins* (K) and are not given degree signs.

Time

We typically measure time in units of years, days, hours, minutes, or seconds. Of these, the SI and metric basic unit of time is the **second (s)**. The standard device now used to determine a second is an atomic clock. A comparison of metric and SI units for measurement is shown in Table 1.1.

FIGURE 1.4 A thermometer is used to determine the temperature of a substance.

Q What kinds of temperature readings have you made today?

TABLE 1.1 Units of Measurement

Measurement	Metric	SI
Length	Meter (m)	Meter (m)
Volume	Liter (L)	Cubic meter (m^3)
Mass	Gram (g)	Kilogram (kg)
Time	Second (s)	Second (s)
Temperature	Celsius degree (°C)	Kelvin (K)

CONCEPT CHECK 1.1

■ **Units of Measurement**

State the type of measurement indicated by each of the following units:

a. kilogram   **b.** liter   **c.** meter   **d.** Celsius degree

ANSWER

a. A kilogram is a unit of mass.   **b.** A liter is a unit of volume.
c. A meter is a unit of length.   **d.** A Celsius degree is a unit of temperature.

SAMPLE PROBLEM   1.1

■ **Units of Measurement**

State the type of measurement (mass, length, volume, temperature, or time) indicated by the unit in each of the following:

a. 45.6 kg   **b.** 1.895 L   **c.** 14 s   **d.** 45 m   **e.** 315 K

SOLUTION

a. mass   **b.** volume   **c.** time   **d.** length   **e.** temperature

STUDY CHECK

Write the name of the metric unit and symbol you would use to express each of the following:

a. length of a football field
b. daytime temperature
c. mass of salt in a shaker

EXPLORE YOUR WORLD

Units Listed on Labels

Read the labels on a variety of products such as sugar, salt, soft drinks, vitamins, and dental floss.

QUESTIONS

1. What metric or SI units of mea–surement are listed on the labels?
2. What type of measurement (mass, volume, etc.) do they indicate?
3. Write the metric or SI amounts in terms of a number plus a unit.

QUESTIONS AND PROBLEMS

Units of Measurement

In every chapter, each magenta-colored, odd-numbered exercise in Questions and Problems is paired with the next even-numbered exercise. The answers for all the magenta, odd-numbered Questions and Problems are given at the end of this chapter. The complete solutions to the odd-numbered Questions and Problems are in the *Study Guide*.

1.1 Compare the units a student in the United States and a student in Mexico would use to measure the following:
   a. your mass
   b. your height
   c. amount of gasoline to fill the gas tank
   d. temperature

1.2 Suppose that a friend tells you the following information. Why are the statements confusing, and how would you make them clear using a metric (SI) unit?
   a. I rode my bicycle for 15 today.
   b. My dog weighs 25.
   c. It is hot today. It is 30.
   d. I started a diet and lost 1.5 last week.

1.3 State the name of the unit and the type of measurement (mass, length, volume, temperature, or time) for each of the following quantities:
   a. 4.8 m
   b. 325 g
   c. 1.5 L
   d. 480 s
   e. 28 °C

1.4 State the name of the unit and the type of measurement (mass, length, volume, temperature, or time) for each of the following quantities:
   a. 0.8 mL
   b. 3.6 m
   c. 14 kg
   d. 35 g
   e. 373 K

1.2 Scientific Notation

In chemistry, we use numbers that are extremely small and extremely large. We might measure something as tiny as the width of a human hair, which is 0.000 008 m. Or perhaps we want to count the number of hairs on the average human scalp, which is about 100 000 hairs. (In this section, we have added spaces to help make the places easier to count in very small or very large numbers.) (See Figure 1.5.) However, it is more convenient to write these small and large numbers in scientific notation.

Item	Value	Scientific Notation
Width of a human hair	0.000 008 m	8×10^{-6} m
Hairs on a human scalp	100 000 hairs	1×10^{5} hairs

Writing a Number in Scientific Notation

A number written in **scientific notation** has two parts: a coefficient and a power of 10. For example, the number 2400 in scientific notation is 2.4×10^{3}. The coefficient is 2.4, and 10^{3} shows that the power of 10 is 3. The coefficient is determined by moving the decimal point three places to the left to give a number from 1 to 9. Because we moved the decimal

FIGURE 1.5 Humans have an average of 1×10^{5} hairs on their scalps. Each hair is about 8×10^{-6} m wide.

Q Why are large and small numbers written in scientific notation?

8×10^{-6} m

point three places to the left, the power of 10 is a positive 3, written as 10^3. For a number greater than 1, the power of 10 is positive.

$$2400. = 2.4 \times 1000 = 2.4 \times 10 \times 10 \times 10 = 2.4 \quad \times \quad 10^3$$

← 3 places   Coefficient   Power of 10

When a number less than 1 is written in scientific notation, the power of 10 is negative. For example, to express the number 0.000 86 in scientific notation, the decimal point is moved to the right four places to give a coefficient of 8.6. By moving the decimal point four places to the right, the power of 10 is a negative 4, or 10^{-4}.

$$0.000\ 86 = \frac{8.6}{10\ 000} = \frac{8.6}{10 \times 10 \times 10 \times 10} = 8.6 \quad \times \quad 10^{-4}$$

4 places →   Coefficient   Power of 10

Table 1.2 gives some examples of numbers written as positive and negative powers of 10. The powers of 10 are a way to keep track of the decimal point in the decimal number. Table 1.3 gives examples of writing measurements in scientific notation.

TABLE 1.2 Some Powers of 10

Number	Multiples of 10	Scientific Notation	
10 000	$10 \times 10 \times 10 \times 10$	1×10^4	
1 000	$10 \times 10 \times 10$	1×10^3	
100	10×10	1×10^2	Some positive
10	10	1×10^1	powers of 10
1	0	1×10^0	
0.1	$\dfrac{1}{10}$	1×10^{-1}	
0.01	$\dfrac{1}{10} \times \dfrac{1}{10} = \dfrac{1}{100}$	1×10^{-2}	
0.001	$\dfrac{1}{10} \times \dfrac{1}{10} \times \dfrac{1}{10} = \dfrac{1}{1000}$	1×10^{-3}	Some negative powers of 10
0.0001	$\dfrac{1}{10} \times \dfrac{1}{10} \times \dfrac{1}{10} \times \dfrac{1}{10} = \dfrac{1}{10\ 000}$	1×10^{-4}	

TABLE 1.3 Some Measurements Written in Scientific Notation

Measured Quantity	Measurement	Scientific Notation
Volume of gasoline used in United States each year	550 000 000 000 L	5.5×10^{11} L
Diameter of Earth	12 800 000 m	1.28×10^7 m
Time for light to travel from the Sun to Earth	500 s	5×10^2 s
Mass of a typical human	68 kg	6.8×10^1 kg
Mass of a hummingbird	0.002 kg	2×10^{-3} kg
Length of a pox virus	0.000 000 3 m	3×10^{-7} m
Mass of a bacterium (mycoplasma)	0.000 000 000 000 000 000 1 kg	1×10^{-19} kg

Scientific Notation and Calculators

You can enter numbers in scientific notation on many calculators using the EE or EXP key. After you enter the coefficient, push the EXP (or EE) key and enter only the power of 10; the EXP function key already includes the $\times$ 10 value. To enter a negative power of 10, push the plus/minus (+/−) key or the minus (−) key (depending on your calculator) but **not** the key that performs the subtraction operation "−". Some calculators require entering the sign before the power.

Number to Enter	Method	Display Reads
4×10^6	4 EXP (EE) 6	$4\ 06$ or 4^{06} or $4\ E06$
2.5×10^{-4}	2.5 EXP (EE) +/− 4	$2.5\ -04$ or 2.5^{-04} or $2.5\ E{-}04$

When a calculator answer appears in scientific notation, it is usually shown in the display as a number from 1 to 9 followed by a space and the power of 10. To express this display in scientific notation, write the number, insert $\times\ 10$, and use the power of 10 as an exponent.

Calculator Display	Expressed in Scientific Notation
$7.52\ 04$ or 7.52^{04} or $7.52\ E04$	7.52×10^4
$5.8{-}02$ or 5.8^{-02} or $5.8\ E{-}02$	5.8×10^{-2}

On many scientific calculators, a number can be converted into scientific notation using the appropriate keys. For example, the number 0.000 52 can be entered followed by hitting the 2nd or 3rd function key and the SCI key. The scientific notation appears in the calculator display as a coefficient and the power of 10.

$$0.000\ 52 \quad \boxed{2^{nd}\ or\ 3^{rd}\ function\ key} \quad \boxed{SCI} \quad = \quad 5.2^{-04}\ or\ 5.2{-}04\ or\ 5.2E{-}4 \quad = 5.2 \times 10^{-4}$$

Key   Key   Display

Converting Scientific Notation to a Standard Number

When a number in scientific notation has a positive power of 10, the standard number is written by moving the decimal point to the right for the same number of places as the power of 10. Placeholder zeros are used to give additional decimal places.

$$8.2 \ \times \ 10^2 \ = \ 8.2 \ \times \ 100 \ = \ 820$$

For a number in scientific notation with a negative power of 10, the standard number is written by moving the decimal point to the left for the same number of places. Placeholder zeros are added in front of the coefficient as needed.

$$4.3 \ \times \ 10^{-3} \ = \ 4.3 \ \times \ \frac{1}{1000} \ = \ 0.0043$$

■ Scientific Notation

Indicate whether the power of 10 is positive or negative when each of the following is written in scientific notation:

a. 45 000 m
b. 0.0092 g
c. 143 mL

ANSWER
a. To make a coefficient between 1 and 9, the decimal point is moved four places to the left, which gives a positive power of 10 (4.5×10^4 m).
b. To make a coefficient between 1 and 9, the decimal point is moved three places to the right, which gives a negative power of 10 (9.2×10^{-3} g).
c. To make a coefficient between 1 and 9, the decimal point is moved two places to the left, which gives a positive power of 10 (1.43×10^2 mL).

■ **Scientific Notation**

1. Write the following measurements in scientific notation:
   a. 0.000 16 L   **b.** 5 220 000 m
2. Write the following as standard numbers:
   a. 7.2×10^{-3} m   **b.** 2.4×10^{5} g

SOLUTION

1. **a.** 1.6×10^{-4} L   **b.** 5.22×10^{6} m
2. **a.** 0.0072 m   **b.** 240 000 g

STUDY CHECK

Write the following measurements in scientific notation:
a. 425 000 m   **b.** 0.000 000 8 g

QUESTIONS AND PROBLEMS

Scientific Notation

1.5 Write the following measurements in scientific notation:
   a. 55 000 m   **b.** 480 g   **c.** 0.000 005 cm
   d. 0.000 14 s   **e.** 0.007 85 L **f.** 670 000 kg

1.6 Write the following measurements in scientific notation:
   a. 180 000 000 g   **b.** 0.000 06 m   **c.** 750 000 kg
   d. 0.15 m   **e.** 0.024 s   **f.** 1500 m³

1.7 Which number in each pair is larger?
   a. 7.2×10^{3} or 8.2×10^{2} **b.** 4.5×10^{-4} or 3.2×10^{-2}
   c. 1×10^{4} or 1×10^{-4} **d.** 0.000 52 or 6.8×10^{-2}

1.8 Which number in each pair is smaller?
   a. 4.9×10^{-3} or 5.5×10^{-9}
   b. 1250 or 3.4×10^{2}
   c. 0.000 000 4 or 5×10^{-8}
   d. 4×10^{-8} or 4×10^{-10}

1.9 Write the following as standard numbers:
   a. 1.2×10^{4} **b.** 8.25×10^{-2}
   c. 4×10^{6} **d.** 5×10^{-3}

1.10 Write the following as standard numbers:
   a. 3.6×10^{-5} **b.** 8.75×10^{4}
   c. 3×10^{-2} **d.** 2.12×10^{5}

1.3 Measured Numbers and Significant Figures

Whenever you make a measurement, you use some type of measuring device. For example, you may use a meterstick to measure your height, a scale to check your weight, and a thermometer to take your temperature. **Measured numbers** are the numbers you obtain when you measure a quantity such as your height, weight, or temperature.

Measured Numbers

Suppose you are going to measure the lengths of the objects in Figure 1.6. You would select a ruler with a scale marked on it. By observing the lines on the scale, you determine the measurement for each object. Perhaps the divisions on the scale are marked as 1 cm. Another ruler might be marked in divisions of 0.1 cm. To report the length, you would first read the numerical value of the marked line. Finally, you estimate by visually dividing the space between the smallest marked lines. This estimated number is the final digit in a measured number.

For example, in Figure 1.6a, the end of the object falls between the lines marked 4 cm and 5 cm. That means that the length is 4 cm plus an estimated digit. If you estimate that the end is halfway between 4 cm and 5 cm, you would report its length as 4.5 cm. However, someone else might report the length as 4.4 cm. The last digit in a measured number can differ because people do not estimate in the same way. The ruler shown in Figure 1.6b is marked with lines at 0.1 cm. With this ruler, you can estimate the value of the hundredth's

LEARNING GOAL

Determine the number of significant figures in measured numbers.

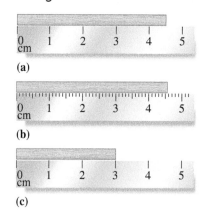

FIGURE 1.6 The lengths of the rectangular objects are measured as **(a)** 4.5 cm and **(b)** 4.55 cm.

Q What is the length of the object in (c)?

place (0.01 cm). Perhaps you would report the length of the object as 4.55 cm, while someone else may report its length as 4.56 cm. Both results are acceptable.

Therefore, there is always uncertainty in every measurement. When a measurement ends right on a marked line, a zero is written as the estimated digit. For example, in Figure 1.6c, the measurement for length is written as 3.0 cm, not 3. This means that the uncertainty of the measurement is in the estimated digit.

Significant Figures

SELF STUDY ACTIVITY
Significant Figures

In a measured number, the **significant figures** (**SFs**) are all the digits including the estimated digit. All nonzero numbers are counted as significant figures. Zeros may or may not be significant, depending on their position in a number. Table 1.4 gives the rules and examples of counting significant figures.

TABLE 1.4 Significant Figures in Measured Numbers

Rule	Measured Number	Number of Significant Figures
1. **A number is a *significant figure* if it is**		
a. not a zero	4.5 g	2
	122.35 m	5
b. a zero between nonzero digits	205 m	3
	5.082 kg	4
c. a zero at the end of a decimal number	50. L	2
	25.0 °C	3
	16.00 g	4
d. any digit in the coefficient of a number written in scientific notation	4.0×10^5 m	2
	5.70×10^{-3} g	3
2. **A zero is *not significant* if it is**		
a. at the beginning of a decimal number	0.0004 lb	1
	0.075 m	2
b. used as a placeholder in a large number without a decimal point	850 000 m	2
	1 250 000 g	3

When one or more zeros in a large number are significant digits, they are shown by writing the number using scientific notation. For example, if the first zero in the measurement 500 m is significant, then it can be shown by writing the measurement as 5.0×10^2 m. In this text, we will place a decimal point after a significant zero at the end of a number. For example, a measurement written as 250. g has three significant figures, which includes the zero. The number could also be written as 2.50×10^2 g. Unless noted otherwise, we will assume that zeros at the end of large standard numbers are not significant. We would interpret 400 000 g as 4×10^5 g with one significant figure.

CONCEPT CHECK 1.3

■ **Significant Zeros**

Underline significant zeros in each of the following measured numbers:

a. 0.000 250 m   **b.** 70.040 g   **c.** 1 020 055 mg

ANSWER

a. 0.000 25<u>0</u> m   **b.** 7<u>0</u>.<u>0</u>40 g   **c.** 1 <u>0</u>2<u>0</u> <u>0</u>55 mg

---

Exact Numbers

Exact numbers are those obtained by counting items or from a definition that compares two units in the same measuring system. Suppose a friend asks you to tell her the number of coats in your closet or the number of classes you are taking in school. Your answer would be given by counting the items. It was not necessary for you to use any type of measuring tool. Suppose someone asks you to state the number of seconds in one minute. Without using any measuring device, you would give the definition: 60 seconds in one minute. Exact numbers are not measured, do not have a limited number of significant figures, and do not affect the number of significant figures in a calculated answer. For more examples of exact numbers, see Table 1.5.

TABLE 1.5 Examples of Some Exact Numbers

Counted Numbers	Defined Equalities	
	U.S. System	Metric System
8 doughnuts	1 ft = 12 in.	1 L = 1000 mL
2 baseballs	1 qt = 4 cups	1 m = 100 cm
5 capsules	1 lb = 16 oz	1 kg = 1000 g

SAMPLE PROBLEM   1.3

■ **Significant Figures**

Identify each of the following numbers as measured or exact, and give the number of significant figures in each measured number:

a. 42.2 g   **b.** three eggs   **c.** 5.0×10^{-4} cm   **d.** 450 000 km   **e.** 3.500×10^5 s

SOLUTION

a. measured; three   **b.** exact
c. measured; two   **d.** measured; two
e. measured; four

STUDY CHECK

State the number of significant figures in each of the following measured numbers:

a. 0.000 35 g   **b.** 2000 m   **c.** 2.0045 L

QUESTIONS AND PROBLEMS

Measured Numbers and Significant Figures

1.11 Identify the numbers in each of the following statements as measured or exact:
  a. A person weighs 155 lb.
  b. The basket holds eight apples.
  c. In the metric system, 1 kg is equal to 1000 g.
  d. The distance from Denver, Colorado, to Houston, Texas, is 1720 km.

1.12 Identify the numbers in each of the following statements as measured or exact:
  a. There are 31 students in the laboratory.
  b. The oldest known flower lived 1.2×10^8 years ago.
  c. The largest gem ever found, an aquamarine, has a mass of 10^4 kg.
  d. A laboratory test shows a blood cholesterol level of 184 mg/100 mL.

1.13 In each set of the following numbers, identify the measured number(s), if any:
  a. 3 hamburgers and 6 oz of meat
  b. one table and four chairs
  c. 0.75 lb of grapes and 350 g of butter
  d. 60 seconds equals 1 minute

1.14 In each set of the following numbers, identify the exact number(s), if any:
  a. 5 pizzas and 50.0 g of cheese
  b. 6 nickels and 16 g of nickel
  c. 3 onions and 3 lb of potatoes
  d. 5 miles and 5 cars

1.15 For each of the following measurements, indicate if the zeros are significant:
  a. 0.0038 m   **b.** 5.04 cm
  c. 800. L   **d.** 3.0×10^{-3} kg
  e. 85 000 g

1.16 For each of the following measurements, indicate if the zeros are significant:
  a. 20.05 g
  b. 5.00 m
  c. 0.000 02 L
  d. 120 000 years
  e. 8.05×10^2 g

1.17 How many significant figures are in each of the following measured quantities?

    a. 11.005 g   **b.** 0.000 32 m

    c. 36 000 000 m   **d.** 1.80×10^4 g

    e. 0.8250 L   **f.** 30.0 °C

1.18 How many significant figures are in each of the following measured quantities?

    a. 20.60 L   **b.** 1036.48 g

    c. 4.00 m   **d.** 20.8 °C

    e. 60 800 000 g   **f.** 5.0×10^{-3} L

1.19 In which of the following pairs do both numbers contain the same number of significant figures?

    a. 20.5 g and 20.50 g   **b.** 405 K and 405.0 K

    c. 0.0012 s and 12 000 s   **d.** 35.00 L and 0.3500 L

1.20 In which of the following pairs do both numbers contain the same number of significant figures?

    a. 0.005 75 g and 5.75×10^{-3} g

    b. 0.0250 m and 0.205 m

    c. 150 000 s and 1.50×10^4 s

    d. 3.8×10^{-2} L and 3.8×10^5 L

1.21 Write each of the following in scientific notation with two significant figures:

    a. 5000 L   **b.** 30 000 g

    c. 100 000 m   **d.** 0.000 25 cm

1.22 Write each of the following in scientific notation with two significant figures:

    a. 5 100 000 g   **b.** 26 000 s

    c. 40 000 m   **d.** 0.000 820 kg

1.4   Significant Figures in Calculations

LEARNING GOAL

Adjust calculated answers to the correct number of significant figures.

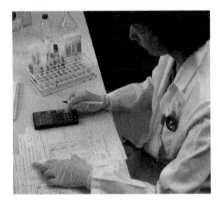

In the sciences, we measure many things: the length of a bacterium, the volume of a gas sample, the temperature of a reaction mixture, or the mass of iron in a sample. The numbers obtained from these types of measurements are often used in calculations. The number of significant figures in the measured numbers limits the number of significant figures that can be given in the calculated answer.

Using a calculator will usually help you to do calculations faster. However, calculators cannot think for you. It is up to you to enter the numbers correctly, press the right function keys, and adjust the calculator display to give an answer with the correct number of significant figures.

Rounding Off

To calculate the area of a carpet that measures 5.5 m by 3.5 m, you multiply 5.5 times 3.5 to obtain the number 19.25 as the area in square meters. However, all four digits cannot be given in the answer because they are not all significant figures. Each measurement of length and width has only two significant figures. This means that the calculated result must be rounded off to give an answer that also has two significant figures, 19 m². When you obtain a calculator result, determine the number of significant figures for the answer and round off using the following rules.

Rules for Rounding Off

    1. If the first digit to be dropped is *4 or less*, then it and all following digits are simply dropped from the number.

    2. If the first digit to be dropped is *5 or greater*, then the last retained digit of the number is increased by 1.

	Three Significant Figures	Two Significant Figures
Example 1: 8.4234 rounds off to	8.42	8.4
Example 2: 14.780 rounds off to	14.8	15
Example 3: 3256 rounds off to	3260 (3.26×10^3)	3300 (3.3×10^3)

CONCEPT CHECK 1.4

■ **Rounding Off**

Select the correct value when 2.8456 m is rounded to each of the following:

    a. three significant figures: 2.84 m   2.85 m   2.8 m   2.90 m

    b. two significant figures: 2.80 m   2.8 m   2.9 m   3.0 m

ANSWER

a. To round 2.8456 m to three significant figures, drop the final digits 56 and increase the last retained digit to give 2.85 m.

b. To round 2.8456 m to two significant figures, drop the final digits 456 to give 2.8 m.

SAMPLE PROBLEM 1.4

■ **Rounding Off**

Round off each of the following numbers to three significant figures:

a. 35.7823 m   **b.** 0.002 627 L   **c.** 3.8268×10^3 g   **d.** 1.2836 kg

SOLUTION

a. 35.8 m   **b.** 0.002 63 L   **c.** 3.83×10^3 g   **d.** 1.28 kg

STUDY CHECK

Round off each of the numbers in Sample Problem 1.4 to two significant figures.

Multiplication and Division

In multiplication or division, the final answer is written so it has the same number of significant figures as the measurement with the fewest SFs.

Example 1

Multiply the following measured numbers: 24.65×0.67

24.65   ☒   0.67   ⊜   *16.5155*   ⟶   17

Four SFs   Two   Calculator   Final answer,
            SFs   display   rounded to two SFs

The answer in the calculator display has more digits than the data allow. The measurement 0.67 has the least number of significant figures: two. Therefore, the calculator answer is rounded off to two significant figures.

Example 2

Solve the following:

$$\frac{2.85 \times 67.4}{4.39}$$

To do this problem on a calculator, enter the numbers and then press the operation keys. In this case, we might press the keys in the following order:

2.85   ☒   67.4   ÷   4.39   ⊜   *43.756264*   ⟶   43.8

Three SFs   Three SFs   Three SFs   Calculator   Final answer, rounded
                                       display   to three SFs

All of the measurements in this problem have three significant figures. Therefore, the calculator result is rounded off to give an answer, 43.8, that also has three significant figures.

Adding Significant Zeros

Sometimes, a calculator displays a small whole number. To give an answer with the correct number of significant figures, you may need to write significant zeros after the calculator result. For example, suppose the calculator display is 4, but you used measurements that have three significant numbers. The answer 4.00 is obtained by placing two significant zeros after the 4.

$$\frac{8.00}{2.00} = \qquad 4 \longrightarrow 4.00$$

3 SFs   Calculator display   Final answer, two zeros
added to give 3 SFs

SAMPLE PROBLEM   1.5

■ **Significant Figures in Multiplication and Division**

Perform the following calculations of measured numbers. Give the answers with the correct number of significant figures:

a. 56.8×0.37 **b.** $\dfrac{71.4}{11}$ **c.** $\dfrac{(2.075)(0.585)}{(8.42)(0.004\ 50)}$ **d.** $\dfrac{25.0}{5.00}$

SOLUTION

a. 21   **b.** 6.5   **c.** 32.0   **d.** 5.00 (add significant zeros)

STUDY CHECK

Perform the following calculations of measured numbers. Give the answers with the correct number of significant figures:

a. $45.26 \times 0.010\ 88$ **b.** $2.6 \div 324$ **c.** $\dfrac{4.0 \times 8.00}{16}$

Addition and Subtraction

In addition or subtraction, the answer is written so that it has the same number of decimal places as the measurement having the fewest decimal places.

Example 3

Add:

2.045	Three decimal places
+ 34.1	One decimal place
36.145	Calculator display
36.1	Answer rounded to one decimal place

Example 4

Subtract:

255	Ones place
− 175.65	Two decimal places
79.35	Calculator display
79	Answer rounded to ones place

When numbers are added or subtracted to give answers ending in zero, the zero does not appear after the decimal point in the calculator display. For example, $14.5\ \text{g} - 2.5\ \text{g} = 12.0\ \text{g}$. However, if you do the subtraction on your calculator, the display shows 12. To give the correct answer, a significant zero is written after the decimal point.

Example 5

Add:

37.12 mL	Two decimal places
+ 21.880 mL	Three decimal places
59.	Calculator display
59.00 mL	Answer; two significant zeros are written after the decimal point

SAMPLE PROBLEM **1.6**

■ **Significant Figures in Addition and Subtraction**

Perform the following calculations, and give the answers with the correct number of decimal places:

a. 27.8 cm + 0.235 cm **b.** 104.45 mL − 0.838 mL + 46 mL
c. 153.247 g − 14.82 g

SOLUTION

a. 28.0 cm **b.** 151 mL **c.** 138.43 g

STUDY CHECK

Perform the following calculations and give the answers with the correct number of decimal places:

a. 82.45 mg + 1.245 mg + 0.000 56 mg **b.** 4.259 L − 3.8 L

QUESTIONS AND PROBLEMS

Significant Figures in Calculations

1.23 Why do we usually need to round off calculations that use measured numbers?

1.24 Why do we sometimes add a zero to a number in a calculator display?

1.25 Round off each of the following numbers to three significant figures:
a. 1.854 **b.** 184.2038
c. 0.004 738 265 **d.** 8807
e. 1.832×10^5

1.26 Round off each of the numbers in problem 1.25 to two significant figures.

1.27 For the following problems, give answers with the correct number of significant figures:
a. 45.7 × 0.034 **b.** 0.002 78 × 5
c. $\dfrac{34.56}{1.25}$ **d.** $\dfrac{(0.2465)(25)}{1.78}$

1.28 For the following problems, give answers with the correct number of significant figures:
a. 400 × 185 **b.** $\dfrac{2.40}{(4)(125)}$
c. 0.825 × 3.6 × 5.1 **d.** $\dfrac{3.5 \times 0.261}{8.24 \times 20.0}$

1.29 For the following problems, give answers with the correct number of decimal places:
a. 45.48 cm + 8.057 cm
b. 23.45 g + 104.1 g + 0.025 g
c. 145.675 mL − 24.2 mL
d. 1.08 L − 0.585 L

1.30 For the following problems, give answers with the correct number of decimal places:
a. 5.08 g + 25.1 g
b. 85.66 cm + 104.10 cm + 0.025 cm
c. 24.568 mL − 14.25 mL
d. 0.2654 L − 0.2585 L

1.5 Prefixes and Equalities

The special feature of the metric system of units is that a **prefix** can be attached to any unit to increase or decrease its size by some factor of 10. For example, the prefixes *milli* and *micro* are used to make the smaller units, milligram (mg) and microgram (μg). Table 1.6 lists some of the metric prefixes, their symbols, and their decimal values.

The prefix *centi* is like cents in a dollar. One cent would be a centidollar, or $\frac{1}{100}$ of a dollar. That also means that one dollar is the same as 100 cents. The prefix *deci* is like dimes in a dollar. One dime would be a decidollar, or $\frac{1}{10}$ of a dollar. That also means that one dollar is the same as 10 dimes.

The U.S. Food and Drug Administration (FDA) has determined the daily values (DVs) of nutrients for adults and children age 4 or older. Some of these recommended daily values, which use prefixes, are listed in Table 1.7.

LEARNING GOAL

Use the numerical values of prefixes to write a metric equality.

SELF STUDY ACTIVITY
Metric System

TABLE 1.6 Metric and SI Prefixes

Prefix	Symbol	Numerical Value	Scientific Notation	Equality
Prefixes That Increase the Size of the Unit				
peta	P	1 000 000 000 000 000	10^{15}	$1\ Pg = 10^{15}\ g$
tera	T	1 000 000 000 000	10^{12}	$1\ Tg = 10^{12}\ g$
giga	G	1 000 000 000	10^{9}	$1\ Gm = 10^{9}\ m$
mega	M	1 000 000	10^{6}	$1\ Mg = 10^{6}\ g$
kilo	k	1 000	10^{3}	$1\ km = 10^{3}\ m$
Prefixes That Decrease the Size of the Unit				
deci	d	0.1	10^{-1}	$1\ dL = 10^{-1}\ L$ $1\ L = 10\ dL$
centi	c	0.01	10^{-2}	$1\ cm = 10^{-2}\ m$ $1\ m = 100\ cm$
milli	m	0.001	10^{-3}	$1\ ms = 10^{-3}\ s$ $1\ s = 10^{3}\ ms$
micro	μ	0.000 001	10^{-6}	$1\ \mu g = 10^{-6}\ g$ $1\ g = 10^{6}\ \mu g$
nano	n	0.000 000 001	10^{-9}	$1\ nm = 10^{-9}\ m$ $1\ m = 10^{9}\ nm$
pico	p	0.000 000 000 001	10^{-12}	$1\ ps = 10^{-12}\ s$ $1\ s = 10^{12}\ ps$
femto	f	0.000 000 000 000 001	10^{-15}	$1\ fs = 10^{-15}\ s$ $1\ s = 10^{15}\ fs$

TABLE 1.7 Daily Values for Selected Nutrients

Nutrient	Amount Recommended
Protein	44 g
Vitamin C	60 mg
Vitamin B_{12}	6 μg
Calcium	1000 mg
Iron	18 mg
Iodine	150 μg
Magnesium	400 mg
Potassium	3500 mg
Sodium	2400 mg
Zinc	15 mg

The relationship of a prefix to a unit can be expressed by replacing the prefix with its numerical value. For example, when the prefix *kilo* in kilometer is replaced with its value of 1000, we find that a kilometer is equal to 1000 meters. Other examples follow.

1 **kilo**meter (1 km) = **1000** meters (1000 m = 10^3 m)

1 **kilo**liter (1 kL) = **1000** liters (1000 L = 10^3 L)

1 **kilo**gram (1 kg) = **1000** grams (1000 g = 10^3 g)

CONCEPT CHECK 1.5

■ **Prefixes**

The storage capacity for a hard disk drive (HDD) is specified using prefixes: terabyte (TB), gigabyte (GB), or megabyte (MB). Indicate the storage capacity in bytes of each of the following hard disk drives. Suggest a reason for describing a HDD storage capacity in gigabytes or terabytes:

a. 5 MB   **b.** 1 TB   **c.** 2 GB

ANSWER

a. 5 MB = 5 000 000 (5×10^6) bytes
b. 1 TB = 1 000 000 000 000 (1×10^{12}) bytes
c. 2 GB = 2 000 000 000 (2×10^9) bytes

Expressing HDD capacity in gigabytes or terabytes gives a more reasonable number to work with than a number with many zeros or a large power of 10.

SAMPLE PROBLEM   1.7

■ Prefixes

Fill in the blanks with the correct prefix:

a. 1000 grams = 1 _____ gram   **b.** 0.01 meter = 1 _____ meter
c. 1×10^6 liters = 1 _____ liter

SOLUTION

a. The prefix for 1000 is *kilo*; 1000 grams = 1 kilogram.
b. The prefix for 0.01 is *centi*; 0.01 meter = 1 centimeter.
c. The prefix for 1×10^6 is *mega*; 1×10^6 liters = 1 megaliter.

STUDY CHECK

Write the correct prefix in the blanks:

a. 1 000 000 000 seconds = 1 _____ second
b. 0.01 meter = 1 _____ meter

Measuring Length

An ophthalmologist may measure the diameter of the retina of an eye in centimeters (cm), whereas a surgeon may need to know the length of a nerve in millimeters (mm). When the prefix *centi* is used with the unit meter, it indicates the unit centimeter, a length that is one-hundredth of a meter (0.01 m). A *millimeter* measures a length of 0.001 m. There are 1000 mm in a meter.

If we compare the lengths of a millimeter and a centimeter, we find that 1 mm is 0.1 cm; there are 10 mm in 1 cm. These comparisons are examples of **equalities**, which show the relationship between two units that measure the same quantity. For example, in the equality 1 m = 100 cm, each quantity describes the same length but in a different unit. Note that each quantity in the equality expression has both a number and a unit.

First Quantity   **Second Quantity**

    1   m   =   100   cm
    ↑   ↑   ↑   ↑
Number + unit   Number + unit

Some Length Equalities

1 m = 100 cm = 1×10^2 cm
1 m = 1000 mm = 1×10^3 mm
1 cm = 10 mm   = 1×10^1 mm

Some metric units for length are compared in Figure 1.7.

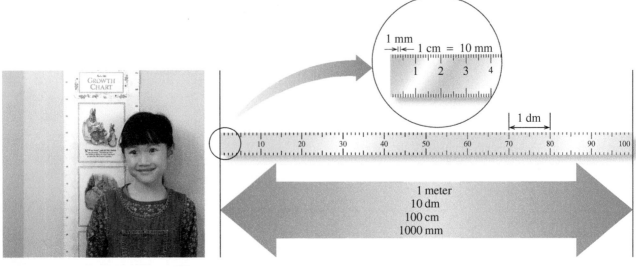

FIGURE 1.7 The metric length of 1 meter is the same length as 10 dm, 100 cm, and 1000 mm.

Q How many millimeters (mm) are in 1 centimeter (cm)?

Measuring Volume

Volumes of 1 L or smaller are common in the health sciences. When a liter is divided into 10 equal portions, each portion is a deciliter (dL). There are 10 dL in 1 L. Laboratory results for blood work are often reported in mass per deciliter. Table 1.8 lists typical laboratory tests for some substances in the blood.

When a liter is divided into a thousand parts, each smaller part is a milliliter (mL). In a 1-L container of physiological saline, there are 1000 mL of solution. (See Figure 1.8.)

Some Volume Equalities

$$1 \text{ L} = 10 \text{ dL} \quad = 1 \times 10^1 \text{ dL}$$
$$1 \text{ L} = 1000 \text{ mL} = 1 \times 10^3 \text{ mL}$$
$$1 \text{ dL} = 100 \text{ mL} \ \ = 1 \times 10^2 \text{ mL}$$

The **cubic centimeter** (**cm^3** or **cc**) is the volume of a cube with dimensions of 1 cm on each side. A cubic centimeter has the same volume as a milliliter, and the units are often used interchangeably.

$$1 \text{ cm}^3 = 1 \text{ cc} = 1 \text{ mL}$$

When you see *1 cm*, you are reading about length; when you see *1 cc* or *1 cm^3* or *1 mL*, you are reading about volume. Units of volume are illustrated in Figure 1.9.

TABLE 1.8 Some Typical Laboratory Test Values

Substance in Blood	Typical Range
Albumin	3.5–5.0 g/dL
Ammonia	20–150 µg/dL
Calcium	8.5–10.5 mg/dL
Cholesterol	105–250 mg/dL
Iron (male)	80–160 µg/dL
Protein (total)	6.0–8.0 g/dL

FIGURE 1.8 A plastic intravenous fluid container contains 1000 mL.

Q How many liters of solution are in the intravenous fluid container?

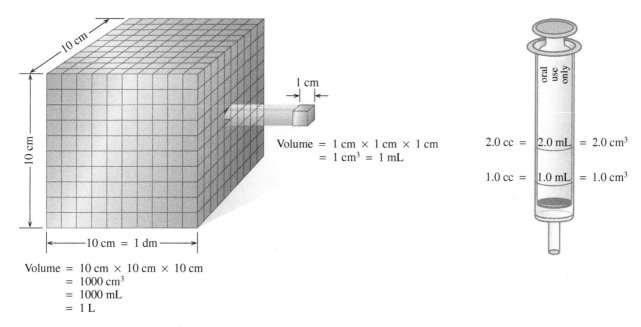

FIGURE 1.9 A cube measuring 10 cm on each side has a volume of 1000 cm³, or 1 L; a cube measuring 1 cm on each side has a volume of 1 cm³ (cc) or 1 mL.

Q What is the relationship between a milliliter (mL) and a cubic centimeter (cm³)?

Measuring Mass

When you get a physical examination, your mass is recorded in kilograms, whereas the results of your laboratory tests are reported in grams, milligrams (mg), or micrograms (μg). A kilogram equals 1000 g. One gram represents the same mass as 1000 mg, and 1 mg equals 1000 μg.

Some Mass Equalities

$$1 \text{ kg} = 1000 \text{ g} \quad = 1 \times 10^3 \text{ g}$$
$$1 \text{ g} = 1000 \text{ mg} = 1 \times 10^3 \text{ mg}$$
$$1 \text{ mg} = 1000 \text{ μg} = 1 \times 10^3 \text{ μg}$$

SAMPLE PROBLEM   1.8

■ Writing Metric Relationships

Complete the following list of metric equalities:
a. 1 L = _____ dL
b. 1 km = _____ m
c. 1 m = _____ cm
d. 1 cm³ = _____ mL

SOLUTION

a. 10 dL   **b.** 1000 m   **c.** 100 cm   **d.** 1 mL

STUDY CHECK

Complete the following metric equalities:
a. 1 kg = _____ g
b. 1 mL = _____ L

QUESTIONS AND PROBLEMS

Prefixes and Equalities

1.31 The speedometer is marked in both km/h and mph. What is the meaning of each abbreviation?

1.32 In a French car, the odometer reads 2250. What units would this be? What units would it be if this were an odometer in a car made for the United States?

1.33 How does the prefix *kilo* affect the gram unit in kilogram?

1.34 How does the prefix *centi* affect the meter unit in centimeter?

1.35 Write the abbreviation for each of the following units:
  a. milligram   **b.** deciliter
  c. kilometer   **d.** kilogram
  e. microliter   **f.** nanogram

1.36 Write the complete name for each of the following units:
  a. cm   **b.** kg
  c. dL   **d.** Gm
  e. μg   **f.** mg

1.37 Write the numerical values for each of the following prefixes:
  a. centi   **b.** kilo
  c. milli   **d.** deci
  e. mega   **f.** pico

1.38 Write the complete name (prefix + unit) for each of the following numerical values:
  a. 0.10 g   **b.** 1×10^{-6} g
  c. 1000 g   **d.** 0.01 g
  e. 0.001 g   **f.** 1×10^{12} g

1.39 Complete the following metric relationships:
  a. 1 m = _____ cm   **b.** 1 km = _____ m
  c. 1 mm = _____ m   **d.** 1 L = _____ mL

1.40 Complete the following metric relationships:
  a. 1 kg = _____ g   **b.** 1 mL = _____ L
  c. 1 g = _____ kg   **d.** 1 g = _____ mg

1.41 For each of the following pairs, which is the larger unit?
  a. milligram or kilogram   **b.** milliliter or microliter
  c. cm or km   **d.** kL or dL
  e. nanometer or picometer

1.42 For each of the following pairs, which is the smaller unit?
  a. mg or g   **b.** centimeter or millimeter
  c. mm or μm   **d.** mL or dL
  e. mg or Mg

1.6 Writing Conversion Factors

LEARNING GOAL

Write a conversion factor for two units that describe the same quantity.

Many problems in chemistry and the health sciences require a change of units. You make changes in units every day. For example, suppose you spent 2.0 hours (h) on your homework, and someone asked you how many minutes that was. You must have multiplied 2.0 h × 60 min/h, because you knew an equality (1 h = 60 min) that related the two units. When you expressed 2.0 h as 120 min, you did not change the amount of time you spent studying. You changed only the unit of measurement used to express the time. You can write every equality in the form of a fraction called a **conversion factor** in which one of the quantities is the numerator, and the other is the denominator. Two conversion factors are always possible from an equality because a factor can be inverted. Be sure to include the units when you write the conversion factors.

Two Conversion Factors for the Equality 1 h = 60 min

$$\frac{\text{Numerator} \longrightarrow}{\text{Denominator} \longrightarrow} \quad \frac{60 \text{ min}}{1 \text{ h}} \quad \text{and} \quad \frac{1 \text{ h}}{60 \text{ min}}$$

These factors are read as "60 minutes per 1 hour," and "1 hour per 60 minutes." The term *per* means "divide." Some common relationships are given in Table 1.9. It is important that the equality you select to construct a conversion factor is a true relationship.

When an equality shows the relationship for two units from the same system (metric or U.S.), it is considered a definition and exact. It is not used to determine significant figures. When an equality shows the relationship of units from two different systems, the number is measured and counts toward the significant figures in a calculation. For example, in the equality 1 lb = 454 g, the measured number 454 has three significant figures. The number 1 in 1 lb is considered to be exact. An exception is the relationship of 1 in. = 2.54 cm: the value 2.54 has been defined as exact.

TABLE 1.9 Some Common Equalities

Quantity	U.S.	Metric (SI)	Metric–U.S.
Length	1 ft = 12 in.	1 km = 1000 m	2.54 cm = 1 in.
	1 yard = 3 ft	1 m = 1000 mm	1 m = 39.4 in.
	1 mile = 5280 ft	1 cm = 10 mm	1 km = 0.621 mi
Volume	1 qt = 4 cups	1 L = 1000 mL	946 mL = 1 qt
	1 qt = 2 pt	1 dL = 100 mL	1 L = 1.06 qt
	1 gallon = 4 qt	1 mL = 1 cm³	
Mass	1 lb = 16 oz	1 kg = 1000 g	1 kg = 2.20 lb
		1 g = 1000 mg	454 g = 1 lb
Time		1 h = 60 min	
		1 min = 60 s	

Metric Conversion Factors

We can write metric conversion factors for the metric relationships we have studied. For example, from the equality for meters and centimeters, we can write the following factors:

Metric Equality	Conversion Factors
1 m = 100 cm	$\dfrac{100 \text{ cm}}{1 \text{ m}}$ and $\dfrac{1 \text{ m}}{100 \text{ cm}}$

Both are proper conversion factors for the relationship; one is just the inverse of the other. The usefulness of conversion factors is enhanced by the fact that we can turn a conversion factor over and use its inverse.

Metric–U.S. System Conversion Factors

Suppose you need to convert from pounds, a unit in the U.S. system, to kilograms in the metric (or SI) system. A relationship you could use is

1 kg = 2.20 lb

The corresponding conversion factors would be

$$\frac{2.20 \text{ lb}}{1 \text{ kg}} \quad \text{and} \quad \frac{1 \text{ kg}}{2.20 \text{ lb}}$$

Figure 1.10 illustrates the contents of some packaged foods in both metric and U.S. units.

FIGURE 1.10 In the U.S., the contents of many packaged foods are listed in both U.S. and metric units.

Q What are some advantages of using the metric system?

■ **Identifying Conversion Factors**

Identify the correct conversion factors for the equality for gigagrams and grams.

a. $\dfrac{1 \text{ Gg}}{1 \times 10^9 \text{g}}$ **b.** $\dfrac{1 \times 10^{-9}\text{g}}{1 \text{ Gg}}$ **c.** $\dfrac{1 \times 10^9 \text{ Gg}}{1 \text{ g}}$ **d.** $\dfrac{1 \times 10^9 \text{g}}{1 \text{ Gg}}$

ANSWER

Using the prefix table, we find the equality for gigagrams and grams is $1 \text{ Gg} = 1 \times 10^9$ g. Answers **a.** and **d.** are correctly written conversion factors.

SAMPLE PROBLEM 1.9

■ **Writing Conversion Factors from Equalities**

Write conversion factors for the relationship for the following pairs of units:

a. milligrams and grams **b.** quarts and milliliters

SOLUTION

Equality	Conversion Factors		
a. 1 g = 1000 mg	$\dfrac{1 \text{ g}}{1000 \text{ mg}}$	and	$\dfrac{1000 \text{ mg}}{1 \text{ g}}$
b. 1 qt = 946 mL	$\dfrac{1 \text{ qt}}{946 \text{ mL}}$	and	$\dfrac{946 \text{ mL}}{1 \text{ qt}}$

STUDY CHECK

A zeptosecond (zs) is a very small quantity of time. As an equality, it is written

$1 \text{ zs} = 1 \times 10^{-21}$ s

Write the conversion factors for this equality.

EXPLORE YOUR WORLD

SI and Metric Equalities on Product Labels

Read the labels on some food products or use the labels in Figure 1.10. List the amount of product given in different units. Write a relationship for two of the amounts for the same product and container. Look for measurements of grams and pounds or quarts and milliliters.

QUESTIONS

1. Use the stated measurement to derive a metric–U.S. conversion factor.
2. How do your results compare to the conversion factors we have described in this text?

Conversion Factors Stated Within a Problem

Many times, a problem specifies an equality that is true only for that problem. It might be the cost of 1 kilogram of oranges or the speed of a car in kilometers per hour. Such equalities are easy to miss when you first read a problem. Let's see how conversion factors are written from statements made within a problem.

1. The motorcycle was traveling at a speed of 85 km/h.

   Equality: 1 h = 85 km

   Conversion factors: $\dfrac{85 \text{ km}}{1 \text{ h}}$ and $\dfrac{1 \text{ h}}{85 \text{ km}}$

2. One tablet contains 500 mg of vitamin C.

   Equality: 1 tablet = 500 mg of vitamin C

   Conversion factors: $\dfrac{500 \text{ mg vitamin C}}{1 \text{ tablet}}$ and $\dfrac{1 \text{ tablet}}{500 \text{ mg vitamin C}}$

Conversion Factors for a Percentage, ppm, and ppb

Sometimes a percentage is given in a problem. The term *percent* (%) means parts per 100 parts. To write a percentage as a conversion factor, we choose a unit and express the numerical relationship of the parts of this unit to 100 parts of the whole. For example, an athlete might have 18% (18 percent) body fat by mass. (See Figure 1.11.) The percent quantity can be written as 18 mass units of body fat in every 100 mass units of body mass. Different mass units such as grams, kilograms (kg), or pounds (lb) can be used, but both units in the factor must be the same.

Percent quantity: 18% body fat by mass

Equality: 18 kg of body fat = 100 kg of body mass

Conversion factors: $\dfrac{100 \text{ kg body mass}}{18 \text{ kg body fat}}$ and $\dfrac{18 \text{ kg body fat}}{100 \text{ kg body mass}}$

or

Equality: 18 lb of body fat = 100 lb of body mass

Conversion factors: $\dfrac{100 \text{ lb body mass}}{18 \text{ lb body fat}}$ and $\dfrac{18 \text{ lb body fat}}{100 \text{ lb body mass}}$

FIGURE 1.11 The thickness of the skin fold at the waist measured in millimeters (mm) is used to determine the amount of body fat.

Q What is the percent body fat of an athlete with a body mass of 100 kg and 16 kg of body fat?

When scientists want to indicate ratios with particularly small percentage values, they use numerical relationships called *parts per million* (ppm) or *parts per billion* (ppb). The ratio of parts per million indicates milligrams of a substance per kilogram (mg/kg). The ratio of parts per billion gives the micrograms per kilogram (μg/kg). For example, the maximum amount of lead allowed by FDA in glazed pottery bowls is 5 ppm, which is 5 mg/kg.

ppm quantity: 5 ppm lead in glaze

Equality: 5 mg lead = 1 kg glaze

Conversion factors: $\dfrac{5 \text{ mg lead}}{1 \text{ kg glaze}}$ and $\dfrac{1 \text{ kg glaze}}{5 \text{ mg lead}}$

SAMPLE PROBLEM   1.10

■ Conversion Factors Stated in a Problem

Write the conversion factors for each of the following statements:

a. There are 325 mg of aspirin in 1 tablet.
b. One kilogram of bananas costs $1.25 at the grocery store.
c. The EPA has set the maximum level for mercury in tuna at 0.1 ppm.

SOLUTION

a. $\dfrac{325 \text{ mg aspirin}}{1 \text{ tablet}}$ and $\dfrac{1 \text{ tablet}}{325 \text{ mg aspirin}}$

b. $\dfrac{\$1.25}{1 \text{ kg bananas}}$ and $\dfrac{1 \text{ kg bananas}}{\$1.25}$

c. $\dfrac{0.1 \text{ mg mercury}}{1 \text{ kg tuna}}$ and $\dfrac{1 \text{ kg tuna}}{0.1 \text{ mg mercury}}$

STUDY CHECK

What conversion factors can be written for the following statements?

a. A cyclist in the Tour de France bicycle race rides at the average speed of 62.2 km/h.

b. The permissible level of arsenic in water is 10 ppb.

GREEN CHEMISTRY NOTE

Toxicology and Risk-Benefit Assessment

Each day we make choices about what we do or what we eat, often without thinking about the risks associated with these choices. We are aware of the risks of cancer from smoking, and we know there is a greater risk of having an accident if we cross a street where there is no light or crosswalk.

A basic concept of toxicology is the statement of Paracelsus that the right dose is the difference between a poison and a cure. To evaluate the level of danger from various substances, natural or synthetic, a risk assessment is made by exposing laboratory animals to the substances and monitoring the health effects. Often, doses much greater than humans might encounter are given to the test animals.

Many hazardous chemicals or substances have been identified by these tests. One measure of toxicity is the LD_{50}, or "lethal dose," which is the concentration of the substance that causes death in 50% of the test animals. A dosage is typically measured in milligrams per kilogram (mg/kg) of body mass or micrograms per kilogram (μg/kg).

Dosage	Units
parts per million (ppm)	milligrams per kilogram (mg/kg)
parts per billion (ppb)	micrograms per kilogram (μg/kg)

Other evaluations also need to be made, but it is easy to compare LD_{50} values. Parathion, a pesticide, with an LD_{50} of 3 mg/kg would be highly toxic. That means that half the test animals given 3 mg of parathion per kg body mass would be expected to die. Salt (sodium chloride) with an LD_{50} of 3000 mg/kg has a much lower toxicity. You would need to ingest a huge amount of salt before

any toxic effect would be observed. Although the risk to animals based on dose can be evaluated in the laboratory, it is more difficult to determine the impact in the environment because there is also a difference between continued exposure and a single, large dose of the substance.

Table 1.10 lists some LD_{50} values and compares pesticides and common substances in our everyday lives, in order of increasing toxicity.

TABLE 1.10 Some LD_{50} Values for Pesticides and Common Materials Tested in Rats

Substance	LD_{50} (mg/kg)
Table sugar	29 700
Baking soda	4220
Table salt	3000
Ethanol	2080
Aspirin	1100
Caffeine	192
Sodium cyanide	6
Parathion	3

QUESTIONS AND PROBLEMS

Writing Conversion Factors

1.43 Why can two conversion factors be written for an equality such as 1 m = 100 cm?

1.44 How can you check that you have written the correct conversion factors for an equality?

1.45 Write the equality and two conversion factors for the following pairs of units:

a. centimeters and meters

b. milligrams and grams

c. liters and milliliters

d. deciliters and milliliters

1.46 Write the equality and two corresponding conversion factors for the following pairs of units:
  a. centimeters and inches
  b. pounds and kilograms
  c. pounds and grams
  d. quarts and milliliters

1.47 Write the equality and two conversion factors for each of the following statements:
  a. One yard is 3 feet.
  b. One mile is 5280 feet.
  c. One minute is 60 seconds.
  d. A car goes 27 miles on 1 gallon of gas.
  e. Sterling silver is 93% by mass silver.

1.48 Write the equality and two conversion factors for each of the following statements:
  a. One gallon is 4 quarts.
  b. At the store, oranges are $1.29 per lb.

  c. There are 7 days in 1 week.
  d. One dollar has four quarters.
  e. A ring contains 58% by mass gold.

1.49 Write the conversion factors for each of the following statements:
  a. A bee flies at an average speed of 3.5 m per second.
  b. The daily requirement for potassium is 3500 mg.
  c. An automobile traveled 46.0 km on 1.0 gal of gasoline.
  d. The label on a bottle reads 50 mg Atenolol per tablet.
  e. The pesticide level in plums was 29 ppb.

1.50 Write the conversion factors for each of the following statements:
  a. The label on a bottle reads 10 mg of furosemide per mL.
  b. The daily requirement for iodine is 150 µg.
  c. The nitrate level in well water was 32 ppm.
  d. A DVD contains 17 gigabytes of information.
  e. The price of a gallon of gas is $3.19.

1.7 Problem Solving

The process of problem solving in chemistry often requires the conversion of an initial quantity given in one unit to the same quantity but in different units. By using one or more of the conversion factors we discussed in the previous section, the initial unit can be converted to the final unit:

Given quantity × One or more conversion factors = Desired quantity

Initial unit ⟶ Final unit

You may use a sequence similar to the steps in the following guide to problem solving (GPS):

Guide to Problem Solving (GPS) Using Conversion Factors

STEP 1 **Given/Need** State the initial unit given in the problem and the final unit needed.

STEP 2 **Plan** Write out a sequence of units that starts with the initial unit and progresses to the final unit for the answer. Be sure you can supply the equality for each unit conversion.

STEP 3 **Equalities/Conversion Factors** For each change of unit in your plan, state the equality and corresponding conversion factors. Recall that equalities are derived from the metric (SI) system, the U.S. system, and statements within a problem.

STEP 4 **Set Up Problem** Write the initial quantity and unit, and set up conversion factors that connect the units. Be sure to arrange the units in each factor so the unit in the denominator cancels the preceding unit in the numerator. Check that the units cancel properly to give the final unit. Carry out the calculations, count the significant figures in each measured number, and give a final answer with the correct number of significant figures.

Suppose a problem requires the conversion of 164 lb to kilograms. One part of this statement (164 lb) is the given quantity (initial unit), while another part (kilograms) is the final unit needed for the answer. Once you identify these units, you can determine which equalities you need to convert the initial unit to the final unit.

STEP 1 **Given** 164 lb   **Need** kg

STEP 2 **Plan** It is helpful to decide on a plan of units. When we look at the initial units given and the final units needed, we see that one is a metric unit, and the other is

LEARNING GOAL

Use conversion factors to change from one unit to another.

a unit in the U.S. system of measurement. Therefore, the connecting conversion factor must be one that includes a metric and a U.S. unit.

$$\text{lb} \quad \begin{array}{c} \text{Metric–U.S.} \\ \text{factor} \end{array} \quad \text{kg}$$

STEP 3   **Equalities/Conversion Factors**   From the discussion on U.S. and metric equalities, we can write the following equality and conversion factors:

$$1 \text{ kg} = 2.20 \text{ lb}$$

$$\frac{2.20 \text{ lb}}{1 \text{ kg}} \quad \text{and} \quad \frac{1 \text{ kg}}{2.20 \text{ lb}}$$

STEP 4   **Set Up Problem**   Now we can write the setup to solve the problem using the unit plan and a conversion factor. First, write down the initial unit, 164 lb. Then multiply by the conversion factor that has the unit lb in the denominator (bottom number) to cancel out the initial unit. The unit kg in the numerator (top number) gives the final unit for the answer.

Unit for answer goes here

$$164 \text{ lb} \quad \times \quad \frac{1 \text{ kg}}{2.20 \text{ lb}} \quad = \quad 74.5 \text{ kg}$$

Given   Conversion factor   Answer
(initial unit)   (cancels initial unit)   (desired unit)

Look at how the units cancel. The unit that you want in the answer is the one that remains after all the other units have cancelled out. This is a helpful way to check that a problem is set up properly.

$$\text{lb} \times \frac{\text{kg}}{\text{lb}} = \text{kg} \quad \text{Unit needed for answer}$$

The calculation done on a calculator gives the numerical part of the answer. The calculator answer is adjusted to give a final answer with the proper number of significant figures.

$$164 \times \frac{1}{2.20} = 74.54545455 = 74.5$$

3 SFs   3 SFs   Calculator display   3 SFs (rounded)

The value of 74.5 combined with the final unit, kg, gives the final answer of 74.5 kg. With few exceptions, answers to numerical problems contain a number and a unit.

CONCEPT CHECK 1.7

■ **Cancellation of Units**

Cancel the units in the following set up and give the unit of the final answer.

$$3.5 \text{ L} \times \frac{1 \times 10^3 \text{ mL}}{1 \text{ L}} \times \frac{0.48 \text{ g}}{1 \text{ mL}} \times \frac{1 \times 10^3 \text{ mg}}{1 \text{ g}} =$$

ANSWER
All like units cancel to give mg in the numerator as the final unit for the answer.

$$3.5 \text{ L} \times \frac{1 \times 10^3 \text{ mL}}{1 \text{ L}} \times \frac{0.48 \text{ g}}{1 \text{ mL}} \times \frac{1 \times 10^3 \text{ mg}}{1 \text{ g}} = \text{final unit is mg}$$

SAMPLE PROBLEM 1.11

■ **Problem Solving Using Metric Factors**

The daily recommended amount of potassium in the diet is 3500 mg. How many grams of potassium are needed each day?

SOLUTION

STEP 1   **Given**   3500 mg   **Need**   g

STEP 2   **Plan**   When we look at the initial units given and the final units needed, we see that both are metric units. Therefore, the connecting conversion factor must relate two metric units.

     mg   Metric factor   g

STEP 3   **Equalities/Conversion Factors**   From the discussion on prefixes and metric equalities, we can write the following equality and conversion factors:

$$1 \text{ g} = 1000 \text{ mg}$$

$$\frac{1 \text{ g}}{1000 \text{ mg}} \quad \text{and} \quad \frac{1000 \text{ mg}}{1 \text{ g}}$$

STEP 4   **Set Up Problem**   We write the setup using the unit plan and a conversion factor starting with the initial unit, 3500 mg. The final answer (g) is obtained by using the conversion factor that cancels the unit mg. Round off the answer to give the proper number of significant figures.

Unit for answer goes here

$$3500 \text{ mg} \times \frac{1 \text{ g}}{1000 \text{ mg}} = 3.5 \text{ g}$$

Given   Metric factor   Answer

STUDY CHECK

If 1890 mL of orange juice are prepared from orange juice concentrate, how many liters of orange juice is that?

Using Two or More Conversion Factors

In many problems, two or more conversion factors are needed to complete the change of units. In setting up these problems, one factor follows the other. Each factor is arranged to cancel the preceding unit until the final unit is obtained. Up to this point, we have used the conversion factors one at a time and calculated an answer. You can work all problems in single steps; if you do, be sure to keep one or two extra digits in the intermediate answers and round off only the final answer to the correct number of significant figures. A more efficient way to do these problems is to use a series of two or more conversion factors set up so that the unit in the denominator of each factor cancels the unit in the preceding numerator. Both approaches are illustrated in the following sample problem.

SAMPLE PROBLEM 1.12

■ **Problem Solving Using Two Factors**

During a volcanic eruption on Mauna Loa, Hawaii, the lava flowed at a rate of 33 meters per minute. At this rate, how far, in kilometers, can the lava travel in 45 minutes?

SOLUTION

STEP 1   **Given**   45 min   **Need**   km

STEP 2   **Plan**   min   Rate factor   m   Metric factor   km

STEP 3 **Equalities/Conversion Factors**   In the problem, the information for the rate of lava flow is given as 33 m/min. We will use this rate as one of the equalities as well as the metric equality for meters and kilometers and write conversion factors for each.

$$1 \text{ min} = 33 \text{ m} \qquad\qquad 1 \text{ km} = 1000 \text{ m}$$

$$\frac{1 \text{ min}}{33 \text{ m}} \quad \text{and} \quad \frac{33 \text{ m}}{1 \text{ min}} \qquad\qquad \frac{1 \text{ km}}{1000 \text{ m}} \quad \text{and} \quad \frac{1000 \text{ m}}{1 \text{ km}}$$

STEP 4 **Set Up Problem**   Set up the problem using the rate as a conversion factor to cancel minutes. Then use the metric factor to obtain kilometers in the final factor. Working in single steps, we can use the rate factor to convert from minutes to meters:

$$45 \cancel{\text{ min}} \times \frac{33 \text{ m}}{1 \cancel{\text{ min}}} = 1500 \text{ m}$$

Then we use the metric factor to cancel meters and give kilometers as the needed unit:

$$1500 \cancel{\text{ m}} \times \frac{1 \text{ km}}{1000 \cancel{\text{ m}}} = 1.5 \text{ km}$$

When set up as a series, the first factor cancels minutes, and the second factor cancels meters, which gives kilometers as the final unit for the answer.

$$\cancel{\text{min}} \times \frac{\cancel{\text{m}}}{\cancel{\text{min}}} \times \frac{\text{km}}{\cancel{\text{m}}} = \text{km}$$

$$45 \cancel{\text{ min}} \quad \times \quad \frac{33 \cancel{\text{ m}}}{1 \cancel{\text{ min}}} \quad \times \quad \frac{1 \text{ km}}{1000 \cancel{\text{ m}}} = 1.485 \text{ km} = 1.5 \text{ km}$$

Given	Rate	Metric	Calculator	Answer
(initial unit)	factor	factor	answer	(desired unit)
2 SFs	2 SFs	exact		2 SFs

The calculations are done in a sequence on a calculator to give the numerical part of the answer. The calculator answer is adjusted to give a final answer with the proper number of SFs.

$$45 \;\boxed{\times}\; 33 \;\boxed{\div}\; 1000 \;\boxed{=}\; \qquad 1.485 \quad = \quad 1.5$$

2 SFs	2 SFs	Exact	Calculator display	2 SFs (rounded)

STUDY CHECK

One medium bran muffin contains 4.2 g of fiber. How many ounces (oz) of fiber are obtained by eating three medium bran muffins if 1 lb = 16 oz? (*Hint*: number of muffins → g of fiber → lb → oz.)

Using a sequence of two or more conversion factors is an efficient way to set up and solve problems, especially if you are using a calculator. Once you have the problem set up, the calculations can be done without writing out the intermediate values. This process is worth practicing until you understand unit cancellation and the mathematical calculations.

Clinical Calculations Using Conversion Factors

Conversion factors are also useful for calculating medications. For example, if an antibiotic is available in 5-mg tablets, the dosage can be written as a conversion factor: 5 mg/1 tablet. In many hospitals, the apothecary unit of *grain* (gr) is still in use; there are 65 mg in 1 gr. When you do a medication problem, you often start with a doctor's order that contains the quantity to give the patient. The medication dosage is used as a conversion factor.

SAMPLE PROBLEM 1.13

■ Clinical Factors from a Word Problem

Synthroid is used as a replacement or supplemental therapy for diminished thyroid function. A dosage of 0.200 mg is prescribed with tablets that contain 50 μg of Synthroid. How many tablets are required to provide the prescribed medication?

SOLUTION

STEP 1   **Given**   0.200 mg of Synthroid   **Need**   tablets

STEP 2   **Plan**   mg $\dfrac{\text{Metric}}{\text{factor}}$ μg $\dfrac{\text{Clinical}}{\text{factor}}$ tablets

STEP 3   **Equalities/Conversion Factors**   In the problem, the information for the dosage is given as 50 μg per tablet. We will use this as one of the equalities as well as the metric equality for milligrams and micrograms and write conversion factors for each.

$$1\text{ mg} = 1000\text{ μg} \qquad\qquad 1\text{ tablet} = 50\text{ μg}$$

$$\dfrac{1\text{ mg}}{1000\text{ μg}} \quad\text{and}\quad \dfrac{1000\text{ μg}}{1\text{ mg}} \qquad \dfrac{1\text{ tablet}}{50\text{ μg}} \quad\text{and}\quad \dfrac{50\text{ μg}}{1\text{ tablet}}$$

STEP 4   **Set Up Problem**   The problem can be set up using the metric factor to cancel "milligrams," and then the clinical factor to obtain "tablets" as the final unit.

$$0.200\ \cancel{\text{mg}} \times \dfrac{1000\ \cancel{\text{μg}}}{1\ \cancel{\text{mg}}} \times \dfrac{1\text{ tablet}}{50\ \cancel{\text{μg}}} = 4\text{ tablets}$$

STUDY CHECK

An antibiotic dosage of 500 mg is ordered. If the antibiotic is supplied in liquid form as 250 mg in 5.0 mL, how many mL would be given?

SAMPLE PROBLEM 1.14

■ Using a Percent as a Conversion Factor

Bronze is 80.0% by mass copper and 20.0% by mass tin. A sculptor is preparing to cast a figure that requires 1.75 lb of bronze. How many grams of copper are needed for the bronze figure?

SOLUTION

STEP 1   **Given**   1.75 lb of bronze   **Need**   g of copper

STEP 2   **Plan**   lb of bronze $\dfrac{\text{Metric–U.S.}}{\text{factor}}$ g of bronze $\dfrac{\text{Percent}}{\text{factor}}$ g of copper

STEP 3   **Equalities/Conversion Factors**   Now we can write the equalities and conversion factors. One is the U.S.–metric factor for g and lb. The second is the percent factor derived from the information given in the problem.

$$1\text{ lb of bronze} = 454\text{ g of bronze} \qquad 100\text{ g of bronze} = 80.0\text{ g of copper}$$

$$\dfrac{454\text{ g bronze}}{1\text{ lb bronze}} \quad\text{and}\quad \dfrac{1\text{ lb bronze}}{454\text{ g bronze}} \qquad \dfrac{80.0\text{ g copper}}{100\text{ g bronze}} \quad\text{and}\quad \dfrac{100\text{ g bronze}}{80.0\text{ g copper}}$$

STEP 4   **Set Up Problem**   We can set up the problem using conversion factors to cancel each unit, starting with lb bronze, until we obtain the final factor, g copper, in the numerator. After we count the significant figures in the measured quantities, we write the final answer with three significant figures.

$$1.75 \ \text{lb bronze} \ \times \ \frac{454 \ \text{g bronze}}{1 \ \text{lb bronze}} \ \times \ \frac{80.0 \ \text{g copper}}{100 \ \text{g bronze}} \ = \ 636 \ \text{g of copper}$$

3 SFs   3 SFs   3 SFs   3 SFs

STUDY CHECK

A lean hamburger is 22% fat by weight. How many grams of fat are in 0.25 lb of the hamburger?

QUESTIONS AND PROBLEMS

Problem Solving

1.51 When you convert one unit to another, how do you know which unit of the conversion factor to place in the denominator?

1.52 When you convert one unit to another, how do you know which unit of the conversion factor to place in the numerator?

1.53 Use metric conversion factors to solve the following problems:
 a. The height of a student is 175 cm. How tall is the student in meters?
 b. A cooler has a volume of 5500 mL. What is the capacity of the cooler in liters?
 c. A hummingbird has a mass of 0.0055 kg. What is the mass of the hummingbird in grams?

1.54 Use metric conversion factors to solve the following problems:
 a. The daily requirement of phosphorus is 800 mg. How many grams of phosphorus are recommended?
 b. A glass of orange juice contains 0.85 dL of juice. How many milliliters of orange juice is that?
 c. A package of chocolate instant pudding contains 2840 mg of sodium. How many grams of sodium is that?

1.55 Solve the following problems using one or more conversion factors:
 a. A container holds 0.750 qt of liquid. How many milliliters of lemonade will it hold?
 b. In England, a person is weighed in stones. If one stone has a weight of 14.0 lb, what is the mass, in kilograms, of a person who weighs 11.8 stones?
 c. The femur, or thighbone, is the longest bone in the body. In a 6-ft-tall person, the femur is 19.5 in. long. What is the length of that femur in millimeters?
 d. How many inches thick is an arterial wall that measures 0.50 μm?

1.56 Solve the following problems using one or more conversion factors:
 a. You need 4.0 ounces of a steroid ointment. If there are 16 oz in 1 lb, how many grams of ointment does the pharmacist need to prepare?
 b. During surgery, a person receives 5.0 pints of plasma. How many milliliters of plasma were given?
 c. Solar flares containing hot gases can rise to 120 000 miles above the surface of the sun. What is that distance in kilometers?
 d. A filled gas tank contains 18.5 gallons of unleaded fuel. If a car uses 46 L, how many gallons of fuel remain in the tank?

1.57 The singles portion of a tennis court is 27.0 ft wide and 78.0 ft long.

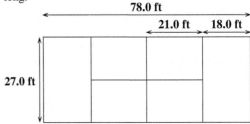

 a. What is the length of the court in meters?
 b. What is the area of the court in square meters (m^2)?
 c. If a serve is measured at 185 km per hour, how many seconds does it take for the tennis ball to travel the length of the court?

1.58 A football field is 300 feet long between goal lines.

 a. How many meters does a player run if he catches the ball on his own goal line and scores a touchdown?
 b. If a player catches the football and runs 45 yards, how many meters did he gain?
 c. If a player runs at a speed of 36 km/h, how many seconds does it take to run from the 50-yard line to the 20-yard line?

1.59 Using conversion factors, solve the following clinical problems:
 a. You have used 250 L of distilled water for a dialysis patient. How many gallons of water is that?
 b. A patient needs 0.024 g of a sulfa drug. There are 8-mg tablets in stock. How many tablets should be given?
 c. The daily dose of ampicillin for the treatment of an ear infection is 115 mg/kg of body weight. What is the daily dose, in mg, for a 34-lb child?

1.60 Using conversion factors, solve the following clinical problems:
 a. The physician has ordered 1.0 g of tetracycline to be given every 6 hours to a patient. If your stock on hand is 500-mg tablets, how many will you need for 1 day's treatment?
 b. An intramuscular medication is given at 5.00 mg/kg of body weight. If you give 425 mg of medication to a patient, what is the patient's weight in pounds?

c. A physician has ordered 325 mg of atropine, intramuscularly. If atropine were available as 0.50 g/mL of solution, how many milliliters would you need to give?

1.61 a. Oxygen makes up 46.7% by mass of Earth's crust. How many grams of oxygen are present if a sample of Earth's crust has a mass of 325 g?

   b. Magnesium makes up 2.1% by mass of Earth's crust. How many grams of magnesium are present if a sample of Earth's crust has a mass of 1.25 g?

   c. A plant fertilizer contains 15% by mass nitrogen (N). In a container of soluble plant food, there are 10.0 oz of fertilizer. How many grams of nitrogen are in the container?

   d. In a candy factory, the nutty chocolate bars contain 22.0% by mass pecans. If 5.0 kg of pecans were used for candy last Tuesday, how many lb of nutty chocolate bars were made?

1.62 a. Water is 11.2% by mass hydrogen. How many kilograms of water would contain 5.0 g of hydrogen?

   b. Water is 88.8% by mass oxygen. How many grams of water would contain 2.25 kg of oxygen?

   c. Blueberry fiber cakes contain 51% dietary fiber. If a package with a net weight of 12 ounces contains 6 cakes, how many grams of fiber are in each cake?

   d. A jar of crunchy peanut butter contains 1.43 kg of peanut butter. If you use 8.0% of the peanut butter for a sandwich, how many ounces of peanut butter did you take out of the container?

1.8 Density

Differences in density determine whether an object will sink or float. In Figure 1.12, the density of lead is greater than the density of water, and the lead object sinks. The cork floats because cork is less dense than water.

The mass and volume of any object can be measured. However, the separate measurements do not tell us how tightly packed the substance might be. If we compare the mass of the object to its volume, we obtain a relationship called **density**:

$$\text{Density} = \frac{\text{mass of substance}}{\text{volume of substance}}$$

LEARNING GOAL

Calculate the density or specific gravity of a substance and use the density or specific gravity to calculate the mass or volume of a substance.

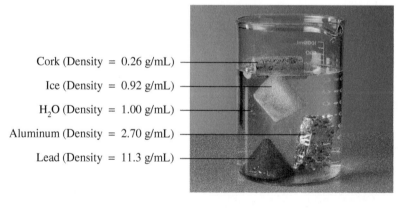

Cork (Density = 0.26 g/mL)

Ice (Density = 0.92 g/mL)

H_2O (Density = 1.00 g/mL)

Aluminum (Density = 2.70 g/mL)

Lead (Density = 11.3 g/mL)

FIGURE 1.12 Objects that sink in water are more dense than water; objects float if they are less dense.

Q Why does a cork float and a piece of lead sink?

In the metric system, the densities of solids and liquids are usually expressed as grams per cubic centimeter (g/cm^3) or grams per milliliter (g/mL). The density of gases is usually stated as grams per liter (g/L). Table 1.11 gives the densities of some common substances.

TABLE 1.11 Densities of Some Common Substances

Solids (at 25 °C)	Density (g/mL)	Liquids (at 25 °C)	Density (g/mL)	Gases (at 0 °C, 1 atm)	Density (g/L)
Cork	0.26	Gasoline	0.66	Hydrogen	0.090
Wood (maple)	0.75	Ethyl alcohol	0.79	Helium	0.179
Ice (at 0 °C)	0.92	Olive oil	0.92	Methane	0.714
Sugar	1.59	Water (at 4 °C)	1.00	Neon	0.90
Bone	1.80	Plasma (blood)	1.03	Nitrogen	1.25
Aluminum	2.70	Milk	1.04	Air (dry)	1.29
Cement	3.00	Mercury	13.6	Oxygen	1.43
Diamond	3.52			Carbon dioxide	1.96
Silver	10.5				
Lead	11.3				
Gold	19.3				

■ **Density**

(a)   (b)

a. In drawing (a), the gray cube has a density of 4.5 g/cm³. Is the density of the green cube the same, less than, or greater than the gray cube?
b. In drawing (b), the gray cube has a density of 4.5 g/cm³. Is the density of the green cube the same, less than, or greater than the gray cube?

ANSWER
a. The green cube has the same volume as the gray cube, but has a greater mass. Thus, the green cube has a density that is greater than the density of the gray cube.
b. The green cube has the same mass as the gray cube, but the green cube has a greater volume. Thus, the green cube has a density that is less than the density of the gray cube.

SAMPLE PROBLEM   1.15

■ **Calculating Density**

A copper sample has a mass of 44.65 g and a volume of 5.0 mL. What is the density of copper?

SOLUTION

Guide to Calculating Density

STEP 1
State the given and needed quantities.

STEP 2
Write the density expression.

STEP 3
Express mass in grams and volume in milliliters (mL) or cm³.

STEP 4
Substitute mass and volume into density expression and solve.

STEP 1   **Given**   mass = 44.65 g; volume = 5.0 mL   **Need**   density (g/mL)

STEP 2   **Plan**   To calculate density, substitute the mass (g) and the volume (mL) of the copper sample into the expression for density.

STEP 3   **Equality/Conversion Factor**

$$\text{Density} = \frac{\text{mass of substance}}{\text{volume of substance}}$$

STEP 4   **Set Up Problem**

$$\text{Density} = \frac{\overset{\text{4 SFs}}{44.65 \text{ g}}}{\underset{\text{2 SFs}}{5.0 \text{ mL}}} = \frac{\overset{\text{2 SFs}}{8.9 \text{ g}}}{1 \text{ mL}} = 8.9 \text{ g/mL}$$

STUDY CHECK

What is the density (g/cm³) of a silver bar that has a mass of 294 g and a volume of 28.0 cm³?

Density of Solids

The density of a solid is calculated from its mass and volume. When a solid is completely submerged, it displaces a volume of water that is equal to the volume of the solid. In Figure 1.13, the water level rises from 35.5 mL to 45.0 mL. This means that 9.5 mL of water is displaced and that the volume of the object is 9.5 mL. The density of the zinc is calculated as follows:

$$\text{Density} = \frac{68.60 \text{ g zinc}}{9.5 \text{ mL}} = 7.2 \text{ g/mL}$$

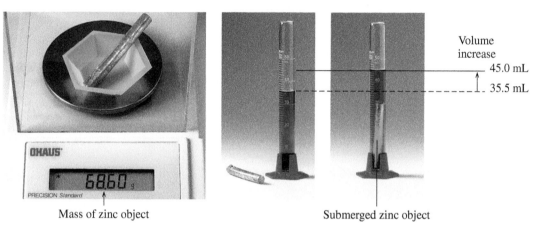

Mass of zinc object   Submerged zinc object

FIGURE 1.13 The density of a solid can be determined by volume displacement because a submerged object displaces a volume of water equal to its own volume.

Q How is the volume of the zinc object determined?

SAMPLE PROBLEM 1.16

■ Using Volume Displacement to Calculate Density

A lead weight used in the belt of a scuba diver has a mass of 226 g. When the weight is placed in a graduated cylinder containing 200.0 mL of water, the water level rises to 220.0 mL. What is the density of the lead weight (g/mL)?

SOLUTION

STEP 1 Given mass = 226 g; water level before object submerged = 200.0 mL; water level after object submerged = 220.0 mL   **Need** density (g/mL)

STEP 2 Plan To calculate density, substitute the mass (g) and the volume (mL) of the lead weight into the expression for density.

STEP 3 Equality/Conversion Factor

$$\text{Density} = \frac{\text{mass of substance}}{\text{volume of substance}}$$

STEP 4 Set Up Problem The volume of the lead weight is equal to the volume of water displaced, which is calculated as follows:

Water level after object submerged	= 220.0 mL
− Water level before object submerged	= 200.0 mL
Water displaced (volume of lead weight) =	20.0 mL

The density is calculated by dividing the mass (g) by the volume (mL). Be sure to use the volume of water the object displaced and not the original volume of water.

$$\text{Density} = \frac{226 \text{ g}}{20.0 \text{ mL}} = \frac{11.3 \text{ g}}{1 \text{ mL}} = 11.3 \text{ g/mL}$$
$$\quad\; 3 \text{ SFs} \qquad\qquad 3 \text{ SFs}$$

STUDY CHECK

A total of 0.500 lb of glass marbles is added to 425 mL of water. The water level rises to a volume of 528 mL. What is the density (g/mL) of the glass marbles?

HEALTH NOTE

Bone Density

The density of our bones determines their health and strength. Our bones are constantly gaining and losing minerals such as calcium, magnesium, and phosphate. In childhood, bones form at a faster rate than they break down. As we age, the breakdown of bone occurs more rapidly than new bone forms. As the loss of bone minerals increases, bones begin to thin, causing a decrease in mass and density. Thinner bones lack strength, which increases the risk of fracture. Hormonal changes, disease, and certain medications can also contribute to the thinning of bone. Eventually, a condition of severe thinning of bone known as *osteoporosis* may occur. *Scanning electron micrographs* (SEMs) show (a) normal bone and (b) bone in osteoporosis caused by the loss of bone minerals.

Bone density is often determined by passing low-dose X-rays through the narrow part at the top of the femur (hip) and the spine (c). These locations are where fractures are more likely to occur, especially as we age. Bones with high density will block more of the X-rays compared to bones that are less dense. The results of a bone density test are compared to a healthy young adult as well as to other people of the same age.

Recommendations to improve bone strength include supplements of calcium and vitamin D and medications such as Fosamax, Evista, or Actonel. Weight-bearing exercise such as walking and lifting weights can also improve muscle strength, which in turn, increases bone strength.

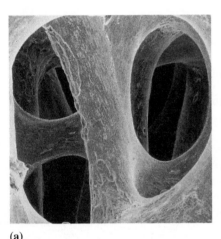

(a)

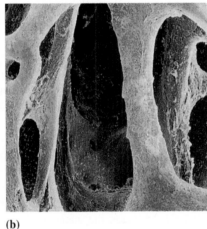

(b)

(c)

Problem Solving Using Density

Density can be used as a conversion factor. For example, if the volume and the density of a sample are known, the mass in grams of the sample can be calculated.

EXPLORE YOUR WORLD

Sink or Float?

1. Fill a large container or bucket with water. Place a can of diet and a can of nondiet soft drink in the water. What happens? Using information on the label, how might you account for your observations?
2. Design an experiment to determine the substance that is the most dense in each of the following:
   a. water and vegetable oil
   b. water and ice
   c. rubbing alcohol and ice
   d. vegetable oil, water, and ice

SAMPLE PROBLEM   1.17

■ Problem Solving Using Density

If the density of milk is 1.04 g/mL, how many grams of milk are in 0.50 qt of milk?

SOLUTION

STEP 1   Given   0.50 qt   **Need**   g

STEP 2   Plan

$$\text{qt} \xrightarrow[\text{factor}]{\text{Metric–U.S.}} \text{L} \xrightarrow[\text{factor}]{\text{Metric}} \text{mL} \boxed{\xrightarrow[\text{factor}]{\text{Density}}} \text{g}$$

STEP 3   Equalities/Conversion Factors

1 L = 1.06 qt	1 L = 1000 mL	1 mL = 1.04 g
$\dfrac{1\ L}{1.06\ qt}$ and $\dfrac{1.06\ qt}{1\ L}$	$\dfrac{1\ L}{1000\ mL}$ and $\dfrac{1000\ mL}{1\ L}$	$\dfrac{1\ mL}{1.04\ g}$ and $\dfrac{1.04\ g}{1\ mL}$

STEP 4   Set Up Problem

$$0.50\ \cancel{qt} \times \frac{1\ \cancel{L}}{1.06\ \cancel{qt}} \times \frac{1000\ \cancel{mL}}{1\ \cancel{L}} \times \frac{1.04\ g}{1\ \cancel{mL}} = 490\ g\ (4.9 \times 10^2\ g)$$

$\quad\quad$ 2 SFs $\quad\quad\quad$ 3 SFs $\quad\quad$ Exact $\quad\quad$ 3 SFs $\quad\quad$ 2 SFs

STUDY CHECK

How many mL of mercury are in a thermometer that contains 20.4 g of mercury? (See Table 1.11 for the density of mercury.)

Specific Gravity

Specific gravity (sp gr) is a ratio between the density of a substance and the density of water. Specific gravity is calculated by dividing the density of a sample by the density of water, which is 1.00 g/mL at 4 °C. A substance with a specific gravity of 1.00 has the same density as water. A substance with a specific gravity of 3.00 is three times as dense as water, whereas a substance with a specific gravity of 0.50 is just one-half as dense as water.

$$\text{Specific gravity} = \frac{\text{density of sample}}{\text{density of water}}$$

In the calculations for specific gravity, the units of density must match. Then all units cancel to leave only a number. Specific gravity is one of the few unitless values you will encounter in chemistry.

An instrument called a *hydrometer* is often used to measure the specific gravity of fluids such as battery fluid or a sample of urine. In Figure 1.14, a hydrometer is used to measure the specific gravity of a fluid.

SAMPLE PROBLEM 1.18

■ Problem Solving with Specific Gravity

John took 2.0 teaspoons (tsp) of cough syrup (sp gr 1.20) for a persistent cough. If there is 5.0 mL in 1 tsp, what was the mass (in grams) of the cough syrup?

SOLUTION

STEP 1   Given   2.0 tsp   **Need**   g

STEP 2   Plan $\text{tsp} \xrightarrow[\text{factor}]{\text{Metric–U.S.}} \text{mL} \boxed{\xrightarrow[\text{factor}]{\text{Density}}} \text{g}$

STEP 3   Equalities/Conversion Factors   For problem solving, it is convenient to convert the specific gravity value (1.20) to density.

$$\text{Density} = (\text{sp gr}) \times 1.00\ \text{g/mL} = 1.20\ \text{g/mL}$$

1 tsp = 5.0 mL	1 mL = 1.20 g
$\dfrac{5.0\ mL}{1\ tsp}$ and $\dfrac{1\ tsp}{5.0\ mL}$	$\dfrac{1\ mL}{1.20\ g}$ and $\dfrac{1.20\ g}{1\ mL}$

Guide to Using Density

STEP 1
State the given and needed quantities.

STEP 2
Write a plan to calculate the needed quantity.

STEP 3
Write equalities and their conversion factors including density.

STEP 4
Set up problem to solve for the needed quantity.

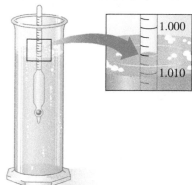

FIGURE 1.14 When the specific gravity of beer measures 1.010 or less with a hydrometer, the fermentation process is complete.

Q If the hydrometer reading is 1.006, what is the density of the liquid?

STEP 4   **Set Up Problem**

$$2.0 \text{ tsp} \times \frac{5.0 \text{ mL}}{1 \text{ tsp}} \times \frac{1.20 \text{ g}}{1 \text{ mL}} = 12 \text{ g of syrup}$$

    2 SFs   2 SFs   3 SFs   2 SFs

STUDY CHECK

An ebony carving has a mass of 275 g. If ebony has a specific gravity of 1.33, what is the volume of the carving?

HEALTH NOTE

Determination of Percentage of Body Fat

Body mass is made up of protoplasm, extracellular fluid, bone, and adipose tissue. One way to determine the amount of adipose tissue is to measure the whole-body density. After the on-land mass of the body is determined, the underwater body mass is obtained by submerging the person in water. Because water helps support the body by giving it buoyancy, the underwater body mass is less. A higher percentage of body fat will make a person more buoyant, causing the underwater mass to be even lower. This occurs because fat has a lower density than the rest of the body.

The difference between the on-land mass and underwater mass, known as the *buoyant force*, is used to determine the body volume. Then the mass and volume of the person are used to calculate body density. For example, suppose a 70.0-kg person has a body volume of 66.7 L.

The body density is calculated as

$$\frac{\text{Body mass}}{\text{Body volume}} = \frac{70.0 \text{ kg}}{66.7 \text{ L}}$$
$$= 1.05 \text{ kg/L or } 1.05 \text{ g/mL}$$

When the body density is determined, it is compared with a chart that correlates the percentage of adipose tissue with body density. A person with a body density of 1.05 g/mL has 21% body fat, according to such a chart. Athletes use this procedure to determine exercise and diet programs.

QUESTIONS AND PROBLEMS

Density

1.63 In an old trunk, you find a piece of metal that you think may be aluminum, silver, or lead. In lab you find it has a mass of 217 g and a volume of 19.2 cm³. Using Table 1.11, what is the metal you found?

1.64 Suppose you have two 100-mL graduated cylinders. In each cylinder there is 40.0 mL of water. You also have two cubes: One is lead, and the other is aluminum. Each cube measures 2.0 cm on each side. After you carefully lower each cube into the water of its own cylinder, what will the new water level be in each of the cylinders?

1.65 Determine the density (g/mL) for each of the following:
    a. A 20.0 mL sample of a salt solution has a mass of 24.0 g.
    b. A cube of butter weighs 0.250 lb and has a volume of 130. mL.
    c. A gem has a mass of 45.0 g. When the gem is placed in a graduated cylinder containing 20.0 mL of water, the water level rises to 34.5 mL.

    d. A syrup is added to an empty container with a mass of 115.25 g. When 0.100 pint of syrup is added, the total mass of the container and syrup is 182.48 g.

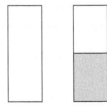

115.25 g   **182.48 g**

1.66 Determine the density (g/mL) for each of the following:
    a. A plastic material weighs 2.68 lb and has a volume of 3.5 L.
    b. The fluid in a car battery if it has a volume of 125 mL and a mass of 155 g.
    c. A 5.00-mL urine sample from a patient suffering from diabetes mellitus has a mass of 5.025 g.
    d. A 10.00 L sample of oxygen gas has a mass of 0.014 kg.

1.67 Use the density values in Table 1.11 to solve the following problems:

a. How many liters of ethanol contain 1.5 kg of alcohol?

b. How many grams of mercury are present in a barometer that holds 6.5 mL of mercury?

c. A sculptor has prepared a mold for casting a bronze figure. The figure has a volume of 225 mL. If bronze has a density of 7.8 g/mL, how many ounces of bronze are needed in the preparation of the bronze figure?

d. How many kilograms of gasoline fill a 12.0-gallon gas tank? (1 gallon = 4 qt)

1.68 Use the density values in Table 1.11 to solve the following problems:

a. A graduated cylinder contains 28.0 mL of water. What is the new water level after 35.6 g of silver metal is submerged in the water?

b. A fish tank holds 35 gallons of water. How many pounds (lb) of water are in the fish tank?

c. The mass of an empty container is 88.25 g. The mass of the container and a liquid with a density of 0.758 g/mL is 150.50 g. What is the volume (mL) of the liquid in the container?

d. A cannon ball made of iron has a volume of 115 cm^3. If iron has a density of 7.86 g/cm^3, what is the mass, in kilograms, of the cannon ball?

1.69 Solve the following specific gravity problems:

a. A urine sample has a density of 1.030 g/mL. What is the specific gravity of the sample?

b. A liquid has a volume of 40.0 mL and a mass of 45.0 g. What is the specific gravity of the liquid?

c. The specific gravity of a vegetable oil is 0.85. What is its density?

1.70 Solve the following specific gravity problems:

a. A 5.0% glucose solution has a specific gravity of 1.02. What is the mass of 500. mL of glucose solution?

b. A bottle containing 325 g of cleaning solution is used for carpets. If the cleaning solution has a specific gravity of 0.850, what volume of solution was used?

c. Butter has a specific gravity of 0.86. What is the mass, in grams, of 2.15 L of butter?

CONCEPT MAP

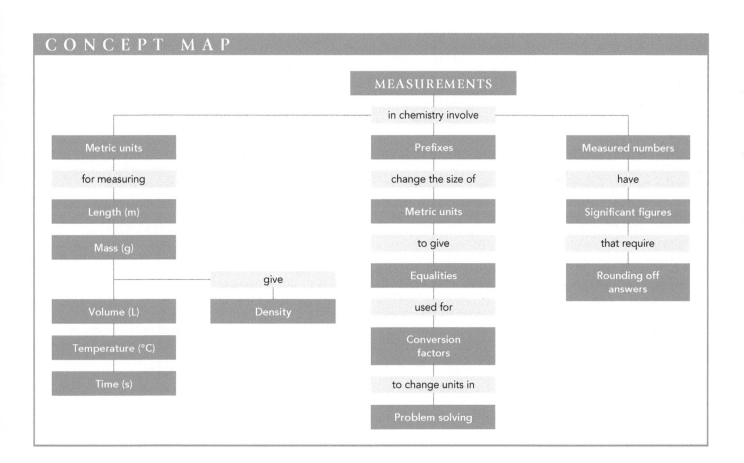

CHAPTER REVIEW

1.1 Units of Measurement

LEARNING GOAL: *Write the names and abbreviations for the units used in measurements of length, volume, time, and mass.*

In science, physical quantities are described in units of the metric or International System (SI). Some important units are meter (m) for length, liter (L) for volume, gram (g) and kilogram (kg) for mass, degree Celsius (°C) and Kelvin (K) for temperature, and second(s) for time.

1.2 Scientific Notation

LEARNING GOAL: *Write a number in scientific notation.*

Large and small numbers can be written using scientific notation in which the decimal point is moved to give a coefficient between 1 and 9 and the number of decimal places moved shown as a power of 10. A large number will have a positive power of 10, while a small number will have a negative power of 10.

1.3 Measured Numbers and Significant Figures

LEARNING GOAL: *Determine the number of significant figures in measured numbers.*

A measured number is any number obtained by using a measuring device. An exact number is obtained by counting items or from a definition; no measuring device is used. Significant figures are the numbers reported in a measurement including the estimated digit. Zeros in front of a decimal number or at the end of a nondecimal number are not significant.

1.4 Significant Figures in Calculations

LEARNING GOAL: *Adjust calculated answers to the correct number of significant figures.*

In multiplication or division, the final answer is written so that it has the same number of significant figures as the measurement with the fewest significant figures. In addition or subtraction, the final answer is written so that it has the same number of decimal places as the measurement with the fewest decimal places.

1.5 Prefixes and Equalities

LEARNING GOAL: *Use the numerical values of prefixes to write a metric equality.*

Prefixes placed in front of a unit change the size of the unit by factors of 10. Prefixes such as *centi*, *milli*, and *micro* provide smaller units; prefixes such as *kilo* provide larger units. An equality relates two metric units that measure the same quantity of length, volume, or mass. Examples of metric equalities are 1 m = 100 cm, 1 L = 1000 mL, and 1 kg = 1000 g.

1.6 Writing Conversion Factors

LEARNING GOAL: *Write a conversion factor for two units that describe the same quantity.*

Conversion factors are used to express a relationship in the form of a fraction. Two factors can be written for any relationship in the metric or U.S. system. A percentage is written as a conversion factor by expressing matching units in the relationship as the parts to 100 parts of the whole. Extremely small percentage values are written as parts per million (ppm) or parts per billion (ppb).

1.7 Problem Solving

LEARNING GOAL: *Use conversion factors to change from one unit to another.*

Conversion factors are useful when changing a quantity expressed in one unit to a quantity expressed in another unit. In the process, a given unit is multiplied by one or more conversion factors that cancel units until the desired answer is obtained.

1.8 Density

LEARNING GOAL: *Calculate the density or specific gravity of a substance, and use the density or specific gravity to calculate the mass or volume of a substance.*

The density of a substance is a ratio of its mass to its volume, usually g/mL or g/cm^3. The units of density can be used as a factor to convert between the mass and volume of a substance. Specific gravity (sp gr) compares the density of a substance to the density of water, 1.00 g/mL.

KEY TERMS

Celsius (°C) temperature scale A temperature scale on which water has a freezing point of 0 °C and a boiling point of 100 °C.

centimeter (cm) A unit of length in the metric system; there are 2.54 cm in 1 in.

conversion factor A ratio in which the numerator and denominator are quantities from an equality or given relationship. For example, the conversion factors for the relationship 1 kg = 2.20 lb are written as the following:

$$\frac{2.20 \text{ lb}}{1 \text{ kg}} \quad \text{and} \quad \frac{1 \text{ kg}}{2.20 \text{ lb}}$$

cubic centimeter (cm³ or cc) The volume of a cube that has 1-cm sides; equal to 1 mL.

density The relationship of the mass of an object to its volume expressed as grams per cubic centimeter (g/cm^3), grams per milliliter (g/mL), or grams per liter (g/L).

equality A relationship between two units that measure the same quantity.

exact number A number obtained by counting or by definition.

gram (g) The metric unit used in measurements of mass.

Kelvin (K) temperature scale A temperature scale on which the lowest possible temperature is 0 K.

kilogram (kg) A metric mass of 1000 g and equal to 2.20 lb. The kilogram is the SI standard unit of mass.

liter (L) The metric unit for volume that is slightly larger than a quart.

mass A measure of the quantity of material in an object.

measured number A number obtained when a quantity is determined by using a measuring device.

meter (m) The metric unit for length that is slightly longer than a yard. The meter is the SI standard unit of length.

metric system A system of measurement used by scientists and in most countries of the world.

milliliter (mL) A metric unit of volume equal to one-thousandth of a L (0.001 L).

prefix The part of the name of a metric unit that precedes the base unit and specifies the size of the measurement. All prefixes are related on a decimal scale.

scientific notation A form of writing large and small numbers using a coefficient from 1 to 9, followed by a power of 10.

second The standard unit of time in the SI and metric system.

SI units The international system of units that modifies the metric system.

significant figures The numbers recorded in a measurement.

specific gravity (sp gr) A relationship between the density of a substance and the density of water:

$$\text{sp gr} = \frac{\text{density of sample}}{\text{density of water}}$$

temperature An indicator of the hotness or coldness of an object.

volume The amount of space occupied by a substance.

UNDERSTANDING THE CONCEPTS

1.71 In which of the following pairs do both numbers contain the same number of significant figures?
   a. 11.0 m and 11.00 m   **b.** 600.0 K and 60 K
   c. 0.000 75 s and 75 000 s   **d.** 255.0 L and 6.240 × 10^{-2} L

1.72 In which of the following pairs do both numbers contain the same number of significant figures?
   a. 5.75 × 10^{-3} g and 0.00287 g   **b.** 8.05 m and 0.0805 m
   c. 150 000 s and 1.5 × 10^2 s   **d.** 0.0038 L and 75 000 mL

1.73 Indicate if each of the following is answered with an exact number or a measured number:

a. number of legs
b. height of table
c. number of chairs at the table
d. area of table top

1.74 Measure the length of each of the objects in figure (a), (b), and (c) using the metric rule in the figure. Indicate the number of significant figures for each and the estimated digit for each.

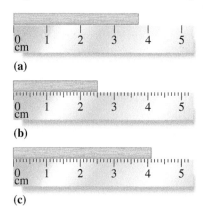

(a)

(b)

(c)

1.75 Measure the length and width of the rectangle using a metric rule:

a. What is the length and width of this rectangle measured in centimeters?
b. What is the length and width of this rectangle measured in millimeters?
c. How many significant figures are in the length measurement?
d. How many significant figures are in the width measurement?

e. What is the area of the rectangle in cm^2?
f. How many significant figures are in the calculated answer for area?

1.76 Each of the following diagrams represents a container of water and a cube. Some cubes float while others sink. Match diagrams A, B, C, or D with one of the following descriptions and explain your choices:

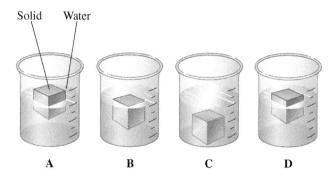

a. The cube has a greater density than water.
b. The cube has a density that is $0.60 - 0.80$ g/mL.
c. The cube has a density that is $1/2$ the density of water.
d. The cube has the same density as water.

1.77 What is the density of the solid object that is weighed and submerged in water?

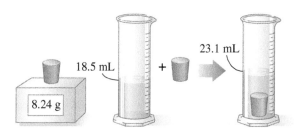

1.78 Consider the following solids. The solids A, B, and C represent gold, silver, and aluminum. If each has a mass of 10.0 g, what is the identity of each solid?

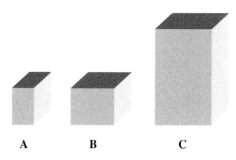

a. Density of aluminum = 2.70 g/mL
b. Density of gold = 19.3 g/mL
c. Density of silver = 10.5 g/mL

ADDITIONAL QUESTIONS AND PROBLEMS

For instructor-assigned homework, go to www.masteringchemistry.com.

1.79 Round off or add zeros to the following calculated answers to give a final answer with three significant figures:
a. 0.000 012 58 L
b. 3.528×10^2 kg
c. 125 111 m
d. 58.703 g
e. 3×10^{-3} s
f. 0.010 826 g

1.80 What is the total mass, in grams, of a dessert containing 137.25 g of vanilla ice cream, 84 g of fudge sauce, and 43.7 g of nuts?

1.81 During a workout at the gym, you set the treadmill at a pace of 55.0 meters per minute. How many minutes will you walk if you cover a distance of 7500 ft?

1.82 A fish company delivers 22 kg of salmon, 5.5 kg of crab, and 3.48 kg of oysters to your seafood restaurant.
   a. What is the total mass, in kilograms, of the seafood?
   b. What is the total number of pounds?

1.83 Bill's recipe for onion soup calls for 4.0 lb of thinly sliced onions. If an onion has an average mass of 115 g, how many onions does Bill need?

1.84 The price of 1 pound (lb) of potatoes is $1.75. If all the potatoes sold today at the store bring in $1420, how many kilograms (kg) of potatoes did grocery shoppers buy?

1.85 The following nutrition information is listed on a box of crackers:

Serving size 0.50 oz (6 crackers)
Fat 4 g per serving
Sodium 140 mg per serving

   a. If the box has a net weight (contents only) of 8.0 oz, about how many crackers are in the box?
   b. If you ate 10 crackers, how many ounces of fat are you consuming?
   c. How many grams of sodium are used to prepare 50 boxes of crackers?

1.86 An aquarium store unit requires 75 000 mL of water. How many gallons of water are needed? (1 gal = 4 qt)

1.87 In Mexico, avocados are 48 pesos per kilogram. What is the cost in cents of an avocado that weighs 0.45 lb if the exchange rate is 10.8 pesos to the dollar?

1.88 Celeste's diet restricts her intake of protein to 24 g per day. If she eats an 8.0-oz burger that is 15.0% protein, has she exceeded her protein limit for the day? How many ounces of a burger would be allowed for Celeste?

1.89 A sunscreen preparation contains 2.50% by mass benzyl salicylate. If a tube contains 4.0 ounces of sunscreen, how many kilograms of benzyl salicylate are needed to manufacture 325 tubes of sunscreen?

1.90 An object has a mass of 3.15 oz. When it is submerged in a graduated cylinder initially containing 325.2 mL of water, the water level rises to 442.5 mL. What is the density (g/mL) of the object?

1.91 What is a cholesterol level of 1.85 g/L in units of mg/dL?

1.92 If a recycling center collects 1254 aluminum cans and there are 22 aluminum cans in 1 pound, what volume, in liters, of aluminum was collected? (See Table 1.11.)

1.93 The water level in a graduated cylinder initially at 215 mL rises to 285 mL after a piece of lead is submerged. What is the mass in grams of the lead? (See Table 1.11.)

1.94 A graduated cylinder contains 155 mL of water. A 15.0-g piece of iron (density = 7.86 g/cm^3) and a 20.0-g piece of lead are added. What is the new water level in the cylinder? (See Table 1.11.)

1.95 How many cubic centimeters (cm^3) of olive oil have the same mass as 1.00 L of gasoline? (See Table 1.11.)

1.96 What is the volume, in quarts, of 1.50 kg of ethyl alcohol? (See Table 1.11.)

1.97 **a.** Some athletes have as little as 3.0% body fat. If such a person has a body mass of 45 kg, how many lb of body fat does that person have?
   b. In a process called *liposuction*, a doctor removes fat deposits from a person's body. If body fat has a density of 0.94 g/mL and 3.0 liters of fat are removed, how many pounds of fat were removed from the patient?

1.98 A mouthwash is 21.6% by mass alcohol. If each bottle contains 0.358 pint of mouthwash with a density of 0.876 g/mL, how many kilograms of alcohol are in 180 bottles of the mouthwash?

1.99 Sterling silver is 92.5% silver by mass with a density of 10.3 g/cm^3. If a cube of sterling silver has a volume of 27.0 cm^3, how many ounces of pure silver are present?

1.100 A typical adult body contains 55% water. If a person has a mass of 65 kg, how many pounds of water does she have in her body?

1.101 For a 180-lb person, calculate the quantities of each of the following that must be ingested to provide the LD$_{50}$ for caffeine given in Table 1.10:
   a. cups of coffee if one cup is 12 fluid ounces and there are 100. mg of caffeine per 6 fl oz of drip-brewed coffee
   b. cans of cola if one can contains 50. mg of caffeine
   c. tablets of No-Doz if one tablet contains 100. mg of caffeine

1.102 The label on a 1-pint bottle of water lists the following components. If the density is the same as pure water and you drink three bottles of water in one day, how many milligrams of each component will you obtain?

Calcium 28 ppm
Fluoride 0.08 ppm
Magnesium 12 ppm
Potassium 3.2 ppm
Sodium 15 ppm

CHALLENGE QUESTIONS

The following groups of questions and problems are related to the topics in this chapter. However, they do not all follow the chapter order, and they require you to combine concepts and skills from several sections. These problems will help you increase your critical thinking skills and prepare for your next exam.

1.103 A balance measures mass to 0.001 g. If you determine the mass of an object that weighs about 30 g, would you record the mass as 30 g, 32 g, 32.1 g, or 32.075 g? Explain your choice by writing two to three complete sentences that describe your thinking.

1.104 When three students use the same meterstick to measure the length of a paper clip, they obtain results of 5.8 cm, 5.75 cm, and 5.76 cm. If the meterstick has millimeter markings, what are some reasons for the different values?

1.105 A car travels at 55 miles per hour and gets 11 kilometers per liter of gasoline. How many gallons of gasoline are needed for a 3.0-hour trip?

1.106 A 50.0-g silver object and a 50.0-g gold object are both added to 75.5 mL of water contained in a graduated cylinder. What is the new water level in the cylinder?

1.107 In the manufacturing of computer chips, cylinders of silicon are cut into thin wafers that are 3.00 inches in diameter and have a mass of 1.50 g of silicon. How thick (mm) is each wafer if silicon has a density of 2.33 g/cm^3? (The volume of a cylinder is $V = \pi r^2 h$.)

1.108 A circular pool with a diameter of 27 ft is filled to a depth of 50. in. Assume the pool is a cylinder ($V = \pi r^2 h$).
   a. What is the volume of water in the pool in cubic meters?

b. The density of water is 1.0 g/cm^3. What is the mass, in kilograms, of the water in the pool?

1.109 A package of aluminum foil is 66.7 yd long, 12 in. wide, and 0.000 30 in. thick. If aluminum has a density of 2.7 g/cm^3, what is the mass, in grams, of the foil?

1.110 An 18-karat gold necklace is 75% gold by mass, 16% silver, and 9.0% copper.

a. What is the mass, in grams, of the necklace if it contains 0.24 oz silver?

b. How many grams of copper are in the necklace?

c. If 18-karat gold has a density of 15.5 g/cm^3, what is the volume in cubic centimeters?

ANSWERS

ANSWERS TO STUDY CHECKS

1.1 **a.** meter; m   **b.** degree Celsius; °C   **c.** gram; g

1.2 **a.** 4.25×10^5 m   **b.** 8×10^{-7} g

1.3 **a.** two   **b.** one   **c.** five

1.4 **a.** 36 m   **b.** 0.0026 L
c. 3.8×10^3 g   **d.** 1.3 kg

1.5 **a.** 0.4924   **b.** 0.0080 or 8.0×10^{-3} **c.** 2.0

1.6 **a.** 83.70 mg   **b.** 0.5 L

1.7 **a.** giga   **b.** centi

1.8 **a.** 1000 g (1×10^3g)   **b.** 0.001 mL (1×10^{-3}mL)

1.9 Conversion factors: $\dfrac{1 \text{ zs}}{1 \times 10^{-23}\text{ s}}$ and $\dfrac{1 \times 10^{-23}\text{ s}}{1 \text{ zs}}$

1.10 **a.** $\dfrac{62.2 \text{ km}}{1 \text{ h}}$ and $\dfrac{1 \text{ h}}{62.2 \text{ km}}$

b. $\dfrac{10 \text{ g arsenic}}{1 \times 10^9 \text{ g water}}$ and $\dfrac{1 \times 10^9 \text{ g water}}{10 \text{ g arsenic}}$

1.11 1.89 L

1.12 0.44 oz

1.13 10 mL

1.14 25 g of fat

1.15 10.5 g/cm^3

1.16 2.20 g/mL

1.17 1.50 mL of mercury

1.18 207 mL

ANSWERS TO SELECTED QUESTIONS AND PROBLEMS

1.1 In the United States, **a.** weight is measured in pounds (lb), **b.** height in feet and inches, **c.** gasoline in gallons, and **d.** temperature in Fahrenheit (°F). In Mexico, **a.** mass is measured in kilograms, **b.** height in meters, **c.** gasoline in liters, and **d.** temperature in Celsius (°C).

1.3 **a.** meter; length   **b.** gram; mass   **c.** liter; volume
d. second; time   **e.** degree Celsius; temperature

1.5 **a.** 5.5×10^4 m   **b.** 4.8×10^2 g   **c.** 5×10^{-6} cm
d. 1.4×10^{-4} s   **e.** 7.85×10^{-3} L   **f.** 6.7×10^5 kg

1.7 **a.** 7.2×10^3 **b.** 3.2×10^{-2}
c. 1×10^4 **d.** 6.8×10^{-2}

1.9 **a.** 12 000   **b.** 0.0825   **c.** 4 000 000   **d.** 0.005

1.11 **a.** measured   **b.** exact   **c.** exact   **d.** measured

1.13 **a.** 6 oz of meat   **b.** none
c. 0.75 lb; 350 g   **d.** none (definitions are exact)

1.15 **a.** not significant   **b.** significant
c. significant   **d.** significant   **e.** not significant

1.17 **a.** 5   **b.** 2   **c.** 2   **d.** 3   **e.** 4   **f.** 3

1.19 Both measurements in part **c** have two significant figures, and both measurements in part **d** have four significant figures.

1.21 **a.** 5.0×10^3 L   **b.** 3.0×10^4 g
c. 1.0×10^5 m   **d.** 2.5×10^{-4} cm

1.23 A calculator often gives more digits than the number of significant figures allowed in the answer.

1.25 **a.** 1.85   **b.** 184   **c.** 0.004 74
d. 8810   **e.** 1.83×10^5

1.27 **a.** 1.6   **b.** 0.01   **c.** 27.6   **d.** 3.5

1.29 **a.** 53.54 cm   **b.** 127.6 g   **c.** 121.5 mL   **d.** 0.50 L

1.31 km/h is kilometers per hour; mi/h (mph) is miles per hour.

1.33 The prefix *kilo* means to multiply by 1000. One kg is the same mass as 1000 g.

1.35 **a.** mg   **b.** dL   **c.** km   **d.** kg   **e.** μL   **f.** ng

1.37 **a.** 0.01   **b.** 1000   **c.** 0.001 (1×10^{-3})
d. 0.1   **e.** 1 000 000 (1×10^6)   **f.** 1×10^{-12}

1.39 **a.** 100 cm   **b.** 1000 m   **c.** 0.001 m   **d.** 1000 mL

1.41 **a.** kilogram   **b.** milliliter   **c.** km
d. kL   **e.** nanometer

1.43 A conversion factor can be inverted to give a second conversion factor.

1.45 **a.** 100 cm = 1 m; $\dfrac{100 \text{ cm}}{1 \text{ m}}$ and $\dfrac{1 \text{ m}}{100 \text{ cm}}$

b. 1000 mg = 1 g; $\dfrac{1000 \text{ mg}}{1 \text{ g}}$ and $\dfrac{1 \text{ g}}{1000 \text{ mg}}$

c. 1 L = 1000 mL; $\dfrac{1000 \text{ mL}}{1 \text{ L}}$ and $\dfrac{1 \text{ L}}{1000 \text{ mL}}$

d. 1 dL = 100 mL; $\dfrac{100 \text{ mL}}{1 \text{ dL}}$ and $\dfrac{1 \text{ dL}}{100 \text{ mL}}$

1.47 **a.** 3 ft = 1 yd; $\dfrac{3 \text{ ft}}{1 \text{ yd}}$ and $\dfrac{1 \text{ yd}}{3 \text{ ft}}$

b. 1 mile = 5280 feet; $\dfrac{5280 \text{ ft}}{1 \text{ mi}}$ and $\dfrac{1 \text{ mi}}{5280 \text{ ft}}$

c. 1 min = 60 sec; $\dfrac{60 \text{ s}}{1 \text{ min}}$ and $\dfrac{1 \text{ min}}{60 \text{ s}}$

d. 1 gal = 27 mi; $\dfrac{1 \text{ gal}}{27 \text{ mi}}$ and $\dfrac{27 \text{ mi}}{1 \text{ gal}}$

e. 93 g silver = 100 g sterling; $\dfrac{93 \text{ g silver}}{100 \text{ g sterling}}$ and $\dfrac{100 \text{ g sterling}}{93 \text{ g silver}}$

1.49 **a.** $\dfrac{3.5 \text{ m}}{1 \text{ s}}$ and $\dfrac{1 \text{ s}}{3.5 \text{ m}}$

b. $\dfrac{3500 \text{ mg potassium}}{1 \text{ day}}$ and $\dfrac{1 \text{ day}}{3500 \text{ mg potassium}}$

c. $\dfrac{46.0 \text{ km}}{1.0 \text{ gal}}$ and $\dfrac{1.0 \text{ gal}}{46.0 \text{ km}}$

d. $\dfrac{50 \text{ mg Atenolol}}{1 \text{ tablet}}$ and $\dfrac{1 \text{ tablet}}{50 \text{ mg Atenolol}}$

e. $\dfrac{29 \ \mu g}{1 \text{ kg}}$ and $\dfrac{1 \text{ kg}}{29 \ \mu g}$

1.51 The unit in the denominator must cancel with the preceding unit.

1.53 a. 1.75 m   **b.** 5.5 L   **c.** 5.5 g

1.55 a. 710. mL   **b.** 75.1 kg   **c.** 495 mm   **d.** 2.0×10^{-5} in.

1.57 a. 23.8 m   **b.** 196 m^2 **c.** 0.463 s

1.59 a. 66 gal   **b.** 3 tablets
   c. 1800 mg (1.8×10^3 mg)

1.61 a. 152 g of oxygen   **b.** 0.026 g of magnesium
   c. 43 g of N   **d.** 50. lb of chocolate bars

1.63 lead; 11.3 g/mL

1.65 a. 1.20 g/mL   **b.** 0.873 g/mL
   c. 3.10 g/mL   **d.** 1.42 g/mL

1.67 a. 1.9 L   **b.** 88 g   **c.** 62 oz   **d.** 30. kg

1.69 a. 1.030   **b.** 1.13   **c.** 0.85 g/mL

1.71 c. 0.000 75 s and 75 000 s
   d. 255.0 L and 6.240×10^{-2} L

1.73 a. exact   **b.** measured   **c.** exact   **d.** measured

1.75 a. length = 6.96 cm; width = 4.75 cm
   b. length = 69.6 mm; width = 47.5 mm
   c. 3 significant figures

d. 3 significant figures
e. 33.1 cm^2
f. 3 significant figures

1.77 1.8 g/mL

1.79 a. 0.000 0126 L   **b.** 3.53×10^2 kg
   c. 125 000 m   **d.** 58.7 g
   e. 3.00×10^{-3} s   **f.** 0.0108 g

1.81 42 min

1.83 16 onions

1.85 a. 96 crackers   **b.** 0.2 oz of fat   **c.** 110 g of sodium

1.87 91 cents

1.89 0.92 kg

1.91 185 mg/dL

1.93 790 g

1.95 720 cm^3

1.97 a. 3.0 lb of body fat   **b.** 6.2 lb

1.99 9.07 oz of pure silver

1.101 a. 80 cups   **b.** 310 cans   **c.** 160 tablets

1.103 You should record the mass as 32.075 g. Because your balance will weigh to the nearest 0.001 g, the mass values should be reported to 0.001 g.

1.105 6.4 gal

1.107 0.141 mm

1.109 3.8×10^2 g of aluminum foil

Energy and Matter

2

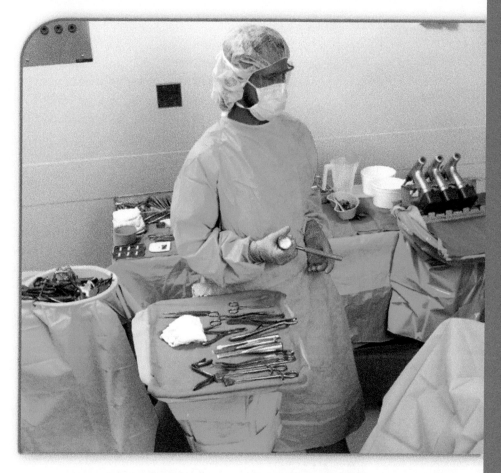

"As a surgical technologist, I assist the doctors during surgeries," says Christopher Ayars, surgical technologist, Kaiser Hospital. *"I am there to help during general or orthopedic surgery by passing instruments, holding retractors, and maintaining the sterile field. Our equipment for surgery is sterilized by steam that is heated to 270 °F, which is the same as 130 °C."*

Surgical technologists assist with surgical procedures by preparing and maintaining surgical equipment, instruments, and supplies; providing patient care in an operating room setting; preparing and maintaining a sterile field; and ensuring that there are no breaks in aseptic technique. Instruments, which have been sterilized, are wrapped and sent to surgery where they are checked again before they are opened.

Almost everything we do involves energy. We use energy when we walk, play tennis, study, and breathe. We use energy when we warm water, cook food, turn on lights, use a washing machine, and drive our cars. Of course, that energy has to come from something. In our bodies, the food we eat provides us with energy. In our homes, schools, and automobiles, burning fossil fuels such as oil, propane, or gasoline provides energy.

Every day, we see a variety of materials with many different shapes and forms. To a scientist, all of these materials are *matter*. Matter is everywhere around us. The orange juice we had for breakfast, the water we put in the coffee maker, the plastic bag we put our sandwich in, our toothbrush and toothpaste, the oxygen we inhale, and the carbon dioxide we exhale are all forms of matter.

When we look around us, we see that matter takes the physical form of a solid, a liquid, or a gas. Water is a familiar substance that we routinely observe in all three states. In the solid state, water can be an ice cube or a snowflake. It is a liquid when it comes out of a faucet or fills a pool. When water evaporates from wet clothes or boils in a pan, it forms a gas, or vapor. In all of these examples, water changes state by gaining or losing energy. For example, energy is added to melt ice cubes and to boil water in a teakettle. In contrast, energy is removed to freeze liquid water in an ice cube tray and to condense water vapor (gas) to liquid.

2.1 Energy

LEARNING GOAL

Identify energy as potential or kinetic and understand the units of energy.

When you are running, walking, dancing, or thinking, you are using energy to do **work**, any activity that requires energy. In fact, **energy** is defined as the ability to do work. Suppose you are climbing a steep hill and you become too tired to go on. At that moment, you do not have sufficient energy to do any more work. Now suppose you sit down and have lunch. In a while you will have obtained energy from the food, and you will be able to do more work and complete the climb.

Potential and Kinetic Energy

All energy can be classified as potential energy or kinetic energy. **Potential energy** is stored energy, whereas **kinetic energy** is the energy of motion. (See Figure 2.1.) Any object that is moving has kinetic energy. A boulder resting on top of a mountain has potential energy because of its location. If the boulder rolls down the mountain, the potential energy becomes kinetic energy. Water stored in a reservoir has potential energy. When it flows over the dam and falls to the stream below, its potential energy is converted to kinetic energy. Foods and fossil fuels have potential energy stored in their molecules. When you digest food or burn gasoline in your car, potential energy is converted to kinetic energy to do work.

FIGURE 2.1 Work is done as the rock climber moves up the cliff. At the top, the climber has more potential energy than when she started the climb.

Q What happens to the potential energy of the climber when she descends?

CONCEPT CHECK 2.1

■ **Potential and Kinetic Energy**

Identify each of the following as an example of mostly potential or kinetic energy:

a. gasoline   **b.** skating   **c.** a candy bar

ANSWER

a. Gasoline is burned to provide energy and heat; it contains potential energy in its molecules.

b. A skater uses energy to move; skating is kinetic energy (energy of motion).

c. A candy bar has stored energy. When digested, its components provide energy for the body to do work.

Heat and Units of Energy

Heat is energy that flows from a warmer object to a cooler one. A frozen pizza feels cold because heat flows from your warm hand to the pizza. Heat is associated with the motion of particles. In the frozen pizza, the particles are moving very slowly. As heat is added and the pizza becomes warmer, the motions of the particles in the pizza increase. Eventually, the particles have enough energy to make the pizza hot and ready to eat.

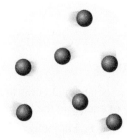

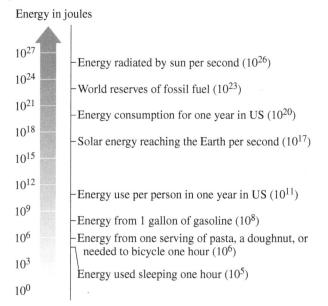

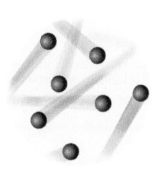

MC™ **TUTORIAL**
Heat

MC™ **TUTORIAL**
Energy Conversions

The SI unit of energy and work is the **joule** (J) (pronounced "jewel"). The joule is a small amount of energy, so scientists often use the kilojoule (kJ). When you heat water for one cup of tea, you use about 75 000 J, or 75 kJ, of heat.

Energy in joules

10^{27} — Energy radiated by sun per second (10^{26})

10^{24} — World reserves of fossil fuel (10^{23})

10^{21} — Energy consumption for one year in US (10^{20})

10^{18} — Solar energy reaching the Earth per second (10^{17})

10^{15}

10^{12} — Energy use per person in one year in US (10^{11})

10^{9} — Energy from 1 gallon of gasoline (10^{8})

10^{6} — Energy from one serving of pasta, a doughnut, or needed to bicycle one hour (10^{6})

10^{3} — Energy used sleeping one hour (10^{5})

10^{0}

You may be more familiar with the unit **calorie (cal)**, from the Latin *caloric*, meaning "heat." The calorie was originally defined as the amount of energy (heat) needed to raise the temperature of one gram of water by 1 °C. Now one calorie is defined as exactly 4.184 J. This equality can also be written as a conversion factor:

1 cal = 4.184 J (exact)

$$\frac{4.184 \text{ J}}{1 \text{ cal}} \quad \text{and} \quad \frac{1 \text{ cal}}{4.184 \text{ J}}$$

One **kilocalorie (kcal)** is equal to 1000 calories, and one *kilojoule* (kJ) is 1000 joules.

1 kcal = 1000 cal
1 kJ = 1000 J

SAMPLE PROBLEM   2.1

■ Energy Units

When 1.0 g of octane fuel burns in an automobile engine, 48 000 J are released. Convert this quantity of energy to the following units:

a. calories   **b.** kilojoules

SOLUTION

a. calories

STEP 1   Given   48 000 J   **Need**   calories (cal)

STEP 2   Plan   J $\boxed{\begin{array}{c}\text{Energy}\\\text{factor}\end{array}}$ cal

STEP 3   Equalities/Conversion Factors

$$1 \text{ cal} = 4.184 \text{ J}$$

$$\frac{1 \text{ cal}}{4.184 \text{ J}} \quad \text{and} \quad \frac{4.184 \text{ J}}{1 \text{ cal}}$$

STEP 4   Set Up Problem

$$48\,000 \text{ J} \times \frac{1 \text{ cal}}{4.184 \text{ J}} = 11\,000 \text{ cal } (1.1 \times 10^4 \text{ cal}) \quad \text{(2 SFs)}$$

b. kilojoules

STEP 1   Given   48 000 J   **Need**   kilojoules

STEP 2   Plan   J $\boxed{\begin{array}{c}\text{Energy}\\\text{factor}\end{array}}$ kJ

STEP 3   Equalities/Conversion Factors

$$1 \text{ kJ} = 1000 \text{ J}$$

$$\frac{1000 \text{ J}}{1 \text{ kJ}} \quad \text{and} \quad \frac{1 \text{ kJ}}{1000 \text{ J}}$$

STEP 4   Set Up Problem

$$48\,000 \text{ J} \times \frac{1 \text{ kJ}}{1000 \text{ J}} = 48 \text{ kJ}$$

STUDY CHECK

The burning of 1.0 g of coal produces 35 000 J of energy. How many kcal are produced?

QUESTIONS AND PROBLEMS

Energy

2.1 Discuss the changes in the potential and kinetic energy of a roller-coaster ride as the roller coaster climbs up a ramp and goes down the other side.

2.2 Discuss the changes in the potential and kinetic energy of a ski jumper taking the elevator to the top of the jump and skiing down the ramp.

2.3 Indicate whether each statement describes potential or kinetic energy:
a. water at the top of a waterfall
b. kicking a ball
c. the energy in a lump of coal
d. a skier at the top of a hill

2.4 Indicate whether each statement describes potential or kinetic energy:
a. the energy in your food
b. a tightly wound spring
c. an earthquake
d. a car speeding down the freeway

2.5 A burning match releases 1.1×10^3 J. Convert the energy released by 20 matches to the following energy units:
a. kilojoules   **b.** calories   **c.** kilocalories

2.6 A person uses 750 kcal to run a race. Convert the energy used for the race to the following energy units:
a. calories   **b.** joules   **c.** kilojoules

2.2 Temperature

Temperature is a measure of how hot or cold a substance is compared to another substance. The temperature is an indication of the kinetic energy of the particles in a substance. Heat flows from a substance with a higher temperature to a substance with a lower temperature until the temperatures of both are the same. When you drink hot coffee or touch a hot pan, heat flows to your mouth or hand, which is at a lower temperature. When you touch an ice cube, it feels cold because heat flows from your hand to the colder ice cube.

LEARNING GOAL

Given a temperature, calculate a corresponding temperature on another temperature scale.

Celsius and Fahrenheit Temperatures

Temperatures in science, and in most of the world, are measured and reported in *Celsius* (°C) units. In the United States, everyday temperatures are commonly reported in *Fahrenheit* (°F) units. A typical room temperature of 22 °C would be the same as 72 °F. A normal human body temperature of 37.0 °C is 98.6 °F.

On the Celsius and Fahrenheit scales, the temperatures of melting ice and boiling water are used as reference points. On the Celsius scale, the freezing point of pure water is defined as exactly 0 °C and the boiling point as exactly 100 °C. On the Fahrenheit scale, pure water freezes at exactly 32 °F and boils at exactly 212 °F. On each scale, the temperature difference between freezing and boiling is divided into smaller units called *degrees*. The Celsius scale has 100 degrees between the freezing and boiling temperatures of water, compared with 180 degrees on the Fahrenheit scale. That makes a Celsius degree almost twice the size of a Fahrenheit degree: 1 °C = 1.8 °F. (See Figure 2.2.)

180 Fahrenheit degrees = 100 Celsius degrees

$$\frac{180 \text{ Fahrenheit degrees}}{100 \text{ Celsius degrees}} = \frac{1.8 \text{ °F}}{1 \text{ °C}}$$

In a chemistry laboratory, temperatures are measured in Celsius degrees. To convert to a Fahrenheit temperature, multiply the Celsius temperature by 1.8 and add 32 degrees. The 32 degrees adjusts the freezing point of 0 °C on the Celsius scale to 32 °F on the Fahrenheit scale. Both values, 1.8 and 32, are exact numbers. The equation for this conversion follows:

$$T_F = \underbrace{\frac{1.8 \text{ °F}(T_C)}{1 \text{ °C}}}_{\substack{\text{Changes} \\ \text{°C to °F}}} + \underbrace{32}_{\substack{\text{Adjusts} \\ \text{freezing point}}} \quad \text{or} \quad T_F = 1.8(T_C) + 32$$

FIGURE 2.2 A comparison of the Fahrenheit, Celsius, and Kelvin temperature scales between the freezing and boiling points of water.

Q What is the difference in the values for freezing on the Fahrenheit, Celsius, and Kelvin temperature scales?

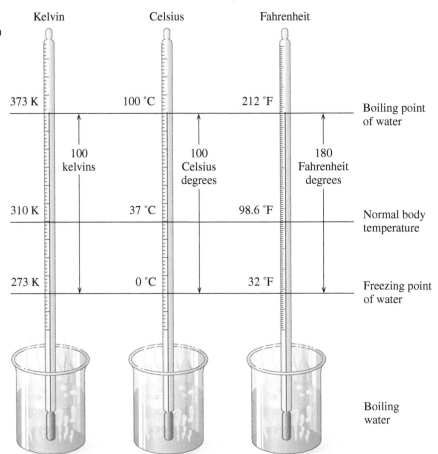

| CONCEPT CHECK | 2.2 |

■ Temperature Scales

A student in your chemistry class has designed a new temperature scale in degrees Zupa. The freezing point on this Zupa scale is 10 °Z, and the boiling point occurs at 130 °Z.

a. What is the relationship between degrees Zupa and degrees Celsius?
b. How would you adjust the freezing point?
c. Write an equation that relates degrees Zupa to degrees Celsius.
d. Convert a temperature of 35 °C to degrees Zupa.

ANSWER

a. On the Celsius scale, there are 100 °C between the freezing and the boiling points of water. On the Zupa scale, there are 120 °Z. Thus, 100 °C = 120 °Z and the conversion factor is 120 °Z/100 °C.
b. The freezing point is adjusted by adding 10 degrees.
c. The equation to convert °C to °Z would be written as

$$T_z = \frac{120 \, °Z \, (T_C)}{100 \, °C} + 10$$

$$T_z = 1.2 \, (T_C) + 10$$

d. $T_z = 1.2(35) + 10 = 42 + 10 = 52 \, °Z$

| SAMPLE PROBLEM | 2.2 |

■ Converting Celsius to Fahrenheit

The temperature of a room is set at 22 °C. If that temperature is lowered by 1 °C, it can save as much as 5% in energy costs. What temperature, in Fahrenheit degrees, should be set to lower the Celsius temperature by 1 °C?

SOLUTION

STEP 1   Given   22 °C − 1 °C = 21 °C   **Need** T_F

STEP 2   Plan T_C Temperature equation T_F

STEP 3   **Equalities/Conversion Factors**

$$T_F = 1.8(T_C) + 32$$

STEP 4   **Set Up Problem**   Substitute the Celsius temperature into the equation and solve.

$$T_F = 1.8(21) + 32 \quad \text{1.8 is exact; 32 is exact}$$

$$T_F = 38 + 32$$

$$= 70.\,°F \qquad \text{Answer to the ones place}$$

In the equation, *the values of 1.8 and 32 are exact numbers*. The answer is reported to the same decimal place as the initial temperature.

STUDY CHECK

In the process of making ice cream, rock salt is added to the crushed ice. If the temperature drops to –11 °C, what is it in °F?

In a chemistry laboratory, temperatures are measured in Celsius degrees. To convert from Fahrenheit to Celsius, the temperature equation is rearranged to solve for T_C. Start with

$$T_F = 1.8(T_C) + 32$$

Then subtract 32 from both sides.

$$T_F - 32 = 1.8(T_C) + 32 - 32$$

$$T_F - 32 = 1.8(T_C)$$

Solve the equation for T_C by dividing both sides by 1.8.

$$\frac{T_F - 32}{1.8} = \frac{\cancel{1.8}(T_C)}{\cancel{1.8}}$$

$$\frac{T_F - 32}{1.8} = T_C$$

SAMPLE PROBLEM   2.3

■ **Converting Fahrenheit to Celsius**

In a type of cancer treatment called *thermotherapy*, temperatures as high as 113 °F are used to destroy cancer cells. What is that temperature in Celsius degrees?

SOLUTION

STEP 1   **Given**   113 °F   **Need** T_C

STEP 2   **Plan** T_F $\begin{array}{c}\text{Temperature}\\\text{equation}\end{array}$ T_C

STEP 3   **Equalities/Conversion Factors**

$$T_C = \frac{T_F - 32}{1.8}$$

STEP 4   **Set Up Problem**   To solve for T_C, substitute the Fahrenheit temperature into the equation, and solve.

$$T_C = \frac{T_F - 32}{1.8}$$

$$T_C = \frac{(113 - 32)}{1.8} \quad \text{32 is exact; 1.8 is exact}$$

$$= \frac{81}{1.8} = 45\,°C \quad \text{Answer to the ones place}$$

STUDY CHECK

A child has a temperature of 103.6 °F. What is this temperature on a Celsius thermometer?

HEALTH NOTE

Variation in Body Temperature

Normal human body temperature is considered to be 37.0 °C, although it varies throughout the day and from person to person. Oral temperatures of 36.1 °C are common in the morning and climb to a high of 37.2 °C between 6 P.M. and 10 P.M. Temperatures above 37.2 °C for a person at rest are usually an indication of disease. Individuals who are involved in prolonged exercise may also experience elevated temperatures. Body temperatures of marathon runners can range from 39 °C to 41 °C because heat production during exercise exceeds the body's ability to lose heat.

Changes of more than 3.5 °C from the normal body temperature begin to interfere with bodily functions. Temperatures above 41 °C, hyperthermia, can lead to convulsions, particularly in children, which may cause permanent brain damage. Heatstroke occurs above 41.1 °C. Sweat production stops, and the skin becomes hot and dry. The pulse rate is elevated, and respiration becomes weak and rapid. The person can become lethargic and lapse into a coma. Damage to internal organs is a major concern, and treatment, which must be immediate, may include immersing the person in an ice-water bath.

At the low temperature extreme of hypothermia, body temperature can drop as low as 28.5 °C. The person may appear cold and pale and have an irregular heartbeat. Unconsciousness can occur if the body temperature drops below 26.7 °C. Respiration becomes slow and shallow, and oxygenation of the tissues decreases. Treatment involves providing oxygen and increasing blood volume with glucose and saline fluids. Injecting warm fluids (37.0 °C) into the peritoneal cavity may restore the internal temperature.

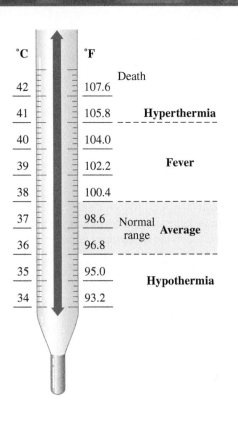

Kelvin Temperature Scale

Scientists have learned that the coldest temperature possible is –273 °C (more precisely, –273.15 °C). On the Kelvin scale, this temperature, called absolute zero, has the value of 0 Kelvin (0 K). Units on the Kelvin scale are called kelvins (K); no degree symbol is used. Because there are no lower temperatures, the Kelvin scale has no negative numbers. Between the freezing and boiling points of water, there are 100 kelvins, which makes a kelvin equal in size to a Celsius degree.

$$1 \text{ K} = 1 \text{ °C}$$

To calculate a Kelvin temperature, add 273 to the Celsius temperature:

$$T_K = T_C + 273$$

Table 2.1 gives a comparison of some temperatures on the three scales.

TABLE 2.1 A Comparison of Temperatures

Example	Fahrenheit (°F)	Celsius (°C)	Kelvin (K)
Sun	9937	5503	5776
A hot oven	450	232	505
A desert	120	49	322
A high fever	104	40	313
Room temperature	70	21	294
Water freezes	32	0	273
An Alaskan winter	–66	–54	219
Helium boils	–452	–269	4
Absolute zero	–459	–273	0

SAMPLE PROBLEM 2.4

■ Converting from Celsius to Kelvin Temperature

A dermatologist may use cryogenic liquid nitrogen at −196 °C to remove skin lesions and some skin cancers. What is the temperature of the liquid nitrogen in K?

SOLUTION

To find the Kelvin temperature, we use the equation:

$T_K = T_C + 273$

$T_K = -196 + 273$

$\quad = 77\ K$

STUDY CHECK

On the planet Mercury, the average night temperature is 13 K, and the average day temperature is 683 K. What are these temperatures in Celsius degrees?

QUESTIONS AND PROBLEMS

Temperature

2.7 Your friend who is visiting from Canada just took her temperature. When she reads 99.8, she becomes concerned that she is quite ill. How would you explain this temperature to your friend?

2.8 You have a friend who is using a recipe for flan from a Mexican cookbook. You notice that he set your oven temperature at 175 °F. What would you advise him to do?

2.9 Solve the following temperature conversions:
a. 37.0 °C = _____ °F
b. 65.3 °F = _____ °C
c. −27 °C = _____ K
d. 62 °C = _____ K
e. 114 °F = _____ °C
f. 72 °F = _____ K

2.10 Solve the following temperature conversions:
a. 25 °C = _____ °F
b. 155 °C = _____ °F
c. −25 °F = _____ °C
d. 224 K = _____ °C
e. 545 K = _____ °C
f. 875 K = _____ °F

2.11 a. A patient with heat stroke has a temperature of 106 °F. What does this read on a Celsius thermometer?
b. Because high fevers can cause convulsions in children, the doctor wants to be called if the child's temperature goes over 40. °C. Should the doctor be called if a child has a temperature of 103 °F?

2.12 a. Hot water is heated to 145 °F. What is the temperature of the hot water in °C?
b. During extreme hypothermia, a young woman's temperature dropped to 20.6 °C. What was her temperature on the Fahrenheit scale?

2.3 Specific Heat

Every substance has the ability to absorb or lose heat with temperature change. When you bake a potato, you place it in a hot oven. If you are cooking pasta, you add the pasta to boiling water. Some substances must absorb more heat than others to reach a certain temperature. These energy requirements for different substances are described in terms of a physical property called specific heat. **Specific heat** (*SH*) is the amount of heat needed to raise the temperature of exactly 1 g of a substance by exactly 1 °C. This temperature change is written as ΔT (*delta T*), where the delta symbol means "a change in."

$$\text{Specific heat}(SH) = \frac{\text{heat}}{\text{grams} \times \Delta T} = \frac{\text{cal(or J)}}{1\ g \times 1\ °C}$$

Now we can write the specific heat for water using our definition of the calorie and joule.

$$\text{Specific heat}(SH) \text{ of } H_2O(l) = \frac{1.00\ \text{cal}}{g\ °C} = \frac{4.184\ J}{g\ °C}$$

If we look at Table 2.2, we see that 1 g of water requires 1.00 cal to increase its temperature by 1 °C. Water has a large specific heat that is about five times the specific heat of aluminum. Aluminum has a specific heat that is about twice that of copper. Therefore, 1 cal (4.184 J) will increase the temperature of 1 g of water by 1 °C. The same amount of heat (1 cal or 4.184 J)

LEARNING GOAL

Use specific heat to calculate heat loss or gain, temperature change, or mass of a sample.

TUTORIAL
Specific Heat Calculations

TABLE 2.2 Specific Heats of Some Substances

Substance	Specific Heat	
	(cal/g °C)	(J/g °C)
Aluminum, Al(s)	0.214	0.897
Copper, Cu(s)	0.0920	0.385
Gold, Au(s)	0.0308	0.129
Iron, Fe(s)	0.108	0.452
Silver, Ag(s)	0.0562	0.235
Titanium, Ti(s)	0.125	0.523
Ammonia, NH_3(g)	0.488	2.04
Ethanol, C_2H_5OH(l)	0.588	2.46
Sodium chloride, NaCl(s)	0.207	0.864
Water, H_2O(l)	1.00	4.184

will also increase the temperature of 1 g of aluminum by about 5 °C and 1 g of copper by 10 °C. The high specific heat of water gives it the capacity to absorb or release large amounts of heat in the body, which maintains an almost constant body temperature.

CONCEPT CHECK 2.3

■ **Specific Heat**

A 1.0-g sample of iron has a temperature of 20 °C. Referring to Table 2.2, what is the final temperature of the iron sample if 1 cal of heat is added to the iron sample?

a. 21 °C   **b.** 25 °C   **c.** 30 °C   **d.** 120 °C   **e.** 200 °C

Explain.

ANSWER

The specific heat of iron (0.108 cal/g °C) is about 10 times smaller than that of water (1.00 cal/g °C). Therefore, the addition of 1 cal of heat would increase the temperature of 1 g of iron about 10 times the temperature increase of 1 g of water, or by 10 °C, to 30 °C (answer **c**).

SAMPLE PROBLEM   2.5

■ **Calculating Specific Heat**

What is the specific heat of lead if 13.6 cal are needed to raise the temperature of 35.6 g of lead by 12.5 °C?

SOLUTION

STEP 1   Given   heat 13.6 cal mass 35.6 g temperature change 12.5 °C
              Need   specific heat (cal/g °C)

STEP 2   Plan   The specific heat (*SH*) is calculated by dividing the heat by the mass (g) and by the temperature change (Δ*T*).

$$SH = \frac{\text{heat}}{\text{mass}\ \Delta T}$$

STEP 3   Substitute the given values into the specific heat relationship.

$$\text{Specific heat } (SH) = \frac{13.6\ \text{cal}}{35.6\ \text{g}\ \ 12.5\ °C} = 0.0306\ \frac{\text{cal}}{\text{g}\ °C}$$

STUDY CHECK

What is the specific heat of sodium metal (J/g °C) if 123 J are needed to raise the temperature of 4.00 g of sodium by 25.0 °C?

Calculations Using Specific Heat

MC™ TUTORIAL
Specific Heat Calculations

When we know the specific heat of a substance, we can rearrange the specific heat to obtain the heat equation.

$$\text{Specific heat } (SH) = \frac{\text{heat}}{\text{grams} \times \Delta T}$$

$$\text{Specific heat } (SH) \times \text{grams} \times \Delta T = \frac{\text{heat}}{\cancel{\text{grams} \times \Delta T}} \times \cancel{\text{grams}} \times \cancel{\Delta T}$$

$$\text{Heat} = \text{mass} \times \Delta T \times \text{specific heat } (SH)$$

The heat lost or gained is calculated by substituting the mass of the substance, the change in temperature, and the specific heat into the heat equation.

$$\text{Heat} = \text{mass} \times \underset{\text{change}}{\text{temperature}} \times \text{specific heat}$$

$$
\begin{array}{lllll}
\text{Heat} & = & \text{mass} & \times \Delta T & \times & SH \\
\text{cal} & = & \cancel{g} & \times °\cancel{C} & \times & \dfrac{\text{cal}}{\cancel{g}\,°\cancel{C}} \\
\text{J} & = & \cancel{g} & \times °\cancel{C} & \times & \dfrac{\text{J}}{\cancel{g}\,°\cancel{C}}
\end{array}
$$

SAMPLE PROBLEM   2.6

■ Calculating Heat with Temperature Increase

How many joules are absorbed by 45.2 g of aluminum (Al) if its temperature rises from 12.5 °C to 76.8 °C? (See Table 2.2.)

SOLUTION

STEP 1   Given   mass = 45.2 g

SH for aluminum = 0.897 J/g °C

Initial temperature = 12.5 °C
Final temperature = 76.8 °C

Need   heat in calories (cal)

STEP 2   Calculate the temperature change. The temperature change ΔT is the difference between the two temperatures.

$$\Delta T = T_{\text{final}} - T_{\text{initial}} = 76.8\,°C - 12.5\,°C = 64.3\,°C$$

STEP 3   Write the heat equation.

$$\text{Heat} = \text{mass} \times \Delta T \times SH$$

STEP 4   Substitute the given values into the equation and solve, making sure units cancel.

$$\text{Heat} = 45.2\,\cancel{g} \times 64.3\,°\cancel{C} \times \frac{0.897\,\text{J}}{\cancel{g}\,°\cancel{C}} = 2610\,\text{J} \ (2.61 \times 10^3\,\text{J})$$

**Guide to Calculations
Using Specific Heat**

STEP 1
List given and needed data.

STEP 2
Calculate temperature change (ΔT).

STEP 3
Write the equation for heat.
Heat = mass × ΔT × SH
and rearrange for unknown.

STEP 4
Substitute given values and
solve, making sure units cancel.

STUDY CHECK

Some cooking pans have a layer of copper on the bottom. How many kilojoules are needed to raise the temperature of 125 g of copper from 22 °C to 325 °C? (See Table 2.2.)

GREEN CHEMISTRY NOTE

Carbon Dioxide and Global Warming

Earth's climate is a product of interactions between sunlight, the atmosphere, and the oceans. The sun provides us with energy in the form of solar radiation. Some of this radiation is reflected back into space. The rest is absorbed by the clouds, atmospheric gases including carbon dioxide, and Earth's surface. For millions of years, concentrations of carbon dioxide have fluctuated. However in the past 100 years, the amount of carbon dioxide (CO_2) gas in our atmosphere has increased significantly. From the years 1000 to 1800, the atmospheric carbon dioxide averaged 280 ppm. But since the beginning of the Industrial Revolution in 1800, the level of atmospheric carbon dioxide has risen from about 280 ppm to about 380 ppm in 2005, or a 35% increase.

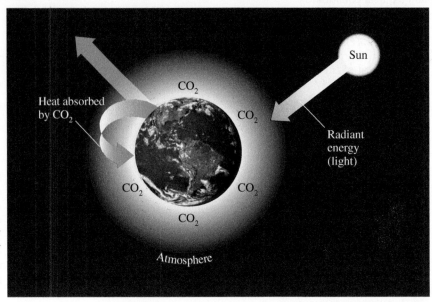

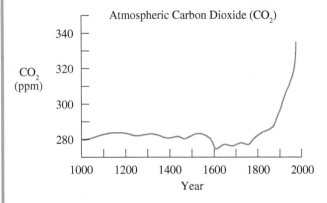

As the atmospheric CO_2 levels increase, more solar radiation is trapped by atmospheric gases, which raises the temperature at Earth's surface. Some scientists have estimated that if the carbon dioxide level doubles from its level before the Industrial Revolution, the average temperature globally could increase by 2.0 °C to 4.4 °C. While this may seem to be a small temperature change, it could have dramatic impact worldwide. Even now, glaciers and snow cover in much of the world have diminished. Ice sheets in Antarctica and Greenland are melting rapidly and breaking apart. Although no one

knows for sure how rapidly the ice in the polar regions is melting, this accelerating change will contribute to a rise in sea level. In the twentieth century, the sea level rose 15 to 23 cm, and some scientists predict the sea level will rise 1 m in this century. Such an increase will have a major impact on coastal areas.

Until recently, the carbon dioxide level was maintained as algae in the oceans and trees in the forests utilized the carbon dioxide. However, the ability of these and other forms of plant life to absorb carbon dioxide is not keeping up with the increase in carbon dioxide levels. Most scientists agree that the primary source of the increase of carbon dioxide is the burning of fossil fuels such as gasoline, coal, and natural gas. The cutting and burning of trees in the rain forests (deforestation) also reduces the amount of carbon dioxide removed from the atmosphere.

Worldwide efforts are being made to reduce the carbon dioxide produced by burning fossil fuels that heat our homes, run our cars, and provide energy for industries. Efforts are being made to explore alternative energy sources and to reduce the effects of deforestation. Meanwhile, we can reduce energy use in our homes by using appliances that are more energy efficient and replacing incandescent light bulbs with fluorescent lights. Such an effort worldwide will reduce the possible impact of global warming and at the same time save our fuel resources.

SAMPLE PROBLEM   2.7

■ Calculating Mass Using Specific Heat

Ethanol has a specific heat of 2.46 J/g °C. When 655 J are added to a sample of ethanol, its temperature rises from 18.2 °C to 32.8 °C. What is the mass in grams of the ethanol sample?

SOLUTION

STEP 1   List given and needed data.

> **Given**   heat = 655 J   *SH* for ethanol = 2.46 J/g °C
>
> Initial temperature = 18.2 °C
>
> Final temperature = 32.8 °C

> **Need**   grams of the ethanol sample

STEP 2   **Calculate the temperature change.** The temperature change, ΔT, is the difference between the two temperatures.

$$\Delta T = 32.8\,^{\circ}\text{C} - 18.2\,^{\circ}\text{C} = 14.6\,^{\circ}\text{C}$$

STEP 3   **Write the heat equation.**

$$\text{Heat} = mass \times \Delta T \times SH$$

The heat equation must be rearranged to solve for mass, which is the heat divided by the temperature change and the specific heat.

STEP 4   **Substitute the given values into the equation and solve, making sure units cancel.**

$$\text{Mass} = \frac{655\,\cancel{J}}{14.6\,\cancel{^{\circ}\text{C}}\,\dfrac{2.46\,\cancel{J}}{\text{g}\,\cancel{^{\circ}\text{C}}}}$$

$$= 18.2\,\text{g}$$

STUDY CHECK

When 8.81 kJ is absorbed by a piece of iron, its temperature rises from 15 °C to 122 °C. What is the mass, in grams, if iron has a specific heat of 0.452 J/g °C?

QUESTIONS AND PROBLEMS

Specific Heat

2.13 If the same amount of heat is supplied to samples of 10.0 g each of aluminum, iron, and copper, all at 15 °C, which sample would reach the highest temperature? (See Table 2.2.)

2.14 Substances A and B are the same mass and at the same initial temperature. When the same amount of heat is added to each, the final temperature of A is 55 °C higher than the temperature of B. What does this tell you about the specific heats of A and B?

2.15 Calculate the specific heat (J/g °C) for each of the following:
   a. a 13.5-g sample of zinc heated from 24.2 °C to 83.6 °C that absorbs 312 J of heat
   b. a 48.2-g sample of a metal that absorbs 345 J when temperature increases from 35.0 °C to 57.9 °C

2.16 Calculate the specific heat (J/g °C) for each of the following:
   a. an 18.5-g sample of tin that absorbs 183 J when its temperature increases from 35.0 °C to 78.6 °C
   b. a 22.5-g sample of a metal that absorbs 645 J when its temperature changes from 36.2 °C to 92.0 °C

2.17 What is the amount of heat required in each of the following?
   a. calories to heat 25 g of water from 15 °C to 25 °C
   b. calories to heat 150 g of water from 0 °C to 75 °C
   c. kilocalories to heat 150 g of water in a kettle from 15 °C to 77 °C

2.18 What is the amount of heat involved in each of the following?
   a. calories given off when 85 g of water cools from 45 °C to 25 °C
   b. calories given off when 25 g of water cools from 86 °C to 61 °C
   c. kilocalories absorbed when 5.0 kg of water warms from 22 °C to 28 °C

2.19 Calculate the energy in joules and calories
   a. required to heat 25.0 g of water from 12.5 °C to 25.7 °C
   b. required to heat 38.0 g of copper (Cu) from 122 °C to 246 °C
   c. lost when 15.0 g of ethanol, C_2H_5OH, cools from 60.5 °C to −42.0 °C
   d. lost when 112 g of iron, Fe, cools from 118 °C to 55 °C

2.20 Calculate the energy in joules and calories
   a. required to heat 5.25 g of water, H_2O, from 5.5 °C to 64.8 °C
   b. lost when 75.0 g of water, H_2O, cools from 86.4 °C to 2.1 °C
   c. required to heat 10.0 g of silver (Ag) from 112 °C to 275 °C
   d. lost when 18.0 g of gold (Au) cools from 224 °C to 118 °C

2.21 Calculate the mass in grams for each of the following:
   a. a gold sample that absorbs 225 J to change its temperature from 15.0 °C to 47.0 °C
   b. an iron object that loses 8.40 kJ when its temperature drops from 168.0 °C to 82.0 °C
   c. a sample of aluminum that absorbs 8.80 kJ when heated from 12.5 °C to 26.8 °C
   d. a sample of titanium that loses 14 200 J when it cools from 185 °C to 42 °C

2.22 Calculate the mass in grams for each of the following:
   a. a sample of water that absorbs 8250 J when its temperature rises from 18.4 °C to 92.6 °C
   b. a pure silver sample that loses 3.22 kJ when its temperature drops from 145 °C to 24 °C
   c. a sample of aluminum that absorbs 1.65 kJ when its temperature rises from 65 °C to 187 °C
   d. an iron bar that loses 2.52 kJ when its temperature drops from 252 °C to 75 °C

2.4 Energy and Nutrition

LEARNING GOAL

Use the energy values to calculate the kilocalories (Cal) or kilojoules (kJ) in a food.

The foods we eat provide energy to do work in the body, which includes the growth and repair of cells. Vitamins and minerals are necessary for health but have little energy value. Carbohydrates are the primary fuel for the body, but if carbohydrate reserves are exhausted, fats and then proteins can be used for energy. For many years in the field of nutrition, the energy from food was measured in Calories or kilocalories. The nutritional unit **Calorie, Cal** (with an uppercase C), is the same as 1000 cal, or 1 kcal. Now the use of kilojoule (kJ) is becoming more prevalent. For example, a baked potato has an energy value of 120 Calories, which is 120 kcal or 500 kJ. A typical diet of 2000 Cal (kcal) is the same as an 8400 kJ diet.

TUTORIAL
Nutritional Energy

Energy Values in Nutrition

1 Cal = 1 kcal = 1000 cal

1 Cal = 4.184 kJ = 4184 J

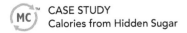
CASE STUDY
Calories from Hidden Sugar

In the laboratory, foods are burned in a calorimeter to determine their energy value. (See Figure 2.3.) Within the calorimeter, a sample of food is placed in a steel combustion chamber filled with oxygen gas. A measured quantity of water surrounds the combustion chamber. After the food sample ignites and burns, the heat released increases the temperature of the water. From the mass of the food and the temperature increase of the water, we can determine the energy content of the food.

We will assume that the energy absorbed by the calorimeter is negligible.

FIGURE 2.3 The caloric value of a food sample is calculated from the heat released when the sample is burned in a calorimeter.

Q What happens to the temperature of water in a calorimeter during the combustion of a food sample?

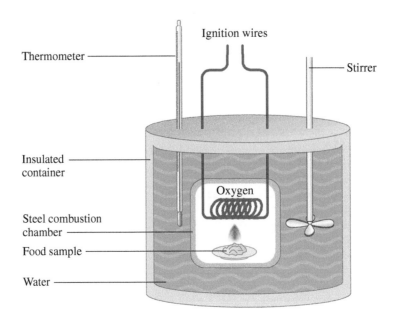

CONCEPT CHECK 2.4

■ **Energy Values of Food**

A 2-oz serving of pasta provides 200 Cal. What is the energy value of pasta in Cal/g?

ANSWER

Using the equalities of 16 oz = 1 lb and 1 lb = 454 g, we can set up some calculations for the energy values of pasta.

$$\frac{200 \text{ Cal}}{2 \text{ oz}} \times \frac{16 \text{ oz}}{1 \text{ lb}} \times \frac{1 \text{ lb}}{454 \text{ g}} = 4 \text{ Cal/g}$$

SAMPLE PROBLEM 2.8

■ **Calculating Food Energy Values**

A 2.3-g sample of butter, a fat, is placed in a calorimeter containing 1900 g of water at an initial temperature of 17 °C. After the complete combustion of the butter, the water has a temperature of 28 °C. Assume that the energy absorbed by the calorimeter is negligible. What is the energy value (kcal/g) and (kJ/g) of butter?

SOLUTION

With a $\Delta T = 11$ °C, the heat in kilocalories and kilojoules absorbed by the water is calculated as follows:

$$\text{Mass} \quad \times \quad \Delta T \quad \times \quad \text{specific heat of water} = \text{heat (kcal or kJ)}$$

$$1900 \text{ g} \times 11 \text{ °C} \times \frac{1.00 \text{ cal}}{\text{g °C}} \times \frac{1 \text{ kcal}}{1000 \text{ cal}} = 21 \text{ kcal}$$

$$1900 \text{ g} \times 11 \text{ °C} \times \frac{4.184 \text{ J}}{\text{g °C}} \times \frac{1 \text{ kJ}}{1000 \text{ J}} = 87 \text{ kJ}$$

Because 2.3 g of fat provided the 21 kcal (87 kJ) of heat, the energy value of butter is calculated as follows:

$$\frac{21 \text{ kcal}}{2.3 \text{ g fat}} = 9.1 \text{ kcal/g of fat} \qquad \frac{87 \text{ kJ}}{2.3 \text{ g fat}} = 38 \text{ kJ/g of fat}$$

STUDY CHECK

A 4.5-g sample of the carbohydrate sucrose, table sugar, is placed in a calorimeter. The water in the container has a mass of 1500 g and an initial temperature of 15 °C. After all the sucrose is burned, the water temperature is 27 °C. What is the energy value, in kcal/g and kJ/g, for sucrose?

Energy Values for Foods

The **energy (caloric) values** of food are the kilocalories or kilojoules obtained from the complete combustion of 1 g of a carbohydrate, fat, or protein. (See Table 2.3.)

TABLE 2.3 Typical Energy (Caloric) Values for the Three Food Types

Food Type	kJ/g	kcal/g
Carbohydrate	17	4
Fat	38	9
Protein	17	4

Using the energy values in Table 2.3, we can calculate the total energy of a food if the mass of each food type is known.

$$\text{Kilojoules} = \text{g} \times \frac{\text{kJ}}{\text{g}}$$

$$\text{Kilocalories} = \text{g} \times \frac{\text{kcal}}{\text{g}}$$

Snack Crackers

Nutrition Facts

Serving Size 14 crackers (31g)
Servings Per Container About 7

Amount Per Serving

Calories 120   Calories from Fat 35
Kilojoules 500   kJ from Fat   150

	% Daily Value*
Total Fat 4g	**6%**
Saturated Fat 0.5g	**3%**
Trans Fat 0g	
Polyunsaturated Fat 0.5%	
Monounsaturated Fat 1.5g	
Cholesterol 0mg	**0%**
Sodium 310mg	**13%**
Total Carbohydrate 19g	**6%**
Dietary Fiber Less than 1g	**4%**
Sugars 2g	
Proteins 2g	

Vitamin A 0%	•	Vitamin C 0%
Calcium 4%	•	Iron 6%

*Percent Daily Values are based on a 2,000 calorie diet. Your daily values may be higher or lower depending on your calorie needs.

	Calories:	2,000	2,500
Total Fat	Less than	65g	80g
Sat Fat	Less than	20g	25g
Cholesterol	Less than	300mg	300mg
Sodium	Less than	2,400mg	2,400mg
Total Carbohydrate		300g	375g
Dietary Fiber		25g	30g

Calories per gram:
Fat 9 • Carbohydrate 4 • Protein 4

EXPLORE YOUR WORLD

Counting Calories

Obtain a food item that has a nutrition label. From the Nutrition Facts information on the label, determine the number of grams of carbohydrate, fat, and protein in one serving. Using energy values, calculate the total Calories for one serving. (Most products round off to the tens place.)

QUESTION

How does your total for the Calories in one serving compare to the Calories stated on the label for a single serving?

Typical values for carbohydrates, fats, and proteins are listed in Table 2.4. On packaged food, the energy content is listed in the Nutrition Facts label on the package, usually in terms of the number of Calories for one serving. The general composition and caloric content of some foods are given in Table 2.4.

TABLE 2.4 General Composition and Energy Content of Some Foods

Food	Carbohydrate (g)	Fat (g)	Protein (g)	Energy*
Banana, 1 medium	26	0	1	460 kJ (110 kcal)
Beef, ground, 3 oz	0	14	22	910 kJ (220 kcal)
Carrots, raw, 1 cup	11	0	1	200 kJ (50 kcal)
Chicken, no skin, 3 oz	0	3	20	460 kJ (110 kcal)
Egg, 1 large	0	6	6	330 kJ (80 kcal)
Milk, 4% fat, 1 cup	12	9	9	700 kJ (170 kcal)
Milk, nonfat, 1 cup	12	0	9	360 kJ (90 kcal)
Potato, baked	23	0	3	440 kJ (100 kcal)
Salmon, 3 oz	0	5	16	460 kJ (110 kcal)
Steak, 3 oz	0	27	19	1350 kJ (320 kcal)

*Energy values are rounded to the tens place.

SAMPLE PROBLEM   2.9

■ Energy Content for a Food

What is the energy content, in kJ and kcal, for a piece of chocolate cake that contains 34 g of carbohydrate, 10 g of fat, and 5 g of protein? Round the answers of kJ and kcal to the tens place.

SOLUTION

Using the energy values for carbohydrate, fat, and protein (Table 2.3), we can calculate the total number of kcal:

Food Type	Mass	Energy Values	Energy
Carbohydrate	$34 \text{ g} \times$	$\dfrac{17 \text{ kJ (or 4 kcal)}}{1 \text{ g}} =$	580 kJ (or 140 kcal)
Fat	$10 \text{ g} \times$	$\dfrac{38 \text{ kJ (or 9 kcal)}}{1 \text{ g}} =$	380 kJ (or 90 kcal)
Protein	$5 \text{ g} \times$	$\dfrac{17 \text{ kJ (or 4 kcal)}}{1 \text{ g}} =$	90 kJ (or 20 kcal)
		Total energy content =	1050 kJ (or 250 kcal)

STUDY CHECK

A 1-oz (28 g) serving of oat-bran hot cereal with half a cup of whole milk contains 22 g of carbohydrate, 7 g of fat, and 10 g of protein. If you eat two servings of the oat bran for breakfast, how many kilocalories will you obtain? Round the final answer to the tens place.

HEALTH NOTE

Losing and Gaining Weight

The number of kilocalories or kilojoules needed in the daily diet of an adult depends on gender, age, and level of physical activity. Some general levels of energy needs are given in Table 2.5.

TABLE 2.5 Typical Energy Requirements for a 70.0-kg (154-lb) Adult

Gender	Energy (kJ)	Energy (kcal)
Female	10 000	2200
Male	12 500	3000

A person gains weight when food intake exceeds energy output. The amount of food a person eats is regulated by the hunger center in the hypothalamus, which is located in the brain. Food intake is normally proportional to the nutrient stores in the body. If these nutrient stores are low, you feel hungry; if they are high, you do not feel like eating.

A person loses weight when food intake is less than energy output. Many diet products contain cellulose, which has no nutritive value but provides bulk and makes you feel full. Some diet drugs depress the hunger center and must be used with caution, because they excite the nervous system and can elevate blood pressure. Because muscular exercise is an important way to expend energy, an increase in daily exercise aids weight loss. Table 2.6 lists some activities and the amount of energy they require.

TABLE 2.6 Energy Expended by a 70.0-kg (154-lb) Adult

Activity	Energy (kJ/hr)	Energy (kcal/hr)
Sleeping	250	60
Sitting	420	100
Walking	840	200
Swimming	2100	500
Running	3100	750

QUESTIONS AND PROBLEMS

Energy and Nutrition

2.23 Using the following data, determine the kilojoules and kilocalories for each food burned in a calorimeter:
  a. one stalk of celery that produces energy to heat 505 g of water from 25.2 °C to 35.7 °C
  b. a waffle that produces energy to heat 4980 g of water from 20.6 °C to 62.4 °C

2.24 Calculate the kilojoules and kilocalories each food provides when burned in a calorimeter:
  a. 1 cup of popcorn that produces energy to change the temperature of 1250 g of water from 25.5 °C to 50.8 °C
  b. a sample of butter that produces energy to increase the temperature of 357 g water from 22.7 °C to 38.8 °C

2.25 Using the energy values for foods, determine each of the following (round final Cal answers to the tens place):
  a. the total Calories for 1 cup of orange juice that contains 26 g of carbohydrate, no fat, and 2 g of protein
  b. the grams of carbohydrate in one apple if the apple has no fat and no protein and provides 72 kcal of energy
  c. the Calories in 1 tablespoon of vegetable oil, which contains 14 g of fat and no carbohydrate or protein

  d. the total Calories in one breakfast roll that has 30.0 g of carbohydrate, 15 g of fat, and 5 g of protein

2.26 Using the energy values for food, determine each of the following (round final Cal answers to tens place):
  a. the total Calories for 2 tablespoons of crunchy peanut butter that contains 6 g of carbohydrate, 16 g of fat, and 7 g of protein
  b. the grams of protein in 1 cup of soup that has 110 Cal with 7 g of fat and 9 g of carbohydrate
  c. the grams of sugar (carbohydrate) in one can of cola if it has 140 Cal and no fat and no protein
  d. the grams of fat in one avocado if it has 405 Calories, 13 g of carbohydrate, and 5 g of protein

2.27 One cup of clam chowder contains 9 g of protein, 12 g of fat, and 16 g of carbohydrate. How many kilocalories are in the clam chowder? How many kilojoules are in the clam chowder? (Round the final answers to the tens place.)

2.28 A high-protein diet contains 70.0 g of carbohydrate, 150 g of protein, and 5.0 g of fat. How many kilocalories does this diet provide? How many kilojoules does this diet provide? (Round the final answers to the tens place.)

2.5 Classification of Matter

LEARNING GOAL

Classify examples of matter as pure substances or mixtures.

TUTORIAL
Classification of Matter

Matter is anything that has mass and occupies space. Matter makes up all the things we use such as water, wood, plates, plastic bags, clothes, and shoes. The different types of matter are classified by their composition.

Pure Substances

A **pure substance** is matter that has a definite composition. There are two kinds of pure substances: elements and compounds. An **element** is the simplest pure substance because it is composed of only one kind of material—for example, silver, iron, or aluminum. A full list of the elements is found on the inside front cover of this text. A **compound** is also a pure substance, but it consists of two or more elements always in the same proportion. In compounds, the elements are held together by attractions called *bonds*. For example, the compound water, H_2O, always has the same proportion of the elements hydrogen and oxygen. The compound, hydrogen peroxide, H_2O_2, is also a combination of the elements hydrogen and oxygen, but in a different ratio.

An important difference between elements and compounds is that chemical processes can break down compounds into simpler substances such as elements. You may know that ordinary table salt is the compound NaCl, which can be broken down into sodium and chlorine as seen in Figure 2.4. Compounds are not broken down through physical methods such as boiling or sifting. Chemical or physical processes cannot break down elements.

Sodium chloride

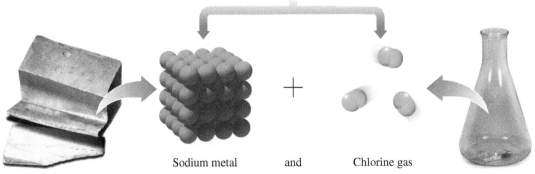

Sodium metal   and   Chlorine gas

FIGURE 2.4 The decomposition of salt, NaCl, produces the elements sodium and chlorine.

Q How do elements and compounds differ?

CONCEPT CHECK 2.5

■ **Pure Substances**

Explain why each of the following pure substances is a compound, and name its elements:

a. a carbohydrate glucose, $C_6H_{12}O_6$, also known as blood sugar
b. nitrogen dioxide, NO_2, a reddish-brown colored gas found in smog

ANSWER
a. Glucose, $C_6H_{12}O_6$, has a definite composition of three elements: carbon, hydrogen, and oxygen.
b. Nitrogen dioxide, NO_2, has a definite composition of two elements: nitrogen and oxygen.

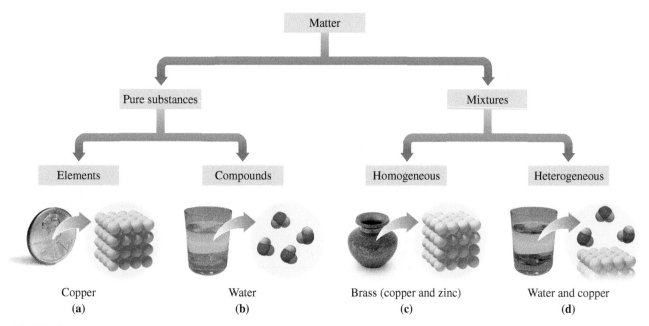

FIGURE 2.5 Matter is organized by its components: elements, compounds, and mixtures. **(a)** The element copper consists of copper atoms. **(b)** The compound water consists of H_2O molecules. **(c)** Brass is a homogeneous mixture of copper and zinc atoms. **(d)** Copper metal in water is a heterogeneous mixture of Cu atoms and H_2O molecules.
Q Why are copper and water pure substances, but brass is a mixture?

Mixtures

Much of the matter in our everyday lives consists of mixtures. (See Figure 2.5.) In a **mixture**, two or more substances are physically mixed, but not chemically combined. The air we breathe is a mixture of mostly oxygen and nitrogen gases. The steel in buildings and railroad tracks is a mixture of iron, nickel, carbon, and chromium. The brass in doorknobs and fixtures is a mixture of zinc and copper. Tea, coffee, and ocean water are mixtures, too. In any mixture, the composition can vary. For example, two sugar–water mixtures may look the same, but one would taste sweeter because it has a higher ratio of sugar to water. Different types of brass have different properties, depending on the ratio of copper to zinc.

Physical processes can be used to separate mixtures because there are no chemical interactions between the components. For example, a mixture of different coins such as nickels, dimes, and quarters can be separated by size; iron particles mixed with sand can be picked up with a magnet; and water is separated from cooked spaghetti by using a strainer. (See Figure 2.6.)

Types of Mixtures

Mixtures are classified as homogeneous or heterogeneous. In a *homogeneous mixture*, also called a *solution*, the composition is uniform throughout the sample. Examples of familiar homogeneous mixtures are air, which contains oxygen and nitrogen gases; and salt water, a solution of salt and water.

Physical method of separation

FIGURE 2.6 A mixture of spaghetti and water is separated using a strainer, a physical method of separation.
Q Why can physical methods be used to separate mixtures but not compounds?

TABLE 2.7 Classification of Matter

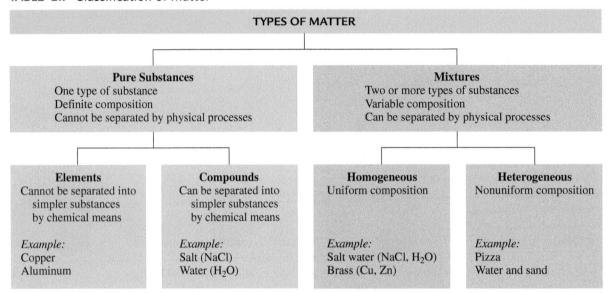

TYPES OF MATTER	
Pure Substances One type of substance Definite composition Cannot be separated by physical processes	**Mixtures** Two or more types of substances Variable composition Can be separated by physical processes

| **Elements**
Cannot be separated into simpler substances by chemical means

Example:
Copper
Aluminum | **Compounds**
Can be separated into simpler substances by chemical means

Example:
Salt (NaCl)
Water (H_2O) | **Homogeneous**
Uniform composition

Example:
Salt water (NaCl, H_2O)
Brass (Cu, Zn) | **Heterogeneous**
Nonuniform composition

Example:
Pizza
Water and sand |

In a *heterogeneous mixture*, the components do not have a uniform composition throughout the sample. For example, a mixture of oil and water is heterogeneous because the oil floats on the surface of the water. Other examples of heterogeneous mixtures include a raisin cookie and a hot fudge sundae. Table 2.7 summarizes the classification of matter.

SAMPLE PROBLEM 2.10

■ **Classifying Pure Substances and Mixtures**

Classify each of the following as a pure substance (element or compound) or a mixture (homogeneous or heterogeneous):

a. ice cream float   **b.** coffee with cream and sugar
c. copper wire   **d.** carbon dioxide (CO_2)

SOLUTION

a. mixture; heterogeneous with a nonuniform composition
b. mixture; homogeneous with uniform composition of coffee, cream, and sugar
c. pure substance; element
d. pure substance; compound with a definite ratio of two elements

STUDY CHECK

A salad dressing is prepared with oil, vinegar, and chunks of blue cheese. Is this a homogeneous or heterogeneous mixture?

QUESTIONS AND PROBLEMS

Classification of Matter

2.29 Classify each of the following pure substances as an element or compound. Give a reason for your answer.
  a. baking soda (NaHCO$_3$)   **b.** oxygen (O_2)
  c. ice (H_2O)   **d.** aluminum foil (Al)

2.30 Classify each of the following pure substances as an element or compound. Give a reason for your answer.
  a. platinum (Pt) in a catalytic converter
  b. vitamin C ($C_6H_8O_6$)
  c. mercury in a thermometer (Hg)
  d. carbon monoxide (CO)

2.31 Classify each of the following mixtures as homogeneous or heterogeneous:
  a. vegetable soup   **b.** saltwater
  c. tea   **d.** tea with ice and a lemon slice
  e. water and sand in an   **f.** fruit salad
       aquarium

2.32 Classify each of the following mixtures as homogeneous or heterogeneous:
  a. homogenized milk   **b.** chocolate chip ice cream
  c. gasoline   **d.** ham and cheese sandwich
  e. chicken noodle soup   **f.** hot tea with sweetener

2.6 States and Properties of Matter

On Earth, matter exists in one of three *physical states*: *solids*, *liquids*, and *gases*. All matter is made up of tiny particles. A **solid**, such as a pebble or a baseball, has a definite shape and volume. You can probably recognize several solids within your reach right now such as books, pencils, or a computer mouse. In a **solid**, strong attractive forces hold the particles close together. The particles are arranged in such a rigid pattern they can only vibrate slowly in their fixed positions. For many solids, this rigid structure produces a crystal such as that seen in amethyst. (See Figure 2.7.)

A **liquid** has a definite volume but not a definite shape. In a **liquid**, the particles move in random directions but are sufficiently attracted to each other to maintain a definite volume, although not a rigid structure. Thus, when oil, water, or vinegar is poured from one container to another, the liquid maintains its own volume but takes the shape of the new container. (See Figure 2.8.)

A **gas** does not have a definite shape or volume. When you inflate a bicycle tire, the air, which is a gas, fills the entire shape and volume of the tire. In a **gas**, the particles are far apart, have little attraction to each other, and move at high speeds, taking the shape and volume of their container. (See Figure 2.9.) Table 2.8 compares the three states of matter.

LEARNING GOAL

Identify the states and properties of matter.

FIGURE 2.7 The solid state of amethyst, a purple form of quartz.

Q Why do these crystals have a definite shape?

FIGURE 2.8 A liquid with a volume of 100 mL takes the shape of its container.

Q Why does a liquid have a definite volume but not a definite shape?

FIGURE 2.9 A gas takes the shape and volume of its container.

Q Why does a gas fill the volume of a container?

CONCEPT CHECK 2.6

■ States of Matter

Identify the state(s) of matter described by the substance in each of the following:

a. Volume does not change in a different container.
b. Has an especially low density.
c. Shape depends on the container.
d. Has a definite shape and volume.

ANSWER
a. Both a solid and a liquid have their own volume that does not depend on the volume of their container.
b. In a gas, the particles are far apart, which gives a small mass per volume, or a low density.
c. Both a liquid and a gas take the shape of their containers.
d. A solid has a rigid arrangement of particles that gives it a definite shape and volume.

Physical Properties and Physical Changes

One way to describe matter is to observe its physical properties. If you were asked to describe yourself, you might list your characteristics such as the color of your eyes and skin, or the length, color, and texture of your hair. **Physical properties** are those characteristics

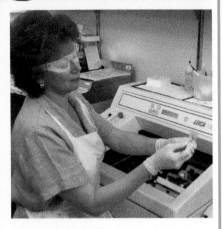

Histologist

"While a patient is in surgery for skin cancer, some tissue around the cancer is sent to us," says Mary Ann Pipe, histology technician. "Using the Mohs surgical technique, we place the tissue block on a glass slide, chill it to −30 °C in a machine called a *cryostat*, and freeze it for longer in another machine called a *heat extractor*. From this frozen block of tissue, we cut extremely thin slices—one-thousandth of an inch—from different depths. We prepare three separate slides from skin at three different depths up to the surface of the skin. We stain the cells pink and blue by placing the slides in hemotoxin, and then in eosin. The slices are a tissue map that the doctor can easily read to determine if the margins around the skin cancer are clear or whether more tissue must be removed."

TABLE 2.8 A Comparison of Solids, Liquids, and Gases

Characteristic	Solid	Liquid	Gas

Ice: H$_2$O (*s*)   Water: H$_2$O (*l*)

Water vapor: H$_2$O (*g*)

Characteristic	Solid	Liquid	Gas
Shape	Has a definite shape	Takes the shape of the container	Takes the shape of the container
Volume	Has a definite volume	Has a definite volume	Fills the volume of the container
Arrangement of particles	Fixed, extremely close	Random, close	Random, far apart
Interaction between particles	Especially strong	Strong	Essentially none
Movement of particles	Extremely slow	Moderate	Exceptionally fast
Examples	Ice, salt, iron	Water, oil, vinegar	Water vapor, helium, air

that can be observed or measured without affecting the identity of a substance. In chemistry, typical physical properties include the shape, state, color, melting point, and boiling point of a substance. For example, you might observe that a penny is round, orange-red, solid, and shiny. Table 2.9 gives examples of physical properties of copper found in pennies, electrical wiring, and copper pans.

TABLE 2.9 Some Physical Properties of Copper

Characteristic	Physical property
Color	Reddish-orange
Odor	Odorless
Melting point	1083 °C
Boiling point	2567 °C
State at 25 °C	Solid
Luster	Shiny
Conduction of electricity	Excellent
Conduction of heat	Excellent

Water is a substance that is commonly found in all three states: solid, liquid, and gas. When matter undergoes a **physical change**, its state or its appearance will change, but its composition remains the same. The solid form of water, snow or ice, has a different appearance than its liquid or gaseous form, but all three forms are water.

The physical appearance of a substance can change in other ways, too. Suppose that you dissolve some salt in water. The appearance of the salt changes, but you could re-form the salt crystals by heating the mixture and evaporating the water. Thus in a physical change, there are no new substances produced. Table 2.10 gives more examples of physical changes.

TABLE 2.10 Examples of Some Physical Changes

Type of Physical Change	Example
Change of state	Water boiling Water freezing
Change of appearance	Dissolving sugar in water
Change of shape	Hammering a gold ingot into shiny gold leaf Drawing copper into thin copper wire
Change of size	Cutting paper into tiny pieces for confetti Grinding pepper into smaller particles

Chemical Properties and Chemical Changes

Chemical properties are those that describe the ability of a substance to change into a new substance. When **chemical changes** take place, the original substances are converted into one or more new substances, which have different chemical and physical properties. For example, wood can burn because it has the chemical property of being flammable. When wood burns, it is converted to ashes and smoke, which have different chemical and physical properties. Rusting or corrosion is a chemical property of iron. In the rain, an iron nail undergoes a chemical change when it reacts with oxygen in the air to form rust, a new substance. Table 2.11 gives examples of chemical changes, and Table 2.12 summarizes physical and chemical properties and changes.

TABLE 2.11 Examples of Some Chemical Changes

Type of Chemical Change	Changes in Chemical Properties
Tarnishing of silver	Shiny, silver metal reacts in air to give a black, grainy coating.
Burning wood	A piece of pine burns with a bright flame, producing heat, ashes, carbon dioxide, and water vapor.
Caramelizing sugar	At high temperatures, white, granular sugar changes to a smooth, caramel-colored substance.
Formation of rust	Iron, which is gray and shiny, combines with oxygen to form orange-red rust.

TABLE 2.12 Summary of Physical and Chemical Properties and Changes

	Physical	Chemical
Property	A characteristic of the substance such as color, shape, odor, luster, size, melting point, and density.	A characteristic that indicates the ability of a substance to form another substance: paper can burn, iron can rust, and silver can tarnish.
Change	A change in a physical property that retains the identity of the substance: a change of state, a change in size, or a change in shape.	A change in which the original substance is converted to one or more new substances: paper burns, iron rusts, silver tarnishes.

■ Physical and Chemical Properties

Classify each of the following as a physical or chemical property:

a. Water is a liquid at room temperature.
b. Gasoline is flammable.
c. Aluminum foil has a shiny appearance.

ANSWER

a. A liquid is a state of matter, which makes it a physical property.
b. The burning or flammability of gasoline changes it to different substances with new properties, which is a chemical property.
c. The shininess of a substance does not change the type of substance; it is a physical property.

■ Physical and Chemical Changes

Classify each of the following as a physical or chemical change:

a. An ice cube melts to form liquid water.
b. Bleach removes a stain.
c. An enzyme breaks down the lactose in milk.
d. Peppercorns are ground into flakes.

SOLUTION

a. Physical change; the ice cube changes state.
b. Chemical change; a change occurs in the composition of the stain.
c. Chemical change; a change occurs in the composition of lactose.
d. Physical change; a change of size does not change composition.

STUDY CHECK

Which of the following are chemical changes?

a. Water freezes on a pond.
b. Gas bubbles form when baking powder is placed in vinegar.
c. A log is chopped for firewood.
d. A log is burned in a fireplace.

QUESTIONS AND PROBLEMS

States and Properties of Matter

2.33 Indicate whether each of the following describes a gas, a liquid, or a solid:
  a. This substance has no definite volume or shape.
  b. The particles in a substance do not interact strongly with each other.
  c. The particles in a substance are held in a definite structure.

2.34 Indicate whether each of the following describes a gas, a liquid, or a solid:
  a. The substance has a definite volume but takes the shape of the container.
  b. The particles in this substance are very far apart.
  c. This substance occupies the entire volume of the container.

2.35 Describe each of the following as a physical or chemical property:
  a. Chromium is a steel-gray solid.
  b. Hydrogen reacts readily with oxygen.
  c. Nitrogen freezes at −210 °C.
  d. Milk will sour when left in a warm room.

2.36 Describe each of the following as a physical or chemical property:
  a. Neon is a colorless gas at room temperature.
  b. Apple slices turn brown when exposed to air.
  c. Phosphorus will ignite when exposed to air.
  d. At room temperature, mercury is a liquid.

2.37 What type of change, physical or chemical, takes place in each of the following?
  a. Water vapor condenses to form rain.
  b. Cesium metal reacts explosively with water.
  c. Gold melts at 1064 °C.
  d. A puzzle is cut into 1000 pieces.
  e. Sugar dissolves in water.

2.38 What type of change, physical or chemical, takes place in each of the following?
  a. Gold is hammered into thin sheets.
  b. A silver pin tarnishes in the air.
  c. A tree is cut into boards at a sawmill.
  d. Food is digested.
  e. A chocolate bar melts.

2.39 Describe each property of the element fluorine as physical or chemical.
  a. is highly reactive
  b. is a gas at room temperature
  c. has a pale, yellow color
  d. will explode in the presence of hydrogen
  e. has a melting point of –220 °C .

2.40 Describe each property of the element zirconium as physical or chemical.
  a. melts at 1852 °C
  b. is resistant to corrosion
  c. has a grayish-white color
  d. ignites spontaneously in air when finely divided
  e. is a shiny metal

2.7 Changes of State

Matter undergoes a **change of state** when it is converted from one state to another state. (See Figure 2.10.)

When heat is added to a solid, the particles in the rigid structure move faster. At a temperature called the **melting point (mp)**, the particles in the solid gain sufficient energy to overcome the attractive forces that hold them together. The particles in the solid separate and move about in random patterns. The substance is **melting**, changing from a solid to a liquid.

LEARNING GOAL

Describe the changes of state between solids, liquids, and gases; calculate the energy involved.

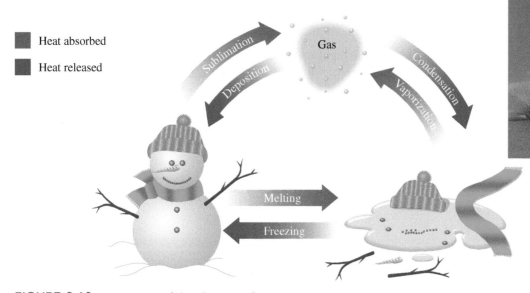

- Heat absorbed
- Heat released

FIGURE 2.10 A summary of the changes of state.
Q Is heat added or released when liquid water freezes?

If the temperature of a liquid is lowered, the reverse process takes place. Kinetic energy is lost, the particles slow down, and attractive forces pull the particles close together. The substance is **freezing**. A liquid changes to a solid at its **freezing point (fp)**, which is the same temperature as the melting point. Every substance has its own freezing (melting) point: Water freezes (melts) at 0 °C, gold freezes (melts) at 1064 °C, and nitrogen freezes (melts) at –210 °C.

During a change of state, the temperature of a substance remains constant. Suppose we have a glass containing ice and water. The ice melts when heat is added at 0 °C, forming more liquid. The liquid freezes when heat is removed at 0 °C.

Heat of Fusion

During melting, energy called the **heat of fusion** is added to separate the particles of a solid. For example, 334 joules (80. calories) of heat are needed to melt 1 g of ice at its melting point (0 °C).

Heat of Fusion for Water

$$\frac{334\ \text{J}}{1\ \text{g of H}_2\text{O}} \qquad \frac{80.\ \text{cal}}{1\ \text{g of H}_2\text{O}}$$

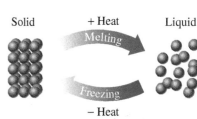

The heat of fusion (334 J/g or 80. cal/g) is also the amount of heat that must be removed to freeze 1 g of water at its freezing point (0 °C). Water is sometimes sprayed in fruit orchards during especially cold and sometimes subfreezing weather. If the air temperature drops to 0 °C, the water begins to freeze. Heat is released as the water molecules bond together, which warms the air and protects the fruit.

To determine the amount of heat needed to melt a sample of ice, multiply the mass of the ice by its heat of fusion. There is no temperature change in the calculation because temperature remains constant as long as the ice is melting.

Calculating Heat to Melt (or Freeze) Water

Heat = mass × heat of fusion

$$J = g \times \frac{334\ J}{g}$$

$$cal = g \times \frac{80.\ cal}{g}$$

SAMPLE PROBLEM 2.12

■ Heat of Fusion

Ice cubes at 0 °C with a mass of 26 g are added to your soft drink.

a. How much heat (joules) must be added to melt all the ice at 0 °C?
b. What happens to the temperature of your soft drink? Why?

SOLUTION

a. The heat in joules required to melt the ice is calculated as follows:

STEP 1	**Given** 26 g of $H_2O(s)$ **Need** joules to melt ice	
STEP 2	g of ice Heat of fusion J	
STEP 3	**Equalities/Conversion Factors**	

$$1\ g\ H_2O(s \longrightarrow l) = 334\ J$$

$$\frac{334\ J}{1\ g\ H_2O} \quad and \quad \frac{1\ g\ H_2O}{334\ J}$$

STEP 4   **Set Up Problem**

$$26\ \cancel{g\ H_2O} \times \frac{334\ J}{1\ \cancel{g\ H_2O}} = 8700\ J$$

b. The soft drink will be colder because heat from the soft drink is providing the energy to melt the ice.

STUDY CHECK

In a freezer, 150. g water at 0 °C is placed in an ice cube tray. How much heat, in kilojoules, must be removed to form ice cubes at 0 °C?

Guide to Calculations Using Heat of Fusion/Vaporization

STEP 1
List grams of substance and change of state.

STEP 2
Write the plan to convert grams to heat and desired unit.

STEP 3
Write the heat conversion factor and metric factor if needed.

STEP 4
Set up the problem with factors.

Boiling and Condensation

Water in a mud puddle disappears, unwrapped food dries out, and clothes hung on a clothesline dry. **Evaporation** is taking place as molecules of liquid water with sufficient energy escape from the liquid surface and enter the gas phase. (See Figure 2.11a.) The loss of the "hot" water molecules removes heat, which cools the remaining liquid water. As heat is added, more and more water molecules evaporate. At the **boiling point (bp)**, the molecules of a liquid acquire the energy needed to change to a gas. The **boiling** of a liquid occurs as gas bubbles form throughout the liquid and then rise to the surface and escape. (See Figure 2.11b.)

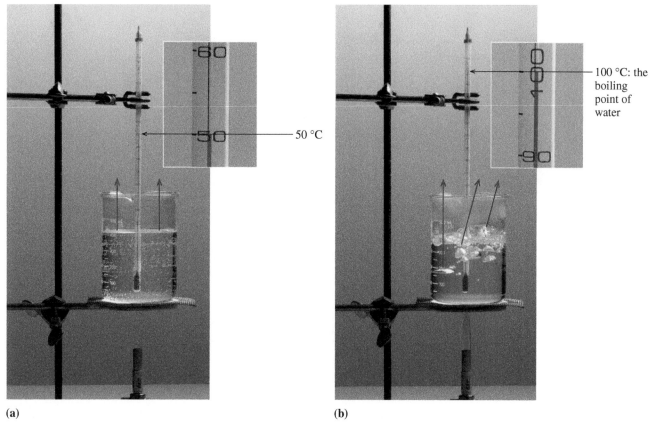

(a)   (b)

FIGURE 2.11 **(a)** Evaporation occurs at the surface of a liquid. **(b)** Boiling occurs as bubbles of gas form throughout the liquid.

Q Why does water evaporate faster at 80 °C than at 20 °C?

When heat is removed, a reverse process takes place. In condensation, water vapor is converted back to liquid as the water molecules lose kinetic energy and slow down. Condensation occurs at the same temperature as boiling but differs because heat is removed. You may have noticed that condensation occurs when you take a hot shower and the water vapor forms water droplets on a mirror. Because a substance loses heat as it condenses, its surroundings become warmer. That is why, when a rainstorm is approaching, we notice a warming of the air as gaseous water molecules condense to rain.

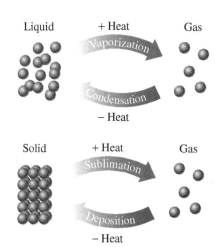

Sublimation

In a process called **sublimation**, the particles on the surface of a solid change directly to a gas with no temperature change and without going through the liquid state. In the reverse process of sublimation called *deposition*, gas particles change directly to solid.

Heat of Sublimation for Water

$$\frac{2590 \text{ J}}{1 \text{ g of } H_2O} \qquad \frac{620. \text{ cal}}{1 \text{ g of } H_2O}$$

For example, dry ice, which is solid carbon dioxide (CO_2), undergoes sublimation at −78 °C. It is called "dry" because it does not form a liquid as it warms. In extremely cold areas, snow does not melt but sublimes directly to water vapor. In a frost-free refrigerator, the water in the ice on the walls of the freezer and in frozen foods sublimes when warm air is circulated through the compartment during the defrost cycle. When frozen foods are left in the freezer for a long time, so much water sublimes that foods, especially meat, become dry and shrunken, a condition called *freezer burn*. Deposition occurs in a freezer when water vapor forms ice crystals on the surface of freezer bags and frozen food.

Freeze-dried foods prepared by sublimation are convenient for long-term storage and for camping and hiking. A food that has been frozen is placed in a vacuum chamber where it dries as the ice sublimes. The dried food retains all of its nutritional value and needs only

water to be edible. A food that is freeze-dried does not need refrigeration because bacteria cannot grow without moisture.

Heat of Vaporization

The energy that must be added to vaporize exactly 1 g of liquid to gas at its boiling point is called the **heat of vaporization**. For water, 540 cal or 2260 J are needed to convert 1 g of water to vapor at 100 °C. This amount of heat is released when 1 g of water vapor (gas) changes to liquid at 100 °C. Therefore, 540 cal/g or 2260 J/g is also the *heat of condensation* of water.

Heat of Vaporization for Water

$$\frac{2260 \text{ J}}{1 \text{ g of } H_2O} \qquad \frac{540 \text{ cal}}{1 \text{ g of } H_2O}$$

To calculate the amount of heat added to vaporize (or removed to condense) a sample of water, the mass of the sample is multiplied by the heat of vaporization. As before, no temperature change occurs during a change of state.

Calculating Heat to Vaporize (or Condense) Water

Heat = mass × heat of vaporization

$$\text{cal} = \cancel{g} \times \frac{540 \text{ cal}}{\cancel{g}}$$

$$\text{J} = \cancel{g} \times \frac{2260 \text{ J}}{\cancel{g}}$$

Just as substances have different melting and boiling points, they also have different heats of fusion and heats of vaporization, as shown in Table 2.13. The heat of vaporization is always greater than the heat of fusion. (See Figure 2.12.)

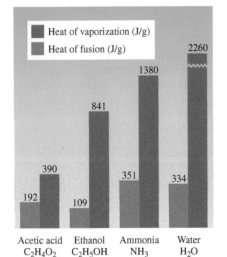

FIGURE 2.12 For any substance, the heat of vaporization is greater than the heat of fusion.

Q Why does the formation of a gas require more energy than the formation of a liquid of the same substance?

TABLE 2.13 Heats of Fusion and Heats of Vaporization for Selected Substances

Liquid	Formula	Melting Point (°C)	Heat of Fusion (J/g)	Boiling Point (°C)	Heat of Vaporization (J/g)
Water	H_2O	0	334	100	2260
Ethanol	C_2H_5OH	−114	109	78	841
Ammonia	NH_3	−78	351	−33	1380
Acetone	C_3H_6O	−95	98	56	335
Mercury	Hg	−39	11	357	294
Acetic acid	$C_2H_4O_2$	17	192	118	390

HEALTH NOTE

Steam Burns

Hot water at 100 °C will cause burns and damage to the skin. However, getting steam on the skin is even more dangerous. If 25 g of hot water at 100 °C falls on a person's skin, the temperature of the water will drop to body temperature, 37 °C. The heat released during cooling burns the skin. The amount of heat can be calculated from the temperature change, 63 °C.

$$25 \text{ g} \times 63 \text{ °C} \times \frac{4.184 \text{ J}}{\text{g °C}} = 6600 \text{ J released}$$

For comparison, we can calculate the amount of heat released when 25 g of steam at 100 °C hits the skin. First, the steam condenses to water (liquid) at 100 °C:

$$25 \text{ g} \times \frac{2260 \text{ J}}{1 \text{ g}} = 57\,000 \text{ J released}$$

The total amount of heat released from the condensation and cooling of the steam is calculated as follows:

Condensation (100 °C) = 57 000 J
Cooling (100 °C to 37 °C) = 6600 J
Heat released = 64 000 J (rounded)

The amount of heat released from steam is 10 times greater than the heat from the same amount of hot water.

SAMPLE PROBLEM 2.13

■ Using Heat of Vaporization

In a sauna, 150 g of water is converted to steam at 100 °C. How many kilocalories of heat are needed?

SOLUTION

STEP 1   Given 150 g of $H_2O(l)$ to $H_2O(g)$ **Need** kilocalories of heat to change state

STEP 2   Plan g of H_2O → Heat of vaporization → cal → Metric factor → kcal

STEP 3   Equalities/Conversion Factors

1 g H_2O ($l \rightarrow g$) = 540 cal   1 kcal = 1000 cal

$$\frac{540 \text{ cal}}{1 \text{ g } H_2O} \text{ and } \frac{1 \text{ g } H_2O}{540 \text{ cal}} \qquad \frac{1000 \text{ cal}}{1 \text{ kcal}} \text{ and } \frac{1 \text{ kcal}}{1000 \text{ cal}}$$

STEP 4   **Set Up Problem**

$$150 \ \text{g} \ \cancel{H_2O} \ \times \ \frac{540 \ \cancel{cal}}{1 \ \text{g} \ \cancel{H_2O}} \ \times \ \frac{1 \ \text{kcal}}{1000 \ \cancel{cal}} \ = \ 81 \ \text{kcal}$$

STUDY CHECK

When steam from a pan of boiling water reaches a cool window, it condenses. How much heat, in kilocalories (kcal), is released when 25 g of steam condenses at 100 °C?

Heating and Cooling Curves

All the changes of state during the heating of a solid can be illustrated visually. In a heating curve, the temperature is shown on the vertical axis, and the addition of heat is shown on the horizontal axis. (See Figure 2.13a.)

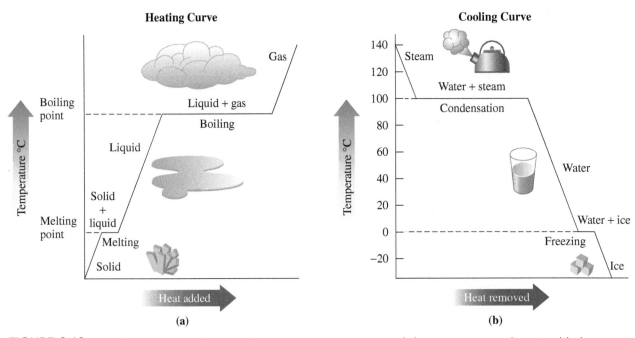

FIGURE 2.13 (a) A heating curve diagrams the temperature increases and changes in state as heat is added. **(b)** A cooling curve for water.

Q What does the horizontal line at 100 °C represent on the heating and cooling curves for water?

Steps on a Heating Curve

The first diagonal line indicates a warming of a solid as heat is added. When the melting temperature is reached, a horizontal line, or plateau, indicates that the solid is melting. As melting takes place, the solid is changing to a liquid without any change in temperature.

Once all of the particles are in the liquid state, heat that is added will increase the temperature of the liquid. This increase is drawn as a diagonal line from the melting point to the boiling point temperature. Once the liquid reaches its boiling point, a horizontal line indicates that the temperature remains constant as liquid changes to gas. Because the heat of vaporization is larger than the heat of fusion, the horizontal line at the boiling point is longer than the line at the melting point. Once all the liquid becomes a gas, adding more heat increases the temperature of the gas.

■ Heating Curve

Using the melting and boiling points of acetone in Table 2.13, identify the state or change of state as heat is added to a sample of acetone starting at –110 °C and stopping at 70 °C. (*Hint*: Sketch the heating curve.)

a. –95 °C   **b.** –80 °C

c. 0 °C   **d.** 70 °C

ANSWER

a. A horizontal line at –95 °C indicates the melting of acetone.

b. At –80 °C, which is higher than the melting point, acetone is a liquid.

c. At 0 °C, which is higher than the melting point, acetone is a liquid.

d. At 70 °C, which is higher than the boiling point, acetone is a gas.

Steps on a Cooling Curve

A cooling curve is a diagram of the cooling process. In the diagram, the temperature is plotted on the vertical axis, and the removal of heat is plotted on the horizontal axis. (See Figure 2.13b.) Initially, a diagonal line to the boiling (condensation) point is drawn to show that heat is removed from a substance, cooling the gas until it begins to condense. A horizontal line (plateau) is drawn at the condensation point (same as the boiling point) to indicate the change of state as the gas condenses to form a liquid. After all of the gas has changed into liquid, further cooling lowers the temperature. The decrease in temperature is shown as a diagonal line from the condensation point temperature to the freezing point temperature. At the freezing point, another horizontal line indicates that liquid is changing to solid at the freezing point temperature. Once all of the substance is frozen, a loss of heat decreases the temperature below its freezing point, which is shown as a diagonal line below the freezing point.

Combining Energy Calculations

Up to now, we have calculated one step in a heating or cooling curve. However, many problems require a combination of steps that include a temperature change as well as a change of state. The heat is calculated for each step separately and then added together to find the total energy as seen in Sample Problem 2.14.

SELF STUDY ACTIVITY
MC™ Heat, Energy, and Changes of State

■ Combining Heat Calculations

Using Table 2.13 and the specific heat of ethanol (2.46 J/g °C), calculate the total heat, in joules, needed to convert 15.0 g of ethanol at 25.0 °C to gas at 78.0 °C.

SOLUTION

STEP 1   Given   15.0 g of ethanol at 25.0 °C

Need   heat (J) needed to warm the ethanol and change it to gas

STEP 2   When several changes occur, draw a diagram of heating and changes of state.

Total heat = joules needed to warm ethanol from 25.0 °C to 78.0 °C
+ joules to change liquid to gas at 78.0 °C

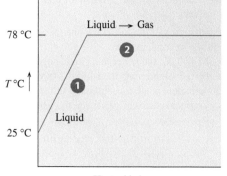

STEP 3   **Equalities/Conversion Factors**

$$SH_{ethanol} = \frac{2.46\ J}{g\ °C}$$

$$\frac{2.46\ J}{g\ °C} \quad and \quad \frac{g\ °C}{2.46\ J}$$

$$1\ g\ of\ ethano(l \rightarrow g) = 841\ J$$

$$\frac{841\ J}{1\ g\ ethanol} \quad and \quad \frac{1\ g\ ethanol}{841\ J}$$

STEP 4   **Set Up Problem** $\Delta T = 78.0\ °C - 25.0\ °C = 53.0\ °C$

Heat needed to warm ethanol (liquid) (25.0 °C) to ethanol (liquid) (78.0 °C):

$$15.0\ \cancel{g} \times 53.0\ \cancel{°C} \times \frac{2.46\ J}{\cancel{g}\ \cancel{°C}} = 1960\ J$$

Heat needed to change ethanol (liquid) to ethanol (gas) at 78.0 °C:

$$15.0\ \cancel{g} \times \frac{841\ J}{1\ \cancel{g}} = 12\ 600\ J$$

Calculate the total heat:

Heating ethanol (25.0 °C to 78.0 °C)	1 960 J
Changing liquid to gas (at 78.0 °C)	12 600 J
Total heat needed	14 600 J (rounded)

STUDY CHECK

How many kilojoules (kJ) are released when 25.0 g of steam at 100 °C condenses, cools to 0 °C, and freezes? (*Hint*: The solution will require three energy calculations.)

QUESTIONS AND PROBLEMS

Changes of State

2.41 Identify each of the following changes of state as melting, freezing, condensation, sublimation, or deposition:
a. The solid structure of a substance breaks down as liquid forms.
b. Coffee is freeze-dried.
c. Water on the street turns to ice during a cold wintry night.
d. Crystals of ice form on a package of frozen corn.

2.42 Identify each of the following changes of state as melting, freezing, condensation, sublimation, or deposition:
a. Dry ice in an ice-cream cart disappears.
b. Snow on the ground turns to liquid water.
c. Heat is removed from 125 g of liquid water at 0 °C.
d. In a warm room, a person's glasses fog up.

2.43 Calculate the heat needed at 0 °C to make each of the following changes of state. Indicate whether heat was absorbed or released.
a. calories to melt 65 g of ice
b. calories to melt 17 g of ice
c. kilocalories to freeze 225 g of water

2.44 Calculate the heat needed at 0 °C to make each of the following changes of state. Indicate whether heat was absorbed or released.
a. calories to freeze 35 g of water
b. calories to freeze 250 g of water
c. kilocalories to melt 140 g of ice

2.45 Identify each of the following changes of state as evaporation, boiling, or condensation:
a. The water vapor in the clouds changes to rain.
b. Wet clothes dry on a clothesline.
c. Lava flows into the ocean, and steam forms.
d. After a hot shower, your bathroom mirror is covered with water.

2.46 Identify each of the following changes of state as evaporation, boiling, or condensation:
a. At 100 °C, the water in a pan changes to steam.
b. On a cool morning, the windows in your car fog up.
c. A shallow pond dries up in the summer.
d. Your teakettle whistles when the water is ready for tea.

2.47 Calculate the heat change at 100 °C in each of the following problems. Indicate whether heat was absorbed or released.
   a. calories to vaporize 10.0 g of water
   b. kilocalories to vaporize 50.0 g of water
   c. kilocalories to condense 8.0 kg of steam

2.48 Calculate the heat change at 100 °C in each of the following problems. Indicate whether heat was absorbed or released.
   a. calories to condense 10.0 g of steam
   b. kilocalories to condense 75 g of steam
   c. kilocalories to vaporize 44 g of water

2.49 Draw a heating curve for a sample of ice that is heated from –20 °C to 140 °C. Indicate the segment of the graph that corresponds to each of the following:
   a. solid   **b.** melting point   **c.** liquid
   d. boiling point   **e.** gas

2.50 Draw a cooling curve for a sample of steam that cools from 110 °C to –10 °C. Indicate the segment of the graph that corresponds to each of the following:
   a. solid   **b.** freezing point   **c.** liquid
   d. condensation point (boiling point)   **e.** gas

2.51 Using the values for the heat of fusion, specific heat of water, or heat of vaporization, calculate the amount of heat energy in each of the following:
   a. calories needed to warm 20.0 g of water at 15 °C to 72 °C (one step)
   b. calories need to melt 50.0 g of ice at 0 °C and to warm the liquid to 65 °C (two steps)
   c. kilojoules given off when 15 g of steam condenses at 100 °C and the liquid cools to 0 °C (two steps)
   d. kilocalories needed to melt 24 g of ice at 0 °C, to warm the liquid to 100 °C, and to vaporize it at 100 °C (three steps)

2.52 Using the values for the heat of fusion, specific heat of water, or heat of vaporization, calculate the amount of heat energy in each of the following:
   a. calories removed to condense 125 g of steam at 100 °C and to cool the liquid to 15 °C (two steps)
   b. joules needed to melt a 525-g ice cube at 0 °C and to warm the liquid to 15 °C (two steps)
   c. kilocalories removed to condense 85 g of steam at 100 °C, cool the liquid to 0 °C, and freeze it at 0 °C (three steps)
   d. calories to warm 55 mL of water (density = 1.0 g/mL) from 10 °C to 100 °C and vaporize it at 100 °C (two steps)

CONCEPT MAP

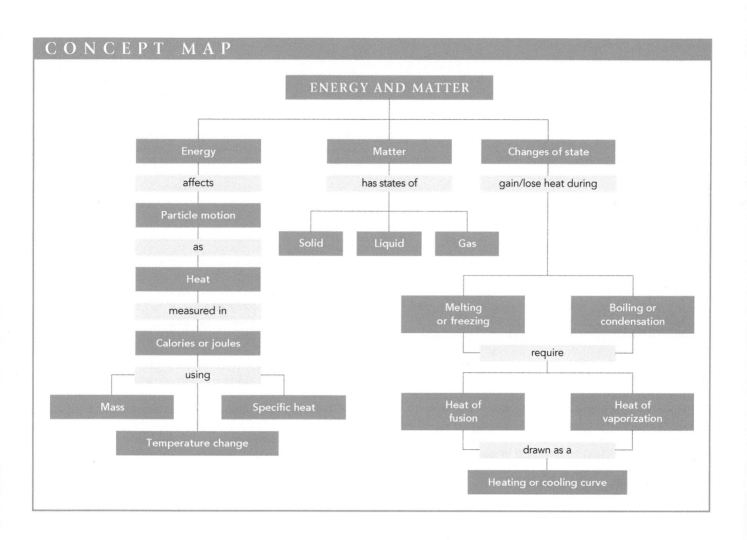

CHAPTER REVIEW

2.1 Energy

LEARNING GOAL: *Identify energy as potential or kinetic and understand the units of energy.*

Energy is the ability to do work. Potential energy is stored energy; kinetic energy is the energy of motion. Common units of energy are the calorie (cal), kilocalorie (kcal), joule (J), and kilojoule (kJ). One cal is equal to 4.184 J.

2.2 Temperature

LEARNING GOAL: *Given a temperature, calculate a corresponding temperature on another temperature scale.*

In science, temperature is measured in Celsius degrees (°C) or kelvins (K). In the United States, the Fahrenheit scale (°F) is still in use. On the Celsius scale, there are 100 units between the freezing point (0 °C) and the boiling point of water (100 °C). On the Fahrenheit scale, there are 180 units between the freezing point (32 °F) and boiling point of water (212 °F). A Fahrenheit temperature is related to its Celsius temperature by the equation $T_F = 1.8 \, T_C + 32$. The SI temperature of Kelvin is related to the Celsius temperature by the equation $T_K = T_C + 273$.

2.3 Specific Heat

LEARNING GOAL: *Use specific heat to calculate heat loss or gain, temperature change, or mass of a sample.*

Specific heat is the amount of energy required to raise the temperature of exactly 1 g of a substance by exactly 1 °C. The heat lost or gained by a substance is determined by multiplying its mass (g), the temperature change (ΔT), and its specific heat (cal/g °C or J/g °C).

2.4 Energy and Nutrition

LEARNING GOAL: *Use the energy values to calculate the kilocalories (kcal) or kilojoules (kJ) in a food.*

The nutritional Calorie is the same amount of energy as 1 kcal or 1000 calories. The energy content of a food is the sum of kilocalories or kilojoules from carbohydrate, fat, and protein.

2.5 Classification of Matter

LEARNING GOAL: *Classify examples of matter as pure substances or mixtures.*

Matter is classified as pure substances or mixtures. Pure substances, which are elements or compounds, have fixed compositions, and mixtures have variable compositions. The substances in mixtures can be separated using physical methods.

2.6 States and Properties of Matter

LEARNING GOAL: *Identify the states and properties of matter.*

Matter is anything that has mass and occupies space. The three states of matter are solid, liquid, and gas. A physical property is a characteristic of a substance. A physical change occurs when physical properties change but not the identity of the substance. A chemical property indicates the ability of a substance to change into another substance. In a chemical change, at least one substance forms a new substance with new physical properties.

2.7 Changes of State

LEARNING GOAL: *Describe the changes of state between solids, liquids, and gases; calculate the energy involved.*

Melting occurs when the particles in a solid absorb enough energy to break apart and form a liquid. The amount of energy required to convert exactly 1 g of solid to liquid is its heat of fusion. For water, 80. cal or 334 J must be added to melt 1 g of ice. Boiling is the vaporization of a liquid at its boiling point. The heat of vaporization is the amount of heat needed to convert exactly 1 g of liquid to vapor. For water, 540 cal or 2260 J are needed to vaporize 1 g of liquid water. A heating or cooling curve illustrates the changes in temperature and state as heat is added to or removed from a substance. Plateaus on the graph indicate changes of state with no change in temperature.

KEY TERMS

boiling The formation of bubbles of gas throughout a liquid.

boiling point (bp) The temperature at which a liquid changes to gas (boils) and gas changes to liquid (condenses).

calorie (cal) The amount of heat energy that raises the temperature of exactly 1 g of water exactly 1 °C; 1 cal = 4.184 J.

Calorie (Cal) A nutritional unit of energy equal to 1000 cal, or 1 kcal.

change of state The transformation of one state of matter to another; for example, from solid to liquid, liquid to solid, and liquid to gas.

chemical change A change during which the original substance is converted into a new substance with a different composition and new chemical and physical properties.

chemical properties The properties that indicate the ability of a substance to change to a new substance.

compound A pure substance consisting of two or more elements, with a definite composition, that can be broken down into simpler substance only by chemical methods.

condensation The change of state of a gas to a liquid.

cooling curve A diagram that illustrates temperature changes and changes of state for a substance as heat is removed.

deposition The reverse process of sublimation, with gas particles changing directly into a solid.

element A pure substance containing only one type of matter, which cannot be broken down by chemical methods.

energy The ability to do work.

energy (caloric) value The kilocalories obtained per gram of the three food types: carbohydrate, fat, and protein.

evaporation The formation of a gas (vapor) by the escape of high-energy molecules from the surface of a liquid.

freezing A change of state from liquid to solid.

freezing point (fp) The temperature at which a liquid changes to a solid (freezes) and a solid changes to a liquid (melts).

gas A state of matter characterized by no definite shape or volume. Particles in a gas move rapidly.

heat The energy associated with the motion of particles in a substance.

heat of fusion The energy required to melt exactly 1 g of a substance at its melting point. For water, 80. cal (334 J) are needed to melt 1 g of ice; 80. cal (334 J) are released when 1 g of water freezes.

heat of vaporization The energy required to vaporize exactly 1 g of a substance at its boiling point. For water, 540 calories (2260 J) are needed to vaporize exactly 1 g of liquid; 1 g of steam gives off 540 cal (2260 J) when it condenses.

heating curve A diagram that shows the temperature changes and changes of state of a substance as it is heated.

joule (J) The SI unit of heat energy; 4.184 J = 1 cal.

kilocalorie (kcal) An amount of heat energy equal to 1000 calories.

kinetic energy The energy of motion.

liquid A state of matter that takes the shape of its container but has a definite volume.

melting A change of state that involves the conversion of a solid to a liquid.

melting point (mp) The temperature at which a solid becomes a liquid (melts). It is the same temperature as the freezing point.

mixture The physical combination of two or more substances that does not change the identities of the substances.

physical change The change in which the physical appearance of a substance changes, but the chemical composition stays the same.

physical properties The properties that can be observed or measured without affecting the identity of a substance.

potential energy An inactive type of energy that is stored for future use.

pure substance Matter composed of elements or compounds that has a definite composition.

solid A state of matter that has its own shape and volume.

specific heat A quantity of heat that changes the temperature of exactly 1 g of a substance by exactly 1 °C.

sublimation The change of state in which a solid is transformed directly to a gas without forming a liquid first.

work An activity that requires energy.

■ UNDERSTANDING THE CONCEPTS

2.53 Select the warmer temperature in each pair.
  a. 10 °C or 10 °F
  b. 30 °C or 15 °F
  c. −10 °C or 32 °F
  d. 200 °C or 200 K

2.54 Compost can be made at home from grass clippings, some kitchen scraps, and dry leaves. As microbes break down organic matter, heat is generated and the compost can reach a temperature of 155 °F, which kills most pathogens. What is this temperature in Celsius degrees?

2.55 After a week, biochemical reactions in compost slow, and the temperature drops to 45 °C. The dark brown organic-rich mixture is ready for use in the garden. What is this temperature in Fahrenheit degrees? In kelvins?

2.56 Determine the energy to heat three cubes (gold, aluminum, and silver), each with a volume of 10.0 cm^3 from 15 °C to 25 °C. Refer to Tables 1.11 and 2.2. What do you notice about the energy needed for each?

2.57 A 70.0-kg person had a quarter-pound cheeseburger, french fries, and a chocolate shake. According to Table 2.6, determine each of the following:

  a. the number of hours of sleep needed to "burn off" the kilocalories in this meal
  b. the number of hours of running needed to "burn off" the kilocalories in this meal

Item	Protein (g)	Fat (g)	Carbohydrate (g)
Cheeseburger	31	29	34
French fries	3	11	26
Chocolate shake	11	9	6

2.58 Identify each of the following as an element, compound, or mixture:

a.

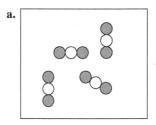

b.

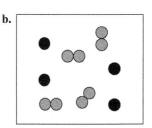

c.

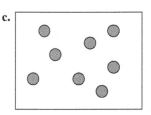

2.59 Which diagram illustrates a heterogeneous mixture? Explain your choice. Which diagrams illustrate a homogeneous mixture? Explain your choice.

 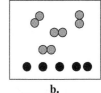

a.   b.   c.

2.60 Classify each of the following as a homogeneous mixture or heterogeneous mixture:
a. lemon-flavored water
b. stuffed mushrooms
c. chicken noodle soup
d. ketchup
e. hard-boiled egg
f. eye drops

2.61 a. How does perspiration during heavy exercise cool the body?
b. Why do clothes dry more quickly on a hot summer day than on a cold winter day?

2.62 a. When a sports injury occurs during a game, a spray such as ethyl chloride may be used to numb an area of the skin. Explain how a substance such as ethyl chloride that evaporates quickly can numb the skin.
b. Why does water in a wide, flat, shallow dish evaporate more quickly than the same amount of water in a tall, narrow glass?

2.63 The following is a heating curve for chloroform, a solvent for fats, oils, and waxes:

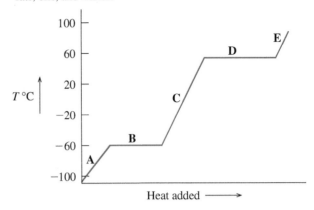

a. What is the melting point of chloroform?
b. What is the boiling point of chloroform?
c. On the heating curve, identify the segments A, B, C, D, and E as solid, liquid, gas, melting, or boiling.
d. At the following temperatures, is chloroform a solid, liquid, or gas? –80 °C; –40 °C; 25 °C; 80 °C

2.64 Associate the following diagrams with a segment on the heating curve for water:

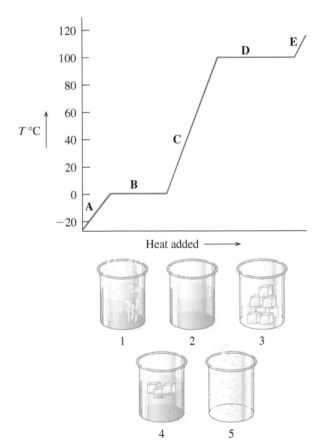

ADDITIONAL QUESTIONS AND PROBLEMS

For instructor-assigned homework, go to www.masteringchemistry.com.

2.65 On a hot day, the beach sand gets hot, but the water stays cool. Compare the specific heat of sand to that of water.

2.66 Why do drops of liquid water form on a glass of iced tea?

2.67 When it rains or snows, the air temperature seems warmer. Explain.

2.68 Water is sprayed on the ground of an orchard when temperatures are near freezing to keep the fruit from freezing. Explain.

2.69 Calculate the following temperatures in degrees Fahrenheit:
a. The highest recorded temperature in the world was 58.0 °C in El Azizia, Libya, on September 13, 1922.
b. The lowest recorded temperature in the world was –89.2 °C in Vostok Station, Antarctica, July 21, 1983.

2.70 Calculate the following temperatures in degrees Celsius:
  a. The highest recorded temperature in the continental United States was 134 °F in Death Valley, California, on July 10, 1913.
  b. The lowest recorded temperature in the continental United States was –70. °F in Rodgers Pass, Montana, on January 20, 1954.

2.71 A large bottle of water (883 g) at 4 °C is removed from the refrigerator. How many kilojoules (kJ) are absorbed to warm the water to a room temperature of 27 °C?

2.72 If you used the 2100 kcal you expend in energy in one day to heat 50 000 g of water at 20. °C, what would be its new temperature?

2.73 A typical diet in the United States provides 15% of its calories from protein, 45% from carbohydrates, and the remainder from fats. Calculate the grams of protein, carbohydrate, and fat to be included each day in diets having the following caloric requirements:
  a. 1200 kcal   **b.** 1900 kcal   **c.** 2600 kcal

2.74 For lunch, your friend has a slice of pizza, a cola soft drink, and ice cream. What is the total number of kilocalories your friend obtained from this meal? How many hours will your friend need to swim to "burn off" the kilocalories in this meal if your friend has a mass of 70.0 kg? (See Table 2.6.)

Item	Protein (g)	Fat (g)	Carbohydrate (g)
Pizza	13	10	29
Cola	0	0	51
Ice cream	8	28	44

2.75 If you want to lose 1 pound of "fat," which is 15% water, how many kilocalories do you need to expend?

2.76 Calculate the Cal (kcal) in 1 cup of whole milk: 12 g of carbohydrate, 9 g of fat, and 9 g of protein.

2.77 Identify each of the following as solid, liquid, or gas:
  a. popcorn in a bag   **b.** water in a garden hose
  c. a computer mouse   **d.** air in a tire
  e. hot tea

2.78 Identify each of the following as solid, liquid, or gas:
  a. vitamin tablets in a bottle   **b.** helium in a balloon
  c. milk in a glass   **d.** the air you breathe
  e. charcoal briquettes on a barbecue

2.79 The melting point of chloroform is –64 °C, and its boiling point is 61 °C. Sketch a heating curve for chloroform from –100 °C to 100 °C.
  a. What is the state of chloroform at –75 °C?
  b. What happens on the curve at –64 °C?
  c. What is the state of chloroform at –18 °C?
  d. What is the state of chloroform at 80 °C?
  e. At what temperature will both solid and liquid be present?

2.80 A pitcher containing 0.75 L of water at 4 °C is removed from the refrigerator. How many kilojoules are needed to warm the water to a room temperature of 27 °C?

2.81 A hot-water bottle contains 725 g of water at 65 °C. If the water cools to body temperature (37 °C), how many kilocalories of heat could be transferred to sore muscles?

2.82 An ice cube tray holds 325 g of water. If the water initially has a temperature of 25 °C, how many kilojoules of heat must be removed to cool and freeze the water at 0 °C?

2.83 How many kilocalories of heat are released when 45 g of steam at 100 °C is converted to liquid water at 15 °C?

2.84 The melting point of benzene is 5.5 °C, and its boiling point is 80.1 °C. Sketch a heating curve for benzene from 0 °C to 100 °C.
  a. What is the state of benzene at 15 °C?
  b. What happens on the curve at 5.5 °C?
  c. What is the state of benzene at 63 °C?
  d. What is the state of benzene at 98 °C?
  e. At what temperature will both liquid and gas be present?

CHALLENGE QUESTIONS

2.85 A 25-g sample of an alloy at 98 °C is placed in 50. g of water at 15 °C. If the final temperature reached by the alloy sample and water is 27 °C, what is the specific heat (cal/g °C) of the alloy?

2.86 A 0.50-g sample of vegetable oil is placed in a calorimeter. When the sample is burned, 18.9 kJ are given off. What is the caloric value, in kcal/g, of the oil?

2.87 How many kilojoules of heat are released when 35.0 g of steam at 100 °C is converted to ice at 0 °C?

2.88 A 45-g piece of ice at 0 °C is added to a sample of water at 8 °C. All of the ice melts, and the temperature of the water decreases to 0 °C. How many grams of water were in the sample?

2.89 Rearrange the heat equation to solve for each of the following:
  a. the mass, in grams, of water that absorbs 8250 J when its temperature rises from 18.3 °C to 92.6 °C
  b. the mass, in grams, of a gold sample that absorbs 225 J when the temperature rises from 15.0 °C to 47.0 °C
  c. the rise in temperature (ΔT) when a 20.0-g sample of iron absorbs 1580 J

  d. the specific heat of a metal when 8.50 g of the metal absorbs 28 cal and the temperature rises from 12 °C to 24 °C

2.90 The combustion of 1.0 g of gasoline releases 11 kcal of heat (density of gasoline = 0.74 g/mL).
  a. How many megajoules are released when 1.0 gal of gasoline burns?
  b. When a color television is on for 2.0 h, 300 kJ are used. How long can a color television run on the energy from 1.0 gal of gasoline?

2.91 A 3.0-kg block of lead is taken from a furnace at 300. °C and placed on a large block of ice at 0 °C. The specific heat of lead is 0.13 J/g °C. If all the heat given up by the lead is used to melt ice, how much ice is melted if the temperature of the lead drops to 0 °C?

2.92 In a large building, oil is used in a steam boiler heating system. The combustion of 1.0 lb of oil provides 2.4×10^7 J.
  a. How many kg of oil are needed to heat 150 kg of water from 22 °C to 100 °C?
  b. How many kg of oil are needed to provide steam from 150 kg of water at 100 °C?

ANSWERS

ANSWERS TO STUDY CHECKS

2.1 8.4 kcal

2.2 12 °F

2.3 39.8 °C

2.4 night –260. °C; day 410. °C

2.5 $SH = 1.23$ J/g °C

2.6 14.6 kJ

2.7 182 g of iron

2.8 4.0 kcal/g of sucrose; 17 kJ/g of sucrose

2.9 380 kcal

2.10 Salad dressing is a heterogeneous mixture with a nonuniform composition.

2.11 b. and d. are chemical changes

2.12 50.1 kJ

2.13 14 kcal; 24 kcal

2.14 75.4 kJ

ANSWERS TO SELECTED QUESTIONS AND PROBLEMS

2.1 As the car goes up the ramp, kinetic energy changes to potential energy. As the car descends, potential energy changes to kinetic energy. At the bottom, all the energy is kinetic.

2.3 a. potential **b.** kinetic **c.** potential **d.** potential

2.5 a. 22 kJ **b.** 5300 cal **c.** 5.3 kcal

2.7 In the United States, the Fahrenheit scale is in common use. On a Fahrenheit thermometer, normal body temperature is 98.6 °F. A temperature of 99.8 °F would indicate a mild fever. On the Celsius scale, her temperature is 37.7 °C.

2.9 a. 98.6 °F **b.** 18.5 °C **c.** 246 K
d. 335 K **e.** 46 °C **f.** 295 K

2.11 a. 41 °C
b. No. The temperature is equivalent to 39 °C.

2.13 Copper has the lowest specific heat of the samples and will reach the highest temperature.

2.15 a. 0.389 J/g °C **b.** 0.313 J/g °C

2.17 a. 250 cal **b.** 11 000 cal **c.** 9.3 kcal

2.19 a. 1380 J; 330. cal **b.** 1810 J; 434 cal
c. 3780 J; 904 cal **d.** 3200 J; 760 cal

2.21 a. 54.5 g of gold **b.** 216 g of iron
c. 686 g of aluminum **d.** 190. g of titanium

2.23 a. 5.30 kcal; 22.2 kJ **b.** 208 kcal; 870. kJ

2.25 a. 110 Cal **b.** 18 g **c.** 130 Cal **d.** 280 Cal

2.27 210 kcal; 870 kJ

2.29 a. compound; contains four elements in definite composition
b. element; consists of one type of pure substance
c. compound; consists of two elements in a definite composition
d. element; consists of one type of pure substance

2.31 a. heterogeneous **b.** homogeneous
c. homogeneous **d.** heterogeneous
e. heterogeneous **f.** heterogeneous

2.29 a. gas **b.** gas **c.** solid

2.33 a. gas **b.** gas **c.** solid

2.35 a. physical **b.** chemical **c.** physical **d.** chemical

2.37 a. physical **b.** chemical **c.** physical
d. physical **e.** physical

2.39 a. chemical **b.** physical **c.** physical
d. chemical **e.** physical

2.41 a. melting **b.** sublimation
c. freezing **d.** deposition

2.43 a. 5200 cal absorbed **b.** 1400 cal absorbed
c. 18 kcal released

2.45 a. condensation **b.** evaporation
c. boiling **d.** condensation

2.47 a. 5400 cal absorbed **b.** 27 kcal absorbed
c. 4300 kcal released

2.49

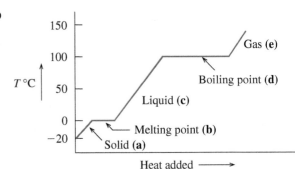

2.51 a. 1100 cal **b.** 7300 cal **c.** 40. kJ **d.** 17 kcal

2.53 a. 10 °C **b.** 30 °C **c.** 32 °F **d.** 200 °C

2.55 113 °F; 318 K

2.57 a. 15 h sleeping **b.** 1.2 h running

2.59 Mixtures b. and c. are not the same throughout and are heterogeneous. Mixture a. is the same throughout and is homogeneous.

2.61 a. The heat from the skin is used to evaporate the water (perspiration). Therefore, the skin is cooled.
b. On a hot day, there are more molecules with sufficient energy to become water vapor.

2.63 a. –60 °C **b.** 60 °C
c. A is solid. B is melting. C is liquid. D is boiling. E is gas.
d. At –80 °C, it is solid; at –40 °C, it is liquid; at 25 °C, it is liquid; at 80 °C, it is gas.

2.65 Sand must have a lower specific heat than water. When both substances absorb the same amount of heat, the final temperature of the sand will be higher than that of water.

2.67 When water vapor condenses or liquid water freezes, heat is released, which warms the air.

2.69 a. 136 °F **b.** –129 °F

2.71 85 kJ

2.73 a. 45 g of protein, 140 g of carbohydrate, 53 g of fat
b. 71 g of protein, 210 g of carbohydrate, 84 g of fat
c. 98 g of protein, 290 g of carbohydrate, 120 g of fat

2.75 3500 kcal

2.77 a. solid **b.** liquid **c.** solid
d. gas **e.** liquid

2.79 a. solid **b.** solid chloroform melts
c. liquid **d.** gas **e.** –64 °C

2.81 20. kcal

2.83 28 kcal

2.85 $\dfrac{0.34 \text{ cal}}{\text{g °C}}$

2.87 105.4 kJ

2.89 a. 26.5 g **b.** 54.5 g of gold **c.** 175 °C **d.** $\dfrac{0.27 \text{ cal}}{\text{g °C}}$

2.91 350 g of ice

COMBINING IDEAS FROM CHAPTERS 1 AND 2

CI.1 Gold, one of the most sought after metals in the world, has a density of 19.3 g/cm^3, a melting point of 1064 °C, a specific heat of 0.129 J/g °C, and a heat of fusion of 63.6 J/g. A gold nugget found in Alaska in 1998 weighs 20.17 lb.

  a. How many significant figures are in the measurement of the nugget's weight?

  b. What is the mass of the nugget in kilograms?

  c. If the nugget is pure gold, what would its volume be in cm^3?

  d. What is the melting point of gold in degrees Fahrenheit and kelvins?

  e. How many kilojoules are required to heat the nugget from 500. °C to 1064 °C and convert all the gold to liquid? How many kcal is that? (*Hint*: Draw a heating curve for gold.)

  f. Gold is sold in troy ounces (ozt). One ozt is equal to 31.1 g. If the current price of gold is $895/ozt, what is the nugget worth?

CI.2 The mileage for a motorcycle with a fuel-tank capacity of 22 L is 35 miles per gal. The density of gasoline is 0.74 g/mL.

  a. How long a trip, in kilometers, can be made on a full tank of gasoline?

  b. If 1 gallon of gasoline costs $3.85, then what would be the price of fuel for the trip?

  c. If the average speed during the trip is 44 mi/h, how many hours will it take to reach the destination?

  d. What is the mass, in kilograms, of the fuel in the tank?

  e. When 1.0 g of gasoline burns, 46 kJ of energy are released. How many kilojoules are produced when the fuel in one full tank is burned?

CI.3 Answer the following questions for the water samples A and B shown in the diagrams:

  a. Which sample has its own shape?

  b. When each sample is transferred to another container, what happens to its volume?

  c. Match the diagrams (1, 2, or 3) that represent the water particles with sample A and B. Give a reason for your choice.

      1   2   3

  d. When the water in sample A changes to sample B, the process is called _____, which occurs at a temperature called the _____.
This is an example of a _____ change.
When the water in sample B changes to sample A, the process is called _____, which occurs at a temperature called the _____.
This is an example of a _____ change.

  e. What happens to the solid water particles when melting occurs?

  f. If the water in sample A has a mass of 19.8 g and a temperature of 45 °C, how much heat, in joules, is removed to form ice at 0 °C?

CI.4 The label of a lemon poppy-seed energy bar lists the nutrition facts as 4 g of fat, 23 g of carbohydrate, and 10 g of protein.

a. Using the energy values of carbohydrate (4 kcal/g), fat (9 kcal/g), and protein (4 kcal/g), what are the kilocalories (Calories) listed for the lemon poppyseed bar?

b. What is the energy value of the energy bar in kilojoules?

c. If the bar has a mass of 48 g, how many kilojoules are obtained from eating 10. g of the bar?

d. If you are walking (840 kJ/h), how many minutes will you need to walk to use the energy from two lemon poppyseed bars?

CI.5 In a box of nails, there are 75 iron nails weighing 0.250 lb. The density of iron is 7.86 g/cm³. The specific heat of iron is 0.450 J/g °C.

a. What is the volume, in cm³, of all the iron nails in the box?

b. If 30 nails are added to a graduated cylinder containing 17.6 mL of water, what is the new level of water in the cylinder?

c. How many joules must be added to the nails in the box to raise the temperature from 16 °C to 125 °C?

CI.6 A hot tub is filled with 450 gal of water, which has a density of 1.0 g/mL.

a. What is the volume, in liters, of the water in the tub?

b. What is the mass, in kilograms, of the water in the tub?

c. How many kilocalories are needed to heat the water from 62 °F to 105 °F?

d. If the hot tub heater provides 1400 kcal per minute, how long, in hours, will it take to heat the water in the hot tub from 62 °F to 105 °F?

ANSWERS

CI.1 a. Four significant figures are in the measurement of 20.17 lb.
    b. 9.17 kg
    c. 475 cm³
    d. 1947 °F; 1337 K
    e. 1250 kJ; 298.8 kcal
    f. $264 000

CI.3 a. B
    b. The volumes of both A and B remain the same.
    c. A is liquid water represented by diagram 2. In liquid water, the water particles are in a random arrangement but close together. B is solid water represented by diagram 1. In solid water, the water particles are fixed in a definite arrangement.

d. freezing; freezing point; 0 °C; physical; melting; melting point; 0 °C; physical

e. The solid water particles break apart from their fixed arrangement to have a more random arrangement, but they are still close together.

f. 10 300 J

CI.5 a. 14.4 cm³
    b. 23.4 mL
    c. 5570 J or 5.57×10^3 J

Atoms and Elements

3

"The unique qualities of semiconducting metals make it possible for us to create so-phisticated electronic circuits," says Tysen Streib, Global Product Manager, Applied Materials. "Elements from columns 3A, 4A, and 5A of the periodic table often make good semiconductors because they readily form covalently bonded crystals. When small amounts of impurities are added, free-flowing electrons or holes can travel through the crystal with very little interference. Without these covalent bonds and loosely bound electrons, we wouldn't have any of the microchips that we use in computers, cell phones, and thousands of other devices."

Materials scientists study the chemical properties of materials to find new uses for them in products such as cars, bridges, and clothing. They also develop materials that can be used as superconductors or in integrated-circuit chips and fuel cells. Chemistry is important in materials science because it provides information about structure and composition.

Visit **www.masteringchemistry.com** for self-study materials and instructor-assigned homework.

All matter is composed of *elements*, of which there are 117 different kinds. Of these, 88 elements occur naturally and make up all the substances in our world. Many elements are already familiar to you. Perhaps you use aluminum in the form of foil or drink soft drinks from aluminum cans. You may have a ring or necklace made of gold, silver, or perhaps platinum. If you play tennis or golf, then you may have noticed that your racket or clubs may be made from the elements titanium or carbon. In our bodies, compounds of calcium and phosphorus form the structure of bones and teeth, iron and copper are needed in the formation of red blood cells, and iodine is required for the proper functioning of the thyroid.

The amounts of certain elements are crucial to the proper growth and function of the body. Low levels of iron can lead to anemia, while low levels of iodine can cause hypothyroidism and goiter. Lab tests are used to confirm that elements such as iron, copper, zinc, or iodine are within normal ranges in a patient's blood serum. A dietitian may recommend beef for iron and zinc, whole grains and leafy green vegetables for magnesium, dairy products for calcium, and iodized table salt and seafood for iodine.

3.1 Elements and Symbols

LEARNING GOAL

Given the name of an element, write its correct symbol; from the symbol, write the correct name.

Elements are primary substances from which all other things are built. Elements cannot be broken down into simpler substances. Over the centuries, elements have been named for planets, mythological figures, minerals, colors, geographic locations, and famous people. Some sources of names of elements are listed in Table 3.1. The names and symbols of all the elements are found on the inside cover of this text.

Chemical symbols are one- and two-letter abbreviations for the names of the elements. Only the first letter of an element's symbol is capitalized. If the symbol has a second letter, it is lowercase so that we know when a different element is indicated. If two letters are capitalized, they represent the symbols of two different elements. For example, the element cobalt has the symbol Co. However, the two capital letters CO specify two elements, carbon (C) and oxygen (O).

One-Letter Symbols		Two-Letter Symbols	
C	carbon	Co	cobalt
S	sulfur	Si	silicon
N	nitrogen	Ne	neon
I	iodine	Ni	nickel

Although most of the symbols use letters from the current names, some are derived from their ancient Latin or Greek names. For example, Na, the symbol for sodium, comes from the Latin word *natrium*. The symbol for iron, Fe, is derived from the Latin name *ferrum*. Table 3.2 lists the names and symbols of some common elements. Learning their names and symbols will greatly help your learning of chemistry. A complete list of all the elements and their symbols appears on the inside front cover of this text.

TABLE 3.1 Some Elements and Their Names

Element	Source of Name
Uranium	The planet Uranus
Titanium	Titans (mythology)
Chlorine	*Chloros*: "greenish yellow" (Greek)
Iodine	*Ioeides*: "violet" (Greek)
Magnesium	Magnesia, a mineral
Californium	California
Curium	Marie and Pierre Curie

CONCEPT CHECK 3.1

■ Symbols of the Elements

The symbol for carbon is C, and the symbol for sulfur is S. However, the symbol for cesium is Cs not CS. Why?

ANSWER

When the symbol for an element has two letters, the first letter is capitalized, but the second letter is lowercase. If both letters are capitalized such as in CS, then two elements—carbon and sulfur—are indicated.

TABLE 3.2 Names and Symbols of Some Common Elements

Name[a]	Symbol	Name[a]	Symbol	Name[a]	Symbol
Aluminum	Al	Gold (*aurum*)	Au	Phosphorus	P
Argon	Ar	Helium	He	Platinum	Pt
Arsenic	As	Hydrogen	H	Potassium (*kalium*)	K
Barium	Ba	Iodine	I	Radium	Ra
Boron	B	Iron (*ferrum*)	Fe	Silicon	Si
Bromine	Br	Lead (*plumbum*)	Pb	Silver (*argentum*)	Ag
Cadmium	Cd	Lithium	Li	Sodium (*natrium*)	Na
Calcium	Ca	Magnesium	Mg	Strontium	Sr
Carbon	C	Manganese	Mn	Sulfur	S
Chlorine	Cl	Mercury (*hydrargyrum*)	Hg	Tin (*stannum*)	Sn
Chromium	Cr	Neon	Ne	Titanium	Ti
Cobalt	Co	Nickel	Ni	Uranium	U
Copper (*cuprum*)	Cu	Nitrogen	N	Zinc	Zn
Fluorine	F	Oxygen	O		

[a]Names given in parentheses are ancient Latin or Greek words from which the symbols are derived.

Aluminum

Carbon

Gold

Silver

Sulfur

SAMPLE PROBLEM 3.1

■ Writing Chemical Symbols

What are the chemical symbols for the following elements?

a. nickel **b.** niobium **c.** nitrogen **d.** neon

SOLUTION

a. Ni **b.** Nb **c.** N **d.** Ne

STUDY CHECK

What are the chemical symbols for silicon, strontium, and silver?

HEALTH NOTE

Latin Names for Elements in Clinical Usage

In medicine, the Latin name *natrium* may be used for sodium, an important electrolyte in body fluids and cells. An increase in serum sodium, a condition called *hypernatremia*, may occur when water is lost because of profuse sweating, severe diarrhea, or vomiting, or when there is inadequate water intake. A decrease in sodium, a condition called *hyponatremia*, may occur when a person takes in a large amount of water or fluid-replacement solutions. Conditions that occur in cardiac failure, liver failure, and malnutrition can also cause hyponatremia.

The Latin name *kalium* may be used for potassium, the most common electrolyte inside the cells. Potassium regulates osmotic pressure, acid–base balance, nerve and muscle excitability, and the function of cellular enzymes. Serum potassium measures potassium outside the cells, which amounts to only 2 percent of total body potassium. An increase in serum potassium (*hyperkalemia*) may occur when cells are severely injured, in renal failure when potassium is not properly excreted, and in Addison's disease. A severe loss of potassium (*hypokalemia*) may occur during excessive vomiting, diarrhea, renal tubular defects, and glucose or insulin therapy.

QUESTIONS AND PROBLEMS

Elements and Symbols

3.1 Write the symbols for the following elements:
   a. copper   **b.** silicon
   c. potassium   **d.** nitrogen
   e. iron   **f.** barium
   g. lead   **h.** strontium

3.2 Write the symbols for the following elements:
   a. oxygen   **b.** lithium
   c. sulfur   **d.** aluminum
   e. hydrogen   **f.** neon
   g. tin   **h.** gold

3.3 Write the name of the element for each of the following symbols:
   a. C   **b.** Cl
   c. I   **d.** Hg
   e. F   **f.** Ar
   g. Zn   **h.** Ni

3.4 Write the name of the element for each of the following symbols:
   a. He   **b.** P
   c. Na   **d.** Mg
   e. Ca   **f.** Br
   g. Cd   **h.** Si

3.5 What elements are in the following substances?
   a. table salt, $NaCl$
   b. plaster casts, $CaSO_4$
   c. Demerol, $C_{15}H_{22}ClNO_2$
   d. antacid, $CaCO_3$

3.6 What elements are in the following substances?
   a. water, H_2O
   b. baking soda, $NaHCO_3$
   c. lye, $NaOH$
   d. sugar, $C_{12}H_{22}O_{11}$

ENVIRONMENTAL NOTE

Toxicity of Mercury

Mercury is a silvery, shiny element that is a liquid at room temperature. Mercury can enter the body through inhalation as a vapor, contact with the skin, or foods or water that have been contaminated with mercury. In the body, mercury destroys proteins and disrupts cell function. Long-term exposure to mercury can damage the brain and kidneys, cause mental retardation, and decrease physical development. Blood, urine, and hair samples are used to test for mercury.

In both freshwater and saltwater, bacteria convert mercury into toxic methylmercury, which primarily attacks the central nervous system (CNS). Because fish absorb methylmercury, we are exposed to mercury when we eat mercury-contaminated fish. As levels of mercury ingested from fish became a concern, the Food and Drug Administration (FDA) set a maximum level of one part mercury per million parts seafood (1 ppm), which is the same as 1 μg mercury in every gram of seafood. Fish higher in the food chain such as swordfish and shark can have such high levels of mercury that the Environmental Protection Agency (EPA) recommends they be consumed no more than once a week.

One of the worst incidents of mercury poisoning occurred in Minamata and Niigata, Japan, in 1950. At that time, the ocean was polluted with high levels of mercury from industrial wastes. Because fish were a major food in the Japanese diet, more than 2000 people were affected with mercury poisoning and died or developed neural damage. In the U.S., between 1988 and 1997, industry decreased the use of mercury by 75% by banning mercury in paint and pesticides, reducing mercury in batteries, and regulating mercury in other products.

This mercury fountain, housed in glass, was designed by Calder for the 1937 World's Fair in Paris

3.2 The Periodic Table

LEARNING GOAL

Use the periodic table to identify the group and the period of an element and decide whether it is a metal, nonmetal, or metalloid.

As more elements were discovered, it became necessary to organize them with some type of classification system. By the late 1800s, scientists recognized that certain elements looked alike and behaved in much the same way. In 1872, a Russian chemist, Dmitri Mendeleev, arranged the 60 elements known at that time into groups with similar properties and placed them in order of increasing mass. Today, this arrangement of 117 elements is known as the **periodic table**. (See Figure 3.1.)

Periodic Table of Elements

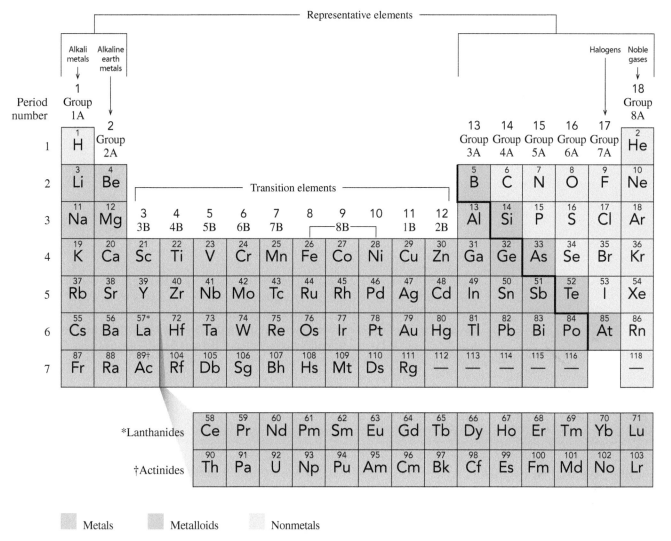

FIGURE 3.1 Groups and periods in the periodic table.
Q What is the symbol of the alkali metal in Period 3?

Periods and Groups

Each horizontal row in the table is called a **period**. The number of elements in the periods increases going down the periodic table. Each row is counted from the top of the table as Period 1 to Period 7. The first period contains only the elements hydrogen (H) and helium (He). The second period contains eight elements: lithium (Li), beryllium (Be), boron (B), carbon (C), nitrogen (N), oxygen (O), fluorine (F), and neon (Ne). The third period also contains eight elements, beginning with sodium (Na) and ending with argon (Ar). The fourth period, which begins with potassium (K), and the fifth period, which begins with rubidium (Rb), have 18 elements each. The sixth period, which begins with cesium (Cs), has 32 elements. The seventh period as of today contains the 31 remaining elements although it could go as high as 32. (See Figure 3.2.)

Each vertical column on the periodic table contains a **group** (or family) of elements that have similar properties. At the top of each column is a number that is assigned to each group. The elements in the first two columns on the left of the periodic table and the last six columns on the right are called the **representative elements**. For many years, they have been given group numbers 1A–8A. On some periodic tables, the group numbers may be written with Roman numerals: IA–VIIIA. In the center of the periodic table is a block

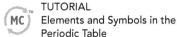

TUTORIAL
Elements and Symbols in the
Periodic Table

FIGURE 3.2 On the periodic table, each vertical column represents a group of elements, and each horizontal row of elements represents a period.

Q Are the elements Si, P, and S part of a group or a period?

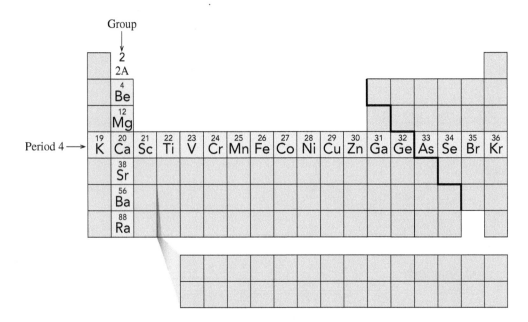

of elements known as the **transition elements**, which are designated with the letter "B." A newer numbering system assigns group numbers of 1 to 18 across the periodic table. Because both systems of group numbers are currently in use, they are both indicated on the periodic table in this text and are included in our discussions of elements and group numbers. The lanthanides and actinides that are part of Periods 6 and 7 are placed at the bottom of the periodic table to allow it to fit on a page.

HEALTH NOTE

Elements Essential to Health

Many elements are essential for the well-being and survival of the human body. The four elements oxygen, carbon, hydrogen, and nitrogen are the most important elements that make up carbohydrates, fats, proteins, and DNA. Most of the hydrogen and oxygen is found in water, which makes up 55% to 60% of our body mass. Some examples and the amounts present in a 60-kg person are listed in Table 3.3.

TABLE 3.3 Elements Essential to Health

Element	Symbol	Amount in a 60-kg Person
Oxygen	O	39 kg
Carbon	C	11 kg
Hydrogen	H	6 kg
Nitrogen	N	1.5 kg
Calcium	Ca	1 kg
Phosphorus	P	600 g
Potassium	K	120 g
Sulfur	S	120 g
Sodium	Na	86 g
Chlorine	Cl	81 g
Magnesium	Mg	16 g
Iron	Fe	3.6 g
Fluorine	F	2.2 g
Zinc	Zn	2.0 g
Copper	Cu	60 mg
Iodine	I	20 mg

Classification of Groups

Several groups in the periodic table have special names. (See Figure 3.3.) Group 1A (1) elements—lithium (Li), sodium (Na), potassium (K), rubidium (Rb), cesium (Cs), and francium (Fr)—make up a family of elements known as the **alkali metals**. (See Figure 3.4.) The elements within this group are soft, shiny metals that are good conductors of heat and electricity and have relatively low melting points. Alkali metals react vigorously with water and form white products when they combine with oxygen.

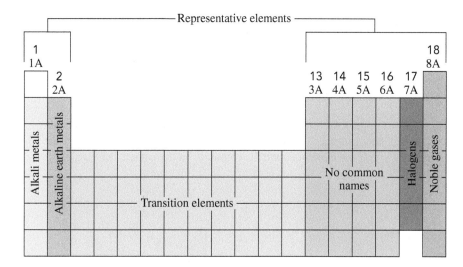

FIGURE 3.3 Certain groups on the periodic table have common names.

Q What is the common name for the group of elements that includes helium and argon?

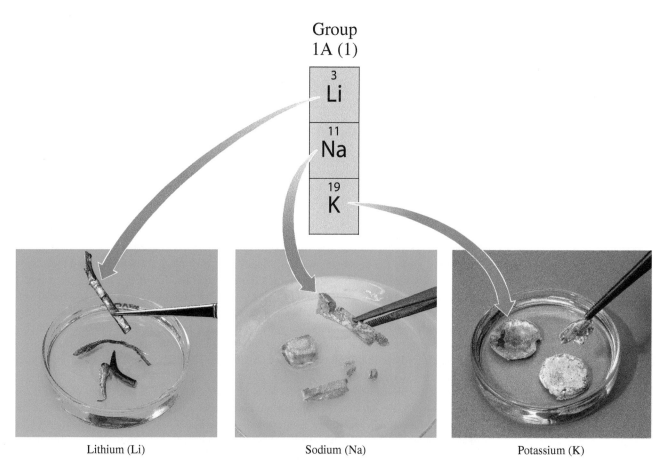

Lithium (Li)   Sodium (Na)   Potassium (K)

FIGURE 3.4 Lithium (Li), sodium (Na), and potassium (K) are some alkali metals from Group 1A (1).

Q What physical properties do these alkali metals have in common?

Group
7A (17)

9   **F**
17   **Cl**
35   **Br**
53   **I**

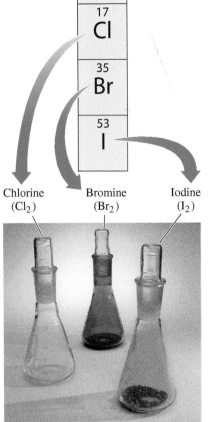

Chlorine   Bromine   Iodine
(Cl₂)   (Br₂)   (I₂)

FIGURE 3.5 Chlorine (Cl₂), bromine (Br₂), and iodine (I₂) are examples of halogens from Group 7A (17).

Q What elements are in the halogen group?

Although hydrogen (H) is at the top of Group 1A (1), it is not an alkali metal and has properties that are distinctly different than the rest of the elements in this group. Thus hydrogen is not included in the classification of alkali metals. In some periodic tables, H is placed at the top of Group 7A (17).

Group 2A (2) elements—beryllium (Be), magnesium (Mg), calcium (Ca), strontium (Sr), barium (Ba), and radium (Ra)—are called the **alkaline earth metals**. They are also shiny metals like those in Group 1A (1), but they are not as reactive.

The **halogens** are found on the right side of the periodic table in Group 7A (17). They include the elements fluorine (F), chlorine (Cl), bromine (Br), iodine (I), and astatine (At), as shown in Figure 3.5. The halogens, especially fluorine and chlorine, are highly reactive and form compounds with most of the elements.

Group 8A (18) contains the **noble gases**: helium (He), neon (Ne), argon (Ar), krypton (Kr), xenon (Xe), and radon (Rn). They are quite unreactive and are seldom found in combination with other elements.

Metals, Nonmetals, and Metalloids

Another feature of the periodic table is the heavy zigzag line that separates the elements into the *metals* and the *nonmetals*. The metals are those elements on the left of the line *except for hydrogen*, and the nonmetals are the elements on the right. (See Figure 3.6.)

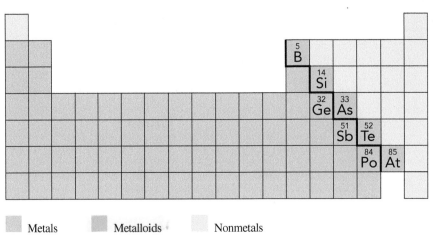

■ Metals   ■ Metalloids   ■ Nonmetals

FIGURE 3.6 Along the heavy zigzag line on the periodic table that separates the metals and nonmetals are metalloids, which exhibit characteristics of both metals and nonmetals.

Q On which side of the heavy zigzag line are the nonmetals located?

In general, most **metals** are shiny solids. They can be shaped into wires (ductile) or hammered into a flat sheet (malleable). Metals are good conductors of heat and electricity. They usually melt at higher temperatures than nonmetals. All of the metals are solids at room temperature, except for mercury (Hg), which is a liquid. Some typical metals are magnesium (Mg), copper (Cu), gold (Au), silver (Ag), iron (Fe), and tin (Sn).

Nonmetals are not especially shiny, malleable, or ductile, and they are often poor conductors of heat and electricity. They typically have low melting points and low densities. You may have heard of nonmetals such as hydrogen (H), carbon (C), nitrogen (N), oxygen (O), chlorine (Cl), and sulfur (S).

Except for aluminum, the elements located along the heavy line are **metalloids**: B, Si, Ge, As, Sb, Te, Po, and At. Metalloids are elements that exhibit some properties that are typical of the metals and other properties that are characteristic of the nonmetals. For example, they are better conductors of heat and electricity than the nonmetals, but not as good as the metals. The metalloids are semiconductors because they can be easily modified to function as conductors or insulators. Table 3.4 compares some characteristics of silver, a metal, with those of antimony, a metalloid, and sulfur, a nonmetal.

TABLE 3.4 Some Characteristics of a Metal, a Metalloid, and a Nonmetal

Silver (Ag)	Antimony (Sb)	Sulfur (S)
Metal	Metalloid	Nonmetal
Shiny	Blue-gray, shiny	Dull, yellow
Extremely ductile	Brittle	Brittle
Can be hammered into sheets (malleable)	Shatters when hammered	Shatters when hammered
Good conductor of heat and electricity	Poor conductor of heat and electricity	Poor conductor, good insulator
Used in coins, jewelry, tableware	Used to harden lead, color glass and plastics	Used in gunpowder, rubber, fungicides
Density 10.5 g/mL	Density 6.7 g/mL	Density 2.1 g/mL
Melting point 962 °C	Melting point 630 °C	Melting point 113 °C

CONCEPT CHECK 3.2

■ Groups and Periods on the Periodic Table

Consider the elements aluminum, silicon, and phosphorus.

a. In what group and period are they found?
b. Identify each as a metal, metalloid, or nonmetal.

ANSWER

a. They are all found in Period 3. Aluminum is in Group 3A (13), silicon is in Group 4A (14), and phosphorus is in Group 5A (15).
b. Aluminum is a metal, silicon is a metalloid, and phosphorus is a nonmetal.

SAMPLE PROBLEM   3.2

■ Classification of Elements

Use the periodic table to classify each of the following elements by its group and period, group name (if any), and if it is a metal, nonmetal, or metalloid:

a. Na   **b.** Si   **c.** I   **d.** Sn

SOLUTION

a. Na (sodium), Group 1A (1), Period 3, is an alkali metal.
b. Si (silicon), Group 4A (14), Period 3, is a metalloid.
c. I (iodine), Group 7A (17), Period 5, halogen, is a nonmetal.
d. Sn (tin), Group 4A (14), Period 5, is a metal.

STUDY CHECK

Give the symbol of the element represented by the following:
a. Group 5A (15), Period 4
b. a noble gas in Period 6
c. a metalloid in Period 2

QUESTIONS AND PROBLEMS

The Periodic Table

3.7 Identify the group or period number described by each of the following statements:
   a. contains the elements C, N, and O
   b. begins with helium
   c. the alkali metals
   d. ends with neon

3.8 Identify the group or period number described by each of the following statements:
   a. contains Na, K, and Rb
   b. the row that begins with Li
   c. the noble gases
   d. contains F, Cl, Br, and I

3.9 Classify each of the following as an alkali metal, alkaline earth metal, transition element, halogen, or noble gas:
   a. Ca   **b.** Fe   **c.** Xe   **d.** Na   **e.** Cl

3.10 Classify each of the following as an alkali metal, alkaline earth metal, transition element, halogen, or noble gas:
   a. Ne   **b.** Mg   **c.** Cu   **d.** Br   **e.** Ba

3.11 Give the symbol of the element described by the following:
   a. Group 4A, Period 2
   b. a noble gas in Period 1
   c. an alkali metal in Period 3
   d. Group 2, Period 4
   e. Group 13, Period 3

3.12 Give the symbol of the element described by the following:
   a. an alkaline earth metal in Period 2
   b. Group 15, Period 3
   c. a noble gas in Period 4
   d. a halogen in Period 5
   e. Group 4A, Period 4

3.13 Identify each of the following elements as a metal, nonmetal, or metalloid:
   a. calcium   **b.** sulfur
   c. a shiny element   **d.** a poor conductor of heat
   e. located in Group 8A   **f.** phosphorus
   g. boron   **h.** silver

3.14 Identify each of the following elements as a metal, nonmetal, or metalloid:
   a. located in Group 2A
   b. a good conductor of electricity
   c. chlorine
   d. arsenic
   e. an element that is not shiny
   f. oxygen
   g. nitrogen
   h. aluminum

HEALTH NOTE

Some Important Trace Elements in the Body

Some metals and nonmetals known as *trace elements* are essential to the proper functioning of the body. Although they are required in minute amounts, their absence can disrupt major biological processes and cause illness. The trace elements listed in Table 3.5 are present in the body combined with other elements. The adult daily value (DV) is the daily recommended amount for an adult.

TABLE 3.5 Some Important Trace Elements in the Body

Element	Adult DV[a]	Biological Function	Deficiency Symptoms	Dietary Sources
Iron (Fe)	10 mg (males) 18 mg (females)	Formation of hemoglobin; enzymes	Dry skin, spoon nails, decreased hemoglobin count, anemia	Liver and other organ meats, oysters, red and dark meats, green leafy vegetables, fortified breads and cereals, egg yolk
Copper (Cu)	2.0–5.0 mg	Necessary in many enzyme systems; growth; aids formation of red blood cells and collagen	Uncommon; anemia; decreased white cell count; bone demineralization	Nuts, organ meats, whole grains, shellfish, eggs, poultry, green leafy vegetables
Zinc (Zn)	15 mg	Amino acid metabolism; enzyme systems; energy production; collagen	Retarded growth and bone formation; skin inflammation; loss of taste and smell; poor healing	Oysters, crab, lamb, beef, organ meats, whole grains
Manganese (Mn)	2.5–5.0 mg	Necessary for some enzyme systems; collagen formation; central nervous system; fat and carbohydrate metabolism; blood clotting	Abnormal skeletal growth; impairment of central nervous system	Whole grains, wheat germ, legumes, pineapple, figs
Iodine (I)	150 mg	Necessary for activity of thyroid gland	Hypothyroidism; goiter; cretinism	Seafood, iodized salt
Fluorine (F)	1.5–4.0 mg	Necessary for solid tooth formation and retention of calcium in bones with aging	Dental cavities	Tea, fish, water in some areas, supplementary drops, toothpaste

[a]Daily value

3.3 The Atom

All the elements listed on the periodic table are made up of atoms. An **atom** is the smallest particle of an element that retains the characteristics of that element. You have probably seen the element aluminum. Imagine that you are tearing a piece of aluminum foil into smaller and smaller pieces. Now imagine that you have a piece so small that you cannot tear it apart further. Then you would have a single atom of aluminum.

The concept of the atom is relatively recent. Although the Greek philosophers in 500 B.C.E. reasoned that everything must contain minute particles they called *atomos*, the idea of atoms did not become a scientific theory until 1808. Then John Dalton (1766–1844) developed an atomic theory that proposed that atoms were responsible for the combinations of elements found in compounds.

Dalton's Atomic Theory

1. All matter is made up of tiny particles called atoms.

2. All atoms of a given element are similar to one another and different from atoms of other elements.

3. Atoms of two or more different elements combine to form compounds. A particular compound is always made up of the same kinds of atoms and always has the same number of each kind of atom.

4. A chemical reaction involves the rearrangement, separation, or combination of atoms. Atoms are never created or destroyed during a chemical reaction.

Although atoms are the building blocks of everything we see around us, we cannot see an atom or even a billion atoms with the naked eye. However, when billions and billions of atoms are packed together, the characteristics of each atom are added to those of the next until we can see the characteristics we associate with the element. For example, a small piece of the shiny, reddish-colored element we call copper consists of many, many copper atoms. A special kind of microscope called a *scanning tunneling microscope* (STM) produces images of individual atoms such as the atoms of carbon in graphite shown in Figure 3.7.

Electrical Charges in an Atom

By the end of the 1800s, experiments with electricity showed that atoms were not solid spheres, but were composed of even smaller bits of matter called **subatomic particles**, three of which are the proton, electron, and neutron. Some of these subatomic particles were discovered because they have electrical charges.

An electrical charge can be positive or negative. Experiments show that like charges repel, or push away from each other. When you brush your hair on a dry day, electrical charges that are alike build up on the brush and in your hair. As a result, your hair flies away from the brush. Opposite or unlike charges attract. The crackle of clothes taken from the clothes dryer indicates the presence of electrical charges. The clinginess of the clothing results from the attraction of opposite, unlike charges, as shown in Figure 3.8.

Structure of the Atom

In 1897, J. J. Thomson, an English physicist, applied electricity to a glass tube and produced streams of small particles called *cathode rays*. Because these rays were attracted to a positively charged electrode, Thomson realized that these particles must be negatively charged. In further experiments, these particles called **electrons** were found to be much smaller than the atom and to have an extremely small mass. Because atoms are neutral, scientists soon discovered that atoms contain positively charged particles called **protons** that are much heavier than the electrons.

Thomson proposed a model for the atom in which the electrons and protons were randomly distributed through the atom. In 1911, Ernest Rutherford worked with Thomson to test this model. In Rutherford's experiment, positively charged particles were aimed at a thin sheet of gold foil. (See Figure 3.9.) If the Thomson model were correct, the particles would travel in straight paths through the gold foil. Rutherford was greatly surprised to

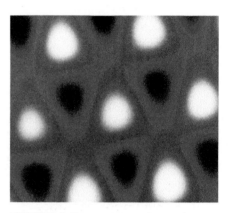

FIGURE 3.7 Graphite, a form of carbon, magnified millions of times by a scanning tunneling microscope. This instrument generates an image of the atomic structure. The round yellow objects are atoms.

Q Why is a microscope with extremely high magnification needed to see atoms?

Positive charges repel

Negative charges repel

Unlike charges attract

FIGURE 3.8 Like charges repel, and unlike charges attract.

Q Why are the electrons attracted to the protons in the nucleus of an atom?

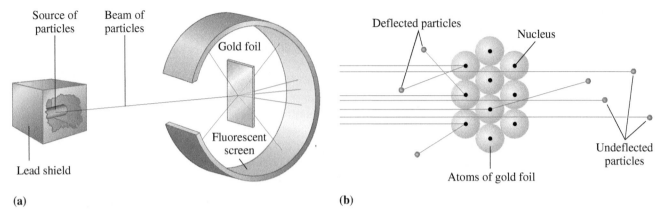

FIGURE 3.9 (a) Positive particles are aimed at a piece of gold foil. (b) Particles that come close to the atomic nuclei are deflected from their straight path.

Q Why are some particles deflected while most pass through the gold foil undeflected?

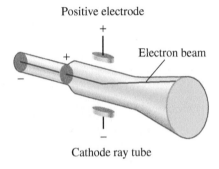

Positive electrode

Electron beam

Cathode ray tube

find that some of the particles were deflected slightly as they passed through the gold foil, and a few particles were deflected so much that they went back in the opposite direction. According to Rutherford, it was as though he had shot a cannonball at a piece of tissue paper, and it bounced back at him. Rutherford realized that the protons must be contained in a small, positively charged region at the center of the atom, which he called the **nucleus**. He proposed that the electrons in the atom occupy the space surrounding the nucleus through which most of the particles traveled undisturbed. Only the particles that came near this dense, positive center were deflected. If an atom were the size of a football stadium, the nucleus would be about the size of a golf ball placed in the center of the field.

Scientists knew that the nucleus was heavier than the mass of the protons and looked for another subatomic particle. Eventually, they discovered that the nucleus also contained a particle called a **neutron**, which is neutral. Thus, the masses of the protons and neutrons in the nucleus determine its mass. (See Figure 3.10.)

Mass of the Atom

All of the subatomic particles are extremely small compared with the things you see around you. One proton has a mass of 1.7×10^{-24} g, and the neutron is about the same. The mass of the electron is 9.1×10^{-28} g, which is much less than a proton or neutron. Because the masses of subatomic particles are so small, chemists use a unit called an

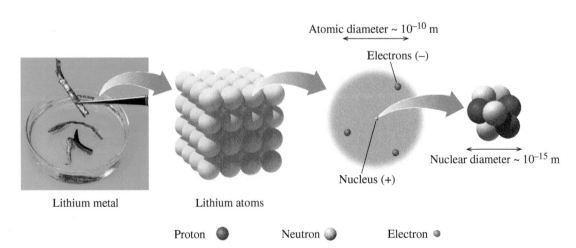

Lithium metal   Lithium atoms

Proton ●   Neutron ●   Electron ●

FIGURE 3.10 In an atom, the protons and neutrons that make up most of the mass of the atom are packed into the tiny volume of the nucleus. The rapidly moving electrons surround the nucleus and account for the large volume of the atom.

Q Why can we say that an atom is mostly empty space?

atomic mass unit (amu). An amu is defined as one-twelfth of the mass of the carbon atom with six protons and six neutrons, a standard with which the mass of every other atom is compared. In biology, the atomic mass unit is called a *dalton* in honor of John Dalton. On the amu scale, the proton and neutron each have a mass of about 1 amu. Because the electron mass is so small, it is usually ignored in atomic mass calculations. Table 3.6 summarizes some information about the subatomic particles in an atom.

TABLE 3.6 Particles in the Atom

Subatomic Particle	Symbol	Electrical Charge	Approximate Mass (amu)	Location in Atom
Proton	p or p^+	1+	1	Nucleus
Neutron	n or n^0	0	1	Nucleus
Electron	e^-	1−	0.0005 ($^1/_{2000}$)	Outside nucleus

SAMPLE PROBLEM 3.3

■ Identifying Subatomic Particles

Is each of the following statements *true* or *false*?

a. Protons are heavier than electrons.
b. Protons are attracted to neutrons.
c. Electrons are so small that they have no electrical charge.
d. The nucleus contains all the protons and neutrons of an atom.

SOLUTION

a. True
b. False; protons are attracted to electrons.
c. False; electrons have a 1− charge.
d. True

STUDY CHECK

True or *false*: The nucleus occupies a large volume in an atom.

EXPLORE YOUR WORLD

Repulsion and Attraction

1. Obtain a tape dispenser with clear tape, a hairbrush, a comb, and a piece of paper. Tear off a piece of the tape about 20 cm long (the length of your hand). Stick the tape to the edge of a table leaving the end hanging down. Tear off a second piece of tape and slowly bring it close to the first one. What happens? Is there an attraction or repulsion?

   Slide your thumb and finger along the tape you are holding. Bring it close to the piece that is hanging from the table. What happens? Is there an attraction or repulsion? Attach the second tape to the edge of the table. Brush your hair and bring the brush close to each piece of tape hanging from the table. What do you observe?

2. Tear a small piece of paper into bits. Brush your hair several times and place the brush just above the bits of paper. Use your knowledge of electrical charges to explain your observations. Try the same experiment using a comb.

QUESTIONS

1. What happens when objects with like charges are placed close together?
2. What happens when objects with unlike charges are placed close together?

QUESTIONS AND PROBLEMS

The Atom

3.15 Is a proton, neutron, or electron described by each of the following?
   a. has the smallest mass
   b. has a 1+ charge
   c. is found outside the nucleus
   d. is electrically neutral

3.16 Is a proton, neutron, or electron described by each of the following?
   a. has a mass about the same as a proton
   b. is found in the nucleus
   c. is attracted to the protons
   d. has a 1− charge

3.17 What did Rutherford determine about the structure of the atom from his gold-foil experiment?

3.18 Why does the nucleus in every atom have a positive charge?

3.19 Is each of the following statements *true* or *false*?
   a. A proton and an electron have opposite charges.
   b. The nucleus contains most of the mass of an atom.
   c. Electrons repel each other.
   d. A proton is attracted to a neutron.

3.20 Is each of the following statements *true* or *false*?
   a. A proton is attracted to an electron.
   b. A neutron has twice the mass of a proton.
   c. Neutrons repel each other.
   d. Electrons and neutrons have opposite charges.

3.21 On a dry day, your hair flies away when you brush it. How would you explain this?

3.22 Sometimes clothes cling together when removed from a dryer. What kinds of charges are on the clothes?

3.4 Atomic Number and Mass Number

LEARNING GOAL

Given the atomic number and the mass number of an atom, state the number of protons, neutrons, and electrons.

All of the atoms of the same element always have the same number of protons. This feature distinguishes atoms of one element from atoms of all the other elements.

Atomic Number

An **atomic number**, which is equal to the number of protons in the nucleus of an atom, is used to identify and define each element.

Atomic number = number of protons in an atom

TUTORIAL
Atomic Number and Mass Number

On the inside front cover of this text is a periodic table, which gives all of the elements in order of increasing atomic number. The atomic number is the whole number that appears above the symbol. For example, a hydrogen atom, with atomic number 1, has 1 proton; a lithium atom, with atomic number 3, has 3 protons; an atom of carbon, with atomic number 6, has 6 protons; gold, with atomic number 79, has 79 protons; and so forth.

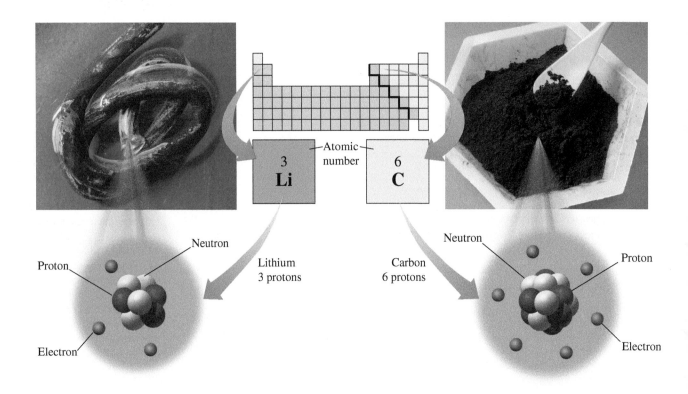

Lithium
3 protons

Carbon
6 protons

An atom is electrically neutral. That means that the number of protons in an atom is equal to the number of electrons. This electrical balance gives an atom an overall electrical charge of zero. Thus, in every atom, the atomic number also gives the number of electrons.

Mass Number

We now know that the protons and neutrons determine the mass of the nucleus. For any atom, the **mass number** is the sum of the number of protons and neutrons in the nucleus.

Mass number = number of protons + number of neutrons

For example, an atom of oxygen that contains 8 protons and 8 neutrons has a mass number of 16.

Most elements have atoms with different numbers of neutrons. For example, some atoms of oxygen have 10 neutrons, which give a mass number of 18 (8 protons and 10 neutrons).

Table 3.7 illustrates the relationship between atomic number, mass number, and the number of protons, neutrons, and electrons in some atoms of different elements.

TABLE 3.7 Composition of Some Atoms of Different Elements

Element	Symbol	Atomic Number	Mass Number	Number of Protons	Number of Neutrons	Number of Electrons
Hydrogen	H	1	1	1	0	1
Nitrogen	N	7	14	7	7	7
Chlorine	Cl	17	35	17	18	17
Chlorine	Cl	17	37	17	20	17
Iron	Fe	26	57	26	31	26
Gold	Au	79	197	79	118	79

CAREER FOCUS

Optician

"When a patient brings in a prescription, I help select the proper lenses, put them into a frame, and fit them properly on the patient's face," says Suranda Lara, optician, Kaiser Hospital. "If a prescription requires a thinner and lighter-weight lens, we formulate that lens. So we have to understand the different materials used to make lenses. Sometimes patients come in with their own glasses that they want to convert to sunglasses. We remove the lenses and put them into a tint bath, which turns them into sunglasses."

Opticians fit and adjust eyewear for patients who have had their eyesight tested by an ophthalmologist or optometrist. Optics and mathematics are used to select materials for frames and lenses that are compatible with patients' facial measurements and lifestyles.

CONCEPT CHECK 3.3

■ Subatomic Particles in Atoms

An atom of silver has a mass number of 109.

a. How many protons are in the nucleus?
b. How many neutrons are in the nucleus?
c. How many electrons are in the atom?

ANSWER

a. Silver (Ag) in Period 5 with atomic number 47 has 47 protons.
b. Neutrons are calculated by subtracting the number of protons from the mass number.

   $109 - 47 = 62$ neutrons for Ag with a mass number of 109

c. In an atom, the number of electrons is equal to the number of protons. An atom of silver with 47 protons has 47 electrons.

SAMPLE PROBLEM 3.4

■ Calculating Numbers of Protons, Neutrons, and Electrons

For an atom of iron that has a mass number of 56, determine the following:

a. the number of protons
b. the number of neutrons
c. the number of electrons

SOLUTION

a. On the periodic table, the atomic number of iron is 26. An iron atom has 26 protons.
b. The number of neutrons in this atom is found by subtracting the atomic number from the mass number. The number of neutrons is 30.

   Mass number − atomic number = number of neutrons
       56   −   26   =   30

c. Because an atom is neutral, the number of electrons is equal to the number of protons. An iron atom has 26 electrons.

STUDY CHECK

How many neutrons are in the nucleus of a bromine atom that has a mass number of 80?

QUESTIONS AND PROBLEMS

Atomic Number and Mass Number

3.23 Would you use atomic number, mass number, or both to obtain the following?
  a. number of protons in an atom
  b. number of neutrons in an atom
  c. number of particles in the nucleus
  d. number of electrons in a neutral atom

3.24 What do you know about the subatomic particles from the following?
  a. atomic number
  b. mass number
  c. mass number − atomic number
  d. mass number + atomic number

3.25 Write the names and symbols of the elements with the following atomic numbers:
  a. 3   **b.** 9   **c.** 20   **d.** 30
  e. 10   **f.** 14   **g.** 53   **h.** 8

3.26 Write the names and symbols of the elements with the following atomic numbers:
  a. 1   **b.** 11   **c.** 19   **d.** 26
  e. 35   **f.** 47   **g.** 15   **h.** 2

3.27 How many protons are there in a neutral atom of the following?
  a. magnesium   **b.** zinc
  c. iodine   **d.** potassium

3.28 How many electrons are there in a neutral atom of the following?
  a. carbon   **b.** fluorine
  c. calcium   **d.** sulfur

3.29 Complete the following table for neutral atoms:

Name of Element	Symbol	Atomic Number	Mass Number	Number of Protons	Number of Neutrons	Number of Electrons
	Al		27			
		12			12	
Potassium					20	
				16	15	
			56			26

3.30 Complete the following table for neutral atoms:

Name of Element	Symbol	Atomic Number	Mass Number	Number of Protons	Number of Neutrons	Number of Electrons
	N		15			
Calcium			42			
				38	50	
		14			16	
		56	138			

3.5 | Isotopes and Atomic Mass

LEARNING GOAL

Give the number of protons, electrons, and neutrons in the isotopes of an element.

 **SELF STUDY ACTIVITY**
Atoms and Isotopes

We have seen that all atoms of the same element have the same number of protons and electrons. However, the atoms of any one element are not identical because they can have different numbers of neutrons.

Isotopes

Isotopes are atoms of the same element that have different numbers of neutrons. For example, all atoms of the element magnesium (Mg) have 12 protons. However, some magnesium atoms have 12 neutrons, others have 13 neutrons, and still others have 14 neutrons. The differences in numbers of neutrons for these magnesium atoms cause their mass numbers to be different but not their chemical behavior. The three isotopes of magnesium have the same atomic number but different mass numbers.

On the periodic table, the atomic number appears above the element symbol. To distinguish between the different isotopes of an element, we write an **atomic symbol** that indicates the mass number in the upper left corner and the atomic number in the lower left corner.

Atomic Symbol for an Isotope of Magnesium

Mass number ⟶
Symbol of element ⟶ $^{24}_{12}\text{Mg}$
Atomic number ⟶

An isotope may be referred to by its name or symbol followed by the mass number such as magnesium-24 or Mg-24. Magnesium has three naturally occurring isotopes, as shown in Table 3.8.

TABLE 3.8 Isotopes of Magnesium

Atomic symbol	$^{24}_{12}Mg$	$^{25}_{12}Mg$	$^{26}_{12}Mg$
Number of protons	12	12	12
Number of electrons	12	12	12
Mass number	**24**	**25**	**26**
Number of neutrons	**12**	**13**	**14**
Mass of isotope (amu)	23.99	24.99	25.98
% abundance	78.70	10.13	11.17

Atomic structure of Mg

Isotopes of Mg

$^{24}_{12}Mg$ $^{25}_{12}Mg$ $^{26}_{12}Mg$

SAMPLE PROBLEM   3.5

■ Identifying Protons and Neutrons in Isotopes

State the number of protons and neutrons in the following isotopes of neon (Ne):

a. $^{20}_{10}Ne$ **b.** $^{21}_{10}Ne$ **c.** $^{22}_{10}Ne$

SOLUTION

The atomic number of Ne is 10; each isotope has 10 protons. The number of neutrons in each isotope is found by subtracting the atomic number (10) from each mass number.

a. 10 protons; 10 neutrons $(20 - 10)$
b. 10 protons; 11 neutrons $(21 - 10)$
c. 10 protons; 12 neutrons $(22 - 10)$

STUDY CHECK

Write an atomic symbol for each of the following isotopes:
a. a nitrogen atom with 8 neutrons
b. an atom with 20 protons and 22 neutrons
c. an atom with mass number 27 and 14 neutrons

Atomic Mass

In laboratory work, a scientist uses samples that contain many atoms of an element. Among those atoms are all of the various isotopes with their different masses. To obtain a convenient mass to work with, chemists use the mass of an "average atom" of each element. This average atom has an **atomic mass**, which is the weighted average of the mass of all of the naturally occurring isotopes of that element. On the periodic table, the atomic mass is given below the symbol of each element.

Most elements consist of several isotopes, which is one reason that the atomic masses on the periodic table are seldom whole numbers. For example, a sample of chlorine atoms consists of two isotopes, $^{35}_{17}Cl$ and $^{37}_{17}Cl$. The atomic mass of chlorine (35.45 amu) indicates that there will be a higher percentage of $^{35}_{17}Cl$ atoms. In fact, there are more than three atoms of $^{35}_{17}Cl$ for every atom of $^{37}_{17}Cl$ in a sample of chlorine atoms.

Calculating Atomic Mass

To determine the atomic mass of an element, the percentage of each isotope and the mass of each isotope must be determined experimentally. For example, a sample of chlorine atoms consists of 75.76% of $^{35}_{17}Cl$ atoms and 24.24% of $^{37}_{17}Cl$ atoms. The atomic mass, known as a *weighted average*, is calculated using the percentage of each isotope and its mass: $^{35}_{17}Cl$ has a mass of 34.97 amu, and $^{37}_{17}Cl$ has a mass of 36.97 amu.

$$\text{Atomic mass of Cl} = \text{mass } ^{35}_{17}Cl \times \frac{^{35}_{17}Cl\%}{100\%} + \text{mass } ^{37}_{17}Cl \times \frac{^{37}_{17}Cl\%}{100\%}$$

$$\underbrace{\qquad\qquad}_{\text{(mass from }^{35}_{17}Cl\text{)}} \qquad \underbrace{\qquad\qquad}_{\text{(mass from }^{37}_{17}Cl\text{)}}$$

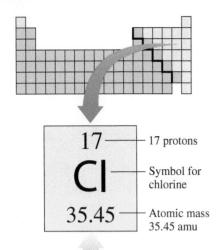

Isotope	Mass (amu)	$\times$	Abundance (%)	=	Contribution to Average Cl Atom
$^{35}_{17}Cl$	34.97	$\times$	$\dfrac{75.76}{100}$	=	26.49 amu
$^{37}_{17}Cl$	36.97	$\times$	$\dfrac{24.24}{100}$	=	8.962 amu
				Atomic mass of Cl =	35.45 amu

The atomic mass of 35.45 amu is the weighted average mass of a sample of Cl atoms, although no individual Cl atom actually has this mass.

Table 3.9 lists the naturally occurring isotopes of selected elements and their atomic masses.

TABLE 3.9 The Atomic Mass of Some Elements

Element	Most Common Naturally Occurring Isotopes	Atomic Mass (weighted average)
Lithium	^6_3Li, ^7_3Li	6.941 amu
Carbon	$^{12}_6C$, $^{13}_6C$, $^{14}_6C$	12.01 amu
Oxygen	$^{16}_8O$, $^{17}_8O$, $^{18}_8O$	16.00 amu
Fluorine	$^{19}_9F$	19.00 amu
Sulfur	$^{32}_{16}S$, $^{33}_{16}S$, $^{34}_{16}S$, $^{36}_{16}S$	32.07 amu
Copper	$^{63}_{29}Cu$, $^{65}_{29}Cu$	63.55 amu

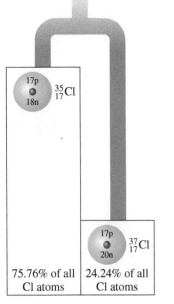

CONCEPT CHECK 3.4

Average Atomic Mass

Magnesium consists of three naturally occurring isotopes: $^{24}_{12}Mg$, $^{25}_{12}Mg$, and $^{26}_{12}Mg$. Using the atomic mass on the periodic table, which isotope of magnesium is the most prevalent in a magnesium sample?

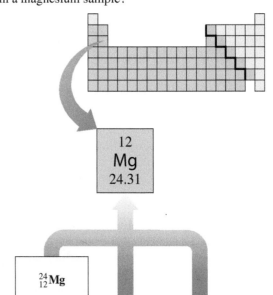

MC TUTORIAL
Atomic Mass Calculations

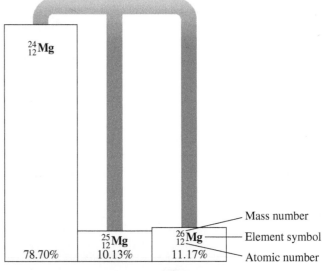

ANSWER

The atomic mass (weighted average) for all isotopes of magnesium is 24.31 amu. Thus, the isotope $^{24}_{12}$Mg must be the most prevalent isotope in a magnesium sample.

SAMPLE PROBLEM   3.6

■ **Calculating Atomic Mass**

Using Table 3.8, calculate the atomic mass for magnesium.

SOLUTION

$^{24}_{12}$Mg	23.99	$\times$	$\dfrac{78.70}{100}$	$=$	18.88 amu
$^{25}_{12}$Mg	24.99	$\times$	$\dfrac{10.13}{100}$	$=$	2.531 amu
$^{26}_{12}$Mg	25.98	$\times$	$\dfrac{11.17}{100}$	$=$	2.902 amu
	Atomic mass of Mg			$=$	24.31 amu

STUDY CHECK

There are two naturally occurring isotopes of boron. $^{10}_{5}$B has a mass of 10.01 amu with an abundance of 19.80%, and $^{11}_{5}$B has a mass of 11.01 amu with an abundance of 80.20%. What is the atomic mass of boron?

QUESTIONS AND PROBLEMS

Isotopes and Atomic Mass

3.31 What are the number of protons, neutrons, and electrons in the following isotopes?
   a. $^{30}_{14}$Si
   b. $^{60}_{27}$Co
   c. $^{80}_{34}$Se
   d. $^{19}_{9}$F

3.32 What are the number of protons, neutrons, and electrons in the following isotopes?
   a. $^{2}_{1}$H
   b. $^{14}_{7}$N
   c. $^{26}_{14}$Si
   d. $^{70}_{30}$Zn

3.33 Write the atomic symbols for isotopes with the following:
   a. 15 protons and 16 neutrons
   b. 35 protons and 45 neutrons
   c. 13 electrons and 14 neutrons
   d. a chlorine atom with 18 neutrons
   e. a mercury atom with 122 neutrons

3.34 Write the atomic symbols for isotopes with the following:
   a. an oxygen atom with 10 neutrons
   b. 4 protons and 5 neutrons
   c. 26 electrons and 30 neutrons
   d. a mass number of 24 and 13 neutrons
   e. a nickel atom with 32 neutrons

3.35 There are four isotopes of sulfur with mass numbers 32, 33, 34, and 36.
   a. Write the atomic symbol for each of these atoms.
   b. How are these isotopes alike?

c. How are they different?
d. Why is the atomic mass of sulfur listed on the periodic table not a whole number?
e. Which isotope is the most abundant in a sample of sulfur?

3.36 There are four isotopes of strontium with mass numbers 84, 86, 87, and 88.
   a. Write the atomic symbol for each of these atoms.
   b. How are these isotopes alike?
   c. How are they different?
   d. Why is the atomic mass of strontium listed on the periodic table not a whole number?
   e. Which isotope is the most abundant in a sample of strontium?

3.37 Copper consists of two isotopes, $^{63}_{29}$Cu and $^{65}_{29}$Cu. If the atomic mass for copper on the periodic table is 63.55, are there more atoms of $^{63}_{29}$Cu or $^{65}_{29}$Cu in a sample of copper?

3.38 There are four naturally occurring isotopes of iron: $^{54}_{26}$Fe, $^{56}_{26}$Fe, $^{57}_{26}$Fe, and $^{58}_{26}$Fe. Use the atomic mass of iron listed on the periodic table to identify the most abundant isotope.

3.39 Two isotopes of gallium are naturally occurring, with $^{69}_{31}$Ga at 60.11% (68.93 amu) and $^{71}_{31}$Ga at 39.89% (70.92 amu). What is the atomic mass of gallium?

3.40 Two isotopes of copper are naturally occurring, with $^{63}_{29}$Cu at 69.09% (62.93 amu) and $^{65}_{29}$Cu at 30.91% (64.93 amu). What is the atomic mass of copper?

3.6 Electron Energy Levels

LEARNING GOAL

Describe the energy levels, sublevels, and orbitals in atoms.

When we listen to a radio, use a microwave oven, turn on a light, see the colors of a rainbow, or have an X-ray, we are using various forms of *electromagnetic radiation*. Light and other electromagnetic radiation consist of energy particles called *photons* that move as a wave of energy. In a wave, the distance between the peaks is called the *wavelength*. In some types of radiation, the peaks are far apart, while in other forms of radiation they are close together. All forms of electromagnetic radiation travel at the speed of light, 3.0×10^8 meters per second, but they differ in energy and wavelength. The energy of radiation is inversely related to its wavelength. High-energy radiation such as X-rays and gamma rays has short wavelengths. X-rays and gamma rays can pass through soft substances but not metal or bone, which is why they are used to scan luggage at airports and to image bones and teeth. Low-energy forms of radiation such as microwaves and radio waves have long wavelengths. The wavelength of a typical AM radio wave or cell phone can be as long as a football field. (See Figure 3.11.)

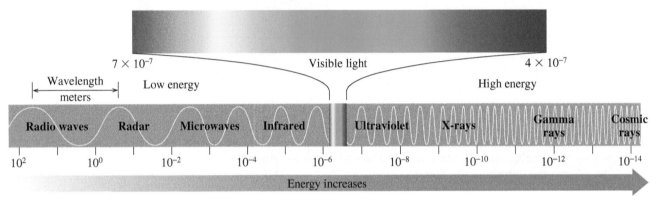

FIGURE 3.11 The electromagnetic spectrum contains radiation with long and short wavelengths in the visible and invisible regions.

Q How does the energy of ultraviolet light compare to that of a microwave?

When sunlight passes through a prism or crystal, the light separates into a continuous color spectrum: red, orange, yellow, green, blue, indigo, and violet. These are the same colors we see in a rainbow that forms when sunlight passes through raindrops acting as prisms. In this visible spectrum, which is the only part of the electromagnetic spectrum that we can see naturally, red light has the longest wavelength and violet light has the shortest wavelength.

When the light emitted from a heated element is passed through a prism, it does not produce a continuous spectrum. Instead, an **atomic spectrum** is produced that consists of lines of different colors separated by dark areas. (See Figure 3.12.) This separation of colors indicates that only certain wavelengths of light are produced when an element is heated, which gives each element a unique atomic spectrum.

Electron Energy Levels

Scientists associated the lines in atomic spectra with changes in the energies of the electrons. In an atom, each electron has a fixed or specific energy known as its energy level.

The energy levels are assigned values called *principal quantum numbers (n)*, which are positive integers ($n = 1$, $n = 2$, ...). Generally, electrons in the lower energy levels are closer to the nucleus, while electrons in the higher energy levels are farther away. The energy of an electron is *quantized*, which means that an electron can only have specific energy values but cannot have values between them.

As an analogy, we can think of the energy levels of an atom as similar to the shelves in a bookcase. The lowest energy level is the first shelf; the second energy level would be the second shelf. If we have a stack of books on the floor, it takes less energy to put them on the bottom shelves first, and then the second shelf, and so on. However, we could never get any book to stay in the space between the shelves. Unlike standard bookcases, however,

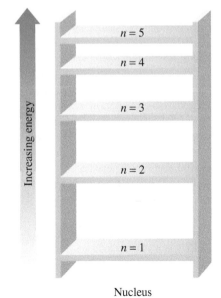

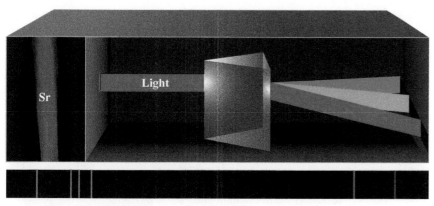

Strontium, Sr

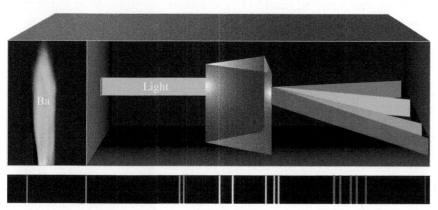

Barium, Ba

FIGURE 3.12 A spectrum unique to each element is produced as light emitted from the heated element passes through a prism, which separates the light into colored lines.

Q Why don't the elements form a continuous spectrum as seen with white light?

there is a big difference in the energy of the first and second energy levels, and thereafter the energy levels are closer.

Principal Quantum Number (*n*)

$1 < 2 < 3 < 4 < 5 < 6 < 7$
Energy of electrons increases →

Changes in Energy Levels

TUTORIAL
Energy Levels

When the electrons in an atom occupy the lowest energy levels, they are in their *ground state*. By absorbing energy equal to the difference in energy levels, an electron is raised to a higher energy level called the *excited state*. An electron loses energy when it falls to a lower energy level and emits electromagnetic radiation equal to the difference in energy levels. (See Figure 3.13.) If the electromagnetic radiation emitted has a wavelength in the visible range, we see a color.

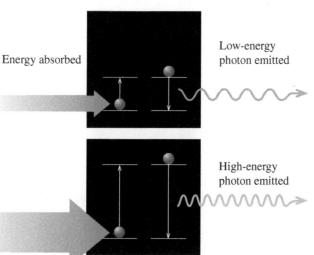

Energy absorbed

Low-energy photon emitted

High-energy photon emitted

FIGURE 3.13 Electrons can absorb a specific amount of energy to move to a higher energy level. When electrons lose energy, photons with specific energies are emitted.

Q How does the energy of a photon of green light compare to the energy of a photon of red light?

There is a limit to the number of electrons allowed in each energy level. Only a few electrons can occupy the lower energy levels, while more electrons can be accommodated in higher energy levels. The maximum number of electrons allowed in any energy level is calculated using the formula $2n^2$ (two times the square of the principal quantum number).

GREEN CHEMISTRY NOTE

Energy-Saving Lightbulbs

A compact fluorescent light (CFL) is a type of fluorescent bulb that is replacing the standard light bulb we use in our homes and workplaces. Compared to a standard light bulb, the CFL has a longer life and uses less electricity. Within about 20 days of use, the fluorescent bulb saves enough money in electricity costs to pay for its higher initial cost.

A standard incandescent light bulb has a thin tungsten filament inside a sealed glass bulb. When the light is switched on, electricity flows through this filament, and electrical energy is converted to heat energy. When the filament reaches a temperature around 2300 °C, we see white light. We say that the light bulb is incandescent.

A fluorescent bulb produces light in a different way. When the switch is turned on, electrons move between two electrodes and collide with mercury atoms in a gas mixture of mercury and argon inside the bulb. When the electrons in the mercury atoms absorb energy from the collisions, electrons are raised to higher energy levels. As electrons fall to lower energy levels, energy in the ultraviolet range is emitted. This ultraviolet light strikes the phosphor coating inside the tube, and fluorescence occurs as visible light is emitted.

The production of light in a fluorescent bulb is more efficient than in an incandescent light bulb. A 75-watt incandescent bulb can be replaced by a 20-watt fluorescent bulb that gives the same amount of light, providing a 70% reduction in electricity costs. A typical light bulb lasts for one to two months, whereas a fluorescent light bulb lasts from one to two years.

Sublevels

Within each energy level, there are one or more **sublevels** that contain electrons with identical energy. The sublevels are identified by the letters *s*, *p*, *d*, and *f*. The number of sublevels within an energy level is equal to the principal quantum number. The first energy level ($n = 1$) has only one sublevel, 1*s*. The second energy level ($n = 2$) has two sublevels, 2*s* and 2*p*. The third energy level ($n = 3$) has three sublevels, 3*s*, 3*p*, and 3*d*. The fourth energy level ($n = 4$) has four sublevels: 4*s*, 4*p*, 4*d*, and 4*f*. (See Figure 3.14.)

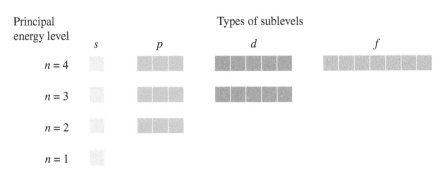

FIGURE 3.14 The number of sublevels in an energy level is the same as the principal quantum number *n*.

Q How many sublevels are in energy level $n = 5$?

Within each energy level, the *s* sublevel has the lowest energy. If there are additional sublevels, the *p* sublevel has the next lowest energy, then the *d* sublevel, and finally the *f* sublevel.

Order of Increasing Energy of Sublevels in an Energy Level

$s < p < d < f$

Lowest $\longrightarrow$ Highest
energy   energy

Energy levels $n = 5$ and higher have as many sublevels as the value of *n*, but only *s*, *p*, *d*, and *f* sublevels are needed to hold the electrons of atoms of the elements known today.

Number of Electrons in Sublevels

A maximum number of electrons can occupy each sublevel. An *s* sublevel holds 1 or 2 electrons. A *p* sublevel takes up to 6 electrons, a *d* sublevel can hold up to 10 electrons, and an *f* sublevel holds a maximum of 14 electrons.

CONCEPT CHECK 3.5

■ Energy Levels and Sublevels

Complete the following table with the notation for principal energy level and sublevels in each energy level:

Energy Level (n)	Sublevels			
	s	*p*	*d*	*f*
			4d	
1				
	2s			
		3p		

ANSWER

Energy Level (n)	Sublevels			
	s	*p*	*d*	*f*
4	4s	4p	4d	4f
1	1s			
2	2s	2p		
3	3s	3p	3d	

Orbitals

There is no way to know the exact location of an electron in an atom. Instead, scientists describe the location of an electron in terms of *probability*. A region in an atom where there is the highest probability of finding an electron is called an **orbital**. Suppose you could draw an imaginary circle with a 100-m radius around your chemistry classroom. There is a high probability of finding you within that area when your chemistry class is in session. Occasionally, though, you may be found outside that circle because you were sick or your car did not start.

Any orbital can have a maximum of two electrons. When an orbital contains two electrons, their spins are in opposite directions. We represent the spins of the electrons in the same orbital with one arrow pointing up and the other pointing down.

Shapes of Orbitals

Each sublevel within an energy level is composed of the same type of orbitals. There is an *s* orbital for each *s* sublevel, *p* orbitals for each *p* sublevel, *d* orbitals for each *d* sublevel,

Electron spinning   Electron spinning
counterclockwise   clockwise

Opposite spins of
electrons in an orbital

FIGURE 3.15 An s orbital represents the region of highest probability of finding an s electron around the nucleus of an atom. All s orbitals are spherical, but the size increases at higher energy levels.

Q Is the probability high or low of finding an s electron outside an s orbital?

and *f* orbitals for each *f* sublevel. Each type of orbital has a unique shape. In an *s* orbital, the electrons are most likely found in a region with a spherical shape. Every *s* orbital can hold one or two electrons; there is just one *s* orbital for every *s* sublevel. Although the shape of every *s* orbital is spherical, there is an increase in the size of the *s* orbitals in higher energy levels. (See Figure 3.15.)

A *p* sublevel consists of three *p* orbitals, each of which has two lobes. The three *p* orbitals are arranged in three different directions (*x*, *y*, and *z* axes) around the nucleus. (See Figure 3.16.) Because each *p* orbital can hold up to two electrons, the three *p* orbitals can accommodate six electrons in a *p* sublevel. At higher energy levels, the shape of *p* orbitals is the same, but the volume increases.

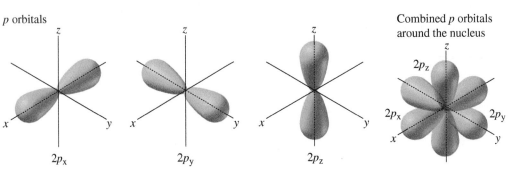

FIGURE 3.16 Each p orbital has a dumbbell shape and aligns along a different axis from other p orbitals. Each holds a maximum of two electrons.

Q What is the maximum number of electrons possible in a p sublevel?

A *d* sublevel consists of five *d* orbitals. Each *d* orbital can hold as many as two electrons, which means that a *d* sublevel can have a maximum of 10 electrons. In the *f* sublevel, there are seven *f* orbitals. Each *f* orbital can hold up to two electrons, which means that the *f* sublevel can have as many as 14 electrons. The shapes of *d* orbitals and *f* orbitals are more complex, and we have not included them in this text.

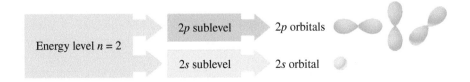

The number of electrons in the orbitals determines the number of electrons in the sublevels in each energy level. (See Table 3.10.)

TABLE 3.10 Electron Capacity and Orbitals in Energy Levels 1–4

Energy Level (n)	Electron Capacity ($2n^2$)	Orbitals	Maximum Number of Electrons in Sublevels
1	$2(1)^2 = 2$	1s	2
2	$2(2)^2 = 8$	2s	2
		2p 2p 2p	6
3	$2(3)^2 = 18$	3s	2
		3p 3p 3p	6
		3d 3d 3d 3d 3d	10
4	$2(4)^2 = 32$	4s	2
		4p 4p 4p	6
		4d 4d 4d 4d 4d	10
		4f 4f 4f 4f 4f 4f 4f	14

SAMPLE PROBLEM   3.7

■ **Energy Levels, Sublevels, and Orbitals**

Indicate the type and number of orbitals in each of the following energy levels or sublevels:

a. 3p sublevel   **b.** $n = 2$ **c.** $n = 3$ **d.** 4d sublevel

SOLUTION

a. The 3p sublevel contains three 3p orbitals.
b. The $n = 2$ principal energy level consists of 2s (one) and 2p (three) orbitals.
c. The $n = 3$ principal energy level consists of 3s (one), 3p (three), and 3d (five) orbitals.
d. The 4d sublevel contains five 4d orbitals.

STUDY CHECK

What is similar and what is different for 1s, 2s, and 3s orbitals?

QUESTIONS AND PROBLEMS

Electron Energy Levels

3.41 Describe the shape of the following orbitals:
    a. 1s   **b.** 2p   **c.** 5s

3.42 Describe the shape of the following orbitals:
    a. 3p   **b.** 6s   **c.** 4p

3.43 What is similar about the following?
    a. 1s and 2s orbitals   **b.** 3s and 3p sublevels
    c. 3p and 4p sublevels   **d.** three 3p orbitals

3.44 What is similar about the following?
    a. 5s and 6s orbitals   **b.** 3p and 4p orbitals
    c. 3s and 4s sublevels   **d.** 2s and 2p orbitals

3.45 Indicate the number of each in the following:
    a. orbitals in the 3d sublevel
    b. sublevels in the energy level $n = 1$
    c. orbitals in the 6s sublevel
    d. orbitals in the energy level $n = 3$

3.46 Indicate the number of each in the following:
    a. orbitals in the energy level $n = 2$
    b. sublevels in the energy level $n = 4$
    c. orbitals in the 5f sublevel
    d. orbitals in the 6p sublevel

3.47 Indicate the maximum number of electrons in the following:
    a. 2p orbital
    b. 3p sublevel
    c. principal energy level $n = 4$
    d. 5d sublevel

3.48 Indicate the maximum number of electrons in the following:
    a. 3s sublevel
    b. 4p orbital
    c. principal energy level $n = 3$
    d. 4f sublevel

3.7 Electron Configurations

We can now look at how electrons are arranged in the orbitals within an atom. In an **orbital diagram**, boxes (or circles) represent the orbitals containing electrons. We see from an energy diagram (Figure 3.17) that the electrons in the 1s orbital have a lower energy level than in the 2s orbital.

LEARNING GOAL

Use the periodic table to write orbital diagrams and electron configurations.

Period 1 Hydrogen and Helium

We can begin to draw the orbital diagrams and build the electron configurations for the elements H and He in Period 1. The 1s orbital (which is also the 1s sublevel) is used first because it has the lowest energy. Hydrogen has one electron in the 1s sublevel; helium has two. In the orbital diagram, the electrons for helium are shown with opposite spins.

TUTORIAL
Electron Configurations

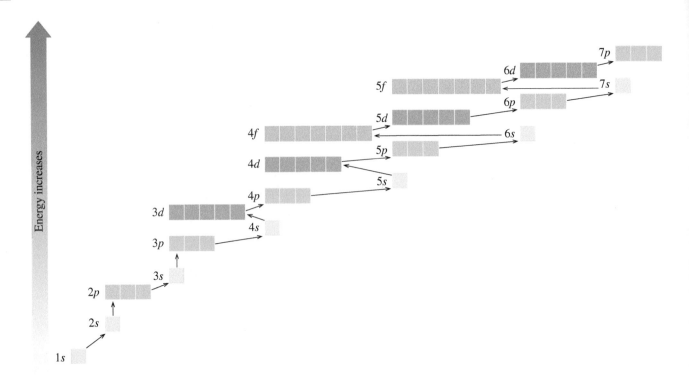

FIGURE 3.17 The sublevels fill in order of increasing energy beginning with 1s. In each sublevel, each orbital will be filled with two electrons before additional electrons go to sublevels of higher energy.

Q Why does the 3d sublevel fill after the 4s sublevel?

The **electron configuration** of an atom is "built up" by placing the electrons of an atom in the sublevels in order of increasing energy. The electron configuration for helium is written as

Sublevel   Number of electrons

$1s^2$ Read as "One s two"

Atomic Number	Element	Orbital Diagram	Electron Configuration
		1s	
1	H	↑	$1s^1$
2	He	↑↓	$1s^2$

Period 2 Lithium to Neon

Period 2 begins with lithium, which has three electrons. The first two electrons fill the 1s orbital, while the third electron goes into the 2s orbital, the sublevel with the next lowest energy. In beryllium, another electron is added to complete the 2s orbital. Because 2p orbitals have equal energy, electrons from boron to nitrogen are added one at a time to give three half-filled 2p orbitals. In a half-filled sublevel, there is less repulsion between electrons when they are placed in separate 2p orbitals. From oxygen to neon, the remaining electrons must pair up using opposite spins until the 2p sublevel is complete. In writing the complete electron configurations for the elements in Period 2, begin with the 1s sublevel followed by the 2s and the 2p sublevels.

An electron configuration can also be written in an *abbreviated configuration*. The electron configuration of the preceding noble gas is replaced by writing its symbol inside square brackets. For example, the electron configuration for lithium, $1s^2 2s^1$, can be abbreviated as $[He]2s^1$, where [He] replaces $1s^2$.

Atomic Number	Element	Orbital Diagram	Electron Configuration	Abbreviated Configuration
		1s 2s		
3	Li	$\uparrow\downarrow$ $\uparrow$	$1s^2 2s^1$	$[He]2s^1$
4	Be	$\uparrow\downarrow$ $\uparrow\downarrow$	$1s^2 2s^2$	$[He]2s^2$
			2p	
5	B	$\uparrow\downarrow$ $\uparrow\downarrow$ $\uparrow$	$1s^2 2s^2 2p^1$	$[He]2s^2 2p^1$
6	C	$\uparrow\downarrow$ $\uparrow\downarrow$ $\uparrow$ $\uparrow$	$1s^2 2s^2 2p^2$	$[He]2s^2 2p^2$
		Unpaired electrons		
7	N	$\uparrow\downarrow$ $\uparrow\downarrow$ $\uparrow$ $\uparrow$ $\uparrow$	$1s^2 2s^2 2p^3$	$[He]2s^2 2p^3$
8	O	$\uparrow\downarrow$ $\uparrow\downarrow$ $\uparrow\downarrow$ $\uparrow$ $\uparrow$	$1s^2 2s^2 2p^4$	$[He]2s^2 2p^4$
9	F	$\uparrow\downarrow$ $\uparrow\downarrow$ $\uparrow\downarrow$ $\uparrow\downarrow$ $\uparrow$	$1s^2 2s^2 2p^5$	$[He]2s^2 2p^5$
10	Ne	$\uparrow\downarrow$ $\uparrow\downarrow$ $\uparrow\downarrow$ $\uparrow\downarrow$ $\uparrow\downarrow$	$1s^2 2s^2 2p^6$	$[He]2s^2 2p^6$

Period 3 Sodium to Argon

In Period 3, electrons enter the orbitals of the 3s and 3p sublevels, but not the 3d sublevel. We notice that the elements sodium to argon, which are directly below the elements lithium to neon in Period 2, have a similar pattern of filling their s and p orbitals. We can write the complete orbital diagram for phosphorus as follows:

1s   2s   2p   3s   3p

$\uparrow\downarrow$ $\uparrow\downarrow$ $\uparrow\downarrow$ $\uparrow\downarrow$ $\uparrow\downarrow$ $\uparrow\downarrow$ $\uparrow$ $\uparrow$ $\uparrow$

For elements in Period 3 and above, we usually write the orbital diagrams for only the electrons in the highest energy levels. In Period 3, the symbol [Ne] replaces the electron configuration of neon, $1s^2 2s^2 2p^6$. The abbreviated configuration is convenient to use for electron configurations that contain several sublevel notations.

Atomic Number	Element	Orbital Diagram (3s and 3p orbitals only)	Electron Configuration	Abbreviated Configuration
		3s 3p		
11	Na	$\uparrow$	$1s^2 2s^2 2p^6 3s^1$	$[Ne]3s^1$
12	Mg	$\uparrow\downarrow$	$1s^2 2s^2 2p^6 3s^2$	$[Ne]3s^2$
13	Al	$\uparrow\downarrow$ $\uparrow$	$1s^2 2s^2 2p^6 3s^2 3p^1$	$[Ne]3s^2 3p^1$
14	Si	$\uparrow\downarrow$ $\uparrow$ $\uparrow$	$1s^2 2s^2 2p^6 3s^2 3p^2$	$[Ne]3s^2 3p^2$
15	P	$\uparrow\downarrow$ $\uparrow$ $\uparrow$ $\uparrow$	$1s^2 2s^2 2p^6 3s^2 3p^3$	$[Ne]3s^2 3p^3$
16	S	$\uparrow\downarrow$ $\uparrow\downarrow$ $\uparrow$ $\uparrow$	$1s^2 2s^2 2p^6 3s^2 3p^4$	$[Ne]3s^2 3p^4$
17	Cl	$\uparrow\downarrow$ $\uparrow\downarrow$ $\uparrow\downarrow$ $\uparrow$	$1s^2 2s^2 2p^6 3s^2 3p^5$	$[Ne]3s^2 3p^5$
18	Ar	$\uparrow\downarrow$ $\uparrow\downarrow$ $\uparrow\downarrow$ $\uparrow\downarrow$	$1s^2 2s^2 2p^6 3s^2 3p^6$	$[Ne]3s^2 3p^6$

SAMPLE PROBLEM   3.8

■ Orbital Diagrams and Electron Configurations

For each of the following elements, write the stated type of electron notation:

a. orbital diagram for silicon
b. electron configuration for phosphorus
c. abbreviated electron configuration for chlorine

SOLUTION

a. Silicon in Period 3 has atomic number 14, which tells us that it has 14 electrons. To write the orbital diagram, we draw boxes for the orbitals up to $3p$.

$1s$	$2s$	$2p$	$3s$	$3p$
↑↓	↑↓	↑↓ ↑↓ ↑↓	↑↓	↑ ↑ ⬚

Add 14 electrons, starting with the $1s$ orbital. Show paired electrons in the same orbital with opposite spins, and place the last 2 electrons in different $3p$ orbitals.

$1s$	$2s$	$2p$	$3s$	$3p$
↑↓	↑↓	↑↓ ↑↓ ↑↓	↑↓	↑ ↑ ⬚

b. The electron configuration gives the electrons that fill the sublevels in order of increasing energy. Phosphorus is in Group 5A (15) in Period 3. In Periods 1 and 2, a total of 10 electrons fill sublevels: $1s^2$, $2s^2$, and $2p^6$. In Period 3, 2 electrons go into $3s^2$. The 3 remaining electrons (total of 15) are placed in the $3p$ sublevel.

P $1s^2 2s^2 2p^6 3s^2 3p^3$

c. In chlorine, the previous noble gas is neon. For the abbreviated configuration, write [Ne] for $1s^2 2s^2 2p^6$ followed by the electrons in the $3s$ and $3p$ sublevels.

[Ne]$3s^2 3p^5$

STUDY CHECK

Write the complete and abbreviated electron configurations for sulfur.

Electron Configurations and the Periodic Table

SELF STUDY ACTIVITY
Bohr's Shell Model

Until now, we have written electron configurations using the energy diagram. As configurations involve more sublevels, this becomes tedious. However, on the periodic table, the atomic numbers are arranged in order of increasing sublevel energy. The electron configurations of the elements are related to their position in the periodic table. Different sections or sublevel blocks within the table correspond to the s, p, d, and f sublevels. (See Figure 3.18.) Therefore, we can "build up" atoms by reading the periodic table from left to right across each period.

1. The **s block** includes the elements hydrogen and helium as well as the elements in Group 1A (1) and Group 2A (2). This means that the final one or two electrons in the elements of the s block are located in s sublevels. The period number indicates the particular s sublevel that is filling: $1s$, $2s$, and so on.

2. The **p block** consists of the elements in Group 3A (13) to Group 8A (18). There are six p block elements in each period because each p sublevel can hold as many as six electrons. The period number indicates the particular p sublevel that is filling: $2p$, $3p$, and so on.

3. The **d block** first appears after calcium (atomic number 20) with the 10 columns of the transition elements. There are 10 elements in the d block because each d sublevel can hold as many as 10 electrons. The particular d sublevel is one less ($n - 1$) than

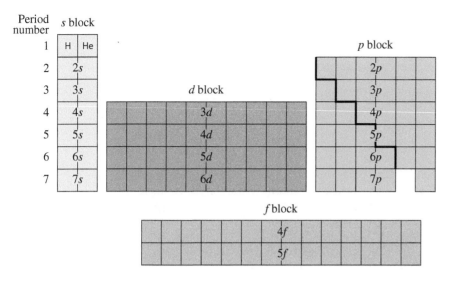

FIGURE 3.18 An electron configuration of an atom follows the order of sublevels on the periodic table.

Q How many electrons are in the 1s, 2s, and 2p sublevels of neon?

the period number. For example, in Period 4, the first d block is the $3d$ sublevel. In Period 5, the second d block is the $4d$ sublevel.

4. The *f block* includes all the elements in the two rows at the bottom of the periodic table. There are 14 elements in each f block because an f sublevel can hold as many as 14 electrons. Elements that have atomic numbers higher than 57 (La) have electrons in the $4f$ block. The particular f sublevel is two fewer $(n - 2)$ than the period number. For example, in Period 6, the first f block is the $4f$ sublevel. In Period 7, the second f block is the $5f$ sublevel.

Writing Electron Configurations Using Sublevel Blocks

Now we can write electron configurations using the sublevel blocks on the periodic table. As before, each configuration begins at H. But now we move across the table writing down each block we come to until we reach the element for which we are writing an electron configuration.

To write the electron configuration for chlorine (atomic number 17) from the sublevel blocks on the periodic table:

Period		**Sublevel Blocks Filled**
1	$1s$ sublevel (H $\longrightarrow$ He)	$1s^2$
2	$2s$ sublevel (Li $\longrightarrow$ Be) then $2p$ sublevel (B $\longrightarrow$ Ne)	$2s^2 \longrightarrow 2p^6$
3	$3s$ sublevel (Na $\longrightarrow$ Mg) then $3p$ sublevel (Al $\longrightarrow$ Cl)	$3s^2 \longrightarrow 3p^?$

Writing the sublevel blocks in order up to chlorine gives

$1s^2 2s^2 2p^6 3s^2 3p^?$

Chlorine is the fifth element in the $3p$ block, which means that chlorine has five $3p$ electrons. The complete electron configuration for chlorine is written as

$1s^2 2s^2 2p^6 3s^2 3p^5$

Period 4

Until now, the filling of sublevels has progressed in order. However, if we look at the sublevel blocks in Period 4, we see that the $4s$ sublevel block fills before the $3d$ orbitals. The $4s$ orbital has a slightly lower energy than the $3d$ orbitals, which means that the $4s$ sublevel has the next lowest energy following the filling of the $3p$ sublevel at the end of Period 3. This order occurs again in Period 5 when the $5s$ orbital fills before the $4d$ orbitals, and again in Period 6 when the $6s$ fills before the $5d$.

At the beginning of Period 4, the one and two remaining electrons in potassium (19) and calcium (20) go into the $4s$ orbital. In scandium, the remaining electron goes into the $3d$ block, which continues to fill until it has 10 electrons at zinc (30). Once the $3d$ block is complete, the next six electrons go into the $4p$ block for elements gallium (31) to krypton (36).

Atomic Number	Element	Electron Configuration	Abbreviated Configuration
4s Block			
19	K	$1s^2 2s^2 2p^6 3s^2 3p^6 4s^1$	$[Ar]4s^1$
20	Ca	$1s^2 2s^2 2p^6 3s^2 3p^6 4s^2$	$[Ar]4s^2$
3d Block			
21	Sc	$1s^2 2s^2 2p^6 3s^2 3p^6 4s^2 3d^1$	$[Ar]4s^2 3d^1$
22	Ti	$1s^2 2s^2 2p^6 3s^2 3p^6 4s^2 3d^2$	$[Ar]4s^2 3d^2$
23	V	$1s^2 2s^2 2p^6 3s^2 3p^6 4s^2 3d^3$	$[Ar]4s^2 3d^3$
24	Cr	$1s^2 2s^2 2p^6 3s^2 3p^6 4s^1 3d^5$	$[Ar]4s^1 3d^5$ (1/2 filled d sublevel is stable)
25	Mn	$1s^2 2s^2 2p^6 3s^2 3p^6 4s^2 3d^5$	$[Ar]4s^2 3d^5$
26	Fe	$1s^2 2s^2 2p^6 3s^2 3p^6 4s^2 3d^6$	$[Ar]4s^2 3d^6$
27	Co	$1s^2 2s^2 2p^6 3s^2 3p^6 4s^2 3d^7$	$[Ar]4s^2 3d^7$
28	Ni	$1s^2 2s^2 2p^6 3s^2 3p^6 4s^2 3d^8$	$[Ar]4s^2 3d^8$
29	Cu	$1s^2 2s^2 2p^6 3s^2 3p^6 4s^1 3d^{10}$	$[Ar]4s^1 3d^{10}$ (filled d sublevel is stable)
30	Zn	$1s^2 2s^2 2p^6 3s^2 3p^6 4s^2 3d^{10}$	$[Ar]4s^2 3d^{10}$
4p Block			
31	Ga	$1s^2 2s^2 2p^6 3s^2 3p^6 4s^2 3d^{10} 4p^1$	$[Ar]4s^2 3d^{10} 4p^1$
32	Ge	$1s^2 2s^2 2p^6 3s^2 3p^6 4s^2 3d^{10} 4p^2$	$[Ar]4s^2 3d^{10} 4p^2$
33	As	$1s^2 2s^2 2p^6 3s^2 3p^6 4s^2 3d^{10} 4p^3$	$[Ar]4s^2 3d^{10} 4p^3$
34	Se	$1s^2 2s^2 2p^6 3s^2 3p^6 4s^2 3d^{10} 4p^4$	$[Ar]4s^2 3d^{10} 4p^4$
35	Br	$1s^2 2s^2 2p^6 3s^2 3p^6 4s^2 3d^{10} 4p^5$	$[Ar]4s^2 3d^{10} 4p^5$
36	Kr	$1s^2 2s^2 2p^6 3s^2 3p^6 4s^2 3d^{10} 4p^6$	$[Ar]4s^2 3d^{10} 4p^6$

Some Exceptions in Sublevel Block Order

Within the filling of the $3d$ sublevel, exceptions occur for chromium and copper. When electrons half-fill or fill a sublevel, it is particularly stable. Thus, chromium has only one electron in the $4s$ and five electrons in the $3d$ sublevel to give the stability of a half-filled d sublevel. In copper, there is one electron in the $4s$ sublevel and 10 electrons in the $3d$ sublevel, which give the stability of a filled d sublevel.

After the $4s$ and $3d$ sublevels are completed, the $4p$ sublevel fills as expected from gallium to krypton, the noble gas that completes Period 4.

CONCEPT CHECK 3.6

■ **Electron Configurations**

Identify the elements that have atoms with each of the following electron configurations:

a. $1s^2 2s^2 2p^5$

b. $1s^2 2s^2 2p^6 3s^2 3p^6 4s^2 3d^{10} 4p^2$

c. $[Ar]4s^2 3d^6$

ANSWER

a. In the p block, Period 2, the fifth element across is F, fluorine.
b. In the p block, Period 4, the second element across is Ge, germanium.
c. In the d block, Period 4, the sixth element across is Fe, iron.

SAMPLE PROBLEM 3.9

■ **Using Sublevel Blocks to Write Electron Configurations**

Use the sublevel blocks on the periodic table to write the electron configuration for bromine.

SOLUTION

STEP 1 Bromine is in the p block and in Period 4.
STEP 2 Beginning with $1s^2$, go across the periodic table writing each filled sublevel block as follows:

Period 1	$1s^2$
Period 2	$2s^2 \longrightarrow 2p^6$
Period 3	$3s^2 \longrightarrow 3p^6$
Period 4	$4s^2 \longrightarrow 3d^{10} \longrightarrow 4p^?$

STEP 3 Five electrons in the $4p$ sublevel for Br ($4p^5$) completes the electron configuration for Br:

$$1s^2 2s^2 2p^6 3s^2 3p^6 4s^2 3d^{10} 4p^5$$

STUDY CHECK

Write the electron configuration for tin.

**Guide to
Writing Electron Configurations
with Sublevel Blocks**

STEP 1
Locate the element on the periodic table.

STEP 2
Write the filled sublevels in order going across each period.

STEP 3
Count the number of electrons in the sublevel for the given element and complete the configuration.

QUESTIONS AND PROBLEMS

Electron Configurations

3.49 Write an orbital diagram for an atom of each of the following:
  a. boron   **b.** aluminum
  c. phosphorus   **d.** argon

3.50 Write an orbital diagram for an atom of each of the following:
  a. fluorine   **b.** sodium
  c. magnesium   **d.** sulfur

3.51 Write a complete electron configuration for an atom of each of the following:
  a. nitrogen   **b.** sodium
  c. sulfur   **d.** arsenic
  e. iron

3.52 Write a complete electron configuration for an atom of each of the following:
  a. carbon   **b.** silicon
  c. phosphorus   **d.** cobalt
  e. gallium

3.53 Write an abbreviated electron configuration for an atom of each of the following:
  a. magnesium   **b.** sulfur
  c. aluminum   **d.** titanium
  e. barium

3.54 Write an abbreviated electron configuration for an atom of each of the following:
  a. sodium   **b.** oxygen

  c. nickel   **d.** tin
  e. silver

3.55 Give the symbol of the element with each of the following electron configurations:
  a. $1s^2 2s^2 2p^6 3s^2 3p^4$
  b. $1s^2 2s^2 2p^6 3s^2 3p^6 4s^2 3d^7$
  c. [Ne]$3s^2 3p^2$
  d. [Ar]$4s^2 3d^{10} 4p^5$

3.56 Give the symbol of the element with each of the following electron configurations:
  a. $1s^2 2s^2 2p^4$
  b. $1s^2 2s^2 2p^6 3s^2 3p^6$
  c. [Ne]$3s^2 3p^1$
  d. [Ar]$4s^2 3d^4$

3.57 Give the symbol of the element that meets the following conditions:
  a. has three electrons in energy level $n = 3$
  b. has two $2p$ electrons
  c. completes the $3p$ sublevel
  d. has two electrons in the $4d$ sublevel

3.58 Give the symbol of the element that meets the following conditions:
  a. has five electrons in the $3p$ sublevel
  b. has three $2p$ electrons
  c. completes the $3s$ sublevel
  d. has four $5p$ electrons

3.59 Give the number of electrons in the indicated orbitals for the following:

a. 3d in zinc   **b.** 2p in sodium

c. 4p in arsenic   **d.** 5s in rubidium

3.60 Give the number of electrons in the indicated orbitals for the following:

a. 3d in manganese   **b.** 5p in antimony

c. 6p in lead   **d.** 3s in magnesium

3.8 | Periodic Trends

LEARNING GOAL

Use the electron configurations of elements to explain periodic trends.

The electron configurations of atoms are an important factor in the physical and chemical behavior of the elements. Going across a period, there is a pattern of regular change in these properties from one group to the next. Known as *periodic properties*, each property increases or decreases across a period. The trend is repeated again in each successive period. We can use the seasonal changes in temperatures as an analogy for periodic properties. In the winter, temperatures are cold and become warmer in the spring. In summer, outdoor temperatures are high, but they are lower in the fall. By winter, we expect cold temperatures again as the pattern of decreasing and increasing temperatures repeats for another year.

Group Number and Valence Electrons

If we could imagine two atoms approaching each other, the first interaction would be between those electrons in the highest filled energy levels. Chemists have determined that the chemical properties of representative elements are mostly the result of these outermost electrons, which are known as the **valence electrons**. Valence electrons occupy the s and p sublevels with the highest quantum number n. The group numbers indicate the number of valence (outer) electrons for the elements in each vertical column. For example, the elements in Group 1A (1) such as lithium, sodium, and potassium, all have one electron in the outer energy level. Looking at the sublevel block, we can represent the valence electron in the alkali metals of Group 1A (1) as ns^1. All the elements in Group 2A (2), the alkaline earth metals, have two (2) valence electrons, ns^2. The halogens in Group 7A (17) have seven (7) valence electrons, ns^2np^5.

We can see the repetition of the outermost s and p electrons for the representative elements in Periods 1 to 4 in Table 3.11. Helium is included in Group 8A (18) because it is a noble gas, but it has only two electrons in its complete energy level.

Atoms of magnesium

$\overset{\displaystyle \cdot}{\underset{\displaystyle \cdot}{Mg}} \cdot$

Electron-dot symbol

$1s^2 2s^2 2p^6 \boxed{3s^2}$

Electron configuration of magnesium

TABLE 3.11 Valence Electrons for Representative Elements in Periods 1–4

1A (1)	2A (2)	3A (13)	4A (14)	5A (15)	6A (16)	7A (17)	8A (18)
1 H $1s^1$							2 He $1s^2$
3 Li $2s^1$	4 Be $2s^2$	5 B $2s^2 2p^1$	6 C $2s^2 2p^2$	7 N $2s^2 2p^3$	8 O $2s^2 2p^4$	9 F $2s^2 2p^5$	10 Ne $2s^2 2p^6$
11 Na $3s^1$	12 Mg $3s^2$	13 Al $3s^2 3p^1$	14 Si $3s^2 3p^2$	15 P $3s^2 3p^3$	16 S $3s^2 3p^4$	17 Cl $3s^2 3p^5$	18 Ar $3s^2 3p^6$
19 K $4s^1$	20 Ca $4s^2$	31 Ga $4s^2 4p^1$	32 Ge $4s^2 4p^2$	33 As $4s^2 4p^3$	34 Se $4s^2 4p^4$	35 Br $4s^2 4p^5$	36 Kr $4s^2 4p^6$

Electron-Dot Symbols

An **electron-dot symbol** is a convenient way to represent the valence electrons. Valence electrons are shown as dots placed on the sides, top, or bottom of the symbol for the element—which side does not matter. However, one to four valence electrons are arranged as single dots. When there are more than four electrons, the electrons begin to pair up. Any of the following would be an acceptable electron-dot symbol for magnesium, which has two valence electrons:

Possible Electron-Dot Symbols for the Two Valence Electrons in Magnesium

Ṁg·   Ṁg   ·Ṁg   ·Mg·   Mg·   ·Mg

Electron-dot symbols for selected elements are given in Table 3.12.

TABLE 3.12 Electron-Dot Symbols for Representative Elements in Periods 1–4

	Group Number							
	1A (1)	2A (2)	3A (13)	4A (14)	5A (15)	6A (16)	7A (17)	8A (18)
Valence Electron Configuration	ns^1	ns^2	ns^2np^1	ns^2np^2	ns^2np^3	ns^2np^4	ns^2np^5	ns^2np^6
	H·							He:
	Li·	Be·	·Ḃ·	·Ċ·	·N̈·	·Ö:	·F̈:	:N̈e:
	Na·	Mg·	·Äl·	·S̈i·	·P̈·	·S̈:	·C̈l:	:Är:
	K·	Ca·	·Ga·	·Ge·	·Äs·	·S̈e:	·B̈r:	:K̈r:

SAMPLE PROBLEM 3.10

▪ Writing Electron-Dot Symbols

Write the electron-dot symbol for each of the following elements:

a. bromine   **b.** aluminum

SOLUTION

a. Because the group number for bromine is 7A (17), bromine has seven valence electrons.

·B̈r:

b. Aluminum, in Group 3A (13), has three valence electrons.

·Äl·

STUDY CHECK

What is the electron-dot symbol for phosphorus?

Atomic Size

Although there are no fixed boundaries to atoms, scientists have a good idea of the typical volume occupied by the electrons in atoms. The *atomic radius*, which is the distance from the nucleus to the valence (outermost) electrons, determines this volume, or atomic size. Going down a group of representative elements, the outermost electrons occupy higher energy levels, which are farther from the nucleus. Therefore, the atomic radius increases from the top to the bottom of each group. For example, in the alkali metals, Li has a valence electron in the $2s$ sublevel, Na has a valence electron in the $3s$ sublevel, K has a valence electron in the $4s$ sublevel, and Rb has a valence electron in the $5s$ sublevel. (See Figure 3.19.)

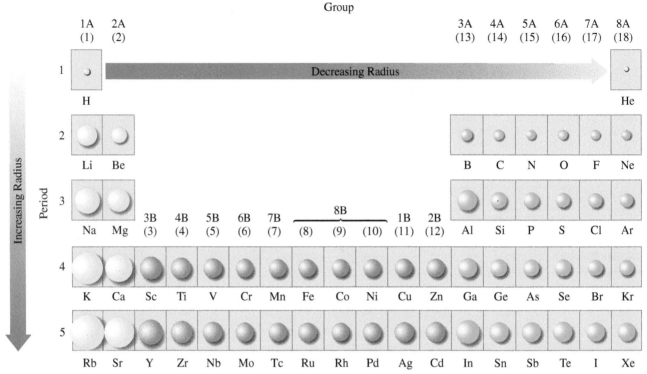

FIGURE 3.19 The atomic radius increases going down a group but decreases going from left to right across a period.
Q Why does the atomic radius increase going down a group?

MC™ TUTORIAL
Ionization Energy

MC™ TUTORIAL
Patterns in the Periodic Table

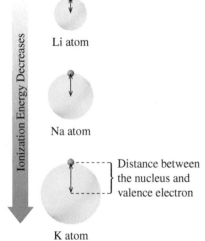

Li atom

Na atom

Distance between the nucleus and valence electron

K atom

Ionization Energy Decreases

The atomic size decreases going across a period. As the positive charge on the nucleus increases, there is an increase in attraction, which pulls all of the electrons closer. Thus, the distance to the outermost electrons decreases, and the atomic size decreases.

Ionization Energy

Electrons are held in atoms by their attraction to the positively charged nucleus. Therefore, energy is required to remove an electron from an atom. The **ionization energy** is the energy needed to remove the least tightly bound electron from an atom in the gaseous (g) state. When an electron is removed from a neutral atom, a particle called a *cation*, with a 1+ charge, is formed.

$$Na(g) + \text{energy (ionization)} \longrightarrow Na^+(g) + e^-$$

The ionization energy decreases going down a group. Less energy is needed to remove an electron because nuclear attraction decreases when electrons are farther from the nucleus. Going across a period from left to right, the ionization energy increases. As the positive charge of the nucleus increases, more energy is needed to remove an electron. (See Figure 3.20.) In Period 1, the valence electrons are close to the nucleus and strongly held. H and He have high ionization energies because a large amount of energy is required to remove an electron. The ionization energy for He is the highest of any element because He has a full, stable, energy level that is disrupted when an electron is removed. The high ionization energies of the noble gases indicate that their electron arrangements are especially stable. The slight decrease in ionization energy for Group 3A (13) occurs because the single p electron is farther from the nucleus and more easily removed than the electrons in the full s sublevel. The next decrease in ionization energy occurs for Group 6A (16) because the removal of a single p electron provides a half-filled, more stable p sublevel. In general, the ionization energy is low for metals and high for nonmetals.

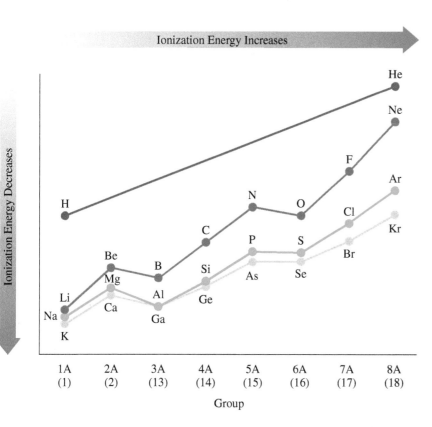

FIGURE 3.20 Ionization energies for the representative elements tend to decrease going down a group and increase going left to right across a period.

Q Why is the ionization energy for Li less than for O?

Atomic Size

a. Match the spheres represented with atoms of Li, Na, K, and Rb.

A.   **B.**   **C.**   **D.**

b. Match the spheres represented with atoms of K, Ge, Ca, and Kr.

A.   **B.**   **C.**   **D.**

ANSWER

a. The element at the top of a group has the smallest atomic radius. Going down the group, the atomic radius increases: Li (with the smallest radius) is C, Na is A, K is D, and Rb (with the largest radius) is B.

b. The element at the beginning of a period has the largest atomic radius. Going across a period, the atomic radius decreases: K (with the largest radius) is B, Ge is A, Ca is C, and Kr (with the smallest radius) is D.

Ionization Energy

Indicate the element in each set that has the higher ionization energy and explain your choice.

a. K or Na   **b.** Mg or Cl   **c.** F, N, or C

SOLUTION

a. Na. In Na, the valence electron is closer to the nucleus.
b. Cl. Attraction for the valence electrons increases across a period, going left to right.
c. F. Because fluorine has more protons than nitrogen or carbon, more energy is needed to remove a valence electron from the fluorine atom.

STUDY CHECK

Arrange Sn, Sr, and I in order of increasing ionization energy.

QUESTIONS AND PROBLEMS

Periodic Trends

3.61 Write the group number using both A and B notation and 1–18 numbering of elements that have the following outer electron configurations:
   a. $2s^2$
   b. $3s^2 3p^3$
   c. $5s^2 4d^{10} 5p^4$

3.62 Write the group number using both A and B notation and 1–18 numbering of elements that have the following outer electron configurations:
   a. $4s^2 4p^5$
   b. $4s^1$
   c. $5s^2 4d^{10} 5p^2$

3.63 Indicate the number of valence (outermost) electrons in each of the following:
   a. aluminum
   b. Group 5A
   c. F, Cl, Br, and I

3.64 Indicate the number of valence (outermost) electrons in each of the following:
   a. Li, Na, K, Rb, and Cs
   b. C, Si, Ge, Sn, and Pb
   c. Group 8A

3.65 Write the group number and electron-dot symbol for each element:
   a. sulfur
   b. nitrogen
   c. calcium
   d. sodium
   e. barium

3.66 Write the group number and electron-dot symbol for each element:
   a. carbon
   b. oxygen
   c. bromine
   d. lithium
   e. chlorine

3.67 Using the symbol M for an atom that is a metal, draw the electron-dot symbol for an atom of a metal in the following groups:
   a. Group 1A (1)
   b. Group 2A (2)

3.68 Using the symbol Nm for an atom that is a nonmetal, draw the electron-dot symbol for an atom of a nonmetal in the following groups:
   a. Group 5A (15)
   b. Group 7A (17)

3.69 Place the elements in each set in order of decreasing atomic radius.
   a. Mg, Al, Si
   b. Cl, Br, I
   c. I, Sb, Sr

3.70 Place the elements in each set in order of decreasing atomic radius.
   a. Cl, S, P
   b. Ge, Si, C
   c. Ba, Ca, Sr

3.71 Select the larger atom in each pair.
   a. Na or Cl
   b. Na or Rb
   c. Na or Mg

3.72 Select the larger atom in each pair.
   a. S or Cl
   b. S or O
   c. S or Se

3.73 Arrange each set of elements in order of increasing ionization energy.
   a. F, Cl, Br
   b. Na, Cl, Al
   c. Cs, Na, K

3.74 Arrange each set of elements in order of increasing ionization energy.
   a. O, N, C
   b. S, P, Cl
   c. As, P, N

3.75 Select the element in each pair with the higher ionization energy.
   a. Br or I
   b. Mg or S
   c. Si or P

3.76 Select the element in each pair with the higher ionization energy.
   a. O or Ne
   b. K or Br
   c. Ca or Ba

CONCEPT MAP

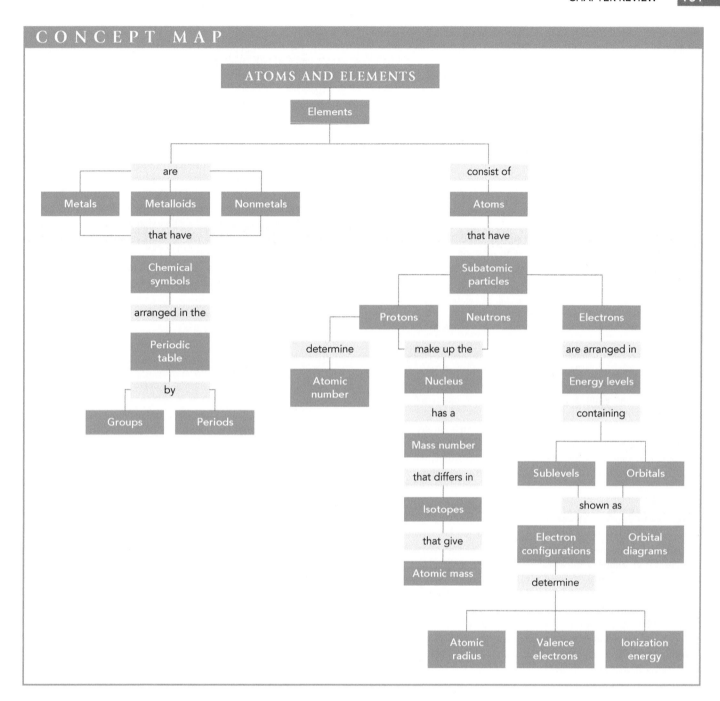

ATOMS AND ELEMENTS

Elements

are

Metals   Metalloids   Nonmetals

that have

Chemical symbols

arranged in the

Periodic table

by

Groups   Periods

consist of

Atoms

that have

Subatomic particles

Protons   Neutrons   Electrons

determine   make up the   are arranged in

Atomic number   Nucleus   Energy levels

has a   containing

Mass number   Sublevels   Orbitals

that differs in   shown as

Isotopes   Electron configurations   Orbital diagrams

that give   determine

Atomic mass   Atomic radius   Valence electrons   Ionization energy

■ CHAPTER REVIEW

3.1 Elements and Symbols
LEARNING GOAL: *Given the name of an element, write its correct symbol; from the symbol, write the correct name.*
Elements are the primary substances of matter. Chemical symbols are one- or two-letter abbreviations of the names of the elements.

3.2 The Periodic Table
LEARNING GOAL: *Use the periodic table to identify the group and period of an element and decide whether it is a metal, nonmetal, or metalloid.*
The periodic table is an arrangement of the elements by increasing atomic number. A vertical column on the periodic table containing elements with similar properties is called a *group*. A horizontal row is

called a *period*. Elements in Group 1A (1) are called the *alkali metals*; Group 2A (2), *alkaline earth metals*; Group 7A (17), the *halogens*; and Group 8A (18), the *noble gases*. On the periodic table, metals are located on the left of the heavy zigzag line, and nonmetals are to the right of the heavy zigzag line. Except for aluminum, elements located on the heavy zigzag line are called *metalloids*.

3.3 The Atom
LEARNING GOAL: *Describe the electrical charge and location in an atom for a proton, a neutron, and an electron.*
An atom is the smallest particle that retains the characteristics of an element. Atoms are composed of three types of subatomic particles. Protons have a positive charge (+), electrons carry a negative charge (−),

and neutrons are electrically neutral. The protons and neutrons are found in the tiny, dense nucleus. Electrons are located outside the nucleus.

3.4 Atomic Number and Mass Number

LEARNING GOAL: *Given the atomic number and the mass number of an atom, state the number of protons, neutrons, and electrons.*

The atomic number gives the number of protons in all the atoms of the same element. In a neutral atom, the number of protons and electrons is equal. The mass number is the total number of protons and neutrons in an atom.

3.5 Isotopes and Atomic Mass

LEARNING GOAL: *Give the number of protons, electrons, and neutrons in the isotopes of an element.*

Atoms that have the same number of protons but different numbers of neutrons are called *isotopes*. The atomic mass of an element is the average mass of all the atoms in a naturally occurring sample of that element.

3.6 Electron Energy Levels

LEARNING GOAL: *Describe the energy levels, sublevels, and orbitals in atoms.*

The atomic spectra of elements are related to the specific energy levels occupied by electrons. When energy is absorbed, an electron moves to a higher energy level; energy is lost when the electron drops to a lower energy level and emits a photon. Each element has it own unique spectrum.

An orbital is a region around the nucleus in which an electron with a specific energy is most likely to be found. Each orbital holds a maximum of two electrons, which must have opposite spins. In each principal energy level (n), electrons occupy orbitals within sublevels.

An s sublevel contains one s orbital, a p sublevel contains three p orbitals, a d sublevel contains five d orbitals, and an f sublevel contains seven f orbitals. Each type of orbital has a unique shape.

3.7 Electron Configurations

LEARNING GOAL: *Use the periodic table to write orbital diagrams and electron configurations.*

Within a sublevel, electrons enter orbitals in the same energy level one at a time until all the orbitals are half-filled. Additional electrons enter with opposite spins until the orbitals in that sublevel are filled with two electrons each. The electrons in an atom can be written in an orbital diagram, which shows the orbitals that are occupied by paired and unpaired electrons. The electron configuration shows the number of electrons in each sublevel. An abbreviated electron configuration places the symbol of a noble gas in brackets to represent the filled sublevels. The periodic table consists of s, p, d, and f sublevel blocks. Beginning with $1s$, an electron configuration is obtained by writing the sublevel blocks in order going across the periodic table until the element is reached.

3.8 Periodic Trends

LEARNING GOAL: *Use the electron configurations of elements to explain periodic trends.*

The properties of elements are related to the valence electrons of the atoms. With only a few minor exceptions, each group of elements has the same arrangement of valence electrons differing only in the energy level. The radius of an atom increases going down a group and decreases going across a period. The energy required to remove a valence electron is the ionization energy, which generally decreases going down a group and generally increases going across a period.

■ KEY TERMS

alkali metal An element in Group 1A (1), except hydrogen, that is a soft, shiny metal with one electron in its outermost energy level.

alkaline earth metal An element in Group 2A (2) that has two electrons in its outermost energy level.

atom The smallest particle of an element that retains the characteristics of the element.

atomic mass The weighted average mass of all the naturally occurring isotopes of an element.

atomic mass unit (amu) A small mass unit used to describe the mass of extremely small particles such as atoms and subatomic particles; 1 amu is equal to one-twelfth the mass of a $^{12}_{6}C$ atom.

atomic number A number that is equal to the number of protons in an atom.

atomic spectrum A series of lines specific for each element produced by photons emitted by electrons dropping to lower energy levels.

atomic symbol An abbreviation used to indicate the mass number and atomic number of an isotope.

chemical symbol An abbreviation that represents the name of an element.

d block The block of ten elements from Groups 3B (3) to 2B (12) in which electrons fill the five d orbitals in d sublevels.

electron A negatively charged subatomic particle having a minute mass that is usually ignored in mass calculations; its symbol is e^-.

electron configuration A list of the number of electrons in each sublevel within an atom, arranged by increasing energy.

electron-dot symbol The representation of an atom that shows valence electrons as dots around the symbol of the element.

f block The block of 14 elements in the rows at the bottom of the periodic table in which electrons fill the seven f orbitals in the $4f$ and $5f$ sublevels.

group A vertical column in the periodic table that contains elements having similar physical and chemical properties.

halogen An element in Group 7A (17)—fluorine, chlorine, bromine, iodine, and astatine—that has seven electrons in its outermost energy level.

ionization energy The energy needed to remove the least tightly bound electron from the outermost energy level of an atom.

isotope An atom that differs only in mass number from another atom of the same element. Isotopes have the same atomic number (number of protons) but different numbers of neutrons.

mass number The total number of neutrons and protons in the nucleus of an atom.

metal An element that is shiny, malleable, ductile, and a good conductor of heat and electricity. The metals are located to the left of the heavy zigzag line on the periodic table.

metalloid Elements with properties of both metals and nonmetals located along the heavy zigzag line on the periodic table.

neutron A neutral subatomic particle having a mass of about 1 amu and found in the nucleus of an atom; its symbol is n or n^0.

noble gas An element in Group 8A (18) of the periodic table, generally unreactive and seldom found in combination with other elements, that has eight electrons (He has two electrons) in its outermost energy level.

nonmetal An element with little or no luster that is a poor conductor of heat and electricity. The nonmetals are located to the right of the heavy zigzag line on the periodic table.

nucleus The compact, extremely dense center of an atom, containing the protons and neutrons of the atom.

orbital The region around the nucleus where electrons of a certain energy are more likely to be found. The *s* orbitals are spherical; the *p* orbitals have two lobes.

orbital diagram A diagram that shows the distribution of electrons in the orbitals of the energy levels.

p block The elements in Groups 3A (13) to 8A (18) in which electrons fill the *p* orbitals in the *p* sublevels.

period A horizontal row of elements in the periodic table.

periodic table An arrangement of elements by increasing atomic number such that elements having similar chemical behavior are grouped in vertical columns.

proton A positively charged subatomic particle having a mass of about 1 amu and found in the nucleus of an atom; its symbol is *p* or p^+.

representative element An element in the first two columns on the left of the periodic table and the last six columns on the right that has a group number of 1A through 8A or 1, 2 and 13 through 18.

s block The elements in Groups 1A (1) and 2A (2) in which electrons fill the *s* orbitals.

subatomic particle A particle within an atom; protons, neutrons, and electrons are subatomic particles.

sublevel A group of orbitals of equal energy within principal energy levels. The number of sublevels in each energy level is the same as the principal quantum number (*n*).

transition element An element in the center of the periodic table that is designated with the letter "B" or the group number of 3 through 12.

valence electrons Electrons in the outermost energy level of an atom.

UNDERSTANDING THE CONCEPTS

3.77 According to Dalton's atomic theory, which of the following are *true*?
 a. Atoms of an element are identical to atoms of other elements.
 b. Every element is made of atoms.
 c. Atoms of two different elements combine to form compounds.
 d. In a chemical reaction, some atoms disappear and new atoms appear.

3.78 Use Rutherford's gold-foil experiment to answer each of the following:
 a. What did Rutherford expect to happen when he aimed particles at the gold foil?
 b. How did the results differ from what he expected?
 c. How did he use the results to propose a model of the atom?

3.79 Match the following with the descriptions below:
 (1) protons   (2) neutrons   (3) electrons
 a. atomic mass   **b.** atomic number
 c. positive charge   **d.** negative charge
 e. mass number – atomic number

3.80 Match the following with the descriptions below:
 (1) protons   (2) neutrons   (3) electrons
 a. mass number   **b.** surround the nucleus
 c. nucleus   **d.** charge of 0
 e. equal to number of electrons

3.81 Consider the following atoms in which X represents the chemical symbol of the element:

$$^{16}_{8}X \quad ^{16}_{9}X \quad ^{18}_{10}X \quad ^{17}_{8}X \quad ^{18}_{8}X$$

 a. What atoms have the same number of protons?
 b. Which atoms are isotopes? Of what element?
 c. Which atoms have the same mass number?
 d. What atoms have the same number of neutrons?

3.82 For each of the following, write the symbol and name for X and the number of protons and neutrons. Which are isotopes of each other?
 a. $^{37}_{17}X$ **b.** $^{56}_{26}X$ **c.** $^{116}_{50}X$ **d.** $^{124}_{50}X$ **e.** $^{116}_{48}X$

ADDITIONAL QUESTIONS AND PROBLEMS

For instructor-assigned homework, go to www.masteringchemistry.com.

3.83 Give the symbol and name of the element found in the following group and period on the periodic table:
 a. Group 2A, Period 3   **b.** Group 7A, Period 4
 c. Group 13, Period 3   **d.** Group 16, Period 2

3.84 The following trace elements have been found to be crucial to the functions of the body. Indicate each as a metal or nonmetal.
 a. zinc   **b.** cobalt
 c. manganese   **d.** iodine
 e. copper   **f.** selenium

3.85 Indicate if each of the following statements is *true* or *false*:
 a. The proton is a negatively charged particle.
 b. The neutron is 2000 times as heavy as a proton.
 c. The atomic mass unit is based on a carbon atom with 6 protons and 6 neutrons.

 d. The nucleus is the largest part of the atom.
 e. The electrons are located outside the nucleus.

3.86 Indicate if each of the following statements is *true* or *false*:
 a. The neutron is electrically neutral.
 b. The masses of the protons and neutrons account for most of the mass of an atom.
 c. The charge of an electron is equal, but opposite, to the charge of a neutron.
 d. The proton and the electron have about the same mass.
 e. The mass number is the number of protons.

3.87 For the following atoms, determine the number of protons, neutrons, and electrons:
 a. $^{27}_{13}Al$ **b.** $^{52}_{24}Cr$ **c.** $^{34}_{16}S$ **d.** $^{56}_{26}Fe$ **e.** $^{136}_{54}Xe$

3.88 For the following atoms, give the number of protons, neutrons, and electrons:
 a. $^{22}_{10}Ne$ **b.** $^{127}_{53}I$ **c.** $^{75}_{35}Br$ **d.** $^{133}_{55}Cs$ **e.** $^{195}_{78}Pt$

3.89 Complete the following table:

Name	Nuclear Symbol	Number of Protons	Number of Neutrons	Number of Electrons
	$^{34}_{16}S$			
		30	40	
Magnesium			14	
	$^{220}_{86}Rn$			

3.90 Complete the following table:

Name	Nuclear Symbol	Number of Protons	Number of Neutrons	Number of Electrons
Potassium			22	
	$^{51}_{23}V$			
		48	64	
Barium			82	

3.91 a. What electron sublevel starts to fill after completion of the 3s sublevel?
  b. What electron sublevel starts to fill after completion of the 4p sublevel?
  c. What electron sublevel starts to fill after completion of the 3d sublevel?
  d. What electron sublevel starts to fill after completion of the 3p sublevel?

3.92 a. What electron sublevel starts to fill after completion of the 5s sublevel?
  b. What electron sublevel starts to fill after completion of the 4d sublevel?
  c. What electron sublevel starts to fill after completion of the 4f sublevel?
  d. What electron sublevel starts to fill after completion of the 5p sublevel?

3.93 a. How many 3d electrons are in Fe?
  b. How many 5p electrons are in Ba?

  c. How many 4d electrons are in I?
  d. How many 6s electrons are in Ba?

3.94 a. How many 3d electrons are in Zn?
  b. How many 4p electrons are in Br?
  c. How many 6p electrons are in Bi?
  d. How many 5s electrons are in Cd?

3.95 What do the elements Ca, Sr, and Ba have in common in terms of their electron configuration? Where are they located in the periodic table?

3.96 What do the elements O, S, and Se have in common in terms of their electron configuration? Where are they located in the periodic table?

3.97 Name the element that corresponds to each of the following:
  a. $1s^2 2s^2 2p^6 3s^2 3p^3$
  b. alkali metal with the smallest atomic radius
  c. $[Kr]5s^2 4d^{10}$
  d. Group 5A element with highest ionization energy
  e. Period 3 element with largest atomic radius

3.98 Name the element that corresponds to each of the following:
  a. $1s^2 2s^2 2p^6 3s^2 3p^6 4s^1 3d^5$
  b. $[Xe]6s^2 4f^{14} 5d^{10} 6p^5$
  c. halogen with the highest ionization energy
  d. Group 6A element with the smallest ionization energy
  e. Period 4 element with smallest atomic radius

3.99 Why is the ionization energy of Ca higher than K but lower than Mg?

3.100 Why is the ionization energy of Cl lower than F but higher than S?

3.101 Of the elements Na, P, Cl, and F, which
  a. is a metal?
  b. has the largest atomic radius?
  c. has the highest ionization energy?
  d. loses an electron most easily?
  e. is found in Group 7A, Period 3?

3.102 Of the elements K, Ca, Br, Kr, which
  a. is a noble gas?
  b. has the smallest atomic radius?
  c. has the lowest ionization energy?
  d. requires the most energy to remove an electron?
  e. is found in Group 2A, Period 4?

CHALLENGE QUESTIONS

3.103 Of the elements K, Mg, Si, S, Cl, and Ar, which
  a. is a metal?
  b. is a metalloid?
  c. is an alkali metal?
  d. has the smallest atomic size?
  e. has an electron arrangement $1s^2 2s^2 2p^6 3s^2 3p^4$?

3.104 Of the elements K, Mg, Si, S, Cl, and Ar, which
  a. has the largest atomic size?
  b. is a halogen?
  c. has an electron arrangement $1s^2 2s^2 2p^6 3s^2 3p^2$?
  d. has the lowest ionization energy?
  e. is in Group 6A (16)?
  f. has the highest ionization energy?

3.105 The most abundant isotope of iron is Fe-56.
  a. How many protons, neutrons, and electrons are in this isotope?
  b. What is the symbol of another isotope of iron with 25 neutrons?
  c. What is the symbol of a different atom with the same mass number and 27 neutrons?

3.106 Give the symbol of the element that has the
  a. smallest atomic radius in Group 6A.
  b. smallest atomic radius in Period 3.
  c. highest ionization energy in Group 15.
  d. lowest ionization energy in Period 3.

3.107 If the diameter of a sodium atom is 3.14×10^{-8} cm, how many sodium atoms would fit along a line exactly 1 inch long?

3.108 A lead atom has a mass of 3.4×10^{-22} g. How many lead atoms are in a cube of lead that has a volume of 2.00 cm^3 if the density of lead is 11.3 g/cm^3?

3.109 Lead consists of four naturally occurring isotopes. Calculate the atomic mass of lead.

Isotope	Mass	Abundance (%)
$^{204}_{82}$Pb	203.97	1.40
$^{206}_{82}$Pb	205.97	24.10
$^{207}_{82}$Pb	206.98	22.10
$^{208}_{82}$Pb	207.98	52.40

3.110 Indium (In) with an atomic mass of 114.8 consists of two naturally occurring isotopes: $^{113}_{49}$In and $^{115}_{49}$In. If 4.30% of a sample of indium is $^{113}_{49}$In, which has a mass of 112.90, what is the mass of the $^{115}_{49}$In?

3.111 Consider three elements with the following abbreviated gas notations:

$X = [Ar]4s^2$ $Y = [Ne]3s^23p^4$

$Z = [Ar]4s^23d^{10}4p^4$

a. Identify each element as a metal, metalloid, or nonmetal.
b. Which element has the largest atomic radius?

c. Which elements have similar properties?
d. Which element has the highest ionization energy?
e. Which element has the smallest atomic radius?

3.112 Indicate if the following sections of orbital diagrams are or are not possible and explain your reason:

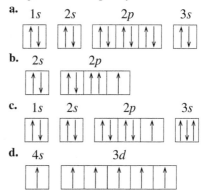

3.113 Consider three elements with the following abbreviated electron configurations:

$X = [Ar]4s^23d^5$ $Y = [Ar]4s^23d^{10}4p^1$

$Z = [Ar]4s^23d^{10}4p^6$

a. Identify each element as a metal, metalloid, or nonmetal.
b. Which element has the smallest atomic radius?
c. Which elements have similar properties?
d. Which element has the highest ionization energy?
e. Which element has a half-filled sublevel?

ANSWERS

ANSWERS TO STUDY CHECKS

3.1 Si, Sr, Ag

3.2 a. As   **b.** Rn   **c.** B

3.3 False; most of the volume in an atom is outside the nucleus.

3.4 45 neutrons

3.5 a. $^{15}_7$N   **b.** $^{42}_{20}$Ca   **c.** $^{27}_{13}$Al

3.6 10.81 amu

3.7 The $1s$, $2s$, and $3s$ orbitals are all spherical, but they increase in volume because the electron is most likely to be found farther from the nucleus for higher energy levels.

3.8 $1s^22s^22p^63s^23p^4$ Complete electron configuration for sulfur (S)
$[Ne]3s^23p^4$ Abbreviated electron configuration for sulfur (S)

3.9 Tin has the electron configuration:
$1s^22s^22p^63s^23p^64s^23d^{10}4p^65s^24d^{10}5p^2$

3.10 $\cdot \ddot{P} \cdot$

3.11 Ionization energy increases going across a period: Sr is lowest, Sn is higher, and I is the highest of this set.

ANSWERS TO SELECTED QUESTIONS AND PROBLEMS

3.1 a. Cu   **b.** Si   **c.** K   **d.** N
e. Fe   **f.** Ba   **g.** Pb   **h.** Sr

3.3 a. carbon   **b.** chlorine   **c.** iodine   **d.** mercury
e. fluorine   **f.** argon   **g.** zinc   **h.** nickel

3.5 a. sodium, chlorine
b. calcium, sulfur, oxygen

c. carbon, hydrogen, chlorine, nitrogen, oxygen
d. calcium, carbon, oxygen

3.7 a. Period 2   **b.** Group 8A (18)
c. Group 1A (1)   **d.** Period 2

3.9 a. alkaline earth metal
b. transition element
c. noble gas
d. alkali metal
e. halogen

3.11 a. C   **b.** He   **c.** Na   **d.** Ca   **e.** Al

3.13 a. metal   **b.** nonmetal   **c.** metal   **d.** nonmetal
e. nonmetal   **f.** nonmetal   **g.** metalloid   **h.** metal

3.15 a. electron   **b.** proton   **c.** electron   **d.** neutron

3.17 Rutherford determined that an atom contains a small, compact nucleus that is positively charged.

3.19 a. b. and **c.** are *true*, but **d.** is *false*. A proton is attracted to an electron, not a neutron.

3.21 In the process of brushing hair, strands of hair become charged with like charges that repel each other.

3.23 a. atomic number   **b.** both
c. mass number   **d.** atomic number

3.25 a. lithium, Li   **b.** fluorine, F
c. calcium, Ca   **d.** zinc, Zn
e. neon, Ne   **f.** silicon, Si
g. iodine, I   **h.** oxygen, O

3.27 a. 12   **b.** 30   **c.** 53   **d.** 19

3.29

Name of Element	Symbol	Atomic Number	Mass Number	Number of Protons	Number of Neutrons	Number of Electrons
Aluminum	Al	13	27	13	14	13
Magnesium	Mg	12	24	12	12	12
Potassium	K	19	39	19	20	19
Sulfur	S	16	31	16	15	16
Iron	Fe	26	56	26	30	26

3.31 a. 14 protons, 16 neutrons, 14 electrons
   b. 27 protons, 33 neutrons, 27 electrons
   c. 34 protons, 46 neutrons, 34 electrons
   d. 9 protons, 10 neutrons, 9 electrons

3.33 a. $^{31}_{15}P$ **b.** $^{80}_{35}Br$ **c.** $^{27}_{13}Al$ **d.** $^{35}_{17}Cl$ **e.** $^{202}_{80}Hg$

3.35 a. $^{32}_{16}S$ $^{33}_{16}S$ $^{34}_{16}S$ $^{36}_{16}S$
   b. They all have the same number of protons and electrons.
   c. They have different numbers of neutrons, which gives them different mass numbers.
   d. The atomic mass of S listed on the periodic table is the weighted average atomic mass of all the naturally occuring isotopes.
   e. The isotope S-32 is most abundant because its atomic mass is closest to the weighted average atomic mass.

3.37 Because the atomic mass of copper is closer to 63 amu, there are more atoms of $^{63}_{29}Cu$.

3.39 69.72 amu

3.41 a. spherical   **b.** two lobes   **c.** spherical

3.43 a. Both are spherical.
   b. Both are part of the third energy level.
   c. Both contain three *p* orbitals.
   d. All have two lobes and belong in the third energy level.

3.45 a. There are five orbitals in the 3*d* sublevel.
   b. There is one sublevel in the $n = 1$ energy level.
   c. There is one orbital in the 6*s* sublevel.
   d. There are nine orbitals in the $n = 3$ energy level.

3.47 a. There is a maximum of 2 electrons in a 2*p* orbital.
   b. There is a maximum of six electrons in the 3*p* sublevel.
   c. There is a maximum of 32 electrons in the $n = 4$ energy level.
   d. There is a maximum of 10 electrons in the 5*d* sublevel.

3.49 a.

1*s*	2*s*	2*p*

b.

1*s*	2*s*	2*p*	3*s*	3*p*

c.

1*s*	2*s*	2*p*	3*s*	3*p*

d.

1*s*	2*s*	2*p*	3*s*	3*p*

3.51 a. N $1s^2 2s^2 2p^3$
   b. Na $1s^2 2s^2 2p^6 3s^1$
   c. S $1s^2 2s^2 2p^6 3s^2 3p^4$
   d. As $1s^2 2s^2 2p^6 3s^2 3p^6 4s^2 3d^{10} 4p^3$
   e. Fe $1s^2 2s^2 2p^6 3s^2 3p^6 4s^2 3d^6$

3.53 a. Mg [Ne]$3s^2$
   b. S [Ne]$3s^2 3p^4$
   c. Al [Ne]$3s^2 3p^1$
   d. Ti [Ar]$4s^2 3d^2$
   e. Ba [Xe]$6s^2$

3.55 a. S   **b.** Co   **c.** Si   **d.** Br

3.57 a. Al   **b.** C   **c.** Ar   **d.** Zr

3.59 a. 10   **b.** 6   **c.** 3   **d.** 1

3.61 a. 2A (2)   **b.** 5A (15)   **c.** 6A (16)

3.63 a. 3   **b.** 5   **c.** 7

3.65 a. Group 6A (16) $\cdot \ddot{S} \colon$ **b.** Group 5A (15) $\cdot \ddot{N} \cdot$
   c. Group 2A (2) $Ca \cdot$ **d.** Group 1A (1) $Na \cdot$
   e. Group 2A (2) $\dot{Ba} \cdot$

3.67 a. $M \cdot$ **b.** $\dot{M} \cdot$

3.69 a. Mg, Al, Si   **b.** I, Br, Cl   **c.** Sr, Sb, I

3.71 a. Na   **b.** Rb   **c.** Na

3.73 a. Br, Cl, F   **b.** Na, Al, Cl   **c.** Cs, K, Na

3.75 a. Br   **b.** S   **c.** P

3.77 a. false   **b.** true   **c.** true   **d.** false

3.79 a. 1 and 2   **b.** 1   **c.** 1   **d.** 3   **e.** 2

3.81 a. $^{16}_8X$, $^{17}_8X$, and $^{18}_8X$ All have eight protons.
   b. $^{16}_8X$, $^{17}_8X$, and $^{18}_8X$ All are isotopes of oxygen.
   c. $^{16}_8X$ and $^{16}_9X$ have mass number 16, whereas $^{18}_8X$ and $^{18}_{10}X$ have mass number 18.
   d. $^{16}_8X$ and $^{18}_{10}X$ both have eight neutrons.

3.83 a. Mg, magnesium   **b.** Br, bromine
   c. Al, aluminum   **d.** O, oxygen

3.85 a. false   **b.** false   **c.** true   **d.** false   **e.** true

3.87 a. 13 protons, 14 neutrons, 13 electrons
   b. 24 protons, 28 neutrons, 24 electrons
   c. 16 protons, 18 neutrons, 16 electrons
   d. 26 protons, 30 neutrons, 26 electrons
   e. 54 protons, 82 neutrons, 54 electrons

3.89

Name	Nuclear Symbol	Number of Protons	Number of Neutrons	Number of Electrons
Sulfur	$^{34}_{16}S$	16	18	16
Zinc	$^{70}_{30}Zn$	30	40	30
Magnesium	$^{26}_{12}Mg$	12	14	12
Radon	$^{220}_{86}Rn$	86	134	86

3.91 a. 3p **b.** 5s **c.** 4p **d.** 4s

3.93 a. 6 **b.** 6 **c.** 10 **d.** 2

3.95 Ca, Sr, and Ba all have two valence electrons ns^2, which places them in Group 2A (2).

3.97 a. phosphorus **b.** lithium (H is a nonmetal)
c. cadmium **d.** nitrogen
e. sodium

3.99 Calcium has a greater number of protons than K. The least tightly bound electron in Ca is farther from the nucleus than in Mg and requires less energy to remove it.

3.101 a. Na **b.** Na **c.** F **d.** Na **e.** Cl

3.103 a. K, Mg **b.** Si **c.** K **d.** Ar **e.** S

3.105 a. 26 protons, 30 neutrons, 26 electrons

b. $^{51}_{26}Fe$ **c.** $^{51}_{24}Cr$

3.107 8.09×10^7 sodium atoms

3.109 207.2 amu

3.111 a. X is a metal; Y and Z are nonmetals.
b. X has the largest atomic radius.
c. Y and Z have six valence electrons and are in Group 6A (16).
d. Y has the highest ionization energy.
e. Y has the smallest atomic radius.

3.113 a. X and Y are metals and Z is a nonmetal.
b. Z
c. X and Y are both metals.
d. Z
e. X

4 Nuclear Chemistry

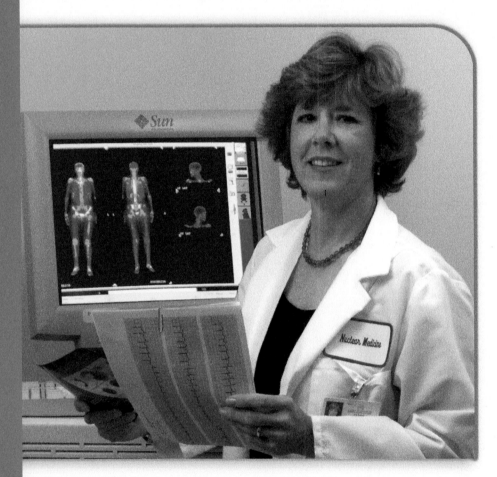

"Everything we do in this department involves radioactive materials," says Julie Goudak, nuclear medicine technologist at Kaiser Hospital. "The radioisotopes are given in several ways. The patient may ingest an isotope, breathe it in, or receive it by an IV injection. We do many diagnostic tests, particularly of the heart function, to determine if a patient needs a cardiac CT scan."

A nuclear medicine technologist administers isotopes that emit radiation to determine the level of function of an organ such as the thyroid or heart, to detect the presence and size of a tumor, or to treat disease. A radioisotope locates in a specific organ, and its radiation is used by a computer to create an image of that organ. From this data, a physician can make a diagnosis and design a treatment program.

Mastering**CHEMISTRY**™

Visit **www.masteringchemistry.com**
for self-study materials and instructor-assigned homework.

A female patient, age 50, complains of nervousness, irritability, increased perspiration, brittle hair, and muscle weakness. Her hands are shaky at times, and her heart often beats rapidly. She has been experiencing weight loss. The doctor decides to test for proper thyroid activity. To get a detailed look at the thyroid, a thyroid scan is ordered. The patient is given a small amount of an iodine radioisotope, which will be taken up by the thyroid. The scan shows a higher than normal rate of uptake of the radioactive iodine, which indicates an overactive thyroid gland, a condition called *hyperthyroidism*. Treatment for hyperthyroidism includes the use of drugs to lower the level of thyroid hormone, the use of radioactive iodine to destroy thyroid cells, or surgical removal of part or the entire thyroid. In our case, the nuclear physician decides to use radioactive iodine. To begin treatment, the patient drinks a solution containing radioactive iodine. In the following few weeks, the cells that take up the radioactive iodine are destroyed by the radiation. Follow-up tests not only show that the patient's thyroid is smaller, but also that the blood level of thyroid hormone is normal once again.

The field of nuclear medicine was established in 1934 with the production of artificial radioactive substances. In 1937, the first radioactive isotope was used to treat a patient with leukemia at the University of California at Berkeley. Major strides in the use of radioactivity in medicine occurred in 1946, when a radioactive iodine isotope was successfully used to diagnose thyroid function and to treat hyperthyroidism and thyroid cancer. During the 1970s and 1980s, a variety of radioactive substances were used to produce images of organs such as the liver, spleen, thyroid gland, kidney, and brain, and to detect heart disease. Today, procedures in nuclear medicine provide information about the function and structure of every organ in the body, which allows the nuclear physician to diagnose and treat diseases early.

4.1 Natural Radioactivity

Most naturally occurring isotopes of elements up to atomic number 19 have stable nuclei. In a stable nucleus, the repulsions between the positively charged protons are balanced by other nuclear forces. Elements with atomic numbers 20 and higher usually have one or more isotopes that have unstable nuclei in which the nuclear forces cannot offset the repulsions between the protons. An unstable nucleus is radioactive, which means that it spontaneously emits small particles of energy called **radiation** to become more stable. Radiation may take the form of alpha (α) and beta (β) particles, positrons (β^+), or pure energy such as gamma (γ) rays. An isotope that emits radiation is called a *radioisotope*. For most types of radiation, there is a change in the number of protons in the nucleus. This change means that an atom of one element is converted into an atom of a different element. This kind of nuclear change was not evident to Dalton when he made his predictions about atoms. Elements with atomic numbers of 93 and higher are produced artificially in nuclear laboratories and consist only of radioactive isotopes.

In Chapter 3, we wrote symbols for the different isotopes of an element. These symbols had the mass number written in the upper left corner and the atomic number in the lower left corner. Recall that the mass number is equal to the number of protons and neutrons in the nucleus and that atomic number is equal to the number of protons. For example, a radioactive isotope of iodine used in the diagnosis and treatment of thyroid conditions has a symbol with a mass number of 131 and an atomic number of 53:

Mass number (protons and neutrons)
Element symbol
Atomic number (protons)

$$^{131}_{53}\text{I}$$

Radioactive isotopes are named specifically by writing the mass number after the element's name or symbol. This isotope is named iodine-131 or I-131. Table 4.1 compares some stable, nonradioactive isotopes with some radioactive isotopes.

LEARNING GOAL

Describe alpha, beta, positron, and gamma radiation.

TABLE 4.1 Stable and Radioactive Isotopes of Some Elements

Magnesium	Iodine	Uranium
Stable Isotopes		
$^{24}_{12}Mg$	$^{127}_{53}I$	None
Magnesium-24	Iodine-127	
Radioactive Isotopes		
$^{23}_{12}Mg$	$^{125}_{53}I$	$^{235}_{92}U$
Magnesium-23	Iodine-125	Uranium-235
$^{27}_{12}Mg$	$^{131}_{53}I$	$^{238}_{92}U$
Magnesium-27	Iodine-131	Uranium-238

TUTORIAL
Types of Radiation

$^{4}_{2}He$

Alpha (α) particle

$^{0}_{-1}e$

Beta (β) particle

Types of Radiation

Different types of radiation are emitted from unstable nuclei to form more stable, lower-energy nuclei. One type of radiation consists of alpha particles. An **alpha particle** is identical to a helium (He) nucleus, which has two protons and two neutrons. An alpha particle has a mass number of 4, an atomic number of 2, and a charge of 2+. The symbol for an alpha particle is the Greek letter alpha (α) or the symbol of a helium nucleus but with the 2+ charge omitted.

A **beta particle** is a high-energy electron that is emitted when a neutron in an unstable nucleus changes into a proton. A beta particle has a charge of 1− and a mass number of 0. It is represented by the Greek letter beta (β) or by the symbol for the electron (e) including the mass number and the charge:

$$^{1}_{0}n \longrightarrow ^{1}_{1}H + ^{0}_{-1}e \ (\text{or } \beta)$$

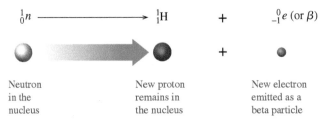

Neutron in the nucleus	New proton remains in the nucleus	New electron emitted as a beta particle

A **positron**, represented as β^{+}, has a positive (1+) charge with a mass number of 0, which makes it similar to a beta (β) particle, but with the opposite charge. We write the symbols of a beta particle and a positron as follows:

	Electron	**Positron**
Mass number		
Charge	$^{0}_{-1}e$	$^{0}_{+1}e$

A positron is produced by an unstable nucleus when a proton is transformed into a neutron and a positron.

$$^{1}_{1}H \longrightarrow ^{1}_{0}n + ^{0}_{+1}e \ (\text{or } \beta^{+})$$

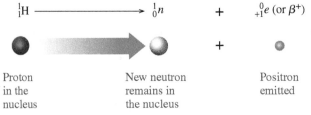

Proton in the nucleus	New neutron remains in the nucleus	Positron emitted

A positron is an example of *antimatter*, a term physicists use to describe a particle that is the exact opposite of another particle, in this case, an electron. When an electron and a positron collide, their minute masses are completely converted to energy in the form of gamma rays.

$$^{0}_{-1}e \ + \ ^{0}_{+1}e \longrightarrow 2\,^{0}_{0}\gamma$$

When the symbol β is used with no charge, it is a beta particle rather than a positron.

Gamma rays are high-energy radiation, released when an unstable nucleus undergoes a rearrangement of its particles to give a more stable, lower-energy nucleus. Gamma rays are often emitted along with other types of radiation. A gamma ray is written as the Greek letter gamma (γ). Because gamma rays are energy only, zeros are used to show that a gamma ray has no mass or charge.

$^{0}_{0}\gamma$

Gamma (γ) ray

Table 4.2 summarizes the types of radiation we will use in nuclear equations.

TABLE 4.2 Some Common Forms of Radiation

Type of Radiation	Symbol		Mass Number	Charge
Alpha particle	α	$^{4}_{2}He$	4	2+
Beta particle	β	$^{0}_{-1}e$	0	1−
Positron	β^{+}	$^{0}_{+1}e$	0	1+
Gamma ray	γ	$^{0}_{0}\gamma$	0	0
Proton	p	$^{1}_{1}H$	1	1+
Neutron	n	$^{1}_{0}n$	1	0

CONCEPT CHECK 4.1

■ Radiation Particles

Identify and write the symbol for each of the following types of radiation:

a. contains two protons and two neutrons
b. has a mass number of 0 and a 1− charge

ANSWER

a. An alpha (α) particle, $^{4}_{2}He$, has two protons and two neutrons.
b. A beta (β) particle, $^{0}_{-1}e$, is like an electron with a mass number of 0 and a 1− charge.

Biological Effects of Radiation

When radiation strikes molecules in its path, electrons may be knocked away, forming unstable ions. For example, when radiation passes through the human body, it may interact with water molecules, removing electrons, and producing H_2O^{+}, which can cause undesirable chemical reactions.

The cells most sensitive to radiation are the ones undergoing rapid division—those of the bone marrow, skin, reproductive organs, and intestinal lining, as well as all cells of growing children. Damaged cells may lose their ability to produce necessary materials. For example, if radiation damages cells of the bone marrow, red blood cells may no longer be produced. If sperm cells, ova, or the cells of a fetus are damaged, birth defects may result. In contrast, cells of the nerves, muscles, liver, and adult bones are much less sensitive to radiation because they undergo little or no cellular division.

Cancer cells are another example of rapidly dividing cells. Because cancer cells are highly sensitive to radiation, large doses of radiation are used to destroy them. The normal tissue that surrounds cancer cells divides at a slower rate and suffers less damage from radiation. However, radiation itself may cause malignant tumors, leukemia, anemia, and genetic mutations.

SELF STUDY ACTIVITY
MC Radiation and Its Biological Effects

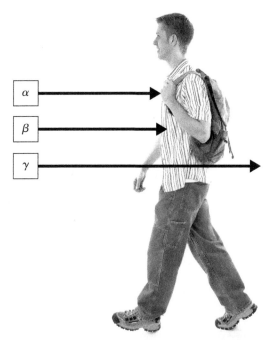

Radiation Protection

Radiologists, doctors, and nurses who work with radioactive isotopes must use proper radiation protection. Proper **shielding** is necessary to prevent exposure. Alpha particles, the heaviest of the radiation particles, travel only a few centimeters in the air before they collide with air molecules, acquire electrons, and become helium atoms. A piece of paper,

TABLE 4.3 Properties of Radiation and Shielding Required

Property	Alpha (α) particle	Beta (β) particle	Gamma (γ) ray
Travel distance in air	2–4 cm	200–300 cm	500 m
Tissue depth	0.05 mm	4–5 mm	50 cm or more
Shielding	Paper, clothing	Heavy clothing, lab coats, gloves	Lead, thick concrete
Typical source	Radium-226	Carbon-14	Technetium-99m

FIGURE 4.1 A person working with radioisotopes wears protective clothing and gloves and stands behind a lead shield.

Q What types of radiation does the lead shield block?

clothing, and our skin are protection against alpha particles. Lab coats and gloves will also provide sufficient shielding. However, if ingested or inhaled, alpha emitters can bring about serious internal damage because of their large mass and high charge.

Beta particles move much faster and farther than alpha particles, traveling as far as several meters through air. They can pass through paper and penetrate as far as 4–5 mm into body tissue. External exposure to beta particles can burn the surface of the skin, but they are stopped before they reach the internal organs. Heavy clothing such as lab coats and gloves are needed to protect the skin from beta particles.

Gamma rays travel great distances through the air and pass through many materials, including body tissues. Only the densest shielding from substances such as lead and concrete will stop them. Because gamma rays penetrate so deeply, exposure to these rays can be extremely hazardous. When preparing radioactive materials, the radiologist wears special gloves and works behind lead-glass windows. Long tongs are used within the work area to pick up vials of radioactive material, keeping them away from the hands and body. Even the syringe used to give an injection of a gamma-emitting radioactive isotope is placed inside a special lead-glass cover. (See Figure 4.1.) Table 4.3 summarizes the shielding materials required for the various types of radiation.

If you work in an environment such as a nuclear medicine facility, try to keep the time you must spend in a radioactive area to a minimum. A certain amount of radiation is emitted every minute. Remaining in a radioactive area twice as long exposes you to twice as much radiation.

Keep your distance! The greater your distance from the radioactive source, the lower the intensity of radiation you will receive. Just by doubling your distance from the radiation source, the intensity of the radiation drops to $\left(\frac{1}{2}\right)^2$ or one-fourth of its previous value.

SAMPLE PROBLEM   4.1

■ **Radiation Protection**

How does the type of shielding for alpha radiation differ from that used for gamma radiation?

SOLUTION

Alpha radiation is stopped by paper and clothing. However, lead or concrete is needed for protection from gamma radiation.

STUDY CHECK

Besides shielding, what other methods help reduce exposure to radiation?

QUESTIONS AND PROBLEMS

Natural Radioactivity

4.1 **a.** How are an alpha particle and a helium nucleus similar?
   b. What symbols are used for alpha particles?
   c. What is the source of an alpha particle?

4.2 **a.** How are a beta particle and an electron similar?
   b. What symbols are used for beta particles?
   c. What is the source of a beta particle?

4.3 Naturally occurring potassium consists of three isotopes: potassium-39, potassium-40, and radioactive potassium-41.
    a. Write the atomic symbol for each isotope.
    b. In what ways are the isotopes similar, and in what ways do they differ?

4.4 Naturally occurring iodine is iodine-127. Medically, radioactive isotopes of iodine-125 and iodine-130 are used.
    a. Write the atomic symbol for each isotope.
    b. In what ways are the isotopes similar, and in what ways do they differ?

4.5 Supply the missing information in the following table:

Medical Use	Atomic Symbol	Mass Number	Number of Protons	Number of Neutrons
Heart imaging	$^{201}_{81}\text{Tl}$			
Radiation therapy		60	27	
Abdominal scan			31	36
Hyperthyroidism	$^{131}_{53}\text{I}$			
Leukemia treatment		32		17

4.6 Supply the missing information in the following table:

Medical Use	Atomic Symbol	Mass Number	Number of Protons	Number of Neutrons
Cancer treatment	$^{60}_{27}\text{Co}$			
Brain scan		99	43	
Blood flow		141	58	
Bone scan		85		47
Lung function	$^{133}_{54}\text{Xe}$			

4.7 Write a symbol for each of the following:
    a. alpha particle   **b.** neutron

c. beta particle   **d.** nitrogen-15
e. iodine-125

4.8 Write a symbol for each of the following:
    a. proton   **b.** gamma ray
    c. electron   **d.** positron
    e. cobalt-60

4.9 Identify each of the following:
    a. $^{0}_{-1}\text{X}$ **b.** $^{4}_{2}\text{X}$
    c. $^{1}_{0}\text{X}$ **d.** $^{24}_{11}\text{X}$
    e. $^{14}_{6}\text{X}$

4.10 Identify each of the following:
    a. $^{1}_{1}\text{X}$ **b.** $^{32}_{15}\text{X}$
    c. $^{0}_{0}\text{X}$ **d.** $^{59}_{26}\text{X}$
    e. $^{0}_{+1}\text{X}$

4.11 a. Why does beta radiation penetrate farther into solid material than alpha radiation?
    b. How does radiation cause damage to cells of the body?
    c. Why does the radiation technician leave the room when taking your X-ray?
    d. What is the purpose of wearing gloves when handling radioactive isotopes?

4.12 a. As a nurse in an oncology unit, you may give an injection of a radioactive isotope. What are three ways you can minimize your exposure to radiation?
    b. Why are cancer cells more sensitive to radiation than nerve cells?
    c. What is the purpose of placing a lead apron on a patient who is receiving routine dental X-rays?
    d. Why are the walls in a radiology office built of lead or thick concrete blocks?

4.2 Nuclear Reactions

When a nucleus spontaneously breaks down by emitting radiation, the process is called **radioactive decay**. The process can be written using the atomic symbols of the original radioactive nucleus, the new nucleus, and the type of radiation emitted. An arrow between the atomic symbols indicates that this is a nuclear equation.

Radioactive nucleus $\longrightarrow$ new nucleus + radiation (α, β, γ, β^{+})

In a nuclear equation, the mass numbers and the atomic numbers must be equal on both sides. In most nuclear equations, there is a change in the number of protons, which gives a different element.

The changes in mass number and atomic number of an unstable nucleus that undergoes radioactive decay are shown in Table 4.4.

LEARNING GOAL

Write an equation showing mass numbers and atomic numbers for radioactive decay.

TABLE 4.4 Mass Number and Atomic Number Changes due to Radiation

Decay Process	Radiation Symbol	Change in Mass Number	Change in Atomic Number	Change in Neutron Number
Alpha emission	$^{4}_{2}\text{He}$	−4	−2	−2
Beta emission	$^{0}_{-1}e$	0	+1	−1
Positron emission	$^{0}_{+1}e$	0	−1	+1
Gamma emission	$^{0}_{0}\gamma$	0	0	0

We will now see how this works in the following examples and sample problems.

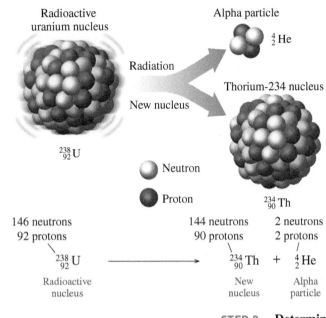

Radioactive uranium nucleus

Alpha particle

$^{4}_{2}$He

Radiation

New nucleus

Thorium-234 nucleus

$^{238}_{92}$U

○ Neutron

● Proton

$^{234}_{90}$Th

146 neutrons
92 protons

$^{238}_{92}$U

Radioactive
nucleus

144 neutrons
90 protons

$^{234}_{90}$Th

New
nucleus

2 neutrons
2 protons

$+ \ ^{4}_{2}$He

Alpha
particle

Alpha Decay

An unstable nucleus undergoes alpha decay by emitting an alpha particle. Because an alpha particle consists of 2 protons and 2 neutrons, the mass number decreases by 4, and the atomic number decreases by 2. For example, uranium-238 emits an alpha particle to form a different nucleus with a mass number of 234. Compared to uranium with 92 protons, the new nucleus has 90 protons, which makes it thorium.

Guide to Completing a Nuclear Equation

In another example of radioactive decay, radium-226 emits an alpha particle to form a nucleus that has a new identity with a different mass number and atomic number.

STEP 1   **Write the incomplete nuclear equation.**

$$^{226}_{88}\text{Ra} \longrightarrow \ ? \ + \ ^{4}_{2}\text{He}$$

STEP 2   **Determine the missing mass number.**   In the equation, the mass number, 226, of the radium is equal to the combined mass numbers of the alpha particle and the new nucleus.

$$226 \quad = \ ? + 4$$
$$226 - 4 = \ ?$$
$$222 \quad = \ ? \ \text{(mass number of new nucleus)}$$

STEP 3   **Determine the missing atomic number.**   The atomic number of radium, 88, must equal the sum of the atomic numbers of the alpha particle and the new nucleus.

$$88 \quad = \ ? + 2$$
$$88 - 2 = \ ?$$
$$86 \quad = \ ? \ \text{(atomic number of new nucleus)}$$

STEP 4   **Determine the symbol of the new nucleus.**
On the periodic table, the element that has atomic number 86 is radon, Rn. The nucleus of this isotope of Rn is written as $^{222}_{86}$Rn.

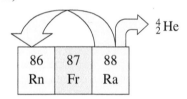

$^{4}_{2}$He

86	87	88
Rn	Fr	Ra

STEP 5   **Complete the nuclear equation.**

$$^{226}_{88}\text{Ra} \longrightarrow \ ^{222}_{86}\text{Rn} \ + \ ^{4}_{2}\text{He}$$

In this nuclear reaction, a radium-226 nucleus decays by releasing an alpha particle and produces a radon-222 nucleus.

CONCEPT CHECK 4.2

■ **Alpha Decay**

Francium-221 emits alpha particles when it decays.

a. Does the new nucleus have a larger or smaller mass number? By how much?
b. Does the new nucleus have a larger or smaller atomic number? By how much?

ANSWER

a. The loss of an alpha particle will give a smaller mass number to the new nucleus. Because an alpha particle is a helium nucleus, $^{4}_{2}$He, the mass number of the new nucleus will decrease by 4 from 221 to 217.
b. The loss of an alpha particle will give a smaller atomic number to the new nucleus. Because an alpha particle is a helium nucleus, $^{4}_{2}$He, the atomic number of the new nucleus will decrease by 2 from 87 to 85.

SAMPLE PROBLEM   4.2

■ Writing an Equation for Alpha Decay

Smoke detectors that are used in homes and apartments contain americium-241, which undergoes alpha decay. When alpha particles collide with air molecules, charged particles are produced that generate an electrical current. When smoke particles enter the detector, they interfere with the formation of charged particles in the air, and the electric current is interrupted. This causes the alarm to sound and warns the occupants of the danger of fire. Complete the following nuclear equation for the decay of americium-241:

$$^{241}_{95}\text{Am} \longrightarrow ? + {}^{4}_{2}\text{He}$$

SOLUTION

STEP 1 **Write the incomplete nuclear equation.**

$$^{241}_{95}\text{Am} \longrightarrow ? + {}^{4}_{2}\text{He}$$

STEP 2 **Determine the missing mass number.** In the equation, the mass number of the americium, 241, is equal to the sum of the mass numbers of the alpha particle and the new nucleus:

$$241 \quad = ? + 4$$
$$241 - 4 = ?$$
$$237 \quad = ? \text{ (mass number of new nucleus)}$$

STEP 3 **Determine the missing atomic number.** The atomic number of americium, 95 must equal the sum of the atomic numbers of the alpha particle and the new nucleus:

$$95 \quad = ? + 2$$
$$95 - 2 = ?$$
$$93 \quad = ? \text{ (atomic number of new nucleus)}$$

STEP 4 **Determine the symbol of the new nucleus.** On the periodic table, the element that has atomic number 93 is neptunium, Np. The symbol of this isotope of Np is written as $^{237}_{93}\text{Np}$.

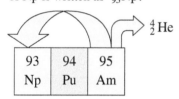

93	94	95
Np	Pu	Am

${}^{4}_{2}\text{He}$

STEP 5 **Complete the nuclear equation.**

$$^{241}_{95}\text{Am} \longrightarrow {}^{237}_{93}\text{Np} + {}^{4}_{2}\text{He}$$

In this nuclear reaction, an Am-241 nucleus decays by releasing an alpha particle and produces a Np-237 nucleus.

STUDY CHECK

Write a balanced nuclear equation for the alpha decay of Po-214.

Guide to Completing a Nuclear Equation

STEP 1
Write the incomplete nuclear equation.

↓

STEP 2
Determine the missing mass number.

↓

STEP 3
Determine the missing atomic number.

↓

STEP 4
Determine the symbol of the new nucleus.

↓

STEP 5
Complete the nuclear equation.

Beta Decay

When an unstable nucleus emits a beta particle, the newly formed proton increases the atomic number by 1, but the mass number stays the same. For example, when carbon-14 decays by beta emission, it becomes nitrogen-14.

In the nuclear equation for beta decay, the mass number of the radioactive nucleus and the mass number of the new nucleus are the same. However, the atomic number of the new nucleus increases by 1, indicating a change of one element into another. For example, the beta decay of a carbon-14 nucleus produces a nitrogen-14 nucleus.

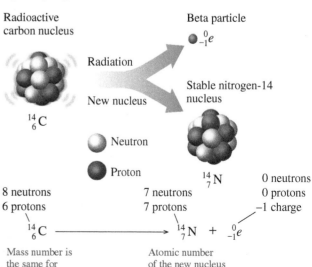

Radioactive carbon nucleus

Radiation

New nucleus

${}^{14}_{6}\text{C}$

8 neutrons
6 protons

${}^{14}_{6}\text{C}$

Mass number is the same for both nuclei

Beta particle
${}^{0}_{-1}e$

Stable nitrogen-14 nucleus

○ Neutron

● Proton

${}^{14}_{7}\text{N}$

7 neutrons
7 protons

0 neutrons
0 protons
−1 charge

$${}^{14}_{6}\text{C} \longrightarrow {}^{14}_{7}\text{N} + {}^{0}_{-1}e$$

Atomic number of the new nucleus increases by 1

GREEN CHEMISTRY NOTE

Radon in Our Homes

The presence of radon has become a much publicized environmental and health issue because of the radiation danger it poses. Radioactive isotopes such as uranium-238 and radium-226 are naturally present in many types of rocks and soils. Radium-226 emits an alpha particle and is converted into radon gas, which diffuses out of the rocks and soil:

$$^{226}_{88}\text{Ra} \longrightarrow {}^{222}_{86}\text{Rn} + {}^{4}_{2}\text{He}$$

Outdoors, radon gas poses little danger because it disperses in the air. However, if the radioactive source is under a house or building, the radon gas can enter the house through cracks in the foundation or other openings. Those who live or work there may inhale the radon. Inside the lungs, radon-222 emits alpha particles to form polonium-218, which is known to cause lung cancer:

$$^{222}_{86}\text{Rn} \longrightarrow {}^{218}_{84}\text{Po} + {}^{4}_{2}\text{He}$$

Some researchers have estimated that 10% of all lung cancer deaths in the United States result from radon gas exposure. The

Environmental Protection Agency (EPA) recommends that the maximum level of radon not exceed 4 picocuries (pCi) per liter of air in a home. One (1) picocurie (pCi) is equal to 10^{-12} curies (Ci): curies are described in section 4.3. In California, 1% of all the houses surveyed exceeded the EPA's recommended maximum radon level.

■ Writing an Equation for Beta Decay

Write the nuclear equation for the beta decay of cobalt-60.

SOLUTION

STEP 1   **Write the incomplete nuclear equation.**

$$^{60}_{27}\text{Co} \longrightarrow ? + {}^{0}_{-1}e$$

STEP 2   **Determine the missing mass number.**   In the equation, the mass number of cobalt, 60, is equal to the sum of the mass numbers of the beta particle and the new nucleus:

$$60 \quad = ? + 0$$
$$60 - 0 = ?$$
$$60 \quad = ? \text{ (mass number of new nucleus)}$$

STEP 3   **Determine the missing atomic number.**   The atomic number of cobalt, 27, must equal the sum of the atomic numbers of the beta particle and the new nucleus:

$$27 \quad = ? - 1$$
$$27 + 1 = ?$$
$$28 \quad = ? \text{ (atomic number of new nucleus)}$$

STEP 4   **Determine the symbol of the new nucleus.**   On the periodic table, the element that has atomic number 28 is nickel (Ni). The symbol of this isotope is written as

$$^{60}_{28}\text{Ni}$$

STEP 5   **Complete the nuclear equation.**

$$^{60}_{27}\text{Co} \longrightarrow {}^{60}_{28}\text{Ni} + {}^{0}_{-1}e$$

In this nuclear reaction, cobalt-60 undergoes beta decay to produce nickel-60.

STUDY CHECK

Write the nuclear equation for the beta decay of iodine-131.

TUTORIAL
Writing Nuclear Equations

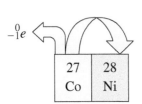

HEALTH NOTE

Beta Emitters in Medicine

The radioactive isotopes of several biologically important elements are beta emitters. When a radiologist wants to treat a malignancy within the body, a beta emitter may be used. The short range of penetration into the tissue by beta particles is advantageous for certain conditions. For example, some malignant tumors increase the fluid within the body tissues. A compound containing phosphorus-32, a beta emitter, is injected into the body cavity where the tumor is located. The beta particles travel only a few millimeters through the tissue, so only the malignancy and any tissue within that range are affected. The growth of the tumor is slowed or stopped, and the production of fluid decreases. Phosphorus-32 is also used to treat leukemia, polycythemia vera (an excessive production of red blood cells), and lymphomas.

$$^{32}_{15}P \longrightarrow ^{32}_{16}S + ^{0}_{-1}e$$

Another beta emitter, iron-59, is used in blood tests to determine the level of iron in the blood and the rate of production of red blood cells by the bone marrow.

$$^{59}_{26}Fe \longrightarrow ^{59}_{27}Co + ^{0}_{-1}e$$

Positron Emission

When a radioactive isotope emits a positron, the mass number does not change. However, the atomic number of the new nucleus decreases by 1. For example, manganese-49 undergoes positron emission to produce chromium-49. The atomic number of chromium (24) and the charge of the positron (+1) added together give the atomic number of manganese (25).

$$^{49}_{25}Mn \longrightarrow ^{49}_{24}Cr + ^{0}_{+1}e$$

MC **TUTORIAL**
Alpha, Beta, and Gamma Emitters

Gamma Emission

Pure gamma emitters are rare, although gamma radiation accompanies most alpha and beta radiation. In radiology, one of the most commonly used gamma emitters is technetium (Tc). Because the unstable isotope of technetium decays quickly, it is written as the *metastable* (symbol m) isotope: technetium-99m, Tc-99m, or $^{99m}_{43}Tc$. By emitting energy in the form of gamma rays, the unstable nucleus becomes more stable.

$$^{99m}_{43}Tc \longrightarrow ^{99}_{43}Tc + ^{0}_{0}\gamma$$

Figure 4.2 summarizes the changes in the nucleus for alpha, beta, positron, and gamma radiation.

Producing Radioactive Isotopes

Today, many radioisotopes are produced in small amounts by converting stable, nonradioactive isotopes into radioactive ones. In a process called *transmutation*, a stable nucleus is bombarded by high-speed particles such as alpha particles, protons, neutrons, and small nuclei. When one of these particles is absorbed, the nucleus becomes a radioactive isotope.

When the nonradioactive isotope boron-10 is bombarded by an alpha particle, it is converted to nitrogen-13, and a neutron is emitted.

Radiation source	Radiation	New nucleus
Alpha emitter	$^{4}_{2}He$	New element
		Mass number −4 Atomic number −2
Beta emitter	$^{0}_{-1}e$	New element
		Mass number same Atomic number +1
Positron emitter	$^{0}_{+1}e$	New element
		Mass number same Atomic number −1
Gamma emitter	γ	Stable nucleus of same element
		Mass number same Atomic number same

FIGURE 4.2 When the nuclei of alpha, beta, positron, and gamma emitters emit radiation, new and more stable nuclei are produced.

Q What changes occur in the number of protons and neutrons when an alpha emitter gives off radiation?

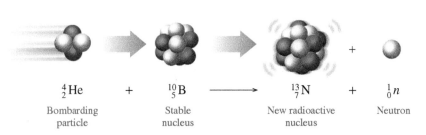

$$^{4}_{2}He + ^{10}_{5}B \longrightarrow ^{13}_{7}N + ^{1}_{0}n$$

Bombarding particle — Stable nucleus — New radioactive nucleus — Neutron

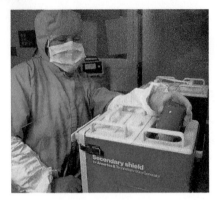

All elements that have an atomic number greater than 92 have been produced by bombardment; none of these elements occurs naturally. Most have been produced in small amounts and exist for such a short time that it is difficult to study their properties. An example is element 105, dubnium (Db), which is produced when californium-249 is bombarded with nitrogen-15:

$$^{249}_{98}\text{Cf} + ^{15}_{7}\text{N} \longrightarrow ^{260}_{105}\text{Db} + 4^{1}_{0}n$$

Technetium-99m is a radioisotope used in nuclear medicine for several diagnostic procedures, including the detection of brain tumors and examinations of the liver and spleen. The source of technetium-99m is molybdenum-99, which is produced in a nuclear reactor by neutron bombardment of molybdenum-98:

$$^{98}_{42}\text{Mo} + ^{1}_{0}n \longrightarrow ^{99}_{42}\text{Mo}$$

Many radiology laboratories have small generators containing molybdenum-99, which decays to give technetium-99m:

$$^{99}_{42}\text{Mo} \longrightarrow ^{99m}_{43}\text{Tc} + ^{0}_{-1}e$$

The technetium-99m radioisotope decays by emitting gamma rays. Gamma emission is desirable for diagnostic work because the gamma rays pass through the body to the detection equipment.

$$^{99m}_{43}\text{Tc} \longrightarrow ^{99}_{43}\text{Tc} + ^{0}_{0}\gamma$$

CONCEPT CHECK 4.3

■ Producing Radioactive Isotopes

Sulfur-32 is bombarded with a neutron to produce a new isotope and an alpha particle. What is the name of the new isotope?

ANSWER

To determine the name of the new isotope, we need to calculate its mass number and atomic number. Combining the mass numbers of S-32 and a neutron (32 + 1) gives a total of 33. Subtracting 4 for the alpha particle gives a mass number of 29 to the new isotope. Combining the atomic numbers of sulfur (16) and the neutron (0) and subtracting 2 for the alpha particle gives an atomic number of 14 to the new isotope. The element that has the atomic number of 14 is silicon. The new nucleus is silicon-29.

SAMPLE PROBLEM   4.4

■ Writing Equations for Isotope Production

Write the equation when zinc-66 absorbs one proton ($^{1}_{1}\text{H}$) during bombardment to form a radioactive isotope.

SOLUTION

STEP 1   Write the incomplete nuclear equation.

$$^{66}_{30}\text{Zn} + ^{1}_{1}\text{H} \longrightarrow ?$$

STEP 2   Determine the missing mass number.   In the equation, the sum of the mass numbers of zinc (66) and the proton (1) must equal the mass number of the new nucleus:

$$66 + 1 = ?$$
$$67 \quad = ? \text{ (mass number of new nucleus)}$$

STEP 3   **Determine the missing atomic number.**   The sum of the atomic numbers of zinc (30) and a proton (1) must equal the atomic number of the new nucleus:

$$30 + 1 = ?$$
$$31 \quad = ? \text{ (atomic number of new nucleus)}$$

STEP 4   **Determine the symbol of the new nucleus.**   On the periodic table, the element that has atomic number 31 is gallium, Ga. The symbol of this isotope of Ga is written as

$$^{67}_{31}\text{Ga}$$

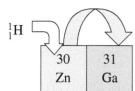

STEP 5   **Complete the nuclear equation.**

$$^{66}_{30}\text{Zn} + {}^{1}_{1}\text{H} \longrightarrow {}^{67}_{31}\text{Ga}$$

Proton   New isotope

STUDY CHECK

The first radioactive isotope was produced in 1933 by the bombardment of aluminum-27 with an alpha particle to produce a radioactive isotope and one neutron. What is the balanced nuclear equation for this transmutation?

QUESTIONS AND PROBLEMS

Nuclear Equations

4.13 Write a balanced nuclear equation for the alpha decay of each of the following:
   a. $^{208}_{84}\text{Po}$ **b.** $^{232}_{90}\text{Th}$ **c.** $^{251}_{102}\text{No}$ **d.** $^{220}_{86}\text{Rn}$

4.14 Write a balanced nuclear equation for the alpha decay of each of the following:
   a. $^{243}_{96}\text{Cm}$ **b.** $^{252}_{99}\text{Es}$ **c.** $^{251}_{98}\text{Cf}$ **d.** $^{261}_{107}\text{Bh}$

4.15 Write a balanced nuclear equation for the beta decay of each of the following:
   a. $^{25}_{11}\text{Na}$ **b.** $^{20}_{8}\text{O}$
   c. strontium-92   **d.** potassium-42

4.16 Write a balanced nuclear equation for the beta decay of each of the following:
   a. $^{44}_{19}\text{K}$ **b.** iron-59   **c.** iron-60   **d.** $^{141}_{56}\text{Ba}$

4.17 Write a balanced nuclear equation for the positron decay of each of the following:
   a. $^{26}_{14}\text{Si}$ **b.** $^{54}_{27}\text{Co}$ **c.** $^{77}_{37}\text{Rb}$ **d.** $^{93}_{45}\text{Rh}$

4.18 Write a balanced nuclear equation for the positron decay of each of the following:
   a. $^{8}_{5}\text{B}$ **b.** $^{13}_{7}\text{N}$ **c.** $^{40}_{19}\text{K}$ **d.** $^{118}_{54}\text{Xe}$

4.19 Complete each of the following nuclear equations:
   a. $^{28}_{13}\text{Al} \longrightarrow ? + {}^{0}_{-1}e$
   b. $? \longrightarrow {}^{86}_{36}\text{Kr} + {}^{1}_{0}n$

   c. $^{66}_{29}\text{Cu} \longrightarrow {}^{66}_{30}\text{Zn} + ?$
   d. $? \longrightarrow {}^{4}_{2}\text{He} + {}^{234}_{90}\text{Th}$
   e. $^{188}_{80}\text{Hg} \longrightarrow ? + {}^{0}_{+1}e$

4.20 Complete each of the following nuclear equations:
   a. $^{11}_{6}\text{C} \longrightarrow {}^{7}_{4}\text{Be} + ?$
   b. $^{35}_{16}\text{S} \longrightarrow ? + {}^{0}_{-1}e$
   c. $? \longrightarrow {}^{90}_{39}\text{Y} + {}^{0}_{-1}e$
   d. $^{210}_{83}\text{Bi} \longrightarrow ? + {}^{4}_{2}\text{He}$
   e. $? \longrightarrow {}^{135}_{59}\text{Pr} + {}^{0}_{+1}e$

4.21 Complete each of the following bombardment reactions:
   a. $^{9}_{4}\text{Be} + {}^{1}_{0}n \longrightarrow ?$
   b. $^{32}_{16}\text{S} + ? \longrightarrow {}^{32}_{15}\text{P}$
   c. $? + {}^{1}_{0}n \longrightarrow {}^{24}_{11}\text{Na} + {}^{4}_{2}\text{He}$
   d. $^{27}_{13}\text{Al} + {}^{4}_{2}\text{He} \longrightarrow ? + {}^{1}_{0}n$

4.22 Complete each of the following bombardment reactions:
   a. $^{40}_{18}\text{Ar} + ? \longrightarrow {}^{43}_{19}\text{K} + {}^{1}_{1}\text{H}$
   b. $^{238}_{92}\text{U} + {}^{1}_{0}n \longrightarrow ?$
   c. $? + {}^{1}_{0}n \longrightarrow {}^{14}_{6}\text{C} + {}^{1}_{1}\text{H}$
   d. $? + {}^{64}_{28}\text{Ni} \longrightarrow {}^{272}_{111}\text{Rg} + {}^{1}_{0}n$

4.3 | Radiation Measurement

One of the most common instruments for detecting beta and gamma radiation is the Geiger counter. It consists of a metal tube filled with a gas such as argon. When radiation enters a window on the end of the tube, it produces charged particles in the gas, which produce an electrical current. Each burst of current is amplified to give a click and a reading on a meter.

$$Ar + radiation \longrightarrow Ar^+ + e^-$$

Radiation is measured in several different ways. We can measure the activity of a radioactive sample or determine the impact of radiation on biological tissue.

Measuring Radiation

When a radiology laboratory obtains a radioisotope, the activity of the sample is measured in terms of the number of nuclear disintegrations per second. The **curie (Ci)**, the original unit of activity, was defined as the number of disintegrations that occur in 1 second for 1 g of radium, which is equal to 3.7×10^{10} disintegrations per second. The unit was named for Marie Curie, a Polish scientist, who, along with her husband, Pierre, discovered the radioactive elements radium and polonium. A newer unit of radiation activity is the **becquerel (Bq)**, which is one disintegration per second.

The **rad (radiation absorbed dose)** is a unit that measures the amount of radiation absorbed by a gram of material such as body tissue. The newer unit for absorbed dose is the **gray (Gy)**, which is equal to 100 rads.

The **rem (radiation equivalent in humans)** measures the biological effects of different kinds of radiation. Although alpha particles do not penetrate the skin, if they should enter the body by some other route, they can cause a lot of damage even though the particles travel only a short distance in tissue. High-energy radiation such as beta particles and high-energy protons and neutrons that penetrate the skin and travel into tissue cause more damage. Gamma rays are dangerous because they travel a long way through tissue and create a great deal of damage.

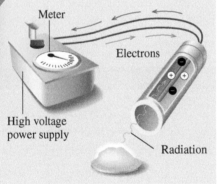

To determine the **equivalent dose** or rem dose, the absorbed dose (rads) is multiplied by a factor that adjusts for biological damage caused by a particular form of radiation. For beta and gamma radiation the factor is 1, so the biological damage in rems is the same as the absorbed radiation (rads). For high-energy protons and neutrons, the factor is about 10, and for alpha particles it is 20.

$$\text{Biological damage (rem)} = \text{absorbed dose (rad)} \times \text{factor}$$

Often the measurement for an equivalent dose will be in units of millirems (mrem). One rem is equal to 1000 mrem. The newer unit is the **sievert (Sv)**. One sievert is equal to 100 rems.

People who work in radiology laboratories wear film badges to determine their exposure to radiation. A film badge consists of a piece of photographic film in a container that is attached to clothing. Periodically, the film badges are collected and developed to determine the level of exposure to radiation.

Table 4.5 summarizes the units used to measure radiation.

TABLE 4.5 Some Units of Radiation Measurement

Measurement	Common Unit	SI Unit	Relationship
Activity	curie (Ci)	becquerel (Bq)	$1\ Ci = 3.7 \times 10^{10}$ Bq
Absorbed dose	rad	gray (Gy)	$1\ Gy = 100$ rad
Biological damage	rem	sievert (Sv)	$1\ Sv = 100$ rem

HEALTH NOTE

Radiation and Food

Food-borne illnesses caused by pathogenic bacteria such as *Salmonella*, *Listeria*, and *Escherichia coli* have become a major health concern in the United States. The Centers for Disease Control and Prevention (CDC) estimates that each year *E. coli* in contaminated foods infects 20 000 people in the United States, and that 500 people die. *E. coli* has been responsible for outbreaks of illness from contaminated ground beef, fruit juices, lettuce, and alfalfa sprouts.

The Food and Drug Administration (FDA) has approved the use of 0.3 kilogray (0.3 kGy) to 1 kGy of radiation produced by cobalt-60 or cesium-137 for the treatment of foods. The irradiation technology is much like that used to sterilize medical supplies. Cobalt pellets are placed in stainless steel tubes, which are arranged in racks. When food moves through the series of racks, the gamma rays pass through the food and kill the bacteria.

It is important for consumers to understand that when food is irradiated, it never comes into contact with the radioactive source. The gamma rays pass through the food to kill bacteria, but that does not make the food radioactive. The radiation kills bacteria because it stops their ability to divide and grow. We cook or heat food thoroughly for the same purpose. Radiation has little effect on the food itself because its cells are no longer dividing or growing. Thus irradiated food is not harmed although small amounts of vitamins may be lost.

Currently, tomatoes, blueberries, strawberries, and mushrooms are being irradiated to allow them to be harvested when completely ripe and extend their shelf life. (See Figure 4.3.) The FDA has also approved the irradiation of pork, poultry, and beef to decrease potential infections and to extend shelf life. Currently, irradiated vegetable and meat products are available in retail markets in South

(a)

(b)

FIGURE 4.3 **(a)** The FDA requires this symbol to appear on irradiated retail foods. **(b)** After two weeks, the irradiated strawberries on the right show no spoilage. Mold is growing on the nonirradiated ones on the left.

Q Why are irradiated foods used on spaceships and in nursing homes?

Africa. Apollo 17 astronauts ate irradiated foods on the moon, and some U.S. hospitals and nursing homes now use irradiated poultry to reduce the possibility of salmonella infections among patients. The extended shelf life of irradiated food also makes it useful for campers and military personnel. Soon consumers concerned about food safety will have a choice of irradiated meats, fruits, and vegetables at the market.

SAMPLE PROBLEM 4.5

(MC) CASE STUDY
Food Irradiation

■ Radiation Measurement

One treatment of bone pain involves intravenous administration of the radioisotope phosphorus-32, which is primarily incorporated into bone. A typical dose of 7 mCi can produce up to 450 rads in the bone. What is the difference between the units of mCi and rads?

SOLUTION

The millicuries (mCi) indicate the activity of the P-32 in terms of nuclei that break down in 1 second. The radiation absorbed dose (rads) is a measure of amount of radiation absorbed by the bone.

STUDY CHECK

If P-32 is a beta emitter, how do the number of rems compare to the rads?

Exposure to Radiation

Every day, we are exposed to low levels of background radiation from naturally occurring radioactive isotopes in the buildings where we live and work, in our food and water, and in the air we breathe. For example, potassium-40 is a naturally occurring isotope that is present in any potassium-containing food. Other naturally occurring radioisotopes in air

HEALTH NOTE

Brachytherapy

The process called *brachytherapy*, or seed implantation, is an internal form of radiation therapy. The prefix *brachy* is from the Greek word for short distance. With internal radiation, a high dose of radiation is delivered to a cancerous area, while normal tissue sustains minimal damage. Because higher doses are used, fewer treatments of shorter duration are needed. Conventional external treatment delivers a lower dose per treatment but requires six to eight weeks of treatments.

Permanent Brachytherapy

One of the most common forms of cancer in males is prostate cancer. In addition to surgery and chemotherapy, one treatment option is to place 40 or more titanium capsules, or "seeds," in the malignant area. Each seed, which is the size of a small grain of rice, contains radioactive iodine-125, palladium-103, or cesium-131. The radiation from the seeds destroys the cancer by interfering with the reproduction of cancer cells. Because the radiation targets the cancer cells, there is minimal damage to normal tissues. Ninety percent (90%) of the radioisotopes decay within a few months because they have short half-lives.

Isotope	I-125	Pd-103	Cs-131
Half-life	60 days	17 days	10 days
Time to deliver 90% of radiation	7 months	2 months	1 month

Almost no radiation passes out of the patient's body. The amount of radiation received by a family member is no greater than that received on a long plane flight. The titanium capsules are left in the body permanently, but the products of decay are not radioactive and cause no further damage.

Temporary Brachytherapy

In another type of treatment for prostate cancer, long needles containing iridium-192 are placed in the tumor. However, the needles are removed after 5 to 10 minutes, depending on the activity of the iridium isotope. Compared to permanent brachytherapy, temporary brachytherapy can deliver a higher dose of radiation over a shorter time. The procedure may be repeated in a few days.

Brachytherapy is also used following breast cancer lumpectomy. An iridium-192 isotope is inserted into the catheter implanted in the space left by the removal of the tumor. The isotope is removed after 5 to 10 minutes, depending on the activity of the iridium source. Radiation is delivered primarily to the tissue surrounding the cavity that contained the tumor and where the cancer is most likely to reoccur. The procedure is repeated twice a day for five days to give an absorbed dose of 34 Gy (3400 rads). The catheter is removed, and no radioactive material remains in the body.

In conventional external beam therapy for breast cancer, a patient receives 2 Gy/treatment once a day for 35 days or about seven weeks, which gives a total absorbed dose of about 100 Gy or 10 000 rads. The external beam therapy irradiates the entire breast including the tumor cavity.

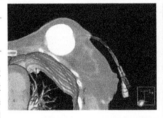
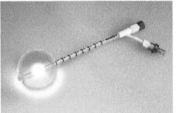

TABLE 4.6 Average Annual Radiation Received by a Person in the United States

Source	Dose (mrem)
Natural	
The ground	20
Air, water, food	30
Cosmic rays	40
Wood, concrete, brick	50
Medical	
Chest X-ray	20
Dental X-ray	20
Hip X-ray	60
Lumbar spine X-ray	70
Mammogram	40
Upper gastrointestinal tract X-ray	200
Other	
Television	20
Air travel	10
Radon	200[a]

[a]Varies widely.

and food are carbon-14, radon-222, strontium-90, and iodine-131. The average person in the United States is exposed to about 360 mrem of radiation annually. Table 4.6 lists some common sources of radiation.

Another source of background radiation is cosmic radiation produced in space by the sun. People who live at high altitudes or travel by airplane receive a greater amount of cosmic radiation because there are fewer molecules in the atmosphere to absorb the radiation. For example, a person living in Denver receives about twice the cosmic radiation as a person living in Los Angeles. A person living close to a nuclear power plant normally does not receive much additional radiation, perhaps 0.1 millirem (mrem) in one year. (One rem equals 1000 mrem.) However, in the accident at the Chernobyl nuclear power plant in 1986 in Ukraine, people in a nearby town were estimated to have received as much as 1 rem/h.

Medical sources of radiation including dental, hip, spine, and chest X-rays and mammograms add to our radiation exposure.

Radiation Sickness

The larger the dose of radiation received at one time, the greater the effect on the body. Exposure to radiation less than 25 rem usually cannot be detected. Whole-body exposure of 100 rem produces a temporary decrease in the number of white blood cells. When the exposure to radiation exceeds 100 rem, a person may experience one or more symptoms of radiation sickness: nausea, vomiting, fatigue, and a reduction in white-cell count. A whole-body dosage greater than 300 rem can decrease the white-cell count to zero. The victim suffers diarrhea, hair loss, and infection. Exposure to radiation of about 500 rem is expected to cause death in 50% of the people receiving that dose. This amount of radiation to the whole body is called the *lethal dose for one-half the population*, or the LD_{50}. The LD_{50} varies for different life forms, as Table 4.7 shows. Radiation dosages of 600 rem or higher would be fatal to all humans within a few weeks.

TABLE 4.7 Lethal Doses of Whole-Body Radiation for Some Life Forms

Life-Form	LD_{50} (rem)
Insect	100 000
Bacterium	50 000
Rat	800
Human	500
Dog	300

QUESTIONS AND PROBLEMS

Radiation Measurement

4.23 a. How does a Geiger counter detect radiation?
  b. What SI unit and what older unit describe the activity of a radioactive sample?
  c. What SI unit and what older unit describe the radiation dose absorbed by tissue?
  d. What is meant by the term kilogray?

4.24 a. What is background radiation?
  b. What are the SI unit and the older unit that describe the biological effect of radiation?
  c. What is meant by the terms mCi and mrem?
  d. Why is a factor used to determine the equivalent dose?

4.25 The recommended dosage of iodine-131 is 4.20 μCi/kg of body weight. How many microcuries of iodine-131 are needed for a 70.0-kg patient with hyperthyroidism?

4.26 a. The dosage of technetium-99m for a lung scan is 20 μCi/kg of body weight. How many millicuries should be given to a 50.0-kg patient? (1 mCi = 1000 μCi)
  b. Suppose a person absorbed 50 mrads of alpha radiation. What would be the equivalent dose in mrems?

4.27 Why would an airline pilot be exposed to more background radiation than the person who works at the ticket counter?

4.28 In radiation therapy, a patient receives high doses of radiation. What symptoms of radiation sickness might the patient exhibit?

4.4 Half-Life of a Radioisotope

The **half-life** of a radioisotope is the amount of time it takes for one-half of a sample to decay. Each radioisotope has a characteristic half-life that depends on the stability of the nucleus. For example, $^{131}_{53}I$ has a half-life of 8.0 days. As $^{131}_{53}I$ decays, it produces a beta particle and the nonradioactive isotope $^{131}_{54}Xe$:

$$^{131}_{53}I \longrightarrow\ ^{131}_{54}Xe +\ ^{0}_{-1}e$$

Suppose we have an initial sample that contains 20. g of $^{131}_{53}I$. In 8.0 days, 10. g, which is one-half of all the $^{131}_{53}I$ in the sample, will decay to give $^{131}_{54}Xe$. The decay process also produces 10. g of the product $^{131}_{54}Xe$. After another half-life or 8.0 days passes, another 5.0 g of $^{131}_{53}I$ will decay.

LEARNING GOAL

Given the half-life of a radioisotope, calculate the amount of radioisotope remaining after one or more half-lives.

20. g of $^{131}_{53}I$ $\xrightarrow{\text{1 half-life}}$ 10. g of $^{131}_{53}I$ $\xrightarrow{\text{2 half-lives}}$ 5 g of $^{131}_{53}I$ $\xrightarrow{\text{3 half-lives}}$ 2.5 g of $^{131}_{53}I$

A third half-life, or another 8.0 days, results in 2.5 g of the $^{131}_{53}I$ decaying to give $^{131}_{54}Xe$, which leaves 2.5 g of $^{131}_{53}I$ still capable of producing radiation. This information is summarized in Table 4.8.

TABLE 4.8 Activity of an $^{131}_{53}\text{I}$ Sample with Time

Time elapsed	0 days	8.0 days	16 days	24 days
Half-lives	0	1	2	3
$^{131}_{53}\text{I}$ remaining	20. g	10. g	5.0 g	2.5 g
$^{131}_{54}\text{Xe}$ produced	0 g	10. g	15.0 g	17.5 g

FIGURE 4.4 The decay curve for iodine-131 shows that one-half of the radioactive sample decays and one-half remains radioactive after each half-life of 8 days.

Q How many grams of the 20.-g sample remain radioactive after 2 half-lives?

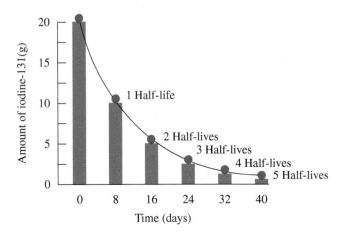

A **decay curve** is a diagram of the decay of a radioactive isotope. Figure 4.4 shows such a curve for the $^{131}_{53}\text{I}$ we have discussed.

CONCEPT CHECK 4.4

■ Half-Lives

Iridium-192, which is used to treat cancer, has a half-life of 74 days. What happens after 74 days if the initial sample of Ir-192 has an activity of 8×10^4 Bq? Why?

ANSWER

In one half-life of iridium-192, or 74 days, half of the iridium-192 atoms will decay. Thus, after 74 days, the activity is half of the initial activity of 8×10^4 Bq, or 4×10^4 Bq.

SAMPLE PROBLEM   4.6

■ Using Half-Lives of a Radioisotope

Phosphorus-32, a radioisotope used in the treatment of leukemia, has a half-life of 14 days. If a sample contains 8.0 g of phosphorus-32, how many grams of phosphorus-32 remain after 42 days?

SOLUTION

STEP 1   **Given**   8.0 g of $^{32}_{15}\text{P}$; 42 days; 14 days/half-life
             Need   g of $^{32}_{15}\text{P}$ remaining

STEP 2   **Plan**

42 days	Half-life	Number of half-lives

8.0 g of $^{32}_{15}\text{P}$	Number of half-lives	g of $^{32}_{15}\text{P}$ remaining

STEP 3   **Equalities/Conversion Factors**

$$1 \text{ half-life} = 14 \text{ days}$$

$$\frac{14 \text{ days}}{1 \text{ half-life}} \quad \text{and} \quad \frac{1 \text{ half-life}}{14 \text{ days}}$$

STEP 4 **Set Up Problem** We can do this problem with two calculations. First, we determine the number of half-lives in the amount of time that has elapsed:

$$\text{Number of half-lives} = 42 \text{ days} \times \frac{1 \text{ half-life}}{14 \text{ days}} = 3 \text{ half-lives}$$

Now we determine how much of the sample decays in three half-lives and how many grams of the phosphorus remain:

$$8.0 \text{ g of } {}^{32}_{15}P \xrightarrow{\text{1 half-life}} 4.0 \text{ g of } {}^{32}_{15}P \xrightarrow{\text{1 half-life}} 2.0 \text{ g of } {}^{32}_{15}P \xrightarrow{\text{1 half-life}} 1.0 \text{ g of } {}^{32}_{15}P$$

STUDY CHECK

Iron-59 has a half-life of 44 days. If the laboratory received 8.0 g of iron-59, how many grams are still active after 176 days?

Naturally occurring isotopes of the elements are typically more stable and therefore usually have long half-lives, as shown in Table 4.9. They disintegrate slowly and produce radiation over a long period of time, even hundreds or millions of years. In contrast, many of the radioisotopes used in nuclear medicine are extremely unstable and have much shorter half-lives. They disintegrate rapidly and produce almost all their radiation in a short period of time. For example, technetium-99m emits half of its radiation in the first six hours. This means that a small amount of the radioisotope given to a patient is essentially gone within two days. The decay products of technetium-99m are totally eliminated by the body.

TABLE 4.9 Half-Lives of Some Radioisotopes

Element	Radioisotope	Half-Life
Naturally Occurring Radioisotopes		
Carbon	${}^{14}_{6}C$	5730 y
Potassium	${}^{40}_{19}K$	1.3×10^9 y
Radium	${}^{226}_{88}Ra$	1600 y
Uranium	${}^{238}_{92}U$	4.5×10^9 y
Some Medical Radioisotopes		
Chromium	${}^{51}_{24}Cr$	28 d
Iodine	${}^{131}_{53}I$	8 d
Iron	${}^{59}_{26}Fe$	44 d
Technetium	${}^{99m}_{43}Tc$	6.0 h
Iridium	${}^{192}_{77}Ir$	74 d

TUTORIAL
Radioactive Half-Lives

SAMPLE PROBLEM 4.7

■ Dating Using Half-Lives

In Los Angeles, the remains of ancient animals have been unearthed from the La Brea Tar Pits. Suppose a bone sample from the tar pits is subjected to the carbon-14 dating method. How long ago did the animal live if the sample shows that two half-lives have passed?

SOLUTION

We can calculate the age of the bone sample by using the half-life of carbon-14 (5730 years):

$$2 \text{ half-lives} \times \frac{5730 \text{ years}}{1 \text{ half-life}} = 11\,500 \text{ years}$$

We would estimate that the animal lived 11 500 years ago, or about 9500 B.C.E.

STUDY CHECK

Suppose that a piece of wood found in a tomb had $\frac{1}{8}$ of its original carbon-14 activity. About how many years ago was the wood part of a living tree?

EXPLORE YOUR WORLD

Modeling Half-Lives

Obtain a piece of paper and a licorice stick or celery stalk. Draw a vertical and a horizontal axis on the paper. Label the vertical axis as radioactive atoms and the horizontal axis as minutes. Place the licorice stick or celery against the vertical axis and mark its height for zero minutes. In the next minute, cut the licorice stick or celery in two. (You can eat the half if you are hungry.) Place the shortened licorice stick or celery at 1 minute on the horizontal axis and mark its height. Every minute, cut the licorice stick or celery in half again and mark the shorter height at the corresponding time. Keep reducing the length by half until you cannot divide the licorice or celery in half any more. Connect the points you made for each minute. What does the curve look like? How does this curve represent the concept of a half-life for a radioisotope?

ENVIRONMENTAL NOTE

Dating Ancient Objects

Radiological dating is a technique used by geologists, archaeologists, and historians to determine the age of ancient objects. The age of an object derived from plants or animals (such as wood, fiber, natural pigments, bone, and cotton and woolen clothing) is determined by measuring the amount of carbon-14, a naturally occurring radioactive form of carbon. In 1960, Willard Libby received the Nobel Prize for his work developing carbon-14 dating techniques during the 1940s. Carbon-14 is produced in the upper atmosphere by the bombardment of $^{14}_{7}N$ by high-energy neutrons from cosmic rays.

$$^{1}_{0}n \ + \ ^{14}_{7}N \ \longrightarrow \ ^{14}_{6}C \ + \ ^{1}_{1}H$$

Neutron from cosmic rays   Nitrogen in atmosphere   Radioactive carbon-14   Proton

The carbon-14 reacts with oxygen to form radioactive carbon dioxide, $^{14}_{6}CO_2$. Living plants continuously absorb carbon dioxide, which incorporates carbon-14 into the plant material. The uptake of carbon-14 stops when the plant dies.

$$^{14}_{6}C \ \longrightarrow \ ^{14}_{7}N \ + \ ^{0}_{-1}e$$

As the carbon-14 decays, the amount of radioactive carbon-14 in the plant material steadily decreases. In a process called **carbon dating**, scientists use the half-life of carbon-14 (5730 years) to calculate the length of time since the plant died. As the plant material ages, the radioactive carbon-14 decays so that the amount of radioactive carbon-14 that remains is less than in the original living plant. For example, a wooden beam found in an ancient Indian dwelling might have one-half of the carbon-14 found in living plants. Because one half-life of carbon-14 is 5730 years, the dwelling was constructed about 5730 years ago. Carbon-14 dating was used to determine that the Dead Sea Scrolls are about 2000 years old.

A radiological dating method used for determining the age of much older items is based on the radioisotope uranium-238, which decays through a series of reactions to lead-206. The uranium-238 isotope has an incredibly long half-life, about 4×10^9 (4 billion) years. Measurements of the amounts of uranium-238 and lead-206 enable geologists to determine the age of rock samples. The older rocks will have a higher percentage of lead-206 because more of the uranium-238 has decayed. The age of rocks brought back from the moon by the Apollo missions, for example, was determined using uranium-238. They were found to be about 4×10^9 years old, approximately the same age calculated for Earth.

QUESTIONS AND PROBLEMS

Half-Life of a Radioisotope

4.29 What is meant by the term *half-life*?

4.30 Why are radioisotopes with short half-lives used for diagnosis in nuclear medicine?

4.31 Technetium-99m is an ideal radioisotope for scanning organs because it has a half-life of 6.0 h and is a pure gamma emitter. Suppose that 80.0 mg were prepared in the technetium generator this morning. How many milligrams would remain after the following intervals?
  a. one half-life   **b.** two half-lives
  c. 18 h   **d.** 24 h

4.32 A sample of sodium-24 with an activity of 12 mCi is used to study the rate of blood flow in the circulatory system. If sodium-24 has a half-life of 15 h, what is the activity of the sodium after 2.5 days?

4.33 Strontium-85, used for bone scans, has a half-life of 65 days. How long will it take for the radiation level of strontium-85 to drop to one-fourth of its original level? To one-eighth?

4.34 Fluorine-18, which has a half-life of 110 min, is used in PET scans. (See section 4.5.) If 100 mg of fluorine-18 is shipped at 8 A.M., how many milligrams of the radioisotope are still active if the sample arrives at the radiology laboratory at 1:30 P.M.?

4.5 Medical Applications Using Radioactivity

LEARNING GOAL

Describe the use of radioisotopes in medicine.

To determine the condition of an organ in the body, a radiologist may give a patient a radioisotope that concentrates in that organ. The cells in the body do not differentiate between a nonradioactive atom and a radioactive one. However, radioactive atoms can be detected because they emit radiation. Some radioisotopes used in nuclear medicine are listed in Table 4.10.

TABLE 4.10 Medical Applications of Radioisotopes

Isotope	Half-Life	Medical Application
Ce-141	32.5 days	Gastrointestinal tract diagnosis; measuring blood flow to the heart
Ga-67	78 h	Abdominal imaging; tumor detection
Ga-68	68 min	Detection of pancreatic cancer
P-32	4.3 days	Treatment of leukemia, excess red blood cells, pancreatic cancer
I-125	60 days	Treatment of brain cancer
I-131	8 days	Imaging of thyroid; treatment of Graves' disease, goiter, and hyperthyroidism; treatment of thyroid and prostate cancer
Sr-85	65 days	Detection of bone lesions; brain scans
Tc-99m	6 h	Imaging of skeleton, heart muscle, brain, liver, heart, lungs, bone, spleen, kidney, and thyroid; most widely used radioisotope in nuclear medicine

Scans with Radioisotopes

After a patient receives a radioisotope, the radiologist determines the level and location of radioactivity emitted by the radioisotope. An apparatus called a *scanner* is used to produce an image of the organ. The scanner moves slowly across the patient's body above the region where the organ containing the radioisotope is located. The gamma rays emitted from the radioisotope in the organ can be used to expose a photographic plate, producing a scan of the organ. On a scan, an area of decreased or increased radiation can indicate conditions such as a disease of the organ, a tumor, a blood clot, or edema.

A common method of determining thyroid function is the use of *radioactive iodine uptake* (RAIU). Taken orally, the radioisotope iodine-131 mixes with the iodine already present in the thyroid. Twenty-four hours later, the amount of iodine taken up by the thyroid is determined. A detection tube held up to the area of the thyroid gland detects the radiation coming from the iodine-131 that has located there. (See Figure 4.5.)

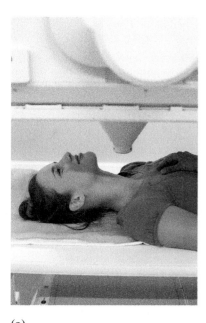

(a)

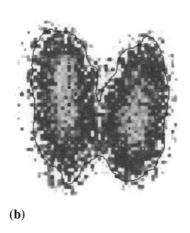

(b)

FIGURE 4.5 (a) A scanner is used to detect radiation from a radioisotope that has accumulated in an organ. (b) A scan of the thyroid shows the accumulation of radioactive iodine-131 in the thyroid.
Q What type of radiation would move through body tissues to create a scan?

HEALTH NOTE

Radiation Doses in Diagnostic and Therapeutic Procedures

We can compare the levels of radiation exposure commonly used during diagnostic and therapeutic procedures in nuclear medicine. In diagnostic procedures, the radiologist uses the minimum amount of radioactive isotope needed to evaluate the condition of an organ or tissue. The doses used in radiation therapy are much greater than those used for diagnostic procedures. For example, a therapeutic dose would be used to destroy the cells in a malignant tumor. Although there will be some damage to surrounding tissue, the healthy cells are more resistant to radiation and can repair themselves. (See Table 4.11.)

TABLE 4.11 Radiation Doses Used for Diagnostic and Therapeutic Procedures

Organ/Condition	Dose (rem)
Diagnostic	
Liver	0.3
Thyroid	50.0
Lung	2.0
Therapeutic	
Lymphoma	4500
Skin cancer	5000–6000
Lung cancer	6000
Brain tumor	6000–7000

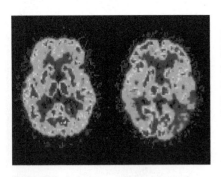

FIGURE 4.6 These PET scans of the brain show a normal brain on the left and a brain affected by Alzheimer's disease on the right.

Q When positrons collide with electrons, what type of radiation is produced that gives an image of an organ?

A patient with a hyperactive thyroid will have a higher than normal level of radioactive iodine, whereas a patient with a hypoactive thyroid will record low values. If the patient has hyperthyroidism, treatment is begun to lower the activity of the thyroid. One treatment involves giving the patient a therapeutic dosage of radioactive iodine, which has a higher radiation count than the diagnostic dose. The radioactive iodine goes to the thyroid, where its radiation destroys some of the thyroid cells. The thyroid produces less thyroid hormone, bringing the hyperthyroid condition under control.

Positron Emission Tomography (PET)

Positron emitters with short half-lives such as carbon-11, oxygen-15, nitrogen-13, and fluorine-18 are used in an imaging method called *positron emission tomography* (PET). A positron-emitting isotope such as fluorine-18 combined with substances in the body such as glucose is used to study brain function, metabolism, and blood flow.

$$^{18}_{9}\text{F} \longrightarrow ^{18}_{8}\text{O} + ^{0}_{+1}e$$

As positrons are emitted, they combine with electrons to produce gamma rays that are detected by computerized equipment to create a three-dimensional image of the organ. (See Figure 4.6.)

SAMPLE PROBLEM   4.8

■ Medical Application of Radioactivity

In the determination of thyroid function, a patient receives an oral dose of sodium iodide (NaI) that contains 10 μCi of iodine-131, which is a beta emitter. Write the nuclear equation for the beta decay of iodine-131.

SOLUTION

We can write the incomplete nuclear equation starting with iodine-131, which has atomic number 53:

$$^{131}_{53}\text{I} \longrightarrow ? + ^{0}_{-1}e$$

In beta decay, the mass number (131) does not change, but the atomic number of the new nucleus increases by 1. The new atomic number is 54, which is xenon (Xe):

$$^{131}_{53}\text{I} \longrightarrow ^{131}_{54}\text{Xe} + ^{0}_{-1}e$$

STUDY CHECK

In an experimental treatment, a patient is given boron-10, which is taken up by malignant tumors. When bombarded with neutrons, boron-10 decays by emitting alpha particles that destroy the surrounding tumor cells. Write the equation for the nuclear reaction for this experimental procedure.

HEALTH NOTE

Other Imaging Methods

Computed Tomography (CT)

Another imaging method used to detect changes within the body is *computed tomography* (CT). A computer monitors the degree of absorption of 30 000 X-ray beams directed at the brain at successive layers. Based on the densities of the tissues and fluids in the brain, the differences in absorption provide a series of images of the brain. This technique is successful in the identification of brain hemorrhages, tumors, and atrophy. (See Figure 4.7.)

Magnetic Resonance Imaging (MRI)

Magnetic resonance imaging (MRI) is a powerful imaging technique that does not involve X-ray radiation. It is the least invasive imaging method available. MRI is based on the absorption of energy when the protons in hydrogen atoms are excited by a strong magnetic field. Hydrogen atoms make up 63% of all the atoms in the body. In the hydrogen nuclei, the protons act like tiny bar magnets. With no external field, the protons have random orientations. However, when placed within a large magnet, the protons align with the magnetic field. A proton aligned with the field has a lower energy than one that is aligned against the field. As the MRI scan proceeds, radiofrequency pulses of energy are applied. When a nucleus absorbs certain energy, its proton "flips" and becomes aligned against the field. Because hydrogen atoms in the body are in different chemical environments, energies of different frequencies are absorbed. The energies absorbed are calculated and converted to color images of the body. MRI is particularly useful in obtaining images of soft tissues because these tissues contain large amounts of water. (See Figure 4.8.)

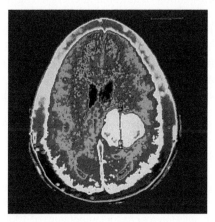

FIGURE 4.7 A CT scan shows a brain tumor (yellow area) in the center of the right side of the brain.
Q What is the type of radiation used to give a CT scan?

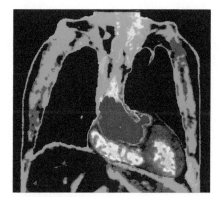

FIGURE 4.8 An MRI scan of the heart and lungs, with the left ventricle shown in red.
Q What is the source of energy in an MRI?

QUESTIONS AND PROBLEMS

Medical Applications Using Radioactivity

4.35 Bone and bony structures contain calcium and phosphorus.
   a. Why would the radioisotopes of calcium-47 and phosphorus-32 be used in the diagnosis and treatment of bone diseases?
   b. The radioisotope strontium-89, a beta emitter, is used to treat bone cancer. Write the nuclear equation and explain why a strontium radioisotope would be used to treat bone cancer.

4.36 **a.** Technetium-99m emits only gamma radiation. Why would this type of radiation be used in diagnostic imaging rather than an isotope that also emits beta or alpha radiation?

   b. A patient with polycythemia vera (excess production of red blood cells) receives radioactive phosphorus-32. Why would this treatment reduce the production of red blood cells in the bone marrow of the patient?

4.37 In a diagnostic test for leukemia, a patient receives 4.0 mL of a solution containing selenium-75. If the activity of the selenium-75 is 45 μCi/mL, what is the dose received by the patient?

4.38 A vial contains radioactive iodine-131 with an activity of 2.0 mCi per milliliter. If the thyroid test requires 3.0 mCi in an "atomic cocktail," how many milliliters are used to prepare the iodine-131 solution?

4.6 Nuclear Fission and Fusion

LEARNING GOAL

Describe the processes of nuclear fission and fusion.

TUTORIAL
Fission and Fusion

During the 1930s, scientists bombarding uranium-235 with neutrons discovered that the U-235 nucleus splits into two medium-weight nuclei and produces a great amount of energy. This was the discovery of nuclear **fission**. The energy generated by splitting the atom was called *atomic* energy. A typical equation for nuclear fission is

$$\,^{1}_{0}n + \,^{235}_{92}U \longrightarrow \,^{91}_{36}Kr + \,^{142}_{56}Ba + 3\,^{1}_{0}n + \text{energy}$$

If we could weigh these products with great accuracy, we would find that their total mass is slightly less than the mass of the starting materials. The missing mass has been converted into energy, consistent with the famous equation derived by Albert Einstein:

$$E = mc^2$$

where E is the energy released, m is the mass lost, and c is the speed of light, 3×10^8 m/s. Even though the mass loss is very small, when it is multiplied by the speed of light squared the result is a large value for the energy released. The fission of 1 g of uranium-235 produces about as much energy as the burning of 3 tons of coal.

Chain Reaction

Fission begins when a neutron collides with the nucleus of a uranium atom. The resulting nucleus is unstable and splits into smaller nuclei. This fission process also releases several neutrons and large amounts of gamma radiation and energy. The neutrons emitted have high energies and bombard more uranium-235 nuclei. As fission continues, there is a rapid increase in the number of high-energy neutrons capable of splitting more uranium atoms, a process called a **chain reaction**. To sustain a nuclear chain reaction, sufficient quantities of uranium-235 must be brought together to provide a critical mass in which almost all the neutrons immediately collide with more uranium-235 nuclei. So much heat and energy are released that an atomic explosion can occur. (See Figure 4.9.)

Nuclear Fusion

In **fusion**, two small nuclei such as those in hydrogen combine to form a larger nucleus. Mass is lost, and a tremendous amount of energy is released, even more than the energy released from nuclear fission. However, a fusion reaction requires a temperature of 100 000 000 °C to overcome the repulsion of the hydrogen nuclei and cause them to undergo fusion. Fusion reactions occur continuously in the sun and other stars, providing us with heat and light. The huge amounts of energy produced by our sun come from the fusion of 6×10^{11} kg of hydrogen every second. The following fusion reaction involves the combination of two isotopes of hydrogen.

$$\,^{3}_{1}H + \,^{2}_{1}H \longrightarrow \,^{4}_{2}He + \,^{1}_{0}n + \text{energy}$$

Scientists expect less radioactive waste with shorter half-lives from fusion reactors. However, fusion is still in the experimental stage because the extremely high temperatures needed have been difficult to reach and even more difficult to maintain. Research groups around the world are attempting to develop the technology needed to make the harnessing of the fusion reaction for energy a reality in our lifetime.

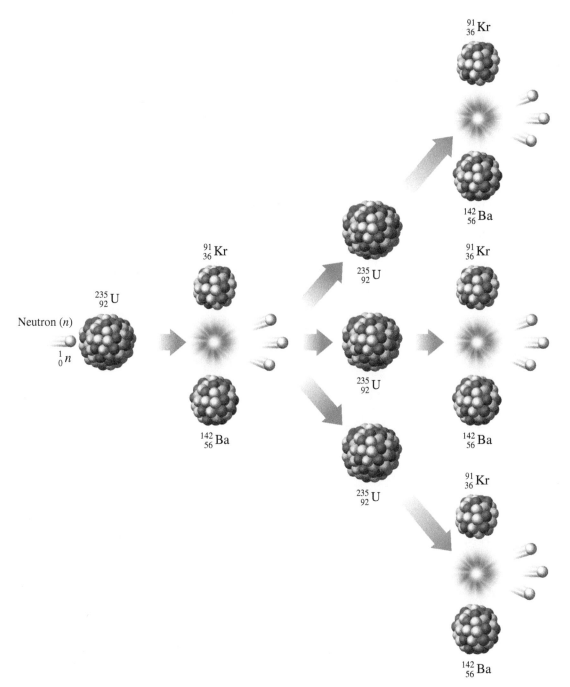

FIGURE 4.9 In a nuclear chain reaction, the fission of each uranium-235 atom produces three neutrons that cause the nuclear fission of more and more uranium-235 atoms.

Q Why is the fission of uranium-235 called a chain reaction?

CONCEPT CHECK 4.5

■ **Identifying Fission and Fusion**

Classify the following as pertaining to nuclear fission, nuclear fusion, or both:

a. Small nuclei combine to form larger nuclei.
b. Large amounts of energy are released.
c. Extraordinarily high temperatures are needed for reaction.

ANSWER
a. When small nuclei are combined, the process is fusion.
b. Large amounts of energy are generated in both the fusion and fission processes.
c. An extremely high temperature is required for fusion.

GREEN CHEMISTRY NOTE

Nuclear Power Plants

In a nuclear power plant, the quantity of uranium-235 is held below a critical mass so that it cannot sustain a chain reaction. The fission reactions are slowed by placing control rods, which absorb some of the fast-moving neutrons, among the uranium samples. In this way, less fission occurs, and there is a slower, controlled production of energy. The heat from the controlled fission is used to produce steam. The steam drives a generator, which produces electricity. Approximately 10% of the electrical energy produced in the United States is generated in nuclear power plants.

Although nuclear power plants help meet some of our energy needs, there are some problems. One of the most serious is the production of radioactive by-products that have long half-lives. It is essential that these waste products be stored safely in a place where they do not contaminate the environment. Early in 1990, the Environmental Protection Agency gave its approval for the storage of radioactive hazardous wastes in chambers 2150 ft underground. In 1998, the Waste Isolation Pilot Plant (WIPP) repository site in New Mexico was ready to receive plutonium waste from former U.S. bomb factories. Although authorities claim the caverns are safe, some people are concerned with the safe transport of the radioactive waste by trucks on the highways.

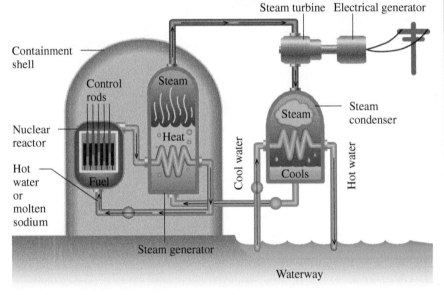

QUESTIONS AND PROBLEMS

Nuclear Fission and Fusion

4.39 What is nuclear fission?

4.40 How does a chain reaction occur in nuclear fission?

4.41 Complete the following fission reaction:

$$^{235}_{92}U + ^{1}_{0}n \longrightarrow ^{131}_{50}Sn + ? + 2\,^{1}_{0}n + energy$$

4.42 In another fission reaction, uranium-235 bombarded with a neutron produces strontium-94, another small nucleus, and 3 neutrons. Write the complete equation for the fission reaction.

4.43 Indicate whether each of the following is characteristic of the fission or fusion process or both:

a. Neutrons bombard a nucleus.
b. The nuclear process occurring in the sun.
c. A large nucleus splits into smaller nuclei.
d. Small nuclei combine to form larger nuclei.

4.44 Indicate whether each of the following is characteristic of the fission or fusion process or both:

a. Extremely high temperatures are required to initiate the reaction.
b. Less radioactive waste is produced.
c. Hydrogen nuclei are the reactants.
d. Large amounts of energy are released when the nuclear reaction occurs.

CONCEPT MAP

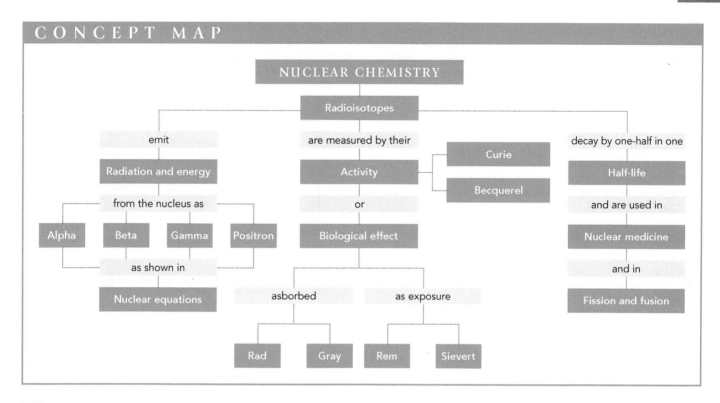

CHAPTER REVIEW

4.1 Natural Radioactivity
LEARNING GOAL: *Describe alpha, beta, positron, and gamma radiation.*
Radioactive isotopes have unstable nuclei that break down (decay), spontaneously emitting alpha (α), beta (β), positron (β), and gamma (γ) radiation. Because radiation can damage the cells in the body, proper protection must be used: shielding, limiting the time of exposure, and distance.

4.2 Nuclear Reactions
LEARNING GOAL: *Write an equation showing mass numbers and atomic numbers for radioactive decay.*
A balanced equation is used to represent the changes that take place in the nuclei of the reactants and products. The new isotopes and the type of radiation emitted can be determined from the symbols that show the mass numbers and atomic numbers of the isotopes in the nuclear reaction. A radioisotope is produced artificially when a nonradioactive isotope is bombarded by a small particle. Many radioactive isotopes used in nuclear medicine are produced in this way.

4.3 Radiation Measurement
LEARNING GOAL: *Describe the detection and measurement of radiation.*
In a Geiger counter, radiation produces charged particles in the gas contained in the tube, which generates an electrical current. The curie (Ci) measures the number of nuclear transformations of a radioactive sample. Activity is also measured in becquerel (Bq) units. The amount of radiation absorbed by a substance is measured in rads or the gray (Gy). The rem and the sievert (Sv) are units used to determine the biological damage from the different types of radiation.

4.4 Half-Life of a Radioisotope
LEARNING GOAL: *Given the half-life of a radioisotope, calculate the amount of radioisotope remaining after one or more half-lives.*
Every radioisotope has its own rate of emitting radiation. The time it takes for one-half of a radioactive sample to decay is called its half-life. For many medical radioisotopes, such as Tc-99m and I-131, half-lives are short. For other isotopes, usually naturally occurring ones such as C-14, Ra-226, and U-238, half-lives are extremely long.

4.5 Medical Applications Using Radioactivity
LEARNING GOAL: *Describe the use of radioisotopes in medicine.*
In nuclear medicine, radioisotopes that go to specific sites in the body are given to the patient. By detecting the radiation they emit, an evaluation can be made about the location and extent of an injury, disease, tumor, or the level of function of a particular organ. Higher levels of radiation are used to treat or destroy tumors.

4.6 Nuclear Fission and Fusion
LEARNING GOAL: *Describe the processes of nuclear fission and fusion.*
In fission, a large nucleus breaks apart into smaller pieces, releasing one or more types of radiation and a great amount of energy. In fusion, small nuclei combine to form a larger nucleus while great amounts of energy are released.

KEY TERMS

alpha particle A nuclear particle identical to a helium nucleus with symbol α or $^{4}_{2}\text{He}$.

becquerel (Bq) A unit of activity of a radioactive sample equal to one disintegration per second.

beta particle A particle identical to an electron with symbol β or $^{0}_{-1}e$ that forms in the nucleus when a neutron changes to a proton and an electron.

carbon dating A technique used to date ancient specimens that contain carbon. The age is determined by the amount of active carbon-14 that remains in the samples.

chain reaction A fission reaction that will continue once it has been initiated by a high-energy neutron bombarding a heavy nucleus such as uranium-235.

curie (Ci) A unit of radiation equal to 3.7×10^{10} disintegrations/s.

decay curve A diagram of the decay of a radioactive element.

equivalent dose The measure of biological damage from an absorbed dose that has been adjusted for the type of radiation.

fission A process in which large nuclei are split into smaller pieces, releasing large amounts of energy.

fusion A reaction in which large amounts of energy are released when small nuclei combine to form larger nuclei.

gamma ray High-energy radiation (with symbol $^{0}_{0}\gamma$) that is emitted by an unstable nucleus.

gray (Gy) A unit of absorbed dose equal to 100 rads.

half-life The length of time it takes for one-half of a radioactive sample to decay.

positron A particle with no mass and a positive charge produced when a proton is transformed into a neutron and a positron.

rad (radiation absorbed dose) A measure of an amount of radiation absorbed by the body.

radiation Energy or particles released by radioactive atoms.

radioactive decay The process by which an unstable nucleus breaks down and releases high-energy radiation.

rem (radiation equivalent in humans) A measure of the biological damage caused by the various kinds of radiation (rad $\times$ radiation biological factor).

scan The image of a site in the body created by the detection of radiation from radioactive isotopes that have accumulated in that site.

shielding Materials used to provide protection from radioactive sources.

sievert (Sv) A unit of biological damage (equivalent dose) equal to 100 rems.

■ UNDERSTANDING THE CONCEPTS

4.45 Consider the following nucleus of a radioactive isotope:

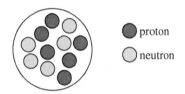

a. What is the nuclear symbol for this isotope?

b. If this isotope decays by emitting a positron, what does the resulting nucleus look like?

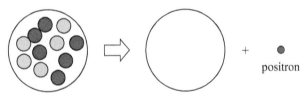

4.46 Sketch the nucleus that emits a beta particle to form the following nucleus:

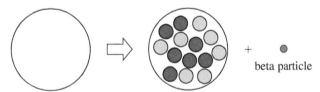

4.47 Sketch the nucleus of the atom to complete the following:

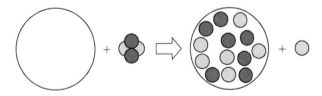

4.48 Complete the following by drawing the nucleus of the atom produced:

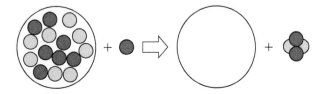

4.49 Carbon dating of small bits of charcoal used in cave paintings has determined that some of the paintings are from 10 000 to 30 000 years old. Carbon-14 has a half-life of 5730 years. In a 1 μg sample of carbon from a live tree, the activity of $^{14}_{6}C$ is 6.4 μCi. If researchers determine that 1 μg of charcoal from a prehistoric cave painting in France has an activity of 0.80 μCi, what is the age of the painting?

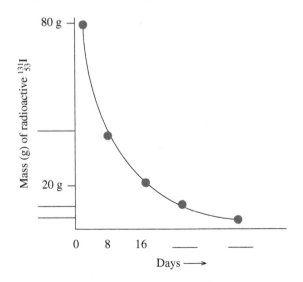

4.50 Using the decay curve for $^{131}_{53}I$, determine the following:

a. the values for the mass of radioactive $^{131}_{53}I$ on the vertical axis

b. the number of days on the horizontal axis

c. the half-life in days of $^{131}_{53}I$

ADDITIONAL QUESTIONS AND PROBLEMS

For instructor-assigned homework, go to www.masteringchemistry.com.

4.51 Give the number of protons and number of neutrons in the nucleus of each the following:
    a. sodium-25   **b.** nickel-61
    c. rubidium-84   **d.** silver-110

4.52 Give the number of protons, neutrons, and electrons in atoms of the following isotopes:
    a. boron-10   **b.** zinc-72
    c. iron-59   **d.** gold-198

4.53 Describe alpha, beta, and gamma radiation in terms of the following:
    a. type of radiation   **b.** symbols

4.54 Describe alpha, beta, and gamma radiation in terms of the following:
    a. depth of tissue penetration
    b. type of shielding needed for protection

4.55 Identify each of the following as alpha decay, beta decay, positron emission, or gamma radiation:
    a. $^{27m}_{13}\text{Al} \longrightarrow ^{27}_{13}\text{Al} + ^{0}_{0}\gamma$
    b. $^{8}_{5}\text{B} \longrightarrow ^{8}_{4}\text{Be} + ^{0}_{+1}e$
    c. $^{220}_{86}\text{Rn} \longrightarrow ^{216}_{84}\text{Po} + ^{4}_{2}\text{He}$

4.56 Identify each of the following as alpha decay, beta decay, positron emission, or gamma radiation:
    a. $^{127}_{55}\text{Cs} \longrightarrow ^{127}_{54}\text{Xe} + ^{0}_{+1}e$
    b. $^{90}_{38}\text{Sr} \longrightarrow ^{90}_{39}\text{Y} + ^{0}_{-1}e$
    c. $^{218}_{85}\text{At} \longrightarrow ^{214}_{83}\text{Bi} + ^{4}_{2}\text{He}$

4.57 Write a balanced nuclear equation for each of the following:
    a. Th-225 (α decay)
    b. Bi-210 (α decay)
    c. cesium-137 (β decay)
    d. tin-126 (β decay)
    e. nitrogen-13 (β^+ emission)

4.58 Write a balanced nuclear equation for each of the following:
    a. potassium-40 (β decay)
    b. sulfur-35 (β decay)
    c. platinum-190 (α decay)
    d. Ra-210 (α decay)
    e. In-113m (γ emission)

4.59 Complete each of the following nuclear equations:
    a. $^{14}_{7}\text{N} + ^{4}_{2}\text{He} \longrightarrow ? + ^{1}_{1}\text{H}$
    b. $^{27}_{13}\text{Al} + ^{4}_{2}\text{He} \longrightarrow ^{30}_{14}\text{Si} + ?$
    c. $^{235}_{92}\text{U} + ^{1}_{0}n \longrightarrow ^{90}_{38}\text{Sr} + 3^{1}_{0}n + ?$

4.60 Complete each of the following nuclear equations:
    a. $^{59}_{27}\text{Co} + ? \longrightarrow ^{56}_{25}\text{Mn} + ^{4}_{2}\text{He}$
    b. $? \longrightarrow ^{14}_{7}\text{N} + ^{0}_{-1}e$
    c. $^{76}_{36}\text{Kr} + ^{0}_{-1}e \longrightarrow ?$

4.61 Write the symbols and a balanced nuclear equation for the following:
    a. When two oxygen-16 atoms collide, one of the products is an alpha particle.
    b. When californium-249 is bombarded by oxygen-18, a new isotope and four neutrons are produced.
    c. Radon-222 undergoes alpha decay.
    d. The particle from **c.** undergoes alpha decay.

4.62 Write the symbols and a balanced nuclear equation for the following:
    a. Polonium-210 decays to give lead-206.
    b. Bismuth-211 decays by emitting an alpha particle.

    c. The product from **b.** emits a beta particle.
    d. When an alpha particle bombards aluminum-27, one product is silicon-30.

4.63 If the amount of radioactive phosphorus-32 in a sample decreases from 1.2 g to 0.30 g in 28 d, what is the half-life of phosphorus-32?

4.64 If the amount of radioactive iodine-123 in a sample decreases from 0.4 g to 0.1 g in 26.2 h, what is the half-life of iodine-123?

4.65 Iodine-131, a beta emitter, has a half-life of 8.0 d.
    a. Write the nuclear equation for the beta decay of iodine-131.
    b. How many grams of a 12.0-g sample of iodine-131 would remain after 40 d?
    c. How many days have passed if 48 g of iodine-131 decayed to 3.0 g of iodine-131?

4.66 Cesium-137, a beta emitter, has a half-life of 30 y.
    a. Write the nuclear equation for the beta decay of cesium-137.
    b. How many grams of a 16-g sample of cesium-137 would remain after 90 y?
    c. How many years will be needed for 28 g of cesium-137 to decay to 3.5 g of cesium-137?

4.67 A nurse was accidentally exposed to potassium-42 while doing some brain scans for possible tumors. The error was not discovered until 36 h later when the activity of the potassium-42 sample was 2.0 μCi. If potassium-42 has a half-life of 12 h, what was the activity of the sample at the time the nurse was exposed?

4.68 A wooden object from the site of an ancient temple has a carbon-14 activity of 10 counts per minute compared with a reference piece of wood cut today that has an activity of 40 counts per minute. If the half-life for carbon-14 is 5730 y, what is the age of the ancient wood object?

4.69 A 120-mg sample of technetium-99m is used for a diagnostic test. If technetium-99m has a half-life of 6.0 h, how much of the technetium-99m sample remains 24 h after the test?

4.70 The half-life of oxygen-15 is 124 s. If a sample of oxygen-15 has an activity of 4000 Bq, how many minutes will elapse before it reaches an activity of 500 Bq?

4.71 What is the purpose of irradiating meats, fruits, and vegetables?

4.72 The irradiation of foods was approved in the United States during the 1980s.
    a. Why have we not seen many irradiated products in our markets?
    b. Would you buy foods that have been irradiated? Why or why not?

4.73 What is the difference between fission and fusion?

4.74 a. What are the products in the fission of uranium-235 that make possible a nuclear chain reaction?
    b. What is the purpose of placing control rods among uranium samples in a nuclear reactor?

4.75 Where does fusion occur naturally?

4.76 Why are scientists continuing to try to build a fusion reactor even though the high temperatures needed have been difficult to reach and maintain?

CHALLENGE QUESTIONS

4.77 Identify each of the following nuclear reactions as alpha decay, beta decay, positron emission, or gamma radiation:

a. $^{27}_{13}\text{Al} \longrightarrow {}^{27}_{13}\text{Al} + {}^{0}_{0}\gamma$

b. $^{8}_{5}\text{B} \longrightarrow {}^{8}_{4}\text{Be} + {}^{0}_{+1}e$

c. $^{90}_{38}\text{Sr} \longrightarrow {}^{90}_{39}\text{Y} + {}^{0}_{-1}e$

d. $^{218}_{85}\text{At} \longrightarrow {}^{214}_{83}\text{Bi} + {}^{4}_{2}\text{He}$

4.78 Complete and balance each of the following nuclear equations:

a. $^{23m}_{12}\text{Mg} \longrightarrow \underline{\quad} + {}^{0}_{0}\gamma$

b. $^{61}_{30}\text{Zn} \longrightarrow {}^{61}_{29}\text{Cu} + \underline{\quad}$

c. $^{241}_{95}\text{Am} + {}^{4}_{2}\text{He} \longrightarrow \underline{\quad} + 2{}^{1}_{0}n$

d. $^{126}_{50}\text{Sn} \longrightarrow \underline{\quad} + {}^{0}_{-1}e$

4.79 Uranium-238 decays in a series of nuclear changes until stable $^{206}_{82}\text{Pb}$ is produced. Complete the following nuclear equations that are part of the $^{238}_{92}\text{U}$ decay series:

a. $^{238}_{92}\text{U} \longrightarrow {}^{234}_{90}\text{Th} + ?$

b. $^{234}_{90}\text{Th} \longrightarrow ? + {}^{0}_{-1}e$

c. $? \longrightarrow {}^{222}_{86}\text{Rn} + {}^{4}_{2}\text{He}$

4.80 The iceman known as "Ötzi" was discovered in a high mountain pass on the Austrian-Italian border. Samples of his hair and bones had carbon-14 activity that was about 50% of that present in new hair or bone. Carbon-14 is a beta emitter.

a. How long ago did "Ötzi" live if the half-life for C-14 is 5730 y?

b. Write a nuclear equation for the decay of carbon-14.

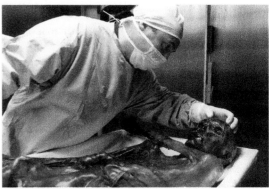

4.81 The half-life for the radioactive decay of calcium-47 is 4.5 d. If a sample has an activity of 4.0 μCi after 18 d, what was the initial activity of the sample?

4.82 A 16-μg sample of sodium-24 decays to 2.0 μg in 45 h. What is the half-life of sodium-24?

4.83 Write a balanced equation for each of the following radioactive emissions:

a. an alpha particle from Hg-180

b. a beta particle from Sn-126

c. a positron from Mn-49

4.84 Write a balanced equation for each of the following radioactive emissions:

a. an alpha particle from Gd-148

b. a beta particle from Sr-90

c. a positron from Al-25

ANSWERS

ANSWERS TO STUDY CHECKS

4.1 Distance from the radioactive source and minimizing the time of exposure

4.2 $^{214}_{84}\text{Po} \longrightarrow {}^{210}_{82}\text{Pb} + {}^{4}_{2}\text{He}$

4.3 $^{131}_{53}\text{I} \longrightarrow {}^{131}_{54}\text{Xe} + {}^{0}_{-1}e$

4.4 $^{27}_{13}\text{Al} + {}^{4}_{2}\text{He} \longrightarrow {}^{30}_{15}\text{P} + {}^{1}_{0}n$

4.5 For β, the factor is 1; rads and rems are equal.

4.6 0.50 g

4.7 17 200 y

4.8 $^{10}_{5}\text{B} + {}^{1}_{0}n \longrightarrow {}^{4}_{2}\text{He} + {}^{7}_{3}\text{Li}$

ANSWERS TO SELECTED QUESTIONS AND PROBLEMS

4.1 a. Both an alpha particle and a helium nucleus have two protons and two neutrons.

b. α, ${}^{4}_{2}\text{He}$

c. An α-particle is emitted from an unstable nucleus during radioactive decay.

4.3 a. $^{39}_{19}\text{K}$, $^{40}_{19}\text{K}$, $^{41}_{19}\text{K}$

b. They all have 19 protons and 19 electrons, but they differ in the number of neutrons.

4.5 Medical Use	Atomic Symbol	Mass Number	Number of Protons	Number of Neutrons
Heart imaging	$^{201}_{81}\text{Tl}$	201	81	120
Radiation therapy	$^{60}_{27}\text{Co}$	60	27	33
Abdominal scan	$^{67}_{31}\text{Ga}$	67	31	36
Hyperthyroidism	$^{131}_{53}\text{I}$	131	53	78
Leukemia treatment	$^{32}_{15}\text{P}$	32	15	17

4.7 a. α, ${}^{4}_{2}\text{He}$ b. ${}^{1}_{0}n$, n c. β, ${}^{0}_{-1}e$

d. $^{15}_{7}\text{N}$ e. $^{125}_{53}\text{I}$

4.9 a. β or ${}^{0}_{-1}e$ b. α or ${}^{4}_{2}\text{He}$ c. ${}^{1}_{0}n$

d. $^{24}_{11}\text{Na}$ e. $^{14}_{6}\text{C}$

4.11 a. Because β particles are much smaller and move faster than α particles, they can penetrate farther into tissue.

b. When radiation interacts with the components of the cells, reactive species are formed that cause undesirable reactions.

c. Radiation technicians leave the room to increase the distance between them and the radiation. Also, a wall that contains lead shields them.

d. Wearing gloves shields the skin from α and β radiation.

4.13 a. $^{208}_{84}\text{Po} \longrightarrow {}^{204}_{82}\text{Pb} + {}^{4}_{2}\text{He}$

b. $^{232}_{90}\text{Th} \longrightarrow {}^{228}_{88}\text{Ra} + {}^{4}_{2}\text{He}$

c. $^{251}_{102}\text{No} \longrightarrow ^{247}_{100}\text{Fm} + ^{4}_{2}\text{He}$

d. $^{220}_{86}\text{Rn} \longrightarrow ^{216}_{84}\text{Po} + ^{4}_{2}\text{He}$

4.15 a. $^{25}_{11}\text{Na} \longrightarrow ^{25}_{12}\text{Mg} + ^{0}_{-1}e$

b. $^{20}_{8}\text{O} \longrightarrow ^{20}_{9}\text{F} + ^{0}_{-1}e$

c. $^{92}_{38}\text{Sr} \longrightarrow ^{92}_{39}\text{Y} + ^{0}_{-1}e$

d. $^{42}_{19}\text{K} \longrightarrow ^{42}_{20}\text{Ca} + ^{0}_{-1}e$

4.17 a. $^{26}_{14}\text{Si} \longrightarrow ^{26}_{13}\text{Al} + ^{0}_{+1}e$

b. $^{54}_{27}\text{Co} \longrightarrow ^{54}_{26}\text{Fe} + ^{0}_{+1}e$

c. $^{77}_{37}\text{Rb} \longrightarrow ^{77}_{36}\text{Kr} + ^{0}_{+1}e$

d. $^{93}_{45}\text{Rh} \longrightarrow ^{93}_{44}\text{Ru} + ^{0}_{+1}e$

4.19 a. $^{28}_{14}\text{Si}$ **b.** $^{87}_{36}\text{Kr}$ **c.** $^{0}_{-1}e$

d. $^{238}_{92}\text{U}$ **e.** $^{188}_{79}\text{Au}$

4.21 a. $^{10}_{4}\text{Be}$ **b.** $^{0}_{-1}e$ **c.** $^{27}_{13}\text{Al}$ **d.** $^{30}_{15}\text{P}$

4.23 a. When radiation enters the Geiger counter, charged particles are produced that create a burst of current that is detected by the instrument.

b. becquerel (Bq), curie (Ci)

c. gray (Gy), rad

d. 1000 Gy

4.25 294 μCi

4.27 When pilots are flying at high altitudes, there is less atmosphere to protect them from cosmic radiation.

4.29 A half-life is the time it takes for one-half of a radioactive sample to decay.

4.31 a. 40.0 mg

b. 20.0 mg

c. 10.0 mg

d. 5.00 mg

4.33 130 days, 195 days

4.35 a. Because the elements Ca and P are part of bone, their radioactive isotopes will also become part of the bony structures of the body where their radiation can be used to diagnose or treat bone diseases.

b. $^{89}_{38}\text{Sr} \longrightarrow ^{89}_{39}\text{Y} + ^{0}_{-1}e$

Strontium (Sr) acts much like calcium (Ca) because both are Group 2A (2) elements. The body will accumulate radioactive strontium in bones in the same way that it incorporates calcium. Once the strontium isotope is absorbed by the bone, the beta radiation will destroy cancer cells.

4.37 180 μCi

4.39 Nuclear fission is the splitting of a large atom into smaller fragments with the release of large amounts of energy.

4.41 $^{103}_{42}\text{Mo}$

4.43 a. fission

b. fusion

c. fission

d. fusion

4.45 a. $^{11}_{6}\text{C}$

b.

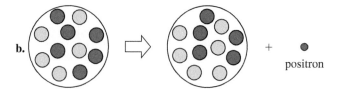

positron

4.47

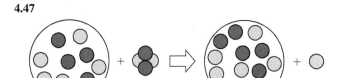

4.49 17 200 years old

4.51 a. 11 protons and 14 neutrons

b. 28 protons and 33 neutrons

c. 37 protons and 47 neutrons

d. 47 protons and 63 neutrons

4.53 a. In alpha decay, a helium nucleus is emitted from a radioisotope. In beta decay, a neutron in an unstable nucleus is converted to a proton and electron, which is emitted as a beta particle. In gamma emission, high-energy radiation is emitted from the nucleus of a radioisotope.

b. $\alpha, ^{4}_{2}\text{He}$ $\beta, ^{0}_{-1}e$ $\gamma, ^{0}_{0}\gamma$

4.55 a. gamma radiation

b. positron emission

c. alpha decay

4.57 a. $^{225}_{90}\text{Th} \longrightarrow ^{221}_{88}\text{Ra} + ^{4}_{2}\text{He}$

b. $^{210}_{83}\text{Bi} \longrightarrow ^{206}_{81}\text{Tl} + ^{4}_{2}\text{He}$

c. $^{137}_{55}\text{Cs} \longrightarrow ^{137}_{56}\text{Ba} + ^{0}_{-1}e$

d. $^{126}_{50}\text{Sn} \longrightarrow ^{126}_{51}\text{Sb} + ^{0}_{-1}e$

e. $^{13}_{7}\text{N} \longrightarrow ^{13}_{6}\text{C} + ^{0}_{+1}e$

4.59 a. $^{17}_{8}\text{O}$ **b.** $^{1}_{1}\text{H}$ **c.** $^{143}_{54}\text{Xe}$

4.61 a. $^{16}_{8}\text{O} + ^{16}_{8}\text{O} \longrightarrow ^{4}_{2}\text{He} + ^{28}_{14}\text{Si}$

b. $^{249}_{98}\text{Cf} + ^{18}_{8}\text{O} \longrightarrow ^{263}_{106}\text{Sg} + 4^{1}_{0}n$

c. $^{222}_{86}\text{Rn} \longrightarrow ^{218}_{84}\text{Po} + ^{4}_{2}\text{He}$

d. $^{218}_{84}\text{Po} \longrightarrow ^{214}_{82}\text{Pb} + ^{4}_{2}\text{He}$

4.63 14 d

4.65 a. $^{131}_{53}\text{I} \longrightarrow ^{0}_{-1}e + ^{131}_{54}\text{Xe}$

b. 0.375 g **c.** 32 d

4.67 16 μCi

4.69 7.5 mg

4.71 The irradiation of meats, fruits, and vegetables kills bacteria such as *E. coli* that can cause food-borne illnesses. In addition, spoilage is deterred, and shelf life is extended.

4.73 In the fission process, an atom splits into smaller nuclei. In fusion, small nuclei combine (fuse) to form a larger nucleus.

4.75 Fusion occurs naturally in the sun and other stars.

4.77 a. gamma radiation

b. positron emission

c. beta decay **d.** alpha decay

4.79 a. $^{238}_{92}\text{U} \longrightarrow ^{234}_{90}\text{Th} + ^{4}_{2}\text{He}$

b. $^{234}_{90}\text{Th} \longrightarrow ^{234}_{91}\text{Pa} + ^{0}_{-1}e$

c. $^{226}_{88}\text{Ra} \longrightarrow ^{222}_{86}\text{Rn} + ^{4}_{2}\text{He}$

4.81 4 half-lives; 64 μCi

4.83 a. $^{180}_{80}\text{Hg} \longrightarrow ^{176}_{78}\text{Pt} + ^{4}_{2}\text{He}$

b. $^{126}_{50}\text{Sn} \longrightarrow ^{126}_{51}\text{Sb} + ^{0}_{-1}e$

c. $^{49}_{25}\text{Mn} \longrightarrow ^{49}_{24}\text{Cr} + ^{0}_{+1}e$

5

Compounds and Their Bonds

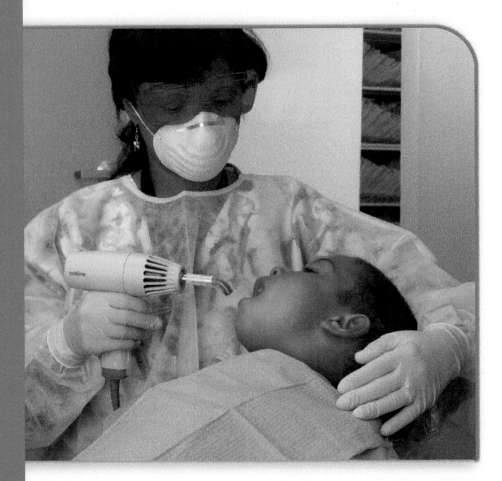

"One way to prevent cavities in children is to apply a thin, plastic coating called a sealant to their teeth," says Dr. Pam Alston, a dentist in private practice. "We look for teeth with deep grooves and pits that trap food. We clean the teeth and apply an etching agent, which helps the sealant bind to the teeth. Then we apply the liquid sealant, which fills in the grooves and pits, and use ultraviolet light to solidify the coating."

The use of fluoride compounds, such as SnF_2 in toothpaste and NaF in water, and mouth rinses have greatly reduced tooth decay. The fluoride ion replaces the hydroxide ion to form $Ca_{10}(PO_4)_6F_2$, which strengthens the enamel and makes it less susceptible to decay. Other compounds used in dentistry are the anesthetic known as laughing gas (N_2O) and Novocaine ($C_{13}H_{20}N_2O_2$).

Mastering**CHEMISTRY**™

Visit **www.masteringchemistry.com** for self-study materials and instructor-assigned homework.

I n nature, atoms of almost all the elements on the periodic table are found in combination with other atoms. Only the atoms of the noble gases—He, Ne, Ar, Kr, Xe, and Rn—do not combine in nature with other atoms. As discussed in Chapter 3, a compound is a pure substance, composed of two or more elements, with a definite composition. In a typical ionic compound, one or more electrons are transferred from the atoms of metals to atoms of nonmetals. The attraction that results is called an *ionic bond*. We use many ionic compounds every day. When we cook or bake, we use ionic compounds such as salt ($NaCl$) and baking soda ($NaHCO_3$). Epsom salts ($MgSO_4$) may be used to soak sore feet. Milk of magnesia ($Mg(OH)_2$) or calcium carbonate ($CaCO_3$) may be taken to settle an upset stomach. In a mineral supplement, iron is present as iron(II) sulfate ($FeSO_4$). Certain sunscreens contain zinc oxide (ZnO) and the tin(II) fluoride (SnF_2) in toothpaste provides fluoride to help prevent tooth decay.

The structures of ionic crystals result in the beautiful facets seen in gems. Sapphires and rubies are made of aluminum oxide (Al_2O_3). Impurities of chromium make rubies red, and iron and titanium make sapphires blue.

In compounds of nonmetals, covalent bonding occurs by atoms sharing one or more valence electrons. There are many more covalent compounds than there are ionic ones, and many simple covalent compounds are present in our everyday lives. For example, water (H_2O), oxygen (O_2), and carbon dioxide (CO_2) are all covalent compounds.

Covalent compounds consist of molecules, which are discrete groups of atoms. A molecule of water (H_2O) consists of two atoms of hydrogen and one atom of oxygen. When you have iced tea, perhaps you add molecules of sugar (sucrose), which is a covalent compound ($C_{12}H_{22}O_{11}$). Other covalent compounds include propane (C_3H_8), alcohol (C_2H_6O), the antibiotic amoxicillin ($C_{16}H_{19}N_3O_5S$), and the antidepressant Prozac ($C_{17}H_{18}F_3NO$).

5.1 Octet Rule and Ions

Most of the elements, except the noble gases, combine to form compounds. The noble gases are so stable that they form compounds only under extreme conditions. One explanation for the stability of noble gases is that they have an octet of 8 valence electrons. The exception is helium, which is stable with 2 electrons that fill its first energy level.

Compounds are the result of the formation of chemical bonds between two or more different elements. Ionic bonds occur when atoms of one element lose valence electrons and the atoms of another element gain valence electrons. Ionic compounds typically occur between metals and nonmetals. For example, atoms of sodium and chlorine form the ionic compound $NaCl$. Covalent bonds occur when atoms of nonmetals share valence electrons and form covalent compounds. For example, atoms of nitrogen and chlorine form the covalent compound NCl_3.

In the formation of either an ionic bond or a covalent bond, atoms lose, gain, or share valence electrons to acquire an octet. This tendency for atoms to attain a noble gas electron configuration is known as the **octet rule** and provides a key to our understanding of the ways in which atoms bond and form compounds.

Positive Ions

In ionic bonding, **ions**, which have electrical charges, form when atoms lose or gain valence electrons to form octets. Because the ionization energies of metals of Groups 1A (1), 2A (2), and 3A (13) are low, these metal atoms readily lose their valence electrons to nonmetals. In doing so, they acquire the electron configuration of a noble gas (8 valence electrons) and form ions with positive charges. For example, when a sodium atom loses its single valence electron, the remaining electrons have the noble gas configuration of neon. By losing an electron, sodium has 10 electrons instead of 11. Because there are still 11 protons in its nucleus, the atom is no longer neutral. It has become a sodium ion and has an

LEARNING GOAL

Using the octet rule, write the symbols of the simple ions for the representative elements.

MC **TUTORIAL**
Octet Rule and Ions

Loss and gain of electrons   Sharing electrons

Ionic bond   Covalent bond

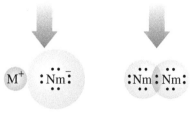
M is a metal
Nm is a nonmetal

electrical charge, called an **ionic charge**, of $1+$. In the symbol for the sodium ion, the ionic charge of $1+$ is written as $+$ in the upper right-hand corner, Na^+.

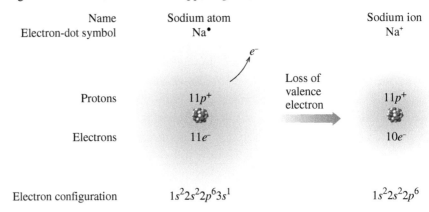

Metals in ionic compounds lose their valence electrons to form positively charged ions called **cations** (pronounced *cat'-ions*). Magnesium, a metal in Group 2A (2), attains a noble gas electron configuration like neon by losing 2 valence electrons to form a positive ion with a 2+ ionic charge. A metal ion is named by its element name. Thus, Mg^{2+} is named the *magnesium* ion.

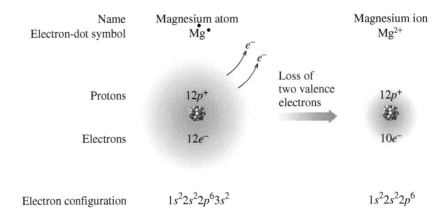

Negative Ions

Nonmetals form negative ions when they gain valence electrons to attain an octet. For example, an atom of chlorine with 7 valence electrons obtains 1 electron to have an octet and the electron configuration of argon, a noble gas. By acquiring an electron, a chlorine atom becomes a particle called a *chloride* ion (Cl^-), which has a $1-$ charge. Ions with negative charges are called **anions** (pronounced *an'-ions*). The name of an anion uses the first syllable of the element name followed by *ide*.

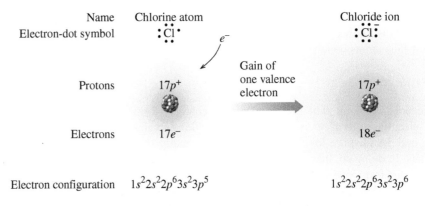

Table 5.1 lists the names of some important metal and nonmetal ions.

TABLE 5.1 Formulas and Names of Some Common Ions

Group Number	Formula of Ion	Name of Ion	Group Number	Formula of Ion	Name of Ion
	Metals			**Nonmetals**	
1A (1)	Li^+	Lithium	5A (15)	N^{3-}	Nitride
	Na^+	Sodium		P^{3-}	Phosphide
	K^+	Potassium	6A (16)	O^{2-}	Oxide
2A (2)	Mg^{2+}	Magnesium		S^{2-}	Sulfide
	Ca^{2+}	Calcium	7A (17)	F^-	Fluoride
	Ba^{2+}	Barium		Cl^-	Chloride
3A (13)	Al^{3+}	Aluminum		Br^-	Bromide
				I^-	Iodide

CONCEPT CHECK 5.1

■ Ions

a. Write the symbol and name of the ion that has 7 protons and 10 electrons.
b. State the number of protons and electrons in a calcium ion, Ca^{2+}.

ANSWER

a. The element with 7 protons is nitrogen. An ion of nitrogen with 10 electrons has an ionic charge of 3— and is called a *nitride* ion, N^{3-}.
b. In a calcium ion, Ca^{2+}, there are 20 protons. The ionic charge of 2+ indicates a loss of 2 electrons, which gives a total of 18 electrons in the calcium ion.

Ionic Charges from Group Numbers

Group numbers can be used to determine the ionic charges for most ions of the representative elements. We have seen that metals lose electrons to form positive ions. The elements in Groups 1A (1), 2A (2), and 3A (13) lose 1, 2, and 3 electrons, respectively. Group 1A (1) metals form ions with 1+ charges, Group 2A (2) metals form ions with 2+ charges, and Group 3A (13) metals form ions with 3+ charges.

The nonmetals from Groups 5A (15), 6A (16), and 7A (17) form negative ions. Group 5A (15) nonmetals usually form ions with 3— charges, Group 6A (16) nonmetals form ions with 2— charges, and Group 7A (17) nonmetals form ions with 1— charges. The nonmetals of Group 4A (14) do not typically form ions. Table 5.2 lists the ionic charges for some common ions of representative elements.

TABLE 5.2 Positive and Negative Ions Have the Same Electron Configuration as the Nearest Noble Gases

Noble Gases		Metals Lose Valence Electrons			Nonmetals Gain Valence Electrons				Noble Gases
		1A (1)	2A (2)	3A (13)	5A (15)	6A (16)	7A (17)		
He	⇐	Li^+							
Ne	⇐	Na^+	Mg^{2+}	Al^{3+}	N^{3-}	O^{2-}	F^-	⇒	Ne
Ar	⇐	K^+	Ca^{2+}		P^{3-}	S^{2-}	Cl^-	⇒	Ar
Kr	⇐	Rb^+	Sr^{2+}				Br^-	⇒	Kr
Xe	⇐	Cs^+	Ba^{2+}				I^-	⇒	Xe

HEALTH NOTE

Some Uses for Noble Gases

Noble gases may be used when an unreactive substance is required. Scuba divers normally use a pressurized mixture of nitrogen and oxygen gases for breathing under water. However, when the air mixture is used at depths where pressure is high, the nitrogen gas is absorbed into the blood, where it can cause mental disorientation. To avoid this problem, a breathing mixture of oxygen and helium may be substituted. The diver still obtains the necessary oxygen, but the unreactive helium that dissolves in the blood does not cause mental disorientation. However, its lower density does change the vibrations of the vocal cords, and the diver will sound like Donald Duck.

Helium is also used to fill blimps and balloons. When dirigibles were first designed, they were filled with hydrogen, the lightest gas. However, when they encountered any type of spark or heating source, the dirigibles exploded violently because of the extreme reactivity of hydrogen gas with oxygen present in the air. Today blimps are filled with unreactive helium gas, which presents no danger of explosion.

Lighting tubes are generally filled with a noble gas such as neon or the filament would soon burn up.

Sizes of Atoms and Their Ions

The size of ions for the representative elements compared to the size of their atoms is much smaller for metals and much larger for nonmetals.

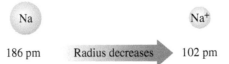

If we look at the relative sizes of the positive ions in Group 1A (1), we see that they are about half the size of their corresponding metal atoms. This size change occurs because metal atoms lose all of their valence electrons from their outermost energy levels. For example, a sodium atom has one electron in the third energy level. When that valence electron is lost and the sodium ion is formed, the outermost energy level becomes the second energy level, which has an octet.

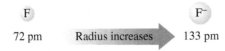

186 pm   Radius decreases   102 pm

The size of nonmetal atoms increases because they gain electrons in the outermost energy level. For example, a valence electron adds to the second energy level of fluorine to complete an octet, which increases the repulsion among the electrons and increases the size of the fluoride ion.

F   F⁻

72 pm   Radius increases   133 pm

SAMPLE PROBLEM   5.1

■ Writing Ions

Consider the elements aluminum and oxygen.

a. Identify each as a metal or a nonmetal.
b. State the number of valence electrons for each.
c. State the number of electrons that must be lost or gained for each to acquire an octet.
d. Write the symbol and name of each resulting ion, including its ionic charge.

SOLUTION

Aluminum	**Oxygen**
a. metal	nonmetal
b. 3 valence electrons	6 valence electrons
c. loses $3e^-$	gains $2e^-$
d. Al^{3+}, aluminum ion	O^{2-}, oxide ion

STUDY CHECK

What are the symbols and names for the ions formed by potassium and sulfur?

HEALTH NOTE

Some Important Ions in the Body

Several ions in body fluids have important physiological and metabolic functions. Some of them are listed in Table 5.3.

TABLE 5.3 Ions in the Body

Ion	Occurrence	Function	Source	Result of Too Little	Result of Too Much
Na^+	Principal cation outside the cell	Regulation and control of body fluids	Salt, cheese, pickles, potato chips, pretzels	Hyponatremia, anxiety, diarrhea, circulatory failure, decrease in body fluid	Hypernatremia, little urine, thirst, edema
K^+	Principal cation inside the cell	Regulation of body fluids and cellular functions	Bananas, orange juice, milk, prunes, potatoes	Hypokalemia (hypopotassemia), lethargy, muscle weakness, failure of neurological impulses	Hyperkalemia (hyperpotassemia), irritability, nausea, little urine, cardiac arrest
Ca^{2+}	Cation outside the cell; 90% of calcium in the body in bone as $Ca_3(PO_4)_2$ or $CaCO_3$	Major cation of bone; needed for muscle contraction	Milk, yogurt, cheese, greens, spinach	Hypocalcemia, tingling fingertips, muscle cramps, osteoporosis	Hypercalcemia, relaxed muscles, kidney stones, deep bone pain
Mg^{2+}	Cation outside the cell; 70% of magnesium in the body in bone structure	Essential for certain enzymes, muscles, nerve control	Widely distributed (part of chlorophyll of all green plants), nuts, whole grains	Disorientation, hypertension, tremors, slow pulse	Drowsiness
Cl^-	Principal anion outside the cell	Gastric juice, regulation of body fluids	Salt	Same as for Na^+	Same as for Na^+

QUESTIONS AND PROBLEMS

Octet Rule and Ions

5.1 State the number of electrons that must be lost by atoms of each of the following elements to acquire a noble gas electron configuration:

a. Li   **b.** Mg
c. Al   **d.** Cs
e. Ba

5.2 State the number of electrons that must be gained by atoms of each of the following elements to acquire a noble gas electron configuration:

a. Cl   **b.** O
c. N   **d.** I
e. P

5.3 Write the symbols of the ions with the following number of protons and electrons:

a. 3 protons, 2 electrons
b. 9 protons, 10 electrons
c. 12 protons, 10 electrons
d. 26 protons, 23 electrons

5.4 Write the symbols of the ions with the following number of protons and electrons:
  a. 30 protons, 28 electrons
  b. 53 protons, 54 electrons
  c. 82 protons, 78 electrons
  d. 15 protons, 18 electrons

5.5 How many protons and electrons are in the following ions?
  a. O^{2-} **b.** K^+
  c. Br^- **d.** S^{2-}

5.6 How many protons and electrons are in the following ions?
  a. Sr^{2+} **b.** F^-
  c. Au^{3+} **d.** Cs^+

5.7 Write the symbol for the ion of each of the following:
  a. chlorine   **b.** potassium
  c. oxygen   **d.** aluminum

5.8 Write the symbol for the ion of each of the following:
  a. fluorine   **b.** calcium
  c. sodium   **d.** lithium

5.9 Select the larger atom or ion in each of the following pairs:
  a. K or K^+ **b.** Cl^- or Cl
  c. Ca or Ca^{2+} **d.** K^+ or Li^+

5.10 Select the smaller atom or ion in each of the following pairs:
  a. S or S^{2-} **b.** Al or Al^{3+}
  c. F^- or Cl^- **d.** I or I^-

5.2 | Ionic Compounds

LEARNING GOAL

Using charge balance, write the correct formula for an ionic compound.

TUTORIAL
Ionic Compounds

Ionic compounds consist of positive and negative ions. The ions are held together by strong attractions between the oppositely charged ions called **ionic bonds**.

Properties of Ionic Compounds

The physical and chemical properties of an ionic compound such as NaCl are very different from those of the original elements. For example, the original elements of NaCl were sodium, which is a soft, shiny metal, and chlorine, which is a yellow-green poisonous gas. As positive and negative ions, however, they form table salt, NaCl, a hard, white, crystalline substance that is common in our diet. In ionic compounds, the attraction between the positive and negative ions is extremely strong, which makes the melting points of ionic compounds high, often more than 500 °C. For instance, the melting point of NaCl is 801 °C. At room temperature, ionic compounds are solids.

The structure of an ionic solid depends on the arrangement of the ions. In a crystal of NaCl, which has a cubic shape, the larger Cl^- ions (green) are packed close together in a structure as shown in Figure 5.1. The smaller Na^+ ions (shown in gray) occupy the holes between the Cl^- ions.

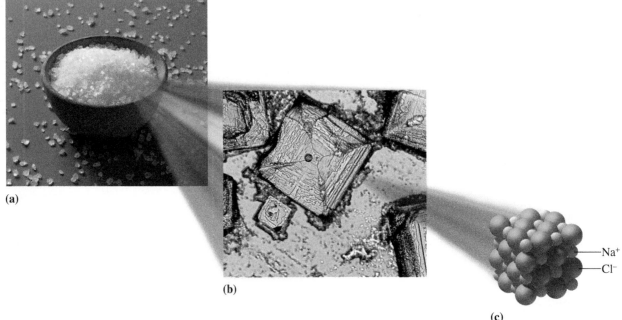

(a)

(b)

(c)

—Na^+
—Cl^-

FIGURE 5.1 **(a)** The elements sodium and chlorine react to form the ionic compound sodium chloride, the compound that makes up table salt. **(b)** Crystals of NaCl under magnification. **(c)** A diagram of the arrangements of Na^+ and Cl^- packed together in a NaCl crystal.
Q What is the type of bonding between Na^+ and Cl^- ions in salt?

Charge Balance in Ionic Compounds

The **formula** of an ionic compound indicates the number and kinds of ions that make up the ionic compound. The sum of the ionic charges in the formula is always zero, which means that the total amount of positive charge is equal to the total amount of negative charge. For example, the NaCl formula indicates that there is one sodium ion, Na^+, for every chloride ion, Cl^-, in the compound. Note that the ionic charges of the ions do not appear in the formula of the ionic compound.

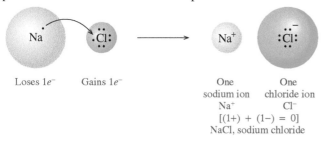

Loses $1e^-$ Gains $1e^-$

One sodium ion Na^+ One chloride ion Cl^-
$[(1+) + (1-) = 0]$
NaCl, sodium chloride

Subscripts in Formulas

Consider a compound of magnesium and chlorine. To achieve an octet, a Mg atom loses its two valence electrons to form Mg^{2+}. Each Cl atom gains one electron to form Cl^-, which has a complete valence energy level. In this example, two Cl^- ions are needed to balance the positive charge of Mg^{2+}. This gives the formula $MgCl_2$, magnesium chloride, in which the subscript 2 shows that two Cl^- were needed for charge balance.

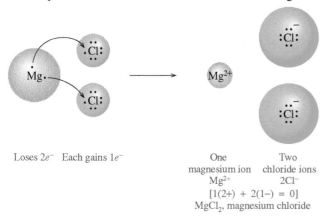

Loses $2e^-$ Each gains $1e^-$

One magnesium ion Mg^{2+} Two chloride ions $2Cl^-$
$[1(2+) + 2(1-) = 0]$
$MgCl_2$, magnesium chloride

Writing Ionic Formulas from Ionic Charges

The subscripts in the formula of an ionic compound represent the number of positive and negative ions that give an overall charge of zero. Thus, we can now write a formula directly from the ionic charges of the positive and negative ions. In the formula of an ionic compound, the cation is written first and is followed by the anion. Suppose we wish to write the formula of the ionic compound containing Na^+ and S^{2-} ions. To balance the ionic charge of the S^{2-} ion, we show two Na^+ ions by using a subscript 2 in the formula. This gives the formula Na_2S, which has an overall charge of zero. When there is no subscript for a symbol such as the S in Na_2S, it assumed to be 1.

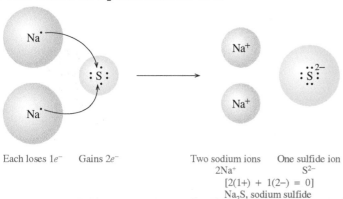

Each loses $1e^-$ Gains $2e^-$

Two sodium ions $2Na^+$ One sulfide ion S^{2-}
$[2(1+) + 1(2-) = 0]$
Na_2S, sodium sulfide

CAREER FOCUS

Physical Therapist

"Physical therapists need to understand how the body, muscles, and joints function in order to recognize when something is not working and which area needs strengthening," says Vincent Leddy, a physical therapist. "Chemistry is important to understanding the body's physiology and how chemical changes in the body affect movement. I went into physical therapy because I enjoy teaching movement to children. I am guiding Maggie into her chair but allowing her to move as much as she can by herself. I help her by giving gentle pressure and reassurance so that she'll be safe in the transition. I work on getting Maggie to use her body, and the occupational therapist works on Maggie's fine motor skills and how she uses her hand on the switch or picks up objects. By using both physical and occupational therapy, we enhance the child's performance."

■ **Writing Formulas from Ionic Charges**

Determine ionic charges and write the formula for the ionic compound formed when lithium and nitrogen react.

ANSWER

Lithium in Group 1A (1) forms Li^+; nitrogen in Group 5A (15) forms N^{3-}. The charge of $3-$ for N^{3-} is balanced by three Li^+ ions. Writing the positive ion first gives the formula Li_3N.

QUESTIONS AND PROBLEMS

Ionic Compounds

5.11 Which of the following pairs of elements are likely to form ionic compounds?
  a. lithium and chlorine
  b. oxygen and chlorine
  c. potassium and oxygen
  d. sodium and neon
  e. sodium and magnesium
  f. nitrogen and chlorine

5.12 Which of the following pairs of elements are likely to form ionic compounds?
  a. helium and oxygen
  b. magnesium and chlorine
  c. chlorine and bromine
  d. potassium and sulfur
  e. sodium and potassium
  f. nitrogen and oxygen

5.13 Write the correct ionic formula for compounds formed between the following ions:

  a. Na^+ and O^{2-} **b.** Al^{3+} and Br^-
  c. Ba^{2+} and O^{2-} **d.** Mg^{2+} and Cl^-
  e. Al^{3+} and S^{2-}

5.14 Write the correct ionic formula for compounds formed between the following ions:
  a. Al^{3+} and Cl^- **b.** Ca^{2+} and S^{2-}
  c. Li^+ and S^{2-} **d.** K^+ and N^{3-}
  e. K^+ and I^-

5.15 Determine the ions and write the correct formula for ionic compounds formed by the following metals and nonmetals:
  a. sodium and sulfur   **b.** potassium and nitrogen
  c. aluminum and iodine   **d.** lithium and oxygen

5.16 Determine the ions and write the correct formula for ionic compounds formed by the following metals and nonmetals:
  a. calcium and chlorine
  b. barium and bromine
  c. sodium and phosphorus
  d. magnesium and oxygen

5.3 | Naming and Writing Ionic Formulas

LEARNING GOAL

Given the formula of an ionic compound, write the correct name; given the name of an ionic compound, write the correct formula.

TUTORIAL
Writing Ionic Formulas

As we determined in section 5.2, the name of a metal ion is the same as its elemental name. The name of a nonmetal ion is obtained by using the first syllable of its elemental name followed by *ide*. The name of the compound includes a space between the names of the metal and nonmetal.

Naming Ionic Compounds Containing Two Elements

In the name of an ionic compound made up of two elements, the metal ion is named followed by the name of the nonmetal ion. Subscripts are never mentioned; they are understood because of the charge balance of the ions in the compound. (See Table 5.4.)

TABLE 5.4   Names of Some Ionic Compounds

Compound	Metal Ion	Nonmetal Ion	Name
NaF	Na^+ Sodium	F^- Fluoride	Sodium fluoride
$MgBr_2$	Mg^{2+} Magnesium	Br^- Bromide	Magnesium bromide
Al_2O_3	Al^{3+} Aluminum	O^{2-} Oxide	Aluminum oxide

SAMPLE PROBLEM 5.2

■ Naming Ionic Compounds

Write the name of the ionic compound Mg_3N_2.

SOLUTION

STEP 1   **Identify the cation and anion.**   The cation from Group 2A (2) is Mg^{2+}, and the anion from Group 5A (15) is N^{3-}.

STEP 2   **Name the cation by its element name.**   The cation Mg^{2+} is magnesium.

STEP 3   **Name the anion by using the first syllable of its element name followed by *ide*.**   The anion N^{3-} is nitride.

STEP 4   **Write the name of the cation first and the name of the anion second.** Mg_3N_2 is named *magnesium nitride*.

STUDY CHECK

Name the compound Ga_2S_3.

Guide to Naming Ionic Compounds with Metals That Form a Single Ion

STEP 1
Identify the cation and anion.

STEP 2
Name the cation by its element name.

STEP 3
Name the anion by using the first syllable of its element name followed by *ide*.

STEP 4
Write the name of the cation first and the name of the anion second.

Metals with Variable Charge

The transition metals typically form two or more kinds of positive ions because they lose their outer electrons as well as electrons from a lower energy level. For example, in some ionic compounds, iron is in the Fe^{2+} form; in other compounds, it takes the Fe^{3+} form. Copper also forms two different ions: Cu^+ is present in some compounds and Cu^{2+} in others. When a metal can form two or more ions, it is not possible to predict the ionic charge from the group number. We say that it has a *variable valence* or *variable charge*.

When different ions are possible for a metal, a naming system is needed to identify the particular cation in a compound. To do this, a Roman numeral that matches the ionic charge is placed in parentheses immediately after the elemental name of the metal. For the cations of iron, Fe^{2+} is named iron(II), and Fe^{3+} is named iron(III). Table 5.5 lists the ions of some common metals that produce two or more ions.

Figure 5.2 shows some common ions and their location on the periodic table. Typically, the transition metals form more than one positive ion. However, zinc, cadmium, and silver

TABLE 5.5 Some Metals That Form More Than One Positive Ion

Element	Possible Ions	Name of Ion
Chromium	Cr^{2+}	Chromium(II)
	Cr^{3+}	Chromium(III)
Copper	Cu^+	Copper(I)
	Cu^{2+}	Copper(II)
Gold	Au^+	Gold(I)
	Au^{3+}	Gold(III)
Iron	Fe^{2+}	Iron(II)
	Fe^{3+}	Iron(III)
Lead	Pb^{2+}	Lead(II)
	Pb^{4+}	Lead(IV)
Tin	Sn^{2+}	Tin(II)
	Sn^{4+}	Tin(IV)

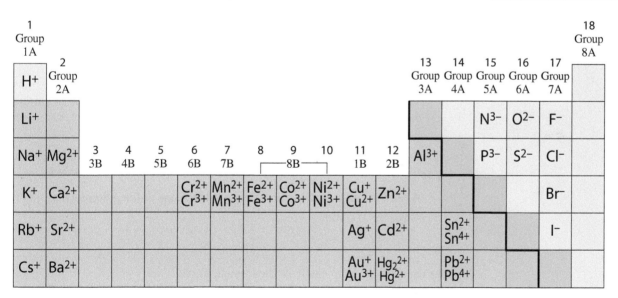

FIGURE 5.2 On the periodic table, positive ions are produced from metals and negative ions are produced from nonmetals.

Q What are the ions produced by calcium, copper, and oxygen?

form only one ion. The ionic charges of silver, cadmium, and zinc are fixed like Group 1A (1), 2A (2), and 3A (13) metals, so their elemental names are sufficient when naming their ionic compounds. Metals in Groups 4A (14) and 5A (15) also form more than one positive ion. For example, lead and tin in Group 4A (14) form cations with charges of 2+ and 4+.

The selection of the correct Roman numeral depends on the ionic charge of the transition metal in the formula. For example, we use charge balance to calculate the charge of the copper cation in the formula $CuCl_2$. Two chloride ions each have a 1− charge, which gives a total negative charge of 2−. To balance the 2− charge, the copper ion must have a positive charge of 2+, which is a Cu^{2+} ion:

$CuCl_2$

Cu charge $+ 2Cl^-$ charge $= 0$

(?) $\qquad + 2(1-) \qquad = 0$

(2+) $\qquad + (2-) \qquad = 0$

To indicate the copper ion Cu^{2+}, we place (II) after *copper* when naming the compound: copper(II) chloride.

Table 5.6 lists names of some ionic compounds in which the metals form two types of positive ions.

TABLE 5.6 Some Ionic Compounds of Metals That Form Two Kinds of Positive Ions

Compound	Systematic Name
$FeCl_2$	Iron(II) chloride
Fe_2O_3	Iron(III) oxide
Cu_3P	Copper(I) phosphide
$CuBr_2$	Copper(II) bromide
$SnCl_2$	Tin(II) chloride
PbS_2	Lead(IV) sulfide

Guide to Naming Ionic Compounds with Variable Charge Metals

STEP 1
Determine the charge of the cation from the anion.

STEP 2
Name the cation by its element name, and use a Roman numeral in parentheses for the charge.

STEP 3
Name the anion by using the first syllable of its element name followed by *ide*.

STEP 4
Write the name of the cation first and the name of the anion second.

SAMPLE PROBLEM   5.3

■ **Naming Ionic Compounds with Variable Charge Metal Ions**

Write the name for Cu_2S.

SOLUTION

STEP 1   Determine the charge of the cation from the anion. The nonmetal S in Group 6A (16) forms the S^{2-} ion. Because there are two Cu ions to balance the S^{2-}, the charge of each Cu ion is 1+.

	Metal	Nonmetal
Elements	Copper	Sulfur
Groups	Transition	6A (16)
Ions	Cu?	S^{2-}
Charge balance	2(1+)	(2−) = 0
Ions	Cu^+	S^{2-}

STEP 2   Name the cation by its element name, and use a Roman numeral in parentheses for the charge.

copper(I)

STEP 3   Name the anion by using the first syllable of its element name followed by *ide*.

sulfide

STEP 4   Write the name of the cation first and the name of the anion second.

copper(I) sulfide

STUDY CHECK

Write the name of the compound with the formula Au_2O.

SAMPLE PROBLEM   5.4

■ **Writing Formulas of Ionic Compounds**

Write the formula for iron(III) chloride.

SOLUTION

STEP 1   **Identify the cation and anion.**   The Roman numeral (III) indicates that the charge of the iron ion is $3+$, Fe^{3+}.

	Metal	**Nonmetal**
Elements	Iron(III)	Chlorine
Groups	Transition	7A (17)
Ions	Fe^{3+}	Cl^-

STEP 1
Identify the cation and anion.

STEP 2
Balance the charges.

STEP 3
Write the formula, cation first, using subscripts from charge balance.

STEP 2   **Balance the charges.**

$$Fe^{3+} \quad Cl^-$$
$$Cl^-$$
$$\underline{Cl^-}$$
$$\mathbf{1(3+) + 3(1-) = 0}$$

Becomes a subscript in the formula

STEP 3   **Write the formula, cation first, using subscripts from the charge balance.**

$FeCl_3$

STUDY CHECK

Write the correct formula for chromium(III) oxide.

QUESTIONS AND PROBLEMS

Naming and Writing Ionic Formulas

5.17 Write names for the following ionic compounds:
  a. Al_2O_3 **b.** $CaCl_2$
  c. Na_2O **d.** Mg_3N_2
  e. KI

5.18 Write names for the following ionic compounds:
  a. $MgCl_2$ **b.** K_3P
  c. Li_2S **d.** LiBr
  e. MgO

5.19 Why is a Roman numeral placed after the name of most transition metal ions?

5.20 The compound $CaCl_2$ is named calcium chloride; the compound $CuCl_2$ is named copper(II) chloride. Explain why a Roman numeral is used in one name but not in the other.

5.21 Write the names of the following Group 4A (14) and transition metal ions (include the Roman numeral when necessary):
  a. Fe^{2+} **b.** Cu^{2+}
  c. Zn^{2+} **d.** Pb^{4+}
  e. Cr^{3+}

5.22 Write the names of the following Group 4A (14) and transition metal ions (include the Roman numeral when necessary):
  a. Ag^+ **b.** Cu^+
  c. Fe^{3+} **d.** Sn^{2+}
  e. Au^{3+}

5.23 Write names for the following ionic compounds:
  a. $SnCl_2$ **b.** FeO
  c. Cu_2S **d.** CuS
  e. $CrBr_3$ **f.** $ZnCl_2$

5.24 Write names for the following ionic compounds:
  a. Ag_3P **b.** PbS
  c. Al_2O_3 **d.** $AuCl_3$
  e. FeS   **f.** Na_3N

5.25 Give the symbol of the cation in each of the following formulas:
  a. $AuCl_3$ **b.** Fe_2O_3
  c. PbI_4 **d.** $SnCl_2$

5.26 Give the symbol of the cation in each of the following formulas:
  a. $FeCl_2$ **b.** CuO
  c. Fe_2S_3 **d.** $CrCl_3$

5.27 Write formulas for the following ionic compounds:
  a. magnesium chloride
  b. sodium sulfide
  c. copper(I) oxide
  d. zinc phosphide
  e. gold(III) nitride
  f. chromium(II) chloride

5.28 Write formulas for the following ionic compounds:
  a. iron(III) oxide
  b. barium fluoride
  c. tin(IV) chloride
  d. silver sulfide
  e. copper(II) chloride
  f. lithium nitride

5.4 Polyatomic Ions

LEARNING GOAL

Write the name and formula of a compound containing a polyatomic ion.

TUTORIAL
Polyatomic Ions

Fertilizer
$NaNO_3$

Na⁺ NO_3^-
Nitrate ion

Plaster molding
$CaSO_4$

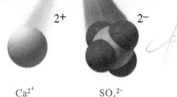

Ca^{2+} SO_4^{2-}
Sulfate ion

FIGURE 5.3 Many products contain polyatomic ions, which are groups of atoms that carry an ionic charge.

Q Why does the sulfate ion have a 2– charge?

An ionic compound with three or more elements contains a **polyatomic ion**, which is a group of atoms that has an ionic charge. Most polyatomic ions consist of a nonmetal such as phosphorus, sulfur, carbon, or nitrogen that has covalent bonds to one or more oxygen atoms. However, the covalent bonds do not contain a sufficient number of electrons to complete some of the octets. Thus, 1, 2, or 3 electrons are gained by the atoms in the group to complete their octets. This electron gain gives the negatively charged polyatomic ions ionic charges of $1-$, $2-$, or $3-$.

Naming Polyatomic Ions

Most polyatomic ions have a negative charge. Only one common polyatomic ion, NH_4^+, has a $1+$ ionic charge. The names of most common negatively charged polyatomic ions end in *ate*. When a related ion has one less oxygen atom, the *ite* ending is used for its name. By recognizing these endings, you can identify a polyatomic ion in the name of a compound. In the halogen family, the ions with just one oxygen atom are named by placing a prefix *hypo* in the name. The hydroxide ion (OH^-) and cyanide ion (CN^-) are exceptions to this naming pattern.

There is no easy way to learn polyatomic ions. You will need to memorize the number of oxygen atoms and the charge associated with each ion, as shown in Table 5.7. By memorizing the formulas and the names of the ions shown in the boxes, you can derive the related ions. For example, the sulfate ion is SO_4^{2-}. We write the formula of the sulfite ion, which has one less oxygen atom, as SO_3^{2-}. Note that the *ate* and *ite* ions of a particular nonmetal have the same ionic charge: sulfate and sulfite ions have $2-$ charges; phosphate and phosphite ions have $3-$ charges; nitrate and nitrite have $1-$ charges; chlorate and chlorite (and other halogens) have $1-$ charges.

The formula of hydrogen carbonate, or *bicarbonate*, can be written by placing a hydrogen cation (H^+) in front of the formula for carbonate, CO_3^{2-}, and decreasing the charge from $2-$ to $1-$ to give HCO_3^-. Some models of polyatomic ions are shown in Figure 5.3.

$$CO_3^{2-} + H^+ = HCO_3^-$$

TABLE 5.7 Names and Formulas of Some Common Polyatomic Ions

Nonmetal Element	Formula of Ion[a]	Name of Ion
Hydrogen	OH^-	Hydroxide
Nitrogen	NH_4^+	Ammonium
	NO_3^-	Nitrate
	NO_2^-	Nitrite
Chlorine	ClO_4^-	Perchlorate
	ClO_3^-	Chlorate
	ClO_2^-	Chlorite
	ClO^-	Hypochlorite
Carbon	CO_3^{2-}	Carbonate
	HCO_3^-	Hydrogen carbonate (or bicarbonate)
	CN^-	Cyanide
	$C_2H_3O_2^-$	Acetate
Sulfur	SO_4^{2-}	Sulfate
	HSO_4^-	Hydrogen sulfate (or bisulfate)
	SO_3^{2-}	Sulfite
	HSO_3^-	Hydrogen sulfite (or bisulfite)
Phosphorus	PO_4^{3-}	Phosphate
	HPO_4^{2-}	Hydrogen phosphate
	$H_2PO_4^-$	Dihydrogen phosphate
	PO_3^{3-}	Phosphite

[a]Boxed formulas show the most common polyatomic ion for each element.

Writing Formulas for Compounds Containing Polyatomic Ions

No polyatomic ion exists by itself. Like any ion, a polyatomic ion must be associated with ions of opposite charge. The bonding between polyatomic ions and other ions is one of electrical attraction. For example, the compound sodium sulfate consists of sodium ions (Na^+) and sulfate ions (SO_4^{2-}) held together by ionic bonds.

To write correct formulas for compounds containing polyatomic ions, we follow the same rules of charge balance that we used for writing the formulas of simple ionic compounds. The total negative and positive charges must equal zero. For example, consider the formula for a compound containing calcium ions and carbonate ions. The ions are written as

$$Ca^{2+} \qquad CO_3^{2-}$$

Calcium ion   Carbonate ion

Ionic charge: $(2+) \ + \ (2-) = 0$

Because one ion of each balances the charge, the formula is written as

$CaCO_3$

Calcium carbonate

When more than one polyatomic ion is needed for charge balance, parentheses are used to enclose the formula of the ion. A subscript is written outside the closing parenthesis of the polyatomic ion to indicate the number needed for charge balance. Consider the formula for magnesium nitrate. The ions are the magnesium ion and the nitrate ion, a polyatomic ion.

$$Mg^{2+} \qquad NO_3^-$$

Magnesium ion   Nitrate ion

To balance the 2+ ionic charge of magnesium, two polyatomic ions of nitrate are needed. In the formula, parentheses are placed around the nitrate ion, as follows:

$$NO_3^-$$

$$Mg^{2+}$$

$$NO_3^-$$

$(2+) \ + \ 2(1-) \ = \ 0$

Magnesium nitrate

$$Mg(NO_3)_2$$

| Parentheses enclose the formula of the nitrate ion | Subscript outside the parentheses indicates the use of two nitrate ions |

SAMPLE PROBLEM 5.5

■ Writing Formulas for Ionic Compounds with Polyatomic Ions

Write the formula of aluminum bicarbonate.

SOLUTION

STEP 1   Identify the cation and anion.   The cation is the aluminum ion, Al^{3+}, and the anion is bicarbonate, HCO_3^-.

	Cation	**Anion**
Ions	Al^{3+}	HCO_3^-

STEP 2   Balance the charges.

$$Al^{3+} \qquad \begin{array}{l} HCO_3^- \\ HCO_3^- \\ HCO_3^- \end{array}$$

_____

$\mathbf{1}(3+) \ + \ \mathbf{3}(1-) = 0$

Becomes a subscript in the formula

STEP 3   **Write the formula, cation first, using subscripts from the charge balance.**   The formula for the compound is written by enclosing the formula of the bicarbonate ion, HCO_3^-, in parentheses and writing the subscript 3 outside the last parenthesis.

$$Al(HCO_3)_3$$

STUDY CHECK

Write the formula for a compound containing ammonium ion(s) and phosphate ion(s).

CONCEPT CHECK 5.3

■ **Polyatomic Ions in Bones and Teeth**

Bone material consists of a mineral substance called calcium hydroxyapatite, $Ca_{10}(PO_4)_6(OH)_2$, a solid formed from calcium ions and polyatomic ions. What polyatomic ions are contained in the mineral substance of bone?

ANSWER

The polyatomic ions are phosphate ions and hydroxide ions.

Naming Compounds Containing Polyatomic Ions

When naming ionic compounds containing polyatomic ions, first we write the positive ion, usually a metal, and then the name of the polyatomic ion. It is important that you learn to recognize the polyatomic ion in the formula and name it correctly. As with other ionic compounds, no prefixes are used.

Na_2SO_4 $FePO_4$ $Al_2(CO_3)_3$

$Na_2 \boxed{SO_4}$ $Fe \boxed{PO_4}$ $Al_2(\boxed{CO_3})_3$

Sodium sulfate   Iron(III) phosphate   Aluminum carbonate

Table 5.8 lists the formulas and names of some ionic compounds that include polyatomic ions and also gives their uses in medicine and industry.

TABLE 5.8 Some Compounds That Contain Polyatomic Ions

Formula	Name	Use
$BaSO_4$	Barium sulfate	Radiopaque medium
$CaCO_3$	Calcium carbonate	Antacid, calcium supplement
$Ca_3(PO_4)_2$	Calcium phosphate	Calcium replenisher
$CaSO_3$	Calcium sulfite	Preservative in cider and fruit juices
$CaSO_4$	Calcium sulfate	Plaster casts
$AgNO_3$	Silver nitrate	Topical anti-infective
$NaHCO_3$	Sodium bicarbonate *or* Sodium hydrogen carbonate	Antacid
$Zn_3(PO_4)_2$	Zinc phosphate	Dental cements
$FePO_4$	Iron(III) phosphate	Food and bread enrichment
K_2CO_3	Potassium carbonate	Alkalizer, diuretic
$Al_2(SO_4)_3$	Aluminum sulfate	Antiperspirant, anti-infective
$AlPO_4$	Aluminum phosphate	Antacid
$MgSO_4$	Magnesium sulfate	Cathartic, Epsom salts

SAMPLE PROBLEM 5.6

■ Naming Compounds Containing Polyatomic Ions

Name the following ionic compounds:

a. $CaSO_4$ b. $Cu(NO_2)_2$

SOLUTION

	STEP 1		STEP 2	STEP 3	STEP 4
Formula	**Cation**	**Anion**	**Name of Cation**	**Name of Anion**	**Name of Compound**
a. $CaSO_4$	Ca^{2+}	SO_4^{2-}	Calcium ion	Sulfate ion	Calcium sulfate
b. $Cu(NO_2)_2$	Cu^{2+}	NO_2^-	Copper(II) ion	Nitrite ion	Copper(II) nitrite

STUDY CHECK

What is the name of $Ca_3(PO_4)_2$?

Guide to Naming Ionic Compounds with Polyatomic Ions

> **STEP 1**
> Identify the cation and polyatomic ion (anion).

> **STEP 2**
> Name the cation using a Roman numeral, if needed.

> **STEP 3**
> Name the polyatomic ion usually ending with *ite* or *ate*.

> **STEP 4**
> Write the name of the compound, cation first and the polyatomic ion second.

QUESTIONS AND PROBLEMS

Polyatomic Ions

5.29 Write the formulas including the charge for the following polyatomic ions:
  a. hydrogen carbonate
  b. ammonium
  c. phosphate
  d. hydrogen sulfate

5.30 Write the formulas including the charge for the following polyatomic ions:
  a. nitrite
  b. sulfite
  c. hydroxide
  d. phosphite

5.31 Name the following polyatomic ions:
  a. SO_4^{2-}
  b. CO_3^{2-}
  c. PO_4^{3-}
  d. NO_3^-

5.32 Name the following polyatomic ions:
  a. OH^-
  b. HSO_3^-
  c. CN^-
  d. NO_2^-

5.33 Complete the following table with the formula of the compound:

	OH^-	NO_2^-	CO_3^{2-}	HSO_4^-	PO_4^{3-}
Li^+					
Cu^{2+}					
Ba^{2+}					

5.34 Complete the following table with the formula of the compound:

	OH^-	NO_3^-	HCO_3^-	SO_3^{2-}	PO_4^{3-}
NH_4^+					
Al^{3+}					
Pb^{4+}					

5.35 Write the formula for the polyatomic ion in each of the following and name each compound:
  a. Na_2CO_3
  b. NH_4Cl
  c. Li_3PO_4
  d. $Cu(NO_2)_2$
  e. $FeSO_3$

5.36 Write the formula for the polyatomic ion in each of the following, and name each compound:
  a. KOH
  b. $NaNO_3$
  c. $CuCO_3$
  d. $NaHCO_3$
  e. $BaSO_4$

5.37 Write the correct formula for the following compounds:
  a. barium hydroxide
  b. sodium sulfate
  c. iron(II) nitrate
  d. zinc phosphate
  e. iron(III) carbonate

5.38 Write the correct formula for the following compounds:
  a. aluminum chlorate
  b. ammonium oxide
  c. magnesium bicarbonate
  d. sodium nitrite
  e. copper(I) sulfate

5.5 Covalent Compounds

A **covalent compound** forms when atoms of two nonmetals achieve stability by sharing electrons. Because of the nonmetals' high ionization energies, electrons are not transferred between atoms. When atoms share electrons, the bond is a **covalent bond**. Thus, in *covalent compounds*, electrons are not transferred from one atom to another, but are shared between atoms of nonmetals to achieve stability. When two or more atoms share electrons, they form **molecules**.

LEARNING GOAL

Given the formula of a covalent compound, write its electron-dot formula.

(MC) SELF STUDY ACTIVITY
Covalent Bonds

Formation of a Hydrogen Molecule

The simplest covalent molecule is hydrogen gas, H_2. When two hydrogen atoms are far apart, they are not attracted to each other. As the atoms move closer, the positive charge of each nucleus attracts the electron of the other atom. This attraction pulls the atoms closer until they share a pair of valence electrons and form a *covalent bond*. In the covalent bond in H_2, the shared electrons give the noble gas configuration of He to each of the H atoms. Thus the atoms bonded in H_2 are more stable than two individual H atoms.

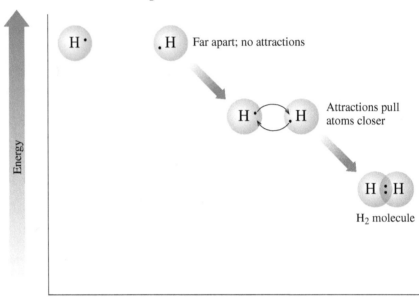

H •   . H   Far apart; no attractions

H :   : H   Attractions pull atoms closer

H : H

H_2 molecule

Energy ↑

Distance between nuclei decreases ⟶

TABLE 5.9 Elements That Exist as Diatomic, Covalent Molecules

Element	Diatomic Molecule	Name
H	H_2	Hydrogen
N	N_2	Nitrogen
O	O_2	Oxygen
F	F_2	Fluorine
Cl	Cl_2	Chlorine
Br	Br_2	Bromine
I	I_2	Iodine

Electron-Dot Formulas of Covalent Molecules

The valence electrons in covalent molecules are shown using an electron-dot formula, which is also known as a Lewis structure. The shared electrons, or *bonding pairs*, are shown as two dots or a single line between atoms. The nonbonding pairs of electrons, or *lone pairs*, are placed on the outside. For example, a fluorine molecule (F_2) consists of two fluorine atoms, Group 7A (17), each with 7 valence electrons. Each F atom achieves an octet by sharing its unpaired valence electrons. In the F_2 molecule, each F atom has the noble gas configuration of neon.

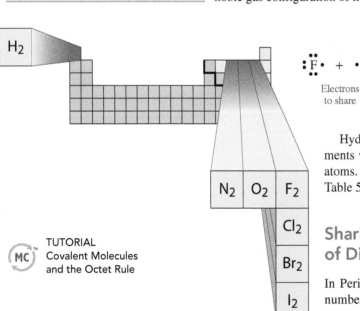

A lone pair

A bonding pair

:F• + •F: ⟶ :F:F: :F—F: = F_2

Electrons to share   A shared pair of electrons   A covalent bond   A fluorine molecule

Hydrogen (H_2) and fluorine (F_2) are examples of nonmetal elements whose natural state is diatomic; that is, they contain two like atoms. The elements that exist as diatomic molecules are listed in Table 5.9.

Sharing Electrons Between Atoms of Different Elements

(MC) TUTORIAL
Covalent Molecules
and the Octet Rule

In Period 2, the number of electrons that an atom shares and the number of covalent bonds it forms are usually equal to the number of electrons needed to acquire a noble gas configuration. For example, carbon has 4 valence electrons. Because carbon needs to acquire 4 more electrons for an octet, it forms 4 covalent bonds by sharing its 4 valence electrons.

Methane, a component of natural gas, is a compound made of carbon and hydrogen. To attain an octet, each carbon atom shares 4 electrons, and each hydrogen atom shares 1 electron. In this molecule, a carbon atom forms 4 covalent bonds with 4 hydrogen atoms. The electron-dot formula for the molecule is written with the carbon atom in the center and the hydrogen atoms on the sides. Table 5.10 gives the formulas of some covalent molecules for Period 2 elements.

Methane, CH_4

TABLE 5.10 Electron-Dot Formulas for Some Covalent Compounds

CH_4	NH_3	H_2O
Formulas Using Electron Dots Only		
H:C:H with H above and below C	H:N:H with H below N	:O:H with H below O
Formulas Using Bonds and Electron Dots		
H—C—H with H above and below C	H—N—H with H below N	:O—H with H below O
Molecular Models		
Methane molecule	Ammonia molecule	Water molecule

While the octet rule is useful, there are exceptions. We have already seen that a hydrogen molecule (H_2) requires just two electrons, or a single bond, to achieve the stability of the nearest noble gas, helium. In $BeCl_2$, Be forms only 2 covalent bonds. In BF_3, the nonmetal B can share only 3 valence electrons to give a total of 6 valence electrons or 3 bonds. The nonmetals typically form octets. However, atoms such as P, S, Cl, Br, and I can share more of their valence electrons and expand the octets to stable valence shells of 10, 12, or even 14 electrons. In PCl_3, the P atom has an octet, but in PCl_5 the P atom has 10 valence electrons or 5 bonds. In H_2S, the S atom has an octet, but in SF_6, there are 12 valence electrons, or 6 bonds to the sulfur atom. Table 5.11 gives the bonding patterns for some nonmetals.

TUTORIAL
Writing Electron-Dot Formulas

TABLE 5.11 Typical Bonding Patterns of Some Nonmetals in Covalent Compounds

1A (1)	3A (13)	4A (14)	5A (15)	6A (16)	7A (17)
[a]H 1 bond					
	[a]B 3 bonds	C 4 bonds	N 3 bonds	O 2 bonds	F 1 bond
		Si 4 bonds	P 3 bonds	S 2 bonds	Cl, Br, I 1 bond

[a]H and B do not form eight-electron octets. H atoms share one electron pair; B atoms share three electron pairs for a set of 6 electrons.

Guide to Writing Electron-Dot Formulas

STEP 1
Determine the arrangement of atoms.

STEP 2
Determine the total number of valence electrons.

STEP 3
Attach each bonded atom to the central atom with a pair of electrons.

STEP 4
Place the remaining electrons as lone pairs to complete octets (two for H, six for B).

SAMPLE PROBLEM 5.7

■ **Writing Electron-Dot Formulas**

Write the electron-dot formula for PCl_3, phosphorus trichloride.

SOLUTION

STEP 1 **Determine the arrangement of atoms.** In PCl_3, the central atom is P because it needs the most electrons.

Cl P Cl
Cl

STEP 2 **Determine the total number of valence electrons.** We can use the group numbers to determine the valence electrons for each of the atoms in the molecule.

Element	Group	Atoms	Valence Electrons	=	Total
P	5A (15)	1 P	$\times 5e^-$	=	$5e^-$
Cl	7A (17)	3 Cl	$\times 7e^-$	=	$21e^-$
		Total valence electrons for PCl_3		=	$26e^-$

STEP 3 **Attach the central atom to each bonded atom by a pair of electrons.**

Cl:P:Cl   or   Cl—P—Cl
Cl   Cl

STEP 4 **Place the remaining electrons as lone pairs to complete octets.** A total of 6 electrons ($3 \times 2e^-$) are needed to bond the central P atom to three Cl atoms. Twenty valence electrons are left:

26 valence e^- − 6 bonding e^- = $20e^-$ remaining

The remaining electrons are placed as lone pairs around the outer Cl atoms first, which uses 18 more electrons.

:Cl:P:Cl: or   :Cl—P—Cl:
:Cl: :Cl:

Use the remaining two electrons to complete the octet for the P atom.

P has an octet

:Cl:P:Cl: or   :Cl—P—Cl:
:Cl: :Cl:

STUDY CHECK

Write the electron-dot formula for Cl_2O (O is the central atom).

Multiple Covalent Bonds

In many covalent compounds, two atoms share two or three pairs of electrons to complete their octets. A **double bond** occurs when two pairs of electrons are shared between two atoms; in a **triple bond**, three pairs of electrons are shared. Atoms of carbon, oxygen, nitrogen, and sulfur are most likely to form multiple bonds. Atoms of hydrogen and the halogens do not form double or triple bonds. Double and triple bonds are formed when single covalent bonds fail to complete the octets of all the atoms in the molecule. For example, in the electron-dot formula for the covalent compound N_2, an octet is achieved when each nitrogen atom shares 3 electrons. Thus, three covalent bonds, or a triple bond, will form.

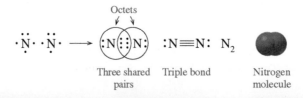

Octets

·N· ·N· ⟶ :N(:::)N: :N≡N: N_2

Three shared pairs   Triple bond   Nitrogen molecule

SAMPLE PROBLEM 5.8

■ Writing Electron-Dot Formulas with Double Bonds

Write the electron-dot formula for CO_2, carbon dioxide.

SOLUTION

STEP 1 **Determine the arrangement of atoms.** In CO_2, the central atom is C.

O C O

STEP 2 **Determine the total number of valence electrons.**

Element	Group	Atoms	Valence Electrons	=	Total
O	6A (16)	2 O	$\times\ 6e^-$	=	$12e^-$
C	4A (14)	1 C	$\times\ 4e^-$	=	$4e^-$
		Total valence electrons for CO_2		=	$16e^-$

STEP 3 **Attach the central atom to each bonded atom by a pair of electrons.**

O:C:O   or   O—C—O

STEP 4 **Arrange remaining electrons as lone pairs to complete octets.** Four (4) electrons ($2 \times 2\ e^-$) are used to bond the central C atom to the O atoms. The number of valence electrons remaining is

16 valence e^- − 4 bonding e^- = $12e^-$ remaining

The remaining 12 electrons are placed as 6 lone pairs to complete the octets for the O atoms.

:Ö:C:Ö: or   :Ö—C—Ö:

If octets are not complete, move one or more electron pairs between the central and attached atoms to form multiple bonds.

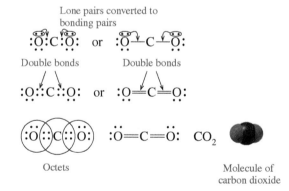

STUDY CHECK

Write the electron-dot formula for HCN (atoms arranged as H C N).

Resonance Structures

When a molecule or polyatomic ion contains multiple bonds, it is often possible to write more than one electron-dot formula for the same arrangement of atoms. Suppose we want to write the electron-dot formula for ozone, O_3, a component in the stratosphere that protects us from the ultraviolet rays of the sun. Although all 18 valence electrons are used, one of the oxygen atoms does not have an octet. One lone pair must be moved to form a double bond. But which one should be used? One possibility is to form a double bond

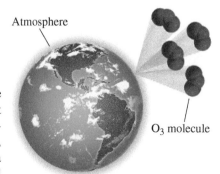

Atmosphere

O_3 molecule

with the O atom on the left. The other possibility is to form a double bond with the O atom on the right.

$$:\ddot{O}—\ddot{O}—\ddot{O}:$$

or

$$:\ddot{O}—\ddot{O}—\ddot{O}:\qquad\qquad :\ddot{O}—\ddot{O}—\ddot{O}:$$

$$:\ddot{O}=\ddot{O}—\ddot{O}: \longleftrightarrow :\ddot{O}—\ddot{O}=\ddot{O}: \quad \text{or} \quad :\ddot{O}—\ddot{O}—\ddot{O}:$$

Resonance structures   Hybrid

Experiments show that the actual bond is equivalent to a "one and a half" bond between the central O atom and each of the attached O atoms. In this *hybrid*, the electrons are shown spread equally over all the O atoms. When two or more electron-dot formulas can be written, they are called **resonance structures** and shown with a double-headed arrow. Although we will write resonance structures of some molecules and ions, the true structure is really a mix, or average, of the possible structures.

CONCEPT CHECK 5.4

■ Resonance Structures

Explain why SCl_2 does not have resonance structures, but SO_2 does.

ANSWER

In the electron-dot formula of SCl_2, the single valence electrons of each chlorine atom complete the octet of the sulfur atom. However, in SO_2, the central sulfur atom must form a double bond with one of the oxygen atoms. Thus, two electron-dot formulas, or resonance structures, are possible.

SAMPLE PROBLEM 5.9

■ Writing Resonance Structures

Write two resonance structures for sulfur dioxide, SO_2.

SOLUTION

STEP 1   **Determine the arrangement of atoms.**   In SO_2, the S atom is the central atom.

O S O

STEP 2   **Determine the total number of valence electrons.**   We can use the group numbers to determine the valence electrons for each atom in the molecule.

Element	Group	Atoms	Valence Electrons	=	Total
S	6A (16)	1 S	$\times\, 6e^-$	=	$6e^-$
O	6A (16)	2 O	$\times\, 6e^-$	=	$12e^-$
		Total valence electrons for SO_2		=	$18e^-$

STEP 3   **Attach the central atom to each bonded atom by a pair of electrons.**   We will use a single line to represent a pair of bonding electrons.

O—S—O

STEP 4   **Arrange the remaining electrons to complete octets.**   Four (4) electrons are used to write single bonds between the S atom and the O atoms. The number of valence electrons that remain is

18 valence e^- − 4 bonding e^- = $14e^-$ remaining

The remaining electrons are placed as lone pairs around the O atoms first. One lone pair remains, which is assigned to the S atom.

$$:\ddot{O}—\ddot{S}—\ddot{O}:$$

The octet for S is completed using one lone pair from an O atom as a bonding pair, and thus forming a double bond. Because two electron-dot formulas can be written using a lone pair from either O atom, two resonance structures are possible.

$$:\ddot{O}-\ddot{S}=\ddot{O}: \longleftrightarrow :\ddot{O}=\ddot{S}-\ddot{O}:$$

STUDY CHECK

Write three resonance structures for SO_3.

QUESTIONS AND PROBLEMS

Covalent Compounds

5.39 What elements on the periodic table are most likely to form covalent compounds?

5.40 How does the bond that forms between Na and Cl differ from a bond that forms between N and Cl?

5.41 State the number of valence electrons, bonding pairs, and lone pairs in each of the following electron-dot formulas:

  a. H:H   **b.** H:$\ddot{B}\ddot{r}$:   **c.** :$\ddot{B}\ddot{r}$:$\ddot{B}\ddot{r}$:

5.42 State the number of valence electrons, bonding pairs, and lone pairs in each of the following electron-dot formulas:

       H   :$\ddot{B}\ddot{r}$:

  a. H:$\ddot{O}$:   **b.** H:$\ddot{N}$:H   **c.** :$\ddot{B}\ddot{r}$:$\ddot{O}$:

                 H

5.43 Write the electron-dot formula for each of the following molecules:

  a. HF   **b.** SF_2 **c.** NBr_3

                          H

  d. CH_3OH (methyl alcohol) H C O H

                             H

                      H H

  e. N_2H_4 (hydrazine) H N N H

5.44 Write the electron-dot formula for each of the following molecules:

  a. H_2O **b.** CCl_4 **c.** SiF_4 **d.** CF_2Cl_2

                    H H

  e. C_2H_6 (ethane) H C C H

                    H H

5.45 When is it necessary to write a multiple bond in an electron-dot formula?

5.46 If the available valence electrons for a molecule do not complete all of the octets in an electron-dot formula, what should you do?

5.47 What is resonance?

5.48 When does a covalent compound have resonance?

5.49 Write the electron-dot formula for each of the following molecules:

  a. CO (carbon monoxide)

  b. H_2CCH_2 (ethylene)

  c. H_2CO (C is the central atom)

5.50 Write the electron-dot formula for each of the following molecules:

  a. HCCH (acetylene)

  b. CS_2 (C is the central atom)

  c. $COCl_2$ (C is the central atom)

5.51 Write resonance structures for $ClNO_2$ (N is the central atom).

5.52 Write resonance structures for N_2O (N N O).

5.6 Naming and Writing Covalent Formulas

When naming a covalent compound, the first nonmetal in the formula is named by its elemental name; the second nonmetal is named by its elemental name with the ending changed to *ide*. Subscripts that indicate two or more atoms of an element are expressed as prefixes placed in front of each name. Table 5.12 lists prefixes used in naming covalent compounds. The names of covalent compounds need prefixes because several different compounds can be formed from the same two nonmetals. For example, carbon and oxygen can form two different compounds: carbon monoxide (CO) and carbon dioxide (CO_2).

When the vowels *o* and *o* or *a* and *o* appear together, the first vowel is omitted as in carbon monoxide. In the name of a covalent compound, the prefix *mono* is usually omitted, as in NO, nitrogen oxide. Traditionally, however, CO is named carbon monoxide. Table 5.13 lists the formulas, names, and commercial uses of some covalent compounds.

LEARNING GOAL

Given the formula of a covalent compound, write its correct name; given the name of a covalent compound, write its formula.

TABLE 5.12 Prefixes Used in Naming Covalent Compounds

1	mono	6	hexa
2	di	7	hepta
3	tri	8	octa
4	tetra	9	nona
5	penta	10	deca

TABLE 5.13 Some Common Covalent Compounds

Formula	Name	Commercial Uses
CS_2	Carbon disulfide	Manufacture of rayon
CO_2	Carbon dioxide	Carbonation of beverages; fire extinguishers; propellant in aerosols; dry ice
NO	Nitrogen oxide	Stabilizer
N_2O	Dinitrogen oxide	Inhalation anesthetic: "laughing gas"
SiO_2	Silicon dioxide	Manufacture of glass
SO_2	Sulfur dioxide	Preserving fruits, vegetables; disinfectant in breweries; bleaching textiles
SF_6	Sulfur hexafluoride	Electrical circuits

CONCEPT CHECK 5.5

■ **Naming Covalent Compounds**

Why is it that the name of the covalent compound BrCl, bromine chloride, does not include a prefix, but the name of OCl_2, oxygen dichloride, does?

ANSWER

When a formula has one atom of each element, no prefix (*mono*) is needed in the name bromine chloride. In OCl_2, two atoms of chlorine are indicated by the prefix *di*, oxygen dichloride.

SAMPLE PROBLEM 5.10

■ **Naming Covalent Compounds**

Name the covalent compound NCl_3.

SOLUTION

We can use the guide for naming covalent compounds to name this covalent compound.

Guide to Naming Covalent Compounds with Two Nonmetals

STEP 1
Name the first nonmetal by its element name.

STEP 2
Name the second nonmetal by using the first syllable of its element name followed by *ide*.

STEP 3
Add prefixes to indicate the number of atoms (subscripts).

STEP 1 **Name the first nonmetal by its element name.**   In NCl_3, the first nonmetal (N) is nitrogen.

STEP 2 **Name the second nonmetal by changing the last part of its element name to *ide*.**   The second nonmetal (Cl) is named *chloride*.

STEP 3 **Add prefixes to indicate the number of atoms of each nonmetal.**   Because there is only one nitrogen atom, the prefix *mono* is understood and not used. The subscript indicating three Cl atoms is shown as the prefix *tri*.

NCl_3 nitrogen trichloride

STUDY CHECK

Write the name of each of the following compounds:

a. $SiBr_4$ **b.** Br_2O

Writing Formulas from the Names of Covalent Compounds

In the name of a covalent compound, the names of two nonmetals are given along with prefixes for the number of atoms of each. To obtain a formula, we write the symbol for each element and a subscript if a prefix indicates two or more atoms.

■ Writing Formulas for Covalent Compounds

Write the formula for diboron trioxide.

SOLUTION

STEP 1   Write the symbols in order of the elements in the name.   The first non-metal is boron and the second nonmetal is oxygen.

B   O

STEP 2   Write prefixes as subscripts.   The prefix *di* in *diboron* indicates that there are two atoms of boron shown as a subscript 2 in the formula. The prefix *tri* in *trioxide* indicates that there are three atoms of oxygen shown as a subscript 3 in the formula.

B_2O_3

STUDY CHECK

What is the formula of iodine heptafluoride?

Guide to Writing Formulas for Covalent Compounds

STEP 1
Write the symbols in the order of the elements in the name.

STEP 2
Write any prefixes as subscripts.

Summary of Naming Compounds

(MC) TUTORIAL
Naming Covalent Compounds

Throughout this chapter we have examined strategies for naming ionic and covalent compounds. Now we can summarize the rules, as illustrated in Figure 5.4. In general, compounds having two elements are named by stating the first element, followed by the second element with an *ide* ending. If the first element is a metal, then the compound is ionic; if the first element is a nonmetal, then the compound is covalent. For ionic compounds, it is necessary to determine whether the metal can form more than one type of positive ion; if so,

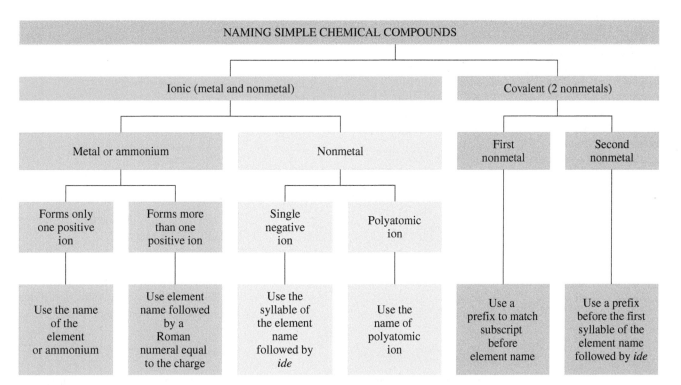

FIGURE 5.4 A flowchart for naming ionic and covalent compounds
Q Why does the name sulfur dichloride have a prefix but magnesium chloride does not?

then a Roman numeral following the name of the metal indicates the particular ionic charge. One exception is the ammonium ion NH_4^+, which is also written first as a positively charged polyatomic ion. In naming covalent compounds having two elements, prefixes are necessary to indicate the number of atoms of each nonmetal as shown in that particular formula. Organic compounds of C and H such as CH_4 and C_2H_6 use a different system of naming that we will discuss in a later chapter. Ionic compounds having three or more elements include some type of polyatomic ion. They are named by ionic rules, but have an *ate* or *ite* ending when the polyatomic ion has a negative charge.

CONCEPT CHECK 5.6

■ Naming Ionic and Covalent Compounds

Identify each of the following compounds as ionic or covalent and give its name:
a. Na_3P **b.** SO_2

ANSWER

a. Na_3P, consisting of a metal and nonmetal, is an ionic compound. Na is a metal that forms a single ion, Na^+, named *sodium*. The single negative ion, P^{3-}, is *phosphide*. The compound is named sodium phosphide.

b. SO_2 consists of two nonmetals; it is covalent. The first element sulfur does not need a prefix because the formula has only one atom. The second element is named *dioxide* because there are two atoms of oxygen. Thus, SO_2 is named sulfur dioxide.

QUESTIONS AND PROBLEMS

Naming and Writing Covalent Formulas

5.53 Name the following covalent compounds:
   a. PBr_3 **b.** CBr_4 **c.** SiO_2
   d. N_2O_3 **e.** $SiBr_4$ **f.** PCl_5

5.54 Name the following covalent compounds:
   a. CS_2 **b.** P_2O_5 **c.** Cl_2O
   d. PCl_3 **e.** IBr_3 **f.** SO_3

5.55 Write the formulas of the following covalent compounds:
   a. carbon tetrachloride   **b.** carbon monoxide
   c. phosphorus trichloride   **d.** dinitrogen tetroxide
   e. boron trifluoride   **f.** sulfur hexafluoride

5.56 Write the formulas of the following covalent compounds:
   a. sulfur dioxide   **b.** silicon tetrachloride
   c. iodine pentafluoride   **d.** dinitrogen oxide
   e. tetraphosphorus hexoxide   **f.** dinitrogen pentoxide

5.57 Name the compounds that are found in the following:
   a. $Al_2(SO_4)_3$ antiperspirant
   b. $CaCO_3$ antacid
   c. N_2O "laughing gas" (inhaled anesthetic)
   d. Na_3PO_4 cathartic
   e. $(NH_4)_2SO_4$ fertilizer
   f. Fe_2O_3 pigment

5.58 Name the compounds that are found in the following:
   a. N_2 Earth's atmosphere
   b. $Mg_3(PO_4)_2$ antacid
   c. $FeSO_4$ iron supplement in vitamins
   d. $MgSO_4$ Epsom salts
   e. Cu_2O fungicide
   f. SnF_2 prevents dental caries

5.7 | Electronegativity and Bond Polarity

In this chapter, we have seen that atoms form chemical bonds by gaining, losing, or sharing valence electrons. In bonds between identical nonmetal atoms, the bonding electrons are shared equally. However, in most compounds, bonds form between atoms of different elements. Then the bonding electrons are attracted to one atom more than the other.

Electronegativity

SELF STUDY ACTIVITY
Electronegativity

Electronegativity is the attraction of an atom for valence electrons in a chemical bond. (See Figure 5.5.) Nonmetals have higher electronegativity values than metals. The nonmetals with the highest electronegativity values are fluorine (4.0) at the top of Group 7A (17)

Electronegativity increases

H
2.1

18
Group
8A

1 Group 1A	2 Group 2A
Li 1.0	Be 1.5
Na 0.9	Mg 1.2
K 0.8	Ca 1.0
Rb 0.8	Sr 1.0
Cs 0.7	Ba 0.9

13 Group 3A	14 Group 4A	15 Group 5A	16 Group 6A	17 Group 7A
B 2.0	C 2.5	N 3.0	O 3.5	F 4.0
Al 1.5	Si 1.8	P 2.1	S 2.5	Cl 3.0
Ga 1.6	Ge 1.8	As 2.0	Se 2.4	Br 2.8
In 1.7	Sn 1.8	Sb 1.9	Te 2.1	I 2.5
Tl 1.8	Pb 1.9	Bi 1.9	Po 2.0	At 2.1

Electronegativity increases (vertical axis label)

FIGURE 5.5 The electronegativity of representative elements indicates the attraction of an atom for valence electrons in a chemical bond. Electronegativity values increase not only across a period but also going up a group.

Q What element on the periodic table has the strongest attraction for shared electrons?

and oxygen (3.5) at the top of Group 6A (16). The metal cesium at the bottom of Group 1A (1) has the lowest electronegativity value of 0.7. Smaller atoms tend to have higher electronegativity values because the valence electrons are closer to their nuclei. Electronegativity values increase from left to right across each period as well as from bottom to top of each group. The values of electronegativity for the transition metals are also low, but we will not include them in our discussion. Note that there are no electronegativity values for the noble gases because they do not typically form bonds.

Types of Bonding

Earlier we discussed bonding as either *ionic*, in which electrons are transferred, or *covalent*, in which electrons were equally shared. The difference in the electronegativity of two atoms can be used to predict the type of bond that forms. In H—H, the electronegativity difference is zero (2.1 − 2.1 = 0), which means the bonding electrons are shared equally. A covalent bond between atoms with identical or very similar electronegativity values is a **nonpolar covalent bond**. However, most covalent bonds are between atoms with different electronegativity values. When electrons are shared unequally, the bond is a **polar covalent bond**. In H—Cl, an electronegativity difference of 3.0 (Cl) − 2.1 (H) = 0.9 means that the H—Cl bond is polar covalent. (See Figure 5.6.)

FIGURE 5.6 In the nonpolar covalent bond of H_2, electrons are shared equally. In the polar covalent bond of HCl, electrons are shared unequally.

Q H_2 has a nonpolar covalent bond, but HCl has a polar covalent bond. Explain.

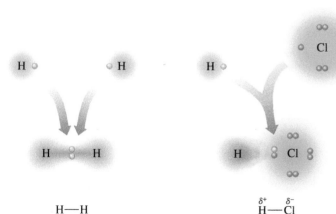

H—H

Equal sharing of electrons
in a nonpolar covalent bond

$$\overset{\delta^+}{H}—\overset{\delta^-}{Cl}$$

Unequal sharing of electrons
in a polar covalent bond (dipole)

In a polar covalent bond, the shared electrons are attracted to the more electronegative atom, which makes it partially negative, whereas the atom with the lower electronegativity becomes partially positive. A polar covalent bond that has a separation of charges is called a **dipole**. The positive and negative ends of the dipole are indicated by the lowercase Greek letter delta with a positive or negative sign, δ^+ and δ^-. Sometimes an arrow pointing from the positive charge to the negative charge ($\longmapsto$) is used to indicate the dipole.

Examples of Dipoles in Polar Covalent Bond

$$\overset{\delta^+}{C}\!-\!\overset{\delta^-}{O} \qquad \overset{\delta^+}{N}\!-\!\overset{\delta^-}{O} \qquad \overset{\delta^+}{Cl}\!-\!\overset{\delta^-}{F}$$

$$\longmapsto \qquad\qquad \longmapsto \qquad\qquad \longmapsto$$

Variations in Bonding

The variations in bonding are continuous; there is no definite point at which one type of bond stops and the next starts. However, we can use some general ranges for predicting the type of bond between atoms. When electronegativity differences are from 0.0 to 0.4, the electrons are shared about equally in a *nonpolar covalent bond*. As the electronegativity difference increases, the shared electrons are attracted more closely to the more electronegative atoms and the polarity of the bond increases. When the electronegativity difference is greater than 0.4 but less than 1.8, the bond is a *polar covalent bond*. (See Table 5.14.)

Eventually, the difference in electronegativity is great enough that the electrons are transferred from one atom to another, which results in an ionic bond. Differences in electronegativity of 1.8 or greater indicate that the bond is an *ionic bond*. (See Table 5.15.)

TABLE 5.14 Electronegativity Difference and Types of Bonds

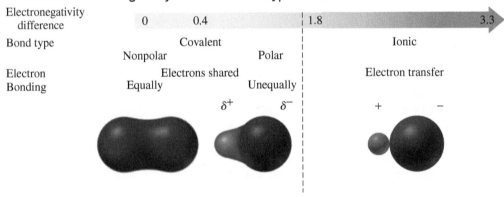

Electronegativity difference	0	0.4	1.8	3.3
Bond type		Covalent	Ionic	
		Nonpolar Polar		
Electron Bonding		Electrons shared Equally Unequally	Electron transfer	

TABLE 5.15 Predicting Bond Type from Electronegativity Differences

Molecule	Bond	Type of Electron Sharing	Electronegativity Difference[a]	Bond Type
H_2	H—H	Shared equally	$2.1 - 2.1 = 0.0$	Nonpolar covalent
Cl_2	Cl—Cl	Shared equally	$3.0 - 3.0 = 0.0$	Nonpolar covalent
CH_4	C—H	Shared equally	$2.5 - 2.1 = 0.4$	Nonpolar covalent
HBr	$\overset{\delta^+}{H}\!-\!\overset{\delta^-}{Br}$	Shared unequally	$2.8 - 2.1 = 0.7$	Polar covalent
HCl	$\overset{\delta^+}{H}\!-\!\overset{\delta^-}{Cl}$	Shared unequally	$3.0 - 2.1 = 0.9$	Polar covalent
NaCl	$Na^+\ Cl^-$	Electron transfer	$3.0 - 0.9 = 2.1$	Ionic
MgO	$Mg^{2+}\ O^{2-}$	Electron transfer	$3.5 - 1.2 = 2.3$	Ionic

[a]Values are taken from Figure 5.5.

■ **Bond Polarity**

Using electronegativity values, classify each bond as nonpolar covalent, polar covalent, or ionic:

N—N   O—H   Cl—As   C—S   O—K

SOLUTION

For each bond, we obtain the electronegativity values and calculate the difference.

Bond	Electronegativity Difference	Type of Bond
N—N	$3.0 - 3.0 = 0.0$	Nonpolar covalent
O—H	$3.5 - 2.1 = 1.4$	Polar covalent
Cl—As	$3.0 - 2.0 = 1.0$	Polar covalent
C—S	$2.5 - 2.5 = 0.0$	Nonpolar covalent
O—K	$3.5 - 0.8 = 2.7$	Ionic

STUDY CHECK

For each of the following pairs, identify the more polar bond:

a. Si—S or Si—N   **b.** O—P or N—P

QUESTIONS AND PROBLEMS

Electronegativity and Bond Polarity

5.59 Describe the trend in electronegativity going from left to right across a period.

5.60 Describe the trend in electronegativity going down a group.

5.61 Approximately what electronegativity difference would you expect for a nonpolar covalent bond?

5.62 Approximately what electronegativity difference would you expect for a polar covalent bond?

5.63 Using the periodic table, arrange the atoms in each of the following sets in order of increasing electronegativity:
a. Li, Na, K   **b.** Na, P, Cl   **c.** O, Ca, Br

5.64 Using the periodic table, arrange the atoms in each of the following sets in order of increasing electronegativity:
a. Cl, F, Br   **b.** B, O, N   **c.** Mg, F, S

5.65 Predict whether each of the following bonds is ionic, polar covalent, or nonpolar covalent:

a. Si—Br   **b.** Li—F   **c.** Br—F
d. Br—Br   **e.** N—P   **f.** C—O

5.66 Predict whether each of the following bonds is ionic, polar covalent, or nonpolar covalent:
a. Si—O   **b.** K—Cl   **c.** S—F
d. P—Br   **e.** Li—O   **f.** O—P

5.67 For each of the following bonds, indicate the positive end with δ^+ and the negative end with δ^-. Write an arrow to show the dipole for each.
a. N—F   **b.** Si—Br   **c.** C—O
d. P—Br   **e.** B—Cl

5.68 For each of the following bonds, indicate the positive end with δ^+ and the negative end with δ^-. Write an arrow to show the dipole for each.
a. Si—Cl   **b.** Se—F   **c.** Br—F
d. N—H   **e.** N—P

5.8 Shapes and Polarity of Molecules

With the information about valence electrons, electron-dot formulas, and polarity of bonds, we can look at the three-dimensional shapes of some molecules.

To predict molecular shape, we look at the geometry of the electron groups around a central atom. The **valence-shell electron-pair repulsion (VSEPR) theory** indicates that the electron groups will move as far apart as possible to reduce the repulsion between their negative charges. Once its electron-dot formula is written, the specific shape of a molecule can be determined.

LEARNING GOAL

Predict the three-dimensional structure of a molecule and classify it as polar or nonpolar.

Two Electron Groups

In $BeCl_2$, two chlorine atoms are bonded to a central beryllium atom. Because Be has a strong attraction for its valence electrons, it forms a covalent rather than ionic compound. With only two electron groups around the central atom, the electron-dot formula of $BeCl_2$ is an exception to the octet rule. The best arrangement of two electron groups for minimal repulsion is to place them on opposite sides of the Be atom. This gives a **linear** shape and a bond angle of 180° to the $BeCl_2$ molecule.

180°

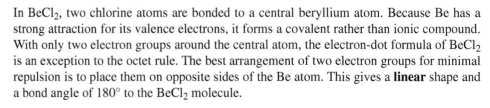

Linear

$$:\ddot{Cl}-Be-\ddot{Cl}:$$

Another example of a linear molecule is CO_2. In predicting shape, a double or triple bond is treated the same as one electron group. Thus, a multiple bond is counted as a single electron group in determining electron repulsion. In CO_2, the two double bonds, which are counted as one electron group each around C, are arranged on opposite sides of the C atom. With two double bonds, the shape of the CO_2 molecule is linear and has a bond angle of 180°.

180°

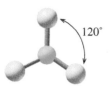

Linear

$$:\ddot{O}=C=\ddot{O}:$$

Three Electron Groups

In BF_3, the central atom B is attached to fluorine atoms by three electron groups (another exception to the octet rule). The arrangement of three electron groups as far apart as possible is called **trigonal planar** and has bond angles of 120°. In BF_3, each electron group is bonded to an atom, which gives BF_3 a trigonal planar structure. Thus, the BF_3 molecule is flat with all the atoms in the same plane and 120° bond angles.

120°

Trigonal planar

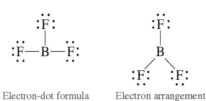

Electron-dot formula   Electron arrangement

In the electron-dot formula for SO_2, there is a single bond, a double bond, and a lone pair of electrons surrounding the S atom. Thus three electron groups surrounding the S atom attain a trigonal planar arrangement for minimal repulsion. But only the bonded atoms attached to the central atom determine the shape and structure of a molecule. Therefore, with two O atoms bonded to the central S atom, the structure of the SO_2 molecule is a **bent** shape. In the SO_2 molecule, the bond angle is slightly affected by the lone pair but close to 120°.

120°
Bent

Electron-dot formula   Electron arrangement

Four Electron Groups

Up to now, the shapes of molecules have been in two dimensions. However, when there are four electron groups around a central atom, the minimum repulsion is obtained by placing four electron groups at the corners of a three-dimensional tetrahedron. A regular tetrahedron consists of four sides that are equilateral triangles. For molecules with four electron groups, the central atom is located in the center of a tetrahedron.

In CH_4, the central atom is bonded to four hydrogen atoms. From the electron-dot formula, CH_4 appears planar with 90° bond angles, but this is not the largest angle possible.

The best arrangement for minimal repulsion is **tetrahedral**, which places the bonded atoms at the corners of a tetrahedron to give bond angles of 109.5°.

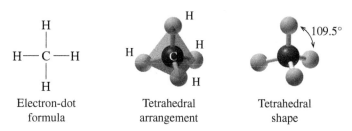

| Electron-dot formula | Tetrahedral arrangement | Tetrahedral shape |

Now we will look at other molecules with four electron groups but only two or three attached atoms. For example, in ammonia, NH_3, the three bonded H atoms and one lone electron pair occupy the corners of a tetrahedron. Because one corner has no bonded atom, the NH_3 molecule has a **trigonal pyramidal** shape. In the NH_3 molecule, the bond angles are decreased by the strong negatively charged lone pair to about 107°.

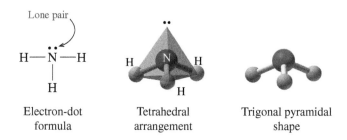

| Electron-dot formula | Tetrahedral arrangement | Trigonal pyramidal shape |

In water, H_2O, there are two bonded H atoms and two lone pairs of electrons. These four electron groups have a tetrahedral arrangement around the central O atom. A molecule with four electron groups but only two bonded atoms has a *bent* shape. In the H_2O molecule, the bond angle is decreased because of the negatively charged lone pairs to about 105°. Table 5.16 gives the molecular shapes for molecules with two, three, and four electron groups.

TUTORIAL
Molecular Shapes

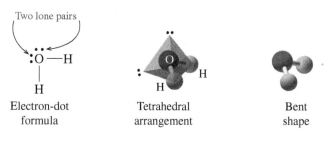

| Electron-dot formula | Tetrahedral arrangement | Bent shape |

SAMPLE PROBLEM 5.13

■ **Predicting Shapes**

Use VSEPR theory to predict the shape of the following molecules:

a. PH_3 **b.** H_2Se

SOLUTION

We will use the guide to predict the shape of molecules.

a. PH_3

STEP 1 **Write the electron-dot formula.** In the electron-dot formula for PH_3, there are four electron groups.

$$H-\overset{\cdot\cdot}{P}-H$$
$$|$$
$$H$$

Guide to Predicting Molecular Shape (VSEPR Theory)

STEP 1
Write the electron-dot formula for the melecule.

STEP 2
Arrange the electron groups around the central atom to minimize repulsion.

STEP 3
Use the atoms bonded to the central atom to determine the molecular shape.

STEP 2 **Arrange the electron groups around the central atom to minimize repulsion.** The four electron groups have a tetrahedral arrangement.

STEP 3 **Use the atoms bonded to the central atom to determine the molecular shape.** Three bonded atoms and one lone pair give PH_3 a trigonal pyramidal shape.

b. H_2Se

STEP 1 **Write the electron-dot formula.** In the electron-dot formula for H_2Se, there are four electron groups.

$$:\overset{..}{Se}-H$$
$$\underset{H}{|}$$

STEP 2 **Arrange the electron groups around the central atom to minimize repulsion.** The four electron groups around Se would have a tetrahedral arrangement.

STEP 3 **Use the atoms bonded to the central atom to determine the molecular shape.** Two bonded atoms and two lone pairs give H_2Se a bent shape.

STUDY CHECK

Predict the shape of CBr_4.

TABLE 5.16 Examples of Shapes of Molecules

Molecule	Electron-Dot Formula	Bonded Atoms	Molecular Shape (angle)	
Two (2) electron groups around the central atom				
$BeCl_2$	$:\overset{..}{\underset{..}{Cl}}:Be:\overset{..}{\underset{..}{Cl}}:$	2	linear (180°)	
CO_2	$:\overset{..}{\underset{..}{O}}::C::\overset{..}{\underset{..}{O}}:$	2	linear (180°)	
Three (3) electron groups around the central atom				
BF_3	$:\overset{..}{\underset{..}{F}}:\overset{..}{\underset{..}{B}}:\overset{..}{\underset{..}{F}}:$	3	trigonal planar (120°)	
SO_2	$:\overset{..}{\underset{..}{O}}:\overset{..}{S}$ $:\overset{..}{\underset{..}{O}}:$	2	bent (120°)	
Four (4) electron groups around the central atom				
CH_4	$H:\overset{..}{\underset{H}{C}}:H$ over/under H	4	tetrahedral (109.5°)	
NH_3	$H:\overset{..}{\underset{H}{N}}:H$	3	trigonal pyramidal (107°)	
H_2O	$:\overset{..}{\underset{H}{O}}:H$	2	bent (105°)	

Polarity of Molecules

We have seen that covalent bonds in molecules can be polar or nonpolar. Molecules can also be polar or nonpolar, depending on their shape. Diatomic molecules such as H_2 and Cl_2 are nonpolar because they contain one nonpolar covalent bond.

H—H   Cl—Cl
    Nonpolar

Molecules with two or more polar bonds can also be nonpolar if the polar bonds have a symmetrical arrangement in the molecule.

In a **polar molecule**, one end of the molecule is more negatively charged than another end. Polarity in a molecule occurs when the polar bonds do not cancel each other. This cancellation depends on the type of atoms, the electron pairs around the central atom, and the shape of the molecule. For example, the HCl molecule is polar because electrons are shared unequally in a polar covalent bond.

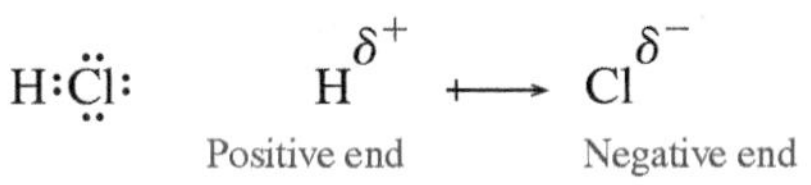

H:C̈l: H$^{\delta+}$ ⟵ Cl$^{\delta-}$
          Positive end   Negative end

In polar molecules with three or more atoms, the shape of the molecule determines whether the dipoles cancel or not. Often there are lone pairs around the central atom. In H_2O, the dipoles do not cancel, which makes the molecule positive at one end and negative at the other end. This gives the molecule a dipole.

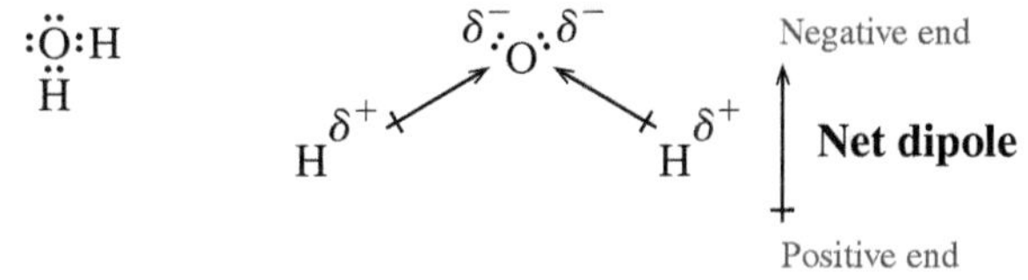

In the molecule NH_3, there are three dipoles, but they do not cancel.

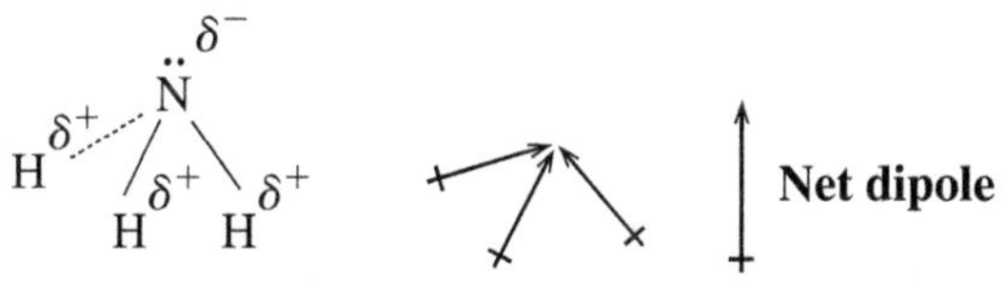

A **nonpolar molecule** occurs when the polar bonds or dipoles in a molecule cancel each other. For example, CO_2 and CCl_4 contain polar bonds. However, the symmetrical arrangement of the polar bonds cancels the dipoles, which makes CO_2 and CCl_4 molecules nonpolar.

Examples of Nonpolar Molecules with Polar Bonds

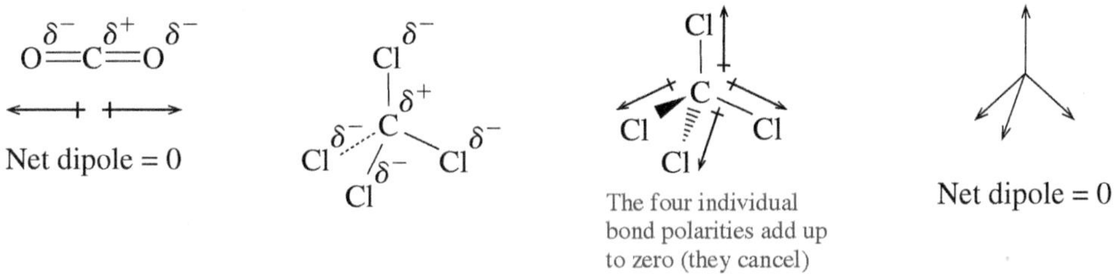

O$\overset{\delta-}{=}$C$\overset{\delta+}{=}$O$^{\delta-}$

Net dipole = 0

The four individual bond polarities add up to zero (they cancel)

Net dipole = 0

SAMPLE PROBLEM 5.14

■ Polarity of Molecules

Determine whether each of the following molecules is polar or nonpolar:

a. $SiCl_4$ **b.** OF_2

SOLUTION

a. The electron-dot formula for $SiCl_4$ has four bonded atoms and no lone pairs.

$$:\ddot{C}l:$$
$$:\ddot{C}l:\ddot{S}i:\ddot{C}l:$$
$$:\ddot{C}l:$$

The molecule would have a tetrahedral shape. With four identical atoms bonded to the central atom and no lone pairs, the polar Si–Cl bonds cancel, and $SiCl_4$ would be non-polar.

b. The electron-dot formula for OF_2 shows four electron groups with two bonded atoms and two lone pairs.

$$:\ddot{O}:\ddot{F}:$$
$$:\ddot{F}:$$

The molecule would have a bent shape. The two polar O–F bonds do not cancel, which makes OF_2 a polar molecule.

STUDY CHECK

Would PCl_3 be a polar or nonpolar molecule?

QUESTIONS AND PROBLEMS

Shapes and Polarity of Molecules

5.69 What is the shape of a molecule if the central atom has four bonded atoms and no lone pairs?

5.70 What is the shape of a molecule if the central atom has two bonded atoms and two lone pairs?

5.71 In the molecule PCl_3, the four electron groups around the phosphorus atom are arranged in a tetrahedral geometry. However, the shape of the molecule is trigonal pyramidal. Why does the shape of the molecule have a different name from the name of the electron group geometry?

5.72 In the molecule H_2S, the four electron groups around the sulfur atom are arranged in a tetrahedral geometry. However, the shape of the molecule is bent. Why does the shape of the molecule have a different name from the name of the electron group geometry?

5.73 Compare the electron-dot formulas of PH_3 and NH_3. Why do these molecules have the same shape?

5.74 Compare the electron-dot formulas CH_4 and H_2O. Why do these molecules have approximately the same angles but different shapes?

5.75 Use the VSEPR theory to predict the shape of each molecule:
   a. OF_2 b. CCl_4 c. HCN   d. SeO_2

5.76 Use the VSEPR theory to predict the shape of each molecule:
   a. NCl_3 b. SCl_2 c. CF_4 d. CS_2

5.77 The molecule Cl_2 is nonpolar, but HCl is polar. Explain.

5.78 The molecules CH_4 and CH_3Cl both contain four bonds. Why is CH_4 nonpolar whereas CH_3Cl is polar?

5.79 Identify the following molecules as polar or nonpolar:
   a. HBr   b. NF_3 c. CBr_4 d. SO_3

5.80 Identify the following molecules as polar or nonpolar:
   a. H_2S b. PBr_3 c. $SiCl_4$ d. SO_2

5.9 Attractive Forces in Compounds

LEARNING GOAL

Describe the attractive forces between ions, polar molecules, and nonpolar molecules.

TUTORIAL
Forces Between Molecules

In gases, the interactions between particles are minimal, which allows gas molecules to move far apart from each other. In solids and liquids, there are sufficient interactions between the particles to hold them close together, although some solids have low melting points whereas others have extremely high melting points. Such differences in properties are explained by looking at the various kinds of attractive forces between particles.

Ionic compounds have high melting points. For example, solid NaCl melts at 801 °C. Large amounts of energy are needed to overcome the strong attractive forces between positive and negative ions. Solids that contain molecules with covalent bonds also have attractive forces, but they are weaker than those of ionic compounds.

Dipole–Dipole Attractions and Hydrogen Bonds

For polar molecules, attractive forces called **dipole–dipole attractions** occur between the positive end of one molecule and the negative end of another. For a polar molecule with a dipole such as HCl, the partially positive H atom of one HCl molecule attracts the partially negative Cl atom in another molecule.

When a hydrogen atom is attached to highly electronegative atoms of fluorine, oxygen, or nitrogen, there are strong dipole–dipole attractions between the polar molecules. This type of attraction, called a **hydrogen bond**, occurs between the partially positive hydrogen atom of one molecule and a lone pair of electrons on a nitrogen, oxygen, or fluorine atom in another molecule. Hydrogen bonds are the strongest type of attractive forces between polar molecules. They are a major factor in the formation and structure of biological molecules such as proteins and DNA.

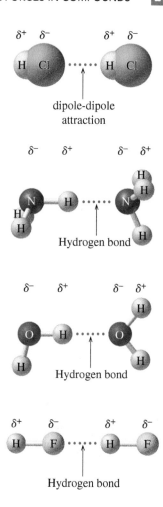

Dispersion Forces

Nonpolar compounds can form solids but only at low temperatures. Very weak attractions called **dispersion forces** occur between nonpolar molecules. Usually, the electrons in a nonpolar molecule are distributed symmetrically. However, electrons may accumulate more in one part of the molecule than another, which forms a temporary dipole. Although dispersion forces are especially weak, they make it possible for nonpolar molecules to form liquids and solids.

The melting points of substances are related to the strength of the attractive forces within the compound. Compounds with weak attractive forces such as dispersion forces have low melting points because only a small amount of energy is needed to separate the molecules and form a liquid. Compounds with hydrogen bonds and dipole–dipole attractions require more energy to break the attractive forces between the molecules. The highest melting points are seen with ionic compounds that have extremely strong attractions between ions. Table 5.17 compares the melting points of some substances with various kinds of attractive forces. The various types of attractions between particles in solids and liquids are summarized in Table 5.18.

TABLE 5.18 Comparison of Bonding and Attractive Forces

Type of Force	Particle Arrangement	Example	Strength
Ionic bonds		Na^+ - - - Cl^-	**Strong**
Hydrogen bonds (X = F, O, or N)	$\overset{\delta^+ \; \delta^-}{H} \; \overset{\delta^+ \; \delta^-}{X} \text{--} H \; X$	$\overset{\delta^+ \; \delta^-}{H} \text{—} \overset{}{F} \text{- - -} \overset{\delta^+ \; \delta^-}{H} \text{—} F$	
Dipole–dipole attractions (X and Y = different nonmetals)	$\overset{\delta^+ \; \delta^-}{Y} \; \overset{\delta^+ \; \delta^-}{X} \text{--} Y \; X$	$\overset{\delta^+ \; \delta^-}{Br} \text{—} Cl \text{- - -} \overset{\delta^+ \; \delta^-}{Br} \text{—} Cl$	
Dispersion forces (Temporary shift of electrons in nonpolar bonds)	$\overset{\delta^+ \; \delta^-}{X} \; \overset{\delta^+ \; \delta^-}{X} \text{--} X \; X$ (temporary dipoles)	$\overset{\delta^+ \; \delta^-}{F} \text{—} F \text{- - -} \overset{\delta^+ \; \delta^-}{F} \text{—} F$	**Weak**

TABLE 5.17 Melting Points of Selected Substances

Substance	Melting Point (°C)
Ionic bonds	
MgF_2	1248
$NaCl$	801
Hydrogen bonds	
H_2O	0
NH_3	−78
Dipole–dipole attractions	
HBr	−89
HCl	−115
Dispersion forces	
Cl_2	−101
F_2	−220
CH_4	−182

SAMPLE PROBLEM 5.15

■ Attractive Forces Between Particles

Indicate the major type of molecular interaction expected of each of the following:

1. dipole–dipole attractions   **2.** hydrogen bonding   **3.** dispersion forces

a. HF   **b.** I_2 **c.** PCl_3

SOLUTION

a. 2: HF is a polar molecule that interacts with other HF molecules by hydrogen bonding.
b. 3: I_2 is nonpolar; only dispersion forces provide attractive forces.
c. 1: The polarity of the PCl_3 molecules provides dipole–dipole attractions.

STUDY CHECK

Why is the boiling point of H_2S lower than that of H_2O?

QUESTIONS AND PROBLEMS

Attractive Forces in Compounds

5.81 Identify the major type of interactive force in each of the following:
  a. BrF   **b.** KCl   **c.** CCl_4 **d.** HF   **e.** Cl_2

5.82 Identify the major type of interactive force in each of the following:
  a. HCl   **b.** MgF_2 **c.** PBr_3 **d.** Br_2 **e.** NH_3

5.83 Identify the strongest attractive forces between molecules of each of the following:
  a. CH_3OH **b.** Cl_2 **c.** HCl
  d. CCl_4 **e.** CH_3CH_3

5.84 Identify the strongest attractive forces between molecules of each of the following:
  a. O_2 **b.** HF   **c.** CH_3Cl **d.** H_2O **e.** NH_3

5.85 Identify the substance in each pair that would have the higher boiling point and explain your choice:
  a. HF or HBr   **b.** HF or NaF
  c. $MgBr_2$ or PBr_3 **d.** CH_4 or CH_3OH

5.86 Identify the substance in each pair that would have the higher boiling point and explain your choice:
  a. $MgCl_2$ or PCl_3 **b.** H_2O or H_2Se
  c. NH_3 or PH_3 **d.** F_2 or HF

CONCEPT MAP

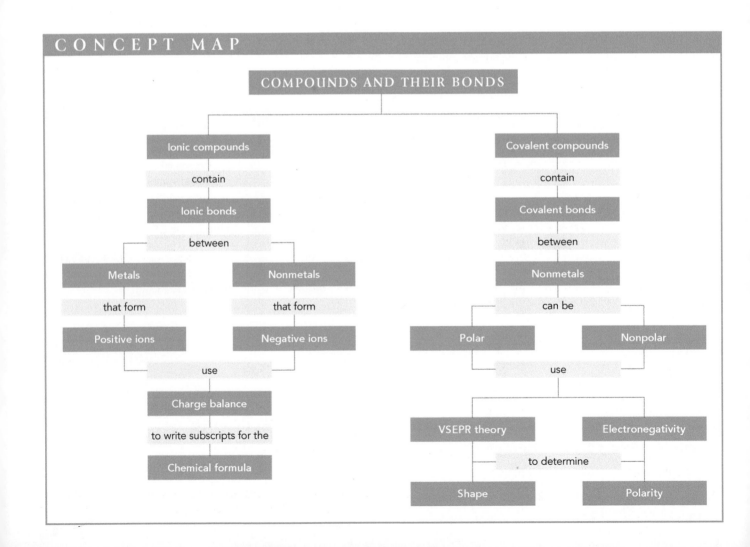

CHAPTER REVIEW

5.1 Octet Rule and Ions

LEARNING GOAL: *Using the octet rule, write the symbols of the simple ions for the representative elements.*

The stability of the noble gases is associated with 8 electrons, an octet, in their valence shells; helium needs 2 electrons for stability. Atoms of elements in Groups 1A–7A (1, 2, 13–17) achieve stability by losing, gaining, or sharing their valence electrons in the formation of compounds. Metals of the representative elements form octets by losing valence electrons to form positively charged ions (cations): Group 1A (1), 1+, Group 2A (2), 2+, and Group 3A (13), 3+. When reacting with metals, nonmetals gain electrons to form octets and form negatively charged ions (anions): Group 5A (15), 3−, Group 6A (16), 2−, Group 7A (17), 1−.

5.2 Ionic Compounds

LEARNING GOAL: *Using charge balance, write the correct formula for an ionic compound.*

The total positive and negative ionic charge is balanced in the formula of an ionic compound. Charge balance in a formula is achieved by using subscripts after each symbol so that the overall charge is zero.

5.3 Naming and Writing Ionic Formulas

LEARNING GOAL: *Given the formula of an ionic compound, write the correct name; given the name of an ionic compound, write the correct formula.*

In naming ionic compounds, the name of the positive ion is first, followed by the name of the negative ion. Ionic compounds containing two elements end with *ide*. Except for Ag, Cd, and Zn, transition metals form cations with two or more ionic charges. The charge of the cation is determined from the total negative charge in the formula and included as a Roman numeral in the name.

5.4 Polyatomic Ions

LEARNING GOAL: *Write the name and formula of a compound containing a polyatomic ion.*

A polyatomic ion is a group of nonmetal atoms that carries an electrical charge; for example, the carbonate ion has the formula $CO_3{}^{2-}$. Most polyatomic ions have names that end with *ate* or *ite*.

5.5 Covalent Compounds

LEARNING GOAL: *Given the formula of a covalent compound, write its electron-dot formula (Lewis structure).*

In a covalent bond, atoms of two nonmetals share electrons such that each atom achieves an octet (or two for hydrogen). In some covalent compounds, double or triple bonds are needed to provide an octet. Resonance structures are possible when two or more electron-dot formulas can be drawn for a molecule with a multiple bond.

5.6 Naming and Writing Covalent Formulas

LEARNING GOAL: *Given the formula of a covalent compound, write its correct name; given the name of a covalent compound, write its formula.*

In the names of covalent compounds, prefixes are used to indicate the subscript in the formula. The first element is named with its name. The second element uses the first syllable of its element name followed by *ide*. Prefixes are added to indicate the number of atoms of each nonmetal.

5.7 Electronegativity and Bond Polarity

LEARNING GOAL: *Use electronegativity to determine the polarity of a bond.*

Electronegativity is the attraction of an atom for the electrons in a bond. The electronegativity values of metals are low, while those of nonmetals are high. If the bonding electrons are shared equally, then it is a nonpolar covalent bond. If the electrons are shared unequally, then it is a polar covalent bond in which the atom with the lower electronegativity is partially positive (δ^+) and the atom with the higher electronegativity is partially negative (δ^-). Atoms that form ionic bonds have large differences in electronegativity.

5.8 Shapes and Polarity of Molecules

LEARNING GOAL: *Predict the three-dimensional structure of a molecule and classify it as polar or nonpolar.*

The VSEPR theory indicates that the repulsion of electrons around a central atom pushes the electron groups as far apart as possible. The shape of a molecule is predicted from the arrangement of the bonded atoms and lone pairs of the central atom. The arrangement of four atoms around a central atom with no lone pairs is tetrahedral. A central atom with three atoms bonded to the central atom and one lone pair has a trigonal pyramidal shape. A central atom with two bonded atoms and two lone pairs has a bent shape.

Molecules are nonpolar if they contain nonpolar covalent bonds or have an arrangement of polar covalent bonds with dipoles that cancel out. In polar molecules, the dipoles do not cancel because there are nonidentical bonded atoms or lone pairs on the central atom.

5.9 Attractive Forces in Compounds

LEARNING GOAL: *Describe the attractive forces between ions, polar molecules, and nonpolar molecules.*

Ionic bonds consist of very strong attractive forces between oppositely charged ions. Attractive forces in polar covalent compounds are weaker than ionic bonds and include dipole–dipole attractions and hydrogen bonds. Nonpolar covalent compounds form solids using temporary dipoles called dispersion forces.

KEY TERMS

anion A negatively charged ion such as Cl^-, O^{2-}, or $SO_4{}^{2-}$.

bent The shape of a molecule with two bonded atoms and two lone pairs.

cation A positively charged ion such as Na^+, Mg^{2+}, Al^{3+}, or $NH_4{}^+$.

covalent bond A bond created by the sharing of valence electrons by atoms.

covalent compound A combination of atoms in which noble gas configurations are attained by sharing electrons.

dipole The separation of positive and negative charge in a polar bond indicated by an arrow that is drawn from the more positive atom to the more negative atom.

dipole–dipole attractions Attractive forces between oppositely charged ends of polar molecules.

dispersion forces Weak dipole bonding that results from a momentary polarization of nonpolar molecules.

double bond A sharing of two pairs of electrons by two atoms.

electronegativity The relative ability of an element to attract electrons in a bond.

formula The group of symbols and subscripts that represent the atoms or ions in a compound.

hydrogen bond The attraction between a partially positive H on one molecule and a strongly electronegative atom of F, O, or N on a nearby molecule.

ion An atom or group of atoms having an electrical charge because of a loss or gain of electrons.

ionic bond The attraction between oppositely charged ions.

ionic charge The difference between the number of protons (positive) and the number of electrons (negative) written in the upper right corner of the symbol for the element or polyatomic ion.

ionic compound A compound of positive and negative ions held together by ionic bonds.

linear The shape of a molecule that has two bonded atoms and no lone pair.

molecule The smallest unit of two or more atoms held together by covalent bonds.

nonpolar covalent bond A covalent bond in which the electrons are shared equally between atoms.

nonpolar molecule A molecule that has only nonpolar bonds or in which the bond dipoles cancel.

octet rule Elements in Groups 1A–7A (1, 2, 13–17) react with other elements by forming ionic or covalent bonds to produce a noble gas configuration, usually eight electrons in the outer shell.

polar covalent bond A covalent bond in which the electrons are shared unequally between atoms.

polar molecule A molecule containing bond dipoles that do not cancel.

polyatomic ion A group of covalently bonded nonmetal atoms that has an overall electrical charge.

resonance structures Two or more electron-dot formulas that can be written for a molecule by placing a multiple bond between different atoms.

tetrahedral The shape of a molecule with four bonded atoms.

trigonal planar The shape of a molecule with three bonded atoms and no lone pair.

trigonal pyramidal The shape of a molecule that has three bonded atoms and one lone pair.

triple bond A sharing of three pairs of electrons by two atoms.

valence-shell electron-pair repulsion (VSEPR) theory A theory that predicts the shape of a molecule by placing the electron pairs on a central atom as far apart as possible to minimize the mutual repulsion of the electrons.

UNDERSTANDING THE CONCEPTS

5.87 a. How does the octet rule explain the formation of a sodium ion?

    b. What noble gas has the same electron configuration as the sodium ion?

    c. Why are Group 1A (1) and Group 2A (2) elements found in many compounds, but not Group 8A (18) elements?

5.88 a. How does the octet rule explain the formation of a chloride ion, Cl^-?

    b. What noble gas has the same electron configuration as the chloride ion, Cl^-?

    c. Why are Group 7A (17) elements found in many compounds, but not Group 8A (18) elements?

5.89 Identify each of the following atoms or ions:

$$\begin{array}{ccccc} 15p^+ \\ 16n \end{array} 18e^- \qquad \begin{array}{c} 8p^+ \\ 8n \end{array} 8e^- \qquad \begin{array}{c} 30p^+ \\ 35n \end{array} 28e^- \qquad \begin{array}{c} 26p^+ \\ 28n \end{array} 23e^-$$

      A   B   C   D

$$\begin{array}{c} 3p^+ \\ 4n \end{array} 2e^- \qquad \begin{array}{c} 7p^+ \\ 8n \end{array} 10e^-$$

      E   F

5.90 Identify each of the following atoms or ions:

    a. 35 protons, 45 neutrons, and 36 electrons

    b. 47 protons, 60 neutrons, and 46 electrons

    c. 50 protons, 68 neutrons, and 46 electrons

    d. 15 protons, 16 neutrons, and 15 electrons

    e. 82 protons, 126 neutrons, and 82 electrons

    f. 34 protons, 46 neutrons, and 36 electrons

5.91 In the following electron-dot formulas, assume X and Y are atoms of nonmetals and all bonds are polar covalent:

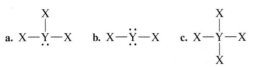

Match each molecule with the correct diagram of its shape and name the shape; indicate if each molecule is polar or nonpolar.

1.   **2.**   **3.**

5.92 Consider the following bonds: Ca—O, C—O, K—O, O—O, and N—O

    a. Which bonds are polar covalent?

    b. Which bonds are nonpolar covalent?

    c. Which bonds are ionic?

    d. Arrange the covalent bonds in order of decreasing polarity.

5.93 Write the formulas and names of the ionic compounds for the elements indicated by the period and electron-dot symbols in the following table:

Period	Electron-Dot Symbols	Formula of Compound	Name of Compound
3	·X· and ·Ÿ·		
3	·Ẋ· and ·Ÿ·		
5	·X· and ·Ÿ:		

5.94 Write the formulas and names of the ionic compounds for the elements indicated by the period and electron-dot symbols in the following table:

Period	Electron-Dot Symbols	Formula of Compound	Name of Compound
2	X· and ·Ÿ·		
4	·X· and ·Ÿ:		
4	·Ẋ· and ·Ÿ·		

5.95 Write the symbols of ions, formulas, and names of their ionic compounds using the electron configurations.

Electron Configurations		Symbols of Ions		Formula of Compound	Name of Compound
Metal	Nonmetal	Cation	Anion		
$1s^22s^1$	$1s^22s^22p^63s^23p^4$				
$1s^22s^22p^63s^23p^64s^2$	$1s^22s^22p^63s^23p^3$				
$1s^22s^22p^63s^1$	$1s^22s^22p^63s^23p^5$				

5.96 Write the symbols of ions, formulas, and names of their ionic compounds using the electron configurations.

Electron Configurations		Symbols of Ions		Formula of Compound	Name of Compound
Metal	Nonmetal	Cation	Anion		
$1s^22s^22p^63s^2$	$1s^22s^22p^3$				
$1s^22s^22p^63s^23p^64s^1$	$1s^22s^22p^4$				
$1s^22s^22p^63s^23p^1$	$1s^22s^22p^63s^23p^5$				

ADDITIONAL QUESTIONS AND PROBLEMS

*For instructor-assigned homework, go to **www.masteringchemistry.com**.*

5.97 Write the symbol for the ion of each of the following:
a. chloride b. potassium c. oxide d. aluminum

5.98 Write the symbol for the ion of each of the following:
a. fluoride b. calcium c. sodium d. lithium

5.99 What is the name of each of the following ions?
a. K^+ b. S^{2-} c. Ca^{2+} d. N^{3-}

5.100 What is the name of each of the following ions?
a. Mg^{2+} b. Ba^{2+} c. I^- d. Cl^-

5.101 Write the formula of each of the following ionic compounds:
a. gold(III) chloride b. lead(IV) oxide
c. silver chloride d. calcium nitride
e. copper(I) phosphide f. chromium(II) chloride

5.102 Write the formula of each of the following ionic compounds:
a. tin(IV) oxide b. iron(III) sulfide
c. lead(IV) sulfide d. chromium(III) iodide
e. lithium nitride f. gold(I) oxide

5.103 Write the electron-dot formula for each of the following:
a. Cl_2O b. CF_4
c. H_2NOH (N is the central atom)
d. H_2CCCl_2

5.104 Write the electron-dot formula for each of the following:
a. H_3COCH_3; the atoms are in the order C O C
b. CS_2; the atoms are in the order S C S
c. NH_3
d. H_2CCHCN; the atoms are in the order C C C N

5.105 Name each of the following covalent compounds:
a. NCl_3 b. SCl_2 c. N_2O
d. F_2 e. PCl_5 f. P_2O_5

5.106 Name each of the following covalent compounds:
a. CBr_4 b. SF_6 c. Br_2
d. N_2O_4 e. SO_2 f. CS_2

5.107 Give the formula for each of the following:
a. carbon monoxide b. diphosphorus pentoxide
c. dihydrogen sulfide d. sulfur dichloride

5.108 Give the formula for each of the following:
a. silicon dioxide b. carbon tetrabromide
c. sulfur trioxide d. dinitrogen oxide

5.109 Classify each of the following compounds as ionic or covalent, and give its name:
a. $FeCl_3$ b. Na_2SO_4 c. N_2O
d. N_2 e. PCl_5 f. CF_4

5.110 Classify each of the following compounds as ionic or covalent, and give its name:
a. $Al_2(CO_3)_3$ b. SF_6 c. Br_2
d. Mg_3N_2 e. SO_2 f. $CrPO_4$

5.111 Write the formulas for the following:
a. tin(II) carbonate b. lithium phosphide
c. silicon tetrachloride d. iron(III) sulfide
e. carbon dioxide f. calcium bromide

5.112 Write the formulas for the following:
a. sodium carbonate b. nitrogen dioxide
c. aluminum nitrate d. copper(I) nitride
e. potassium phosphate f. lead(IV) oxide

5.113 Select the more polar bond in each of the following pairs:
a. C—N or C—O b. N—F or N—Br
c. Br—Cl or S—Cl d. Br—Cl or Br—I
e. N—F or N—O

5.114 Select the more polar bond in each of the following pairs:
a. C—C or C—O b. P—Cl or P—Br
c. Si—S or Si—Cl d. F—Cl or F—Br
e. P—O or P—S

5.115 Show the dipole arrow for each of the following bonds:
a. Si—Cl b. C—N c. F—Cl
d. C—F e. N—O

5.116 Show the dipole arrow for each of the following bonds:
a. C—O b. N—F c. O—Cl
d. S—Cl e. P—F

5.117 Classify each of the following bonds as nonpolar covalent, polar covalent, or ionic:
a. Si—Cl b. C—C c. Na—Cl
d. C—H e. F—F

5.118 Classify each of the following bonds as nonpolar covalent, polar covalent, or ionic:
   a. C—N   **b.** Cl—Cl   **c.** K—Br
   d. H—H   **e.** N—F

5.119 Predict the shape and polarity of each of the following molecules: (Assume that all the bonds are polar.)
   a. A central atom bonded with three identical bonded atoms and no lone pair.
   b. A central atom with two bonded atoms and one lone pair.
   c. A central atom bonded to two identical atoms and no lone pairs.

5.120 Predict the shape and polarity of each of the following molecules: (Assume that all the bonds are polar.)
   a. A central atom with four identical bonded atoms and no lone pairs.
   b. A central atom with three identical bonded atoms and one lone pair.
   c. A central atom with four bonded atoms that are not identical and no lone pair.

5.121 Write the electron-dot formula and determine the shape for each of the following:
   a. NF_3 **b.** $SiBr_4$ **c.** $BeCl_2$ **d.** SO_2

5.122 Write the electron-dot formula and determine the shape for each of the following:
   a. SiH_4 **b.** HCCH
   c. $COCl_2$ (C is the central atom)
   d. BCl_3

5.123 Predict the shape and polarity of each of the following molecules:
   a. H_2S **b.** NF_3 **c.** NCl_3
   d. CH_3Cl **e.** SiF_4

5.124 Predict the shape and polarity of each of the following molecules:
   a. H_2O **b.** CF_4 **c.** GeH_4
   d. PCl_3 **e.** SCl_2

5.125 Indicate the major type of attractive forces—(1) ionic, (2) dipole–dipole attractions, (3) hydrogen bonds, (4) dispersion forces—that occurs between particles of the following:
   a. NH_3 **b.** HI   **c.** Br_2 **d.** Cs_2O

5.126 Indicate the major type of attractive force—(1) ionic, (2) dipole–dipole attraction, (3) hydrogen bond, (4) dispersion forces—that occurs between particles of the following:
   a. $CHCl_3$ **b.** H_2O **c.** LiCl   **d.** Cl_2

CHALLENGE QUESTIONS

5.127 Consider the following electron-dot formulas for elements X and Y:

   X·   ·Ÿ·

   a. What are the group numbers of X and Y?
   b. Will a compound of X and Y be ionic or covalent?
   c. What ions would be formed by X and Y?
   d. What would be the formula of a compound of X and Y?
   e. What would be the formula of a compound of X and chlorine?
   f. What would be the formula of a compound of Y and chlorine?

5.128 Complete the following table for atoms or ions:

Atom or Ion	Number of Protons	Number of Electrons	Electrons Lost/Gained
K^+			
	$12p^+$	$10e^-$	
	$8p^+$		$2e^-$ gained
		$10e^-$	$3e^-$ lost

5.129 One of the ions of tin is tin(IV).
   a. What is the symbol for this ion?
   b. How many protons and electrons are in the ion?
   c. What is the formula of tin(IV) oxide?
   d. What is the formula of tin(IV) phosphate?

5.130 Classify the following compounds as ionic or covalent and name each:
   a. Li_2O **b.** N_2O **c.** CF_4
   d. Cl_2O **e.** MgF_2 **f.** CO
   g. $CaCl_2$ **h.** K_3PO_4

5.131 Name the following compounds:
   a. $FeCl_2$ **b.** Cl_2O_7 **c.** N_2
   d. $Ca_3(PO_4)_2$ **e.** PCl_3 **f.** $Al(NO_3)_3$
   g. $PbCl_4$ **h.** $MgCO_3$ **i.** NO_2
   j. $SnSO_4$ **k.** $Ba(NO_3)_2$ **l.** CuS

5.132 Identify the most important type of attractive forces for each of following:
   a. C_3H_8 **b.** CH_3OH **c.** Br_2
   d. HBr   **e.** IBr

ANSWERS

ANSWERS TO STUDY CHECKS

5.1 K^+ and S^{2-}

5.2 gallium sulfide

5.3 gold(I) oxide

5.4 Cr_2O_3

5.5 $(NH_4)_3PO_4$

5.6 calcium phosphate

5.7 :C̈l:Ö:C̈l: or   :C̈l—Ö—C̈l:

5.8 H:C:::N: or H—C≡N: In HCN, there is a triple bond between C and N atoms.

5.9 :Ö—S=Ö: ⟷ :Ö—S—Ö: ⟷ :Ö=S—Ö:
         | ‖ |
        :O: :O: :O:

5.10 a. silicon tetrabromide   **b.** dibromine oxide

5.11 IF_7

5.12 a. Si—N   **b.** O—P

5.13 tetrahedral

5.14 polar

5.15 H_2O forms hydrogen bonds that are stronger than the dipole–dipole attractions of H_2S. Thus H_2S does not need as much energy to change from liquid to gas.

ANSWERS TO SELECTED QUESTIONS AND PROBLEMS

5.1 a. 1   **b.** 2   **c.** 3   **d.** 1   **e.** 2

5.3 a. Li^+ **b.** F^- **c.** Mg^{2+} **d.** Fe^{3+}

5.5 a. 8 protons, 10 electrons   **b.** 19 protons, 18 electrons
   c. 35 protons, 36 electrons   **d.** 16 protons, 18 electrons

5.7 a. Cl^- **b.** K^+ **c.** O^{2-} **d.** Al^{3+}

5.9 a. K   **b.** Cl^- **c.** Ca   **d.** K^+

5.11 a., c.,

5.13 a. Na_2O **b.** $AlBr_3$ **c.** BaO   **d.** $MgCl_2$ **e.** Al_2S_3

5.15 a. Na^+, S^{2-} Na_2S **b.** K^+, N^{3-} K_3N
   c. Al^{3+}, I^- AlI_3 **d.** Li^+, O^{2-} Li_2O

5.17 a. aluminum oxide   **b.** calcium chloride
   c. sodium oxide   **d.** magnesium nitride
   e. potassium iodide

5.19 Most of the transition metals form more than one positive ion. The specific ion is indicated in a name by writing a Roman numeral that is the same as the ionic charge. For example, iron forms Fe^{2+} and Fe^{3+} ions, which are named iron(II) and iron(III).

5.21 a. iron(II)   **b.** copper(II)
   c. zinc   **d.** lead(IV)
   e. chromium(III)

5.23 a. tin(II) chloride   **b.** iron(II) oxide
   c. copper(I) sulfide   **d.** copper(II) sulfide
   e. chromium(III) bromide   **f.** zinc chloride

5.25 a. Au^{3+} **b.** Fe^{3+} **c.** Pb^{4+} **d.** Sn^{2+}

5.27 a. $MgCl_2$ **b.** Na_2S **c.** Cu_2O
   d. Zn_3P_2 **e.** AuN   **f.** $CrCl_2$

5.29 a. HCO_3^- **b.** NH_4^+ **c.** PO_4^{3-} **d.** HSO_4^-

5.31 a. sulfate   **b.** carbonate
   c. phosphate   **d.** nitrate

5.33

	OH^-	NO_2^-	CO_3^{2-}	HSO_4^-	PO_4^{3-}
Li^+	LiOH	$LiNO_2$	Li_2CO_3	$LiHSO_4$	Li_3PO_4
Cu^{2+}	$Cu(OH)_2$	$Cu(NO_2)_2$	$CuCO_3$	$Cu(HSO_4)_2$	$Cu_3(PO_4)_2$
Ba^{2+}	$Ba(OH)_2$	$Ba(NO_2)_2$	$BaCO_3$	$Ba(HSO_4)_2$	$Ba_3(PO_4)_2$

5.35 a. CO_3^{2-}, sodium carbonate
   b. NH_4^+, ammonium chloride
   c. PO_4^{3-}, lithium phosphate
   d. NO_2^- copper(II) nitrite
   e. SO_3^{2-}, iron(II) sulfite

5.37 a. $Ba(OH)_2$ **b.** Na_2SO_4 **c.** $Fe(NO_3)_2$
   d. $Zn_3(PO_4)_2$ **e.** $Fe_2(CO_3)_3$

5.39 The nonmetallic elements are most likely to form covalent bonds.

5.41 a. 2 valence electrons: 1 bonding pair and 0 lone pairs
   b. 8 valence electrons: 1 bonding pair and 3 lone pairs
   c. 14 valence electrons: 1 bonding pair and 6 lone pairs

5.43 a. HF ($8\,e^-$) H:F̈: or H—F̈:

   b. SF_2 ($20\,e^-$) :F̈:S̈:F̈: or :F̈—S̈—F̈:

   c. NBr_3 ($26\,e^-$) :B̈r:N̈:B̈r: or :B̈r—N̈—B̈r: (with :B̈r: above)

   d. CH_3OH ($14\,e^-$) H:C̈:Ö:H or H—C—Ö—H (with H above and below)

   e. N_2H_4 ($14\,e^-$) H:N̈:N̈:H or H—N—N—H (with H H above)

5.45 When using all the valence electrons does not give complete octets, it is necessary to write multiple bonds.

5.47 Resonance occurs when, for the same molecule or ion, we can write two or more electron-dot formulas that have multiple bonds.

5.49 a. CO ($10\,e^-$) :C:::O: or :C≡O:

   b. H_2CCH_2 ($12\,e^-$) H:C::C:H or H—C=C—H (with H H above and below)

   c. H_2CO ($12\,e^-$) H:C:H or H—C—H (with :O: above)

5.51 a. $ClNO_2$:C̈l—N—Ö: ⟷ :C̈l—N=Ö: (with :O: above)

5.53 a. phosphorus tribromide
   b. carbon tetrabromide
   c. silicon dioxide
   d. dinitrogen trioxide
   e. silicon tetrabromide
   f. phosphorus pentachloride

5.55 a. CCl_4 **b.** CO   **c.** PCl_3
   d. N_2O_4 **e.** BF_3 **f.** SF_6

5.57 a. aluminum sulfate
   b. calcium carbonate
   c. dinitrogen oxide
   d. sodium phosphate
   e. ammonium sulfate
   f. iron(III) oxide

5.59 The electronegativity increases going from left to right across a period.

5.61 A nonpolar covalent bond would have an electronegativity difference of 0.0 to 0.4.

5.63 a. K, Na, Li   **b.** Na, P, Cl   **c.** Ca, Br, O

5.65 a. polar covalent
   b. ionic
   c. polar covalent
   d. nonpolar covalent
   e. polar covalent
   f. nonpolar covalent

5.67 a. $\overset{\delta+}{N}—\overset{\delta-}{F}$ **b.** $\overset{\delta+}{Si}—\overset{\delta-}{Br}$ **c.** $\overset{\delta+}{C}—\overset{\delta-}{O}$

   d. $\overset{\delta+}{P}—\overset{\delta-}{Br}$ **e.** $\overset{\delta+}{B}—\overset{\delta-}{Cl}$

5.69 tetrahedral

5.71 The four electron groups in PCl_3 have a tetrahedral arrangement, but three bonded atoms and one lone pair around a central atom give a trigonal pyramidal shape.

5.73 In both PH_3 and NH_3, there are four electron pairs; three are bonded to atoms, and one is a lone pair. The shapes of both are trigonal pyramidal.

5.75 a. bent   **b.** tetrahedral   **c.** linear   **d.** bent

5.77 Cl_2 is a nonpolar molecule because there is a nonpolar covalent bond between Cl atoms, which have identical electronegativity values. In HCl, the bond is a polar bond, which makes HCl a polar molecule.

5.79 a. polar   **b.** polar
c. nonpolar   **d.** nonpolar

5.81 a. dipole–dipole attractions
b. ionic
c. dispersion forces
d. hydrogen bonds
e. dispersion forces

5.83 a. hydrogen bonding
b. dispersion forces
c. dipole–dipole attractions
d. dispersion forces
e. dispersion forces

5.85 a. HF; hydrogen bonds are stronger than dipole–dipole attractions in HBr.
b. NaF; ionic bonds are stronger than the hydrogen bonds in HF.
c. $MgBr_2$; ionic bonds are stronger than the dipole–dipole attractions in PBr_3.
d. CH_3OH; hydrogen bonds are stronger than the dispersion forces in CH_4.

5.87 a. By losing one valence electron from the third energy level, sodium achieves an octet in the second energy level.
b. Ne
c. Group 1A (1) and 2A (2) elements acquire octets by losing electrons when they form compounds. Group 8A (18) elements are stable with octets (or two electrons for helium).

5.89 a. P^{3-} **b.** O atom   **c.** Zn^{2+} **d.** Fe^{3+}
e. Li^+ **f.** N^{3-}

5.91 a. 2—trigonal pyramidal, polar
b. 1—bent, polar
c. 3—tetrahedral, nonpolar

5.93

Period	Electron-Dot Symbols	Formula of Compound	Name of Compound
3	$\cdot X \cdot$ and $\cdot \ddot{Y} \cdot$	Mg_3P_2	Magnesium phosphide
3	$\cdot \dot{X} \cdot$ and $\cdot \ddot{Y} \cdot$	Al_2S_3	Aluminum sulfide
5	$\cdot X \cdot$ and $\cdot \ddot{Y} :$	SrI_2	Strontium iodide

5.95

Electron Configurations		Symbols of Ions			
Metal	Nonmetal	Cation	Anion	Formula of Compound	Name of Compound
$1s^2 2s^1$	$1s^2 2s^2 2p^6 3s^2 3p^4$	Li^+	S^{2-}	Li_2S	Lithium sulfide
$1s^2 2s^2 2p^6 3s^2 3p^6 4s^2$	$1s^2 2s^2 2p^6 3s^2 3p^3$	Ca^{2+}	P^{3-}	Ca_3P_2	Calcium phosphide
$1s^2 2s^2 2p^6 3s^1$	$1s^2 2s^2 2p^6 3s^2 3p^5$	Na^+	Cl^-	NaCl	Sodium chloride

5.97 a. Cl^- **b.** K^+ **c.** O^{2-} **d.** Al^{3+}

5.99 a. potassium   **b.** sulfide   **c.** calcium   **d.** nitride

5.101 a. $AuCl_3$ **b.** PbO_2 **c.** AgCl
d. Ca_3N_2 **e.** Cu_3P **f.** $CrCl_2$

5.103 a. Cl_2O (20 e^-) $:\ddot{\underset{..}{C}l}:\ddot{\underset{..}{O}}:\ddot{\underset{..}{C}l}:$ or $:\ddot{\underset{..}{C}l}\!-\!\ddot{\underset{..}{O}}\!-\!\ddot{\underset{..}{C}l}:$

b. CF_4 (32 e^-) $:\ddot{\underset{..}{F}}:\overset{\displaystyle :\ddot{F}:}{\underset{\displaystyle :\ddot{F}:}{C}}:\ddot{\underset{..}{F}}:$

c. H_2NOH (14 e^-) $H:\ddot{N}:\ddot{O}:H$ or $H\!-\!\overset{\displaystyle H}{\underset{\displaystyle H}{N}}\!-\!\ddot{\underset{..}{O}}\!-\!H$

d. H_2CCCl_2 (24 e^-) $H:C::C:\ddot{\underset{..}{C}l}:$ or $H\!-\!\overset{\displaystyle H}{C}\!=\!\overset{\displaystyle :\ddot{C}l:}{C}\!-\!\ddot{\underset{..}{C}l}:$

5.105 a. nitrogen trichloride
b. sulfur dichloride
c. dinitrogen oxide
d. fluorine
e. phosphorus pentachloride
f. diphosphorus pentoxide

5.107 a. CO   **b.** P_2O_5 **c.** H_2S **d.** SCl_2

5.109 a. ionic, iron(III) chloride
b. ionic, sodium sulfate
c. covalent, dinitrogen oxide
d. covalent, nitrogen
e. covalent, phosphorus pentachloride
f. covalent, carbon tetrafluoride

5.111 a. $SnCO_3$ **b.** Li_3P **c.** $SiCl_4$
d. Fe_2S_3 **e.** CO_2 **f.** $CaBr_2$

5.113 a. C—O   **b.** N—F   **c.** S—Cl
d. Br—I   **e.** N—F

5.115 a. Si—Cl   **b.** C—N   **c.** F—Cl
$\longrightarrow$ $\longrightarrow$ $\longleftarrow$
d. C—F   **e.** N—O
$\longrightarrow$ $\longrightarrow$

5.117 a. polar covalent
b. nonpolar covalent
c. ionic
d. nonpolar covalent
e. nonpolar covalent

5.119 a. trigonal planar, nonpolar
b. bent, polar
c. linear, nonpolar

5.121 a. NF_3 $:\ddot{\underset{..}{F}}\!-\!\overset{\displaystyle :\ddot{F}:}{N}\!-\!\ddot{\underset{..}{F}}:$ trigonal pyramidal

b. $SiBr_4$ $:\ddot{\underset{..}{B}r}\!-\!\overset{\displaystyle :\ddot{B}r:}{\underset{\displaystyle :\ddot{B}r:}{Si}}\!-\!\ddot{\underset{..}{B}r}:$ tetrahedral

c. $BeCl_2$ $:\ddot{C}l—Be—\ddot{C}l:$ linear

d. SO_2 $\left[:\ddot{O}=\ddot{S}—\ddot{O}:\right] \longleftrightarrow \left[:\ddot{O}—\ddot{S}=\ddot{O}:\right]$ bent (120°)

5.123 a. bent, polar
    b. trigonal pyramidal, polar
    c. trigonal pyramidal, polar
    d. tetrahedral, polar
    e. tetrahedral, nonpolar

5.125 a. (3) hydrogen bond
    b. (2) dipole–dipole attractions
    c. (4) dispersion forces
    d. (1) ionic

5.127 a. X is in Group 1A (1); Y is in Group 6A (16)
    b. ionic   **c.** X^+, Y^{2-} **d.** X_2Y
    e. XCl   **f.** YCl_2

5.129 a. Sn^{4+}
    b. 50 protons, 46 electrons
    c. SnO_2
    d. $Sn_3(PO_4)_4$

5.131 a. iron(II) chloride
    b. dichlorine heptoxide
    c. nitrogen
    d. calcium phosphate
    e. phosphorus trichloride
    f. aluminum nitrate
    g. lead(IV) chloride
    h. magnesium carbonate
    i. nitrogen dioxide
    j. tin(II) sulfate
    k. barium nitrate
    l. copper(II) sulfide

6 Chemical Reactions and Quantities

"In our food science laboratory, I develop a variety of food products, from cake donuts to energy beverages," says Anne Cristofano, senior food technologist at Mattson & Company. *"When I started the donut project, I researched the ingredients, then weighed them out in the lab. I added water to make a batter and cooked the donuts in a fryer. The batter and the oil temperature make a big difference. If I don't get the right taste or texture, I adjust the ingredients, such as sugar and flour, or adjust the temperature."*

A food technologist studies the physical and chemical properties of food and develops scientific ways to process and preserve it for extended shelf life. The food products are tested for texture, color, and flavor. The results of these tests help improve the quality and safety of food.

Mastering**CHEMISTRY**™

Visit **www.masteringchemistry.com** for self-study materials and instructor-assigned homework.

The fuel in our cars burns with oxygen to provide energy to make the car move, play the radio, and run the air conditioner. When we cook our food or bleach our hair, chemical reactions take place. In our bodies, chemical reactions convert food substances into molecules to build muscles and move them. In the leaves of trees and plants, carbon dioxide and water are converted into carbohydrates.

Some chemical reactions are simple, whereas others are quite complex. However, they can all be written with equations used to describe chemical reactions. In every chemical reaction, the atoms in the reacting substances, called *reactants*, are rearranged to give new substances called *products*.

In this chapter, we will see how equations are written and how we can determine the amount of reactant or product involved. We do the same thing at home when we use a recipe to make bread or cookies. At the automotive repair shop, a mechanic does essentially the same thing when adjusting the fuel system of an engine to allow the correct amounts of fuel and oxygen. In the hospital, a respiratory therapist evaluates the level of CO_2 and O_2 in the blood. A certain amount of O_2 must reach the tissues for efficient metabolic reactions. If the oxygenation of the blood is low, then the therapist will oxygenate the patient and recheck the blood oxygen levels.

6.1 Chemical Reactions

As we discussed in Chapter 2, a *chemical change* occurs when a substance is converted into one or more new substances. For example, when silver tarnishes, the shiny silver metal (Ag) reacts with sulfur (S) to become the dull, black substance we call *tarnish* (Ag_2S). (See Figure 6.1.)

LEARNING GOAL

Write a balanced chemical equation from the formulas of the reactants and products for a chemical reaction.

 SELF STUDY ACTIVITY
Chemical Reactions and Equations

A chemical change:
the tarnishing of silver

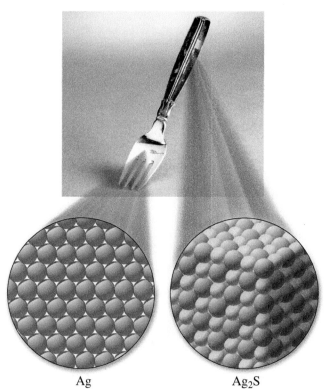

Ag Ag_2S

Silver and tarnish are different substances

FIGURE 6.1 A chemical change produces new substances.
Q Why is the formation of tarnish a chemical change?

FIGURE 6.2 A chemical reaction forms new products with different properties. An antacid ($NaHCO_3$) tablet in water forms bubbles of carbon dioxide (CO_2).

Q What is the evidence for chemical change in this chemical reaction?

TABLE 6.1 Types of Visible Evidence of a Chemical Reaction

1. Change in the color
2. Formation of a gas (bubbles)
3. Formation of a solid (precipitate)
4. Heat (or a flame) produced or heat absorbed

(MC) SELF STUDY ACTIVITY
What Is Chemistry?

A **chemical reaction** always involves chemical change because atoms of the reacting substances form new combinations with new properties. For example, a chemical reaction takes place when an antacid tablet is dropped into a glass of water. The tablet fizzes and bubbles as $NaHCO_3$ and citric acid ($C_6H_8O_7$) in the tablet react to form carbon dioxide (CO_2) gas. (See Figure 6.2.) During a chemical change, new properties become visible, which are an indication that a chemical reaction has taken place. (See Table 6.1.)

CONCEPT CHECK 6.1

■ Evidence of a Chemical Reaction

Indicate why each of the following is a chemical reaction:

a. burning propane fuel in a barbecue
b. using peroxide to change the color of hair

ANSWER

a. The production of heat during burning of propane fuel is evidence of a chemical reaction.
b. The change in hair color is evidence of a chemical reaction.

When you build a model airplane, prepare a new recipe, or mix a medication formulation, you follow a set of directions. These directions tell you what materials to use and the products you will obtain. In chemistry, a **chemical equation** tells us the materials we need and the products that will form in a chemical reaction.

Writing a Chemical Equation

Suppose you work in a bicycle shop, assembling wheels and frames into bicycles. You could represent this process by a simple equation:

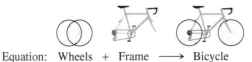

Equation: Wheels + Frame ⟶ Bicycle

When you burn charcoal in a grill, the carbon in the charcoal combines with oxygen to form carbon dioxide. We can represent this reaction by a chemical equation that is much like the one for the bicycle:

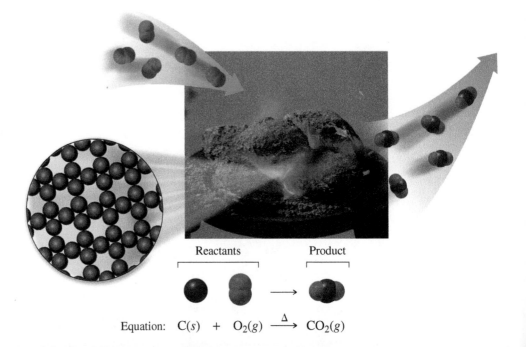

Reactants   Product

Equation: $C(s)$ + $O_2(g)$ $\xrightarrow{\Delta}$ $CO_2(g)$

In an equation, the formulas of the **reactants** are written on the left of the arrow and the formulas of the **products** on the right. When there are two or more formulas on the same side, they are separated by plus (+) signs. The delta sign (Δ) indicates that heat was used to start the reaction.

Generally, the formulas in an equation are followed by letters in parentheses that contain abbreviations for the physical state of the substances: solid (*s*), liquid (*l*), or gas or vapor (*g*). If a substance is dissolved in water, it is an aqueous (*aq*) solution. Table 6.2 summarizes some of the symbols used in equations.

Identifying a Balanced Chemical Equation

When a chemical reaction takes place, the bonds between the atoms of the reactants are broken, and new bonds are formed to give the products. All atoms are conserved, which means that atoms cannot be gained, lost, or changed into other types of atoms during a chemical reaction. Every chemical reaction is written as a **balanced equation** that shows the same number of atoms for each element in the reactants as in the products. For example, the chemical equation we wrote above for burning carbon is *balanced* because there is one carbon atom and two oxygen atoms on each side of the arrow.

$$C(s) + O_2(g) \longrightarrow CO_2(g)$$

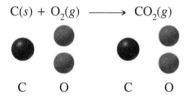

C	O	C	O

Reactant atoms = Product atoms

Now consider the reaction in which hydrogen reacts with oxygen to form water. The formulas of the reactants and products are written as follows:

$$H_2(g) + O_2(g) \longrightarrow H_2O(g)$$

When we add up the atoms of each element on each side of the arrow, we find that the equation is *not balanced*. The number of atoms on the left side does not match the number of atoms on the right side. To balance this equation, we place whole numbers called **coefficients** in front of some of the formulas. If we write a coefficient of 2 in front of H_2O, it represents 2 molecules of water. Now the product consists of 4 hydrogen atoms and 2 oxygen atoms. To obtain 4 H atoms on the reactant side, we must write a coefficient of 2 in front of H_2. Only coefficients can be used to balance a chemical equation; the formulas and their subscripts are never changed. Changing subscripts changes the chemical identities of the reactants and products. Now the numbers of hydrogen atoms and oxygen atoms are the same in the reactants as in the products. The equation is *balanced*.

Balancing a Chemical Equation

We can now show the process of balancing a chemical equation using the reaction of CH_4 with oxygen to produce carbon dioxide and water.

STEP 1   **Write an equation, using the correct formulas of the reactants and products.**

$$CH_4(g) + O_2(g) \longrightarrow CO_2(g) + H_2O(g)$$

TABLE 6.2 Some Symbols Used in Writing Equations

Symbol	Meaning
+	Separates two or more formulas
$\longrightarrow$	Reacts to form products
Δ	Reactants are heated
(*s*)	Solid
(*l*)	Liquid
(*g*)	Gas or vapor
(*aq*)	Aqueous

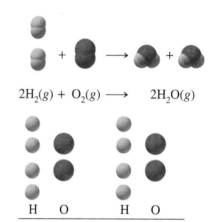

$$2H_2(g) + O_2(g) \longrightarrow \quad 2H_2O(g)$$

H	O	H	O

Reactant atoms = Product atoms

Ⓜ TUTORIAL
Balancing Chemical Equations

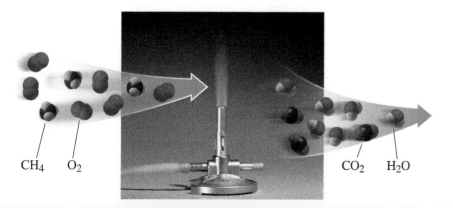

CH₄   O₂   CO₂   H₂O

STEP 2   **Count the atoms of each element in the reactants and products.**   When we compare the atoms on the reactant side and the product side, we see that there are more hydrogen atoms on the left side and more oxygen atoms on the right.

$$CH_4(g) + O_2(g) \longrightarrow CO_2(g) + H_2O(g)$$

Reactants	Products	
1 C	1 C	Balanced
4 H	2 H	Not balanced
2 O	3 O	Not balanced

STEP 3   **Use coefficients to balance each element.**   Because CH_4 has the most atoms of an element (H), we start by balancing the 4 H atoms. This is done by placing a 2 in front of the formula for water, $2H_2O$, which gives a total of 4 H atoms on the product side. This gives a total of 4 O atoms on the product side, which we balance by placing a 2 in front of the formula O_2.

$$CH_4(g) + 2O_2(g) \longrightarrow CO_2(g) + 2H_2O(g)$$

STEP 4   **Check the final equation to confirm that it is balanced.**   In the final equation, the numbers of carbon, hydrogen, and oxygen atoms are the same for both reactants and products.

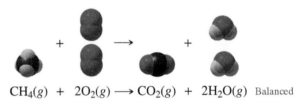

$$CH_4(g) + 2O_2(g) \longrightarrow CO_2(g) + 2H_2O(g) \quad \text{Balanced}$$

Reactants	Products
1 C atom	1 C atom
4 H atoms	4 H atoms
4 O atoms	4 O atoms

In a balanced equation, the coefficients must be the lowest set of whole numbers. Suppose you had added coefficients to the equation and obtained the following:

$$2CH_4(g) + 4O_2(g) \longrightarrow 2CO_2(g) + 4H_2O(g) \quad \text{Incorrect}$$

Although there are equal numbers of atoms on both sides of the equation, this is not written correctly. The correctly balanced equation is obtained by dividing all the coefficients by 2.

CONCEPT CHECK 6.2

■ **Balancing Chemical Equations**

Indicate the number of each in the following equation:

$$Fe_2S_3(s) + 6HCl(aq) \longrightarrow 2FeCl_3(aq) + 3H_2S(g)$$

	Reactants	Products
Atoms of Cl		
Atoms of S		
Atoms of Fe		
Molecules of H_2S		

ANSWER

The total number of atoms in each formula is obtained by multiplying through by its coefficient. The number of molecules is obtained from the coefficient.

	Reactants	Products
Atoms of Cl	6	6
Atoms of S	3	3
Atoms of Fe	2	2
Molecules of H_2S	0	3

SAMPLE PROBLEM   6.1

■ Balancing Chemical Equations

Balance the following equation:

$$Na_3PO_4(aq) + MgCl_2(aq) \longrightarrow Mg_3(PO_4)_2(s) + NaCl(aq)$$

SOLUTION

**Guide to Balancing a
Chemical Equation**

STEP 1
Write an equation using the
correct formulas of the
reactants and products.

STEP 2
Count the atoms or ions of each
element in reactants and products.

STEP 3
Use coefficients to balance
each element.

STEP 4
Check the final equation
for balance.

STEP 1   **Write an equation using the correct formulas.**

$$Na_3PO_4(aq) + MgCl_2(aq) \longrightarrow Mg_3(PO_4)_2(s) + NaCl(aq)$$

STEP 2   **Count the atoms or ions and determine if the equation is balanced.** When we compare the number of ions on the reactant and product sides, we find that the equation is not balanced. In this equation, we can balance the phosphate ion as a group because it appears on both sides of the equation.

Reactants	**Products**	
$Na_3PO_4(aq) + MgCl_2(aq) \longrightarrow$	$Mg_3(PO_4)_2(s) + NaCl(aq)$	
$3 \ Na^+$	$1 \ Na^+$	Not balanced
$1 \ PO_4^{3-}$	$2 \ PO_4^{3-}$	Not balanced
$1 \ Mg^{2+}$	$3 \ Mg^{2+}$	Not balanced
$2 \ Cl^-$	$1 \ Cl^-$	Not balanced

STEP 3   **Use coefficients to balance each element.** We typically begin with the element in a formula that has the highest subscript values, which is $Mg_3(PO_4)_2$. A 3 in front of $MgCl_2$ balances magnesium (Mg), and a 2 in front of Na_3PO_4 balances the phosphate ion (PO_4^{3-}).

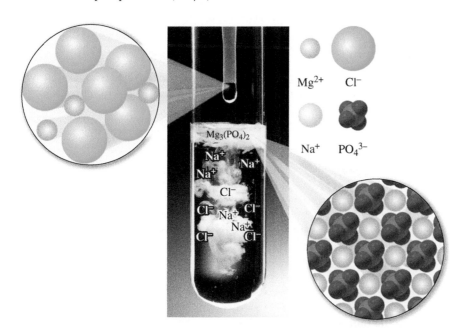

$Mg_3(PO_4)_2$

Mg^{2+} Cl^-

Na^+ PO_4^{3-}

$$2Na_3PO_4(aq) + 3MgCl_2(aq) \longrightarrow 1Mg_3(PO_4)_2(s) + NaCl(aq)$$

Looking again at each of the ions in the reactants and products, we see that the sodium and chloride ions are not yet equal. A 6 in front of the NaCl balances the equation:

$$2Na_3PO_4(aq) + 3MgCl_2(aq) \longrightarrow 1Mg_3(PO_4)_2(s) + 6NaCl(aq)$$

STEP 4   **Check to see that the final equation is balanced.** A check of the total number of atoms indicates the equation is balanced. A coefficient of 1 is understood and not usually written.

Reactants	Products
$6\,Na^+$	$6\,Na^+$
$2\,PO_4{}^{3-}$	$2\,PO_4{}^{3-}$
$3\,Mg^{2+}$	$3\,Mg^{2+}$
$6\,Cl^-$	$6\,Cl^-$

$$2Na_3PO_4(aq) + 3MgCl_2(aq) \longrightarrow Mg_3(PO_4)_2(s) + 6NaCl(aq) \quad \text{Balanced}$$

STUDY CHECK

Balance the following equation:

$$Fe(s) + O_2(g) \longrightarrow Fe_3O_4(s)$$

QUESTIONS AND PROBLEMS

Chemical Reactions

6.1 Determine whether each of the following equations is balanced or not balanced:
a. $S(s) + O_2(g) \longrightarrow SO_3(g)$
b. $2Al(s) + 3Cl_2(g) \longrightarrow 2AlCl_3(s)$
c. $H_2(g) + O_2(g) \longrightarrow H_2O(g)$
d. $C_3H_8(g) + 5O_2(g) \longrightarrow 3CO_2(g) + 4H_2O(g)$

6.2 Determine whether each of the following equations is balanced or not balanced:
a. $PCl_3(s) + Cl_2(g) \longrightarrow PCl_5(s)$
b. $CO(g) + 2H_2(g) \longrightarrow CH_3OH(g)$
c. $2KClO_3(s) \longrightarrow 2KCl(s) + O_2(g)$
d. $Mg(s) + N_2(g) \longrightarrow Mg_3N_2(s)$

6.3 Balance the following equations:
a. $N_2(g) + O_2(g) \longrightarrow NO(g)$
b. $HgO(s) \longrightarrow Hg(l) + O_2(g)$
c. $Fe(s) + O_2(g) \longrightarrow Fe_2O_3(s)$
d. $Na(s) + Cl_2(g) \longrightarrow NaCl(s)$

6.4 Balance the following equations:
a. $Ca(s) + Br_2(l) \longrightarrow CaBr_2(s)$
b. $P_4(s) + O_2(g) \longrightarrow P_4O_{10}(s)$
c. $Sb_2S_3(s) + HCl(aq) \longrightarrow SbCl_3(s) + H_2S(g)$
d. $Fe_2O_3(s) + C(s) \longrightarrow Fe(s) + CO(g)$

6.5 Balance the following equations:
a. $Mg(s) + AgNO_3(aq) \longrightarrow Mg(NO_3)_2(aq) + Ag(s)$
b. $Al(s) + CuSO_4(aq) \longrightarrow Cu(s) + Al_2(SO_4)_3(aq)$
c. $Pb(NO_3)_2(aq) + NaCl(aq) \longrightarrow PbCl_2(s) + NaNO_3(aq)$
d. $Al(s) + HCl(aq) \longrightarrow AlCl_3(aq) + H_2(g)$

6.6 Balance the following equations:
a. $Zn(s) + H_2SO_4(aq) \longrightarrow ZnSO_4(aq) + H_2(g)$
b. $Al(s) + H_2SO_4(aq) \longrightarrow Al_2(SO_4)_3(aq) + H_2(g)$
c. $K_2SO_4(aq) + BaCl_2(aq) \longrightarrow BaSO_4(s) + KCl(aq)$
d. $CaCO_3(s) \longrightarrow CaO(s) + CO_2(g)$

6.2 Types of Reactions

LEARNING GOAL

Identify a chemical reaction as a combination, decomposition, single replacement, or double replacement reaction.

A great number of reactions occur in nature, in biological systems, and in the laboratory. However, some general patterns among all reactions help us to classify them. Most fit into four general reaction types.

Combination Reactions

Two or more reactants	combine to yield	a single product
A + B	$\longrightarrow$	A B

In a **combination reaction**, two or more elements or compounds bond to form one product. For example, sulfur and oxygen combine to form the product sulfur dioxide.

Combination

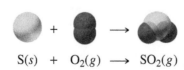

$$S(s) + O_2(g) \longrightarrow SO_2(g)$$

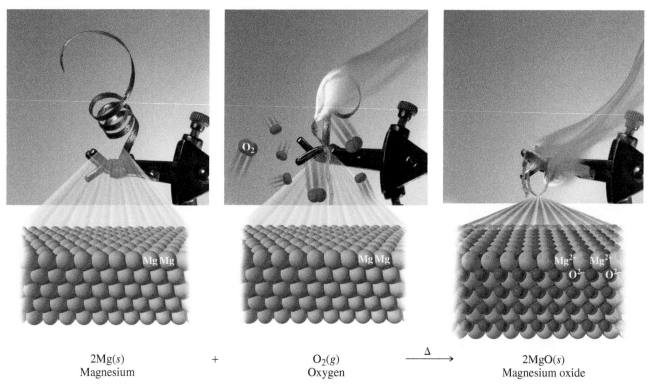

$$2Mg(s) \qquad + \qquad O_2(g) \qquad \xrightarrow{\Delta} \qquad 2MgO(s)$$
Magnesium   Oxygen   Magnesium oxide

FIGURE 6.3 In a combination reaction, two or more substances combine to form one substance as product.
Q What happens to the atoms of the reactants in a combination reaction?

In Figure 6.3, the elements magnesium and oxygen combine to form a single product, magnesium oxide:

$$2Mg(s) + O_2(g) \xrightarrow{\Delta} 2MgO(s)$$

Decomposition Reactions

In a **decomposition reaction**, a reactant splits into two or more simpler products. For example, when mercury(II) oxide is heated, it breaks apart into mercury atoms and oxygen. (See Figure 6.4.)

$$2HgO(s) \xrightarrow{\Delta} 2Hg(l) + O_2(g)$$

Decomposition

A   splits   two or more
reactant   into   products

$$\boxed{A\ B} \longrightarrow \boxed{A} + \boxed{B}$$

Single Replacement Reactions

In a replacement reaction, elements in a compound are replaced by other elements. In a **single replacement reaction**, a reacting element switches place with an element in the other reacting compound.

Single replacement

One element   replaces   another element

$$\boxed{A} + \boxed{B\ C} \longrightarrow \boxed{A\ C} + \boxed{B}$$

In the single replacement reaction shown in Figure 6.5, zinc replaces hydrogen in hydrochloric acid, HCl(aq):

$$Zn(s) + 2HCl(aq) \longrightarrow ZnCl_2(aq) + H_2(g)$$

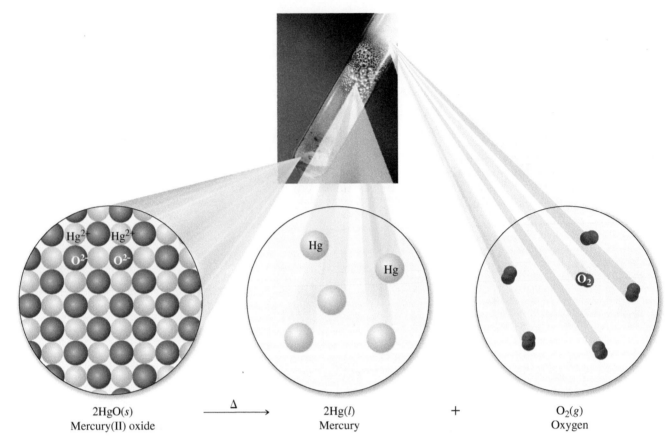

$$2HgO(s) \xrightarrow{\Delta} 2Hg(l) + O_2(g)$$

Mercury(II) oxide   Mercury   Oxygen

FIGURE 6.4 In a decomposition reaction, one reactant breaks down into two or more products.

Q How do the differences in the reactant and products classify this as a decomposition reaction?

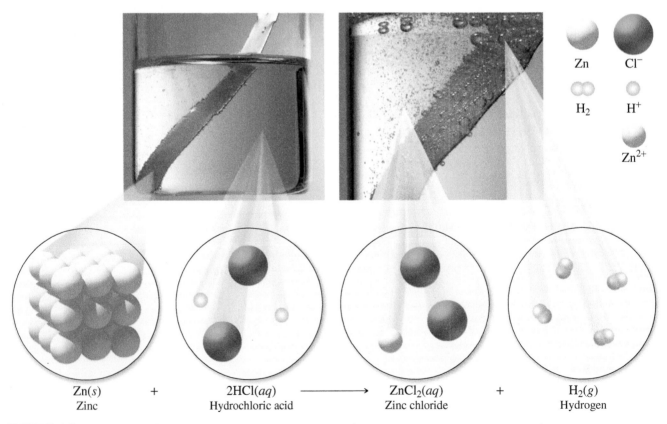

$$Zn(s) + 2HCl(aq) \longrightarrow ZnCl_2(aq) + H_2(g)$$

Zinc   Hydrochloric acid   Zinc chloride   Hydrogen

FIGURE 6.5 In a single replacement reaction, an atom or ion replaces an atom or ion in a compound.

Q What changes in the formulas of the reactants identify this equation as a single replacement?

Double Replacement Reactions

In a **double replacement reaction**, the positive ions in the reacting compounds switch places:

Double replacement

Two elements   replace   each other

A B + C D ⟶ A D + C B

For example, in the reaction shown in Figure 6.6, barium ions change places with sodium ions in the reactants to form sodium chloride and a white solid precipitate of barium sulfate. The formulas of the products depend on the charges of the ions:

$$BaCl_2(aq) + Na_2SO_4(aq) \longrightarrow BaSO_4(s) + 2NaCl(aq)$$

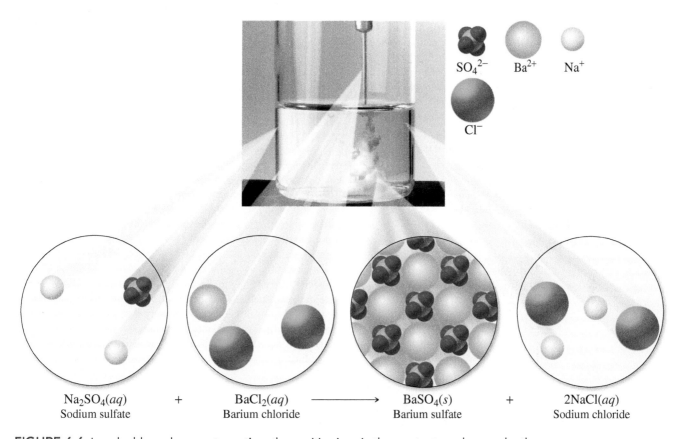

$SO_4{}^{2-}$ Ba^{2+} Na^+

Cl^-

| $Na_2SO_4(aq)$ | + | $BaCl_2(aq)$ | ⟶ | $BaSO_4(s)$ | + | $2NaCl(aq)$ |
| Sodium sulfate | | Barium chloride | | Barium sulfate | | Sodium chloride |

FIGURE 6.6 In a double replacement reaction, the positive ions in the reactants replace each other.
Q How do the changes in the formulas of the reactants identify this equation as a double replacement reaction?

SAMPLE PROBLEM   6.2

▪ Identifying Reactions and Predicting Products

Classify the following reactions as combination, decomposition, single replacement, or double replacement:

a. $2Fe_2O_3(s) + 3C(s) \longrightarrow 3CO_2(g) + 4Fe(s)$
b. $BaCl_2(aq) + K_2SO_4(aq) \longrightarrow BaSO_4(s) + 2KCl(aq)$

SOLUTION

a. In this *single replacement reaction*, a C atom replaces Fe in Fe_2O_3 to form the compound CO_2 and Fe atoms.

b. There are two reactants and two products, but the positive ions have exchanged places, which makes this a *double replacement reaction.*

STUDY CHECK

Nitrogen oxide gas and oxygen gas react to form nitrogen dioxide gas. Write the balanced equation and identify the reaction type.

HEALTH NOTE

Smog and Health Concerns

There are two types of smog. One, photochemical smog, requires sunlight to initiate reactions that produce pollutants such as nitrogen oxides and ozone. The other type of smog—called *industrial* or *London smog*—occurs in areas where coal containing sulfur is burned and the unwanted product, sulfur dioxide, is emitted.

   Photochemical smog is most prevalent in cities where people are dependent on cars for transportation. On a typical day in Los Angeles, for example, nitrogen oxide (NO) emissions from car exhausts increase as traffic increases on the roads. The nitrogen oxide is formed when N_2 and O_2 react at high temperatures in car and truck engines.

$$N_2(g) + O_2(g) \xrightarrow{\Delta} 2NO(g)$$

Then NO reacts with oxygen in the air to produce NO_2, a reddish brown gas that is irritating to the eyes and damaging to the respiratory tract.

$$2NO(g) + O_2(g) \longrightarrow 2NO_2(g)$$

When NO_2 is exposed to sunlight, it is converted into NO and an oxygen atom (O).

$$NO_2(g) \xrightarrow{\text{Sunlight}} NO(g) + O(g)$$
$$\text{Oxygen atom}$$

Oxygen atoms are so reactive that they combine with oxygen molecules in the atmosphere, forming ozone.

$$O(g) + O_2(g) \longrightarrow O_3(g)$$
$$\text{Ozone}$$

In the upper atmosphere (the stratosphere), ozone is beneficial because it protects us from harmful ultraviolet radiation that comes from the sun. However, in the lower atmosphere, ozone irritates the eyes and respiratory tract, where it causes coughing, decreased lung function, and fatigue. It also causes deterioration of fabrics, cracks rubber, and damages trees and crops.

   Industrial smog is prevalent in areas where coal with high sulfur content is burned to produce electricity. During combustion, the sulfur is converted to sulfur dioxide.

$$S(s) + O_2(g) \longrightarrow SO_2(g)$$

The SO_2 is damaging to plants, suppresses growth, and it is corrosive to metals such as steel. SO_2 is also damaging to humans and can cause lung impairment and respiratory difficulties. The SO_2 in the air reacts with more oxygen to form SO_3.

   Acid rain occurs when SO_3 combines with water in the air to form sulfuric acid.

$$2SO_2(g) + O_2(g) \longrightarrow 2SO_3(g)$$
$$SO_3(g) + H_2O(l) \longrightarrow H_2SO_4(aq)$$
$$\text{Sulfuric acid}$$

The presence of sulfuric acid in rivers and lakes causes an increase in the acidity of the water, reducing the ability of animals and plants to survive.

QUESTIONS AND PROBLEMS

Types of Reactions

6.7 **a.** Why is the following called a decomposition reaction?

$$2Al_2O_3(s) \xrightarrow{\Delta} 4Al(s) + 3O_2(g)$$

   b. Why is the following called a single replacement reaction?

$$Br_2(g) + BaI_2(s) \longrightarrow BaBr_2(s) + I_2(g)$$

6.8 **a.** Why is the following called a combination reaction?

$$H_2(g) + Br_2(g) \longrightarrow 2HBr(g)$$

   b. Why is the following called a double replacement reaction?

$$AgNO_3(aq) + NaCl(aq) \longrightarrow AgCl(s) + NaNO_3(aq)$$

6.9 Classify each of the following as a combination, decomposition, single replacement, or double replacement reaction:

a. $4Fe(s) + 3O_2(g) \longrightarrow 2Fe_2O_3(s)$

b. $Mg(s) + 2AgNO_3(aq) \longrightarrow Mg(NO_3)_2(aq) + 2Ag(s)$

c. $CuCO_3(s) \longrightarrow CuO(s) + CO_2(g)$

d. $NaOH(aq) + HCl(aq) \longrightarrow NaCl(aq) + H_2O(l)$

e. $Al_2(SO_4)_3(aq) + 6KOH(aq) \longrightarrow$
$2Al(OH)_3(s) + 3K_2SO_4(aq)$

6.10 Classify each of the following as a combination, decomposition, single replacement, or double replacement reaction:

a. $CuO(s) + 2HCl(aq) \longrightarrow CuCl_2(aq) + H_2O(l)$

b. $2Al(s) + 3Br_2(g) \longrightarrow 2AlBr_3(s)$

c. $Pb(NO_3)_2(aq) + 2NaCl(aq) \longrightarrow$
$PbCl_2(s) + 2NaNO_3(aq)$

d. $C_6H_{12}O_6(aq) \longrightarrow 2C_2H_6O(aq) + 2CO_2(g)$

e. $BaCl_2(aq) + K_2CO_3(aq) \longrightarrow BaCO_3(s) + 2KCl(aq)$

6.11 Try your hand at predicting the products that would result from the following reactions, and balance each equation:

a. combination: $Mg(s) + Cl_2(g) \longrightarrow$

b. decomposition: $HBr(g) \longrightarrow$

c. single replacement: $Mg(s) + Zn(NO_3)_2(aq) \longrightarrow$

d. double replacement: $K_2S(aq) + Pb(NO_3)_2(aq) \longrightarrow$

6.12 Try your hand at predicting the products that would result from the following reactions, and balance each equation:

a. combination: $Ca(s) + O_2(g) \longrightarrow$

b. decomposition: $PbO_2(s) \longrightarrow$

c. single replacement: $KI(s) + Cl_2(g) \longrightarrow$

d. double replacement: $CuCl_2(aq) + Na_2S(aq) \longrightarrow$

6.3 Oxidation–Reduction Reactions

Reactions known as *oxidation* and *reduction* reactions have many important applications in our everyday lives. For example, when you see a rusty nail or tarnish on a silver spoon, you are observing oxidation and reduction reactions.

$$4Fe(s) + 3O_2(g) \longrightarrow 2Fe_2O_3(s)$$
$$\text{Rust}$$

When you turn the lights on in your car, an oxidation–reduction reaction within your car battery provides the electricity. On a cold, wintry day, you might build a wood fire. Burning wood is an oxidation–reduction reaction. When you eat foods with starches in them, you digest the starches to give glucose, which is oxidized in your cells to give you energy along with carbon dioxide and water. Every breath you take provides oxygen to carry out oxidation in your cells.

$$C_6H_{12}O_6(aq) + 6O_2(g) \longrightarrow 6CO_2(g) + 6H_2O(l) + \text{energy}$$

LEARNING GOAL

Define the terms oxidation and reduction.

Oxidation–Reduction

In an **oxidation–reduction reaction** (*redox*), electrons are transferred from one substance to another. If one substance loses electrons, another substance must gain electrons. **Oxidation** is defined as the *loss* of electrons; **reduction** is defined as the *gain* of electrons. One way to remember these definitions is to use the following:

OIL RIG
Oxidation **I**s **L**oss of electrons.
Reduction **I**s **G**ain of electrons.

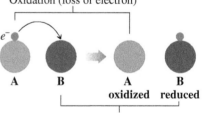

TUTORIAL
Identifying Oxidation–Reduction Reactions

Oxidation–Reduction Involving Ions

In general, atoms of metals lose electrons to form positive ions, whereas nonmetals gain electrons to form negative ions. In terms of oxidation and reduction, atoms of a metal are oxidized, and atoms of a nonmetal are reduced. Let's look at the formation of the ionic compound CaS:

$$Ca(s) + S(s) \longrightarrow CaS(s)$$

When we looked at the formation of ionic compounds, we saw that metals lost electrons and nonmetals gained electrons. Now we can say that metals are oxidized and nonmetals are reduced.

The calcium atom loses two electrons to form calcium ion (Ca^{2+}); calcium is oxidized.

$$Ca \longrightarrow Ca^{2+} + 2e^- \qquad \text{Oxidation; loss of electrons}$$

At the same time, the sulfur atom gains electrons to form sulfide ion (S^{2-}). The elemental forms of calcium and sulfur have no ionic charge; they are neutral. Many oxidation–reduction reactions include a reactant or product written in its elemental form such as $O_2(g)$ or $Zn(s)$.

$$S + 2e^- \longrightarrow S^{2-} \qquad \text{Reduction; gain of electrons}$$

Therefore, the formation of CaS involves two reactions that occur simultaneously, one an oxidation and the other a reduction:

$$Ca + S \longrightarrow Ca^{2+} + S^{2-} = CaS$$

In every oxidation–reduction reaction, the number of electrons lost is equal to the number of electrons gained.

Reduced		**Oxidized**
Na		$Na^+ + e^-$
Ca	Oxidation: lose e^- →	$Ca^{2+} + 2e^-$
$2Br^-$	← Reduction: gain e^-	$Br_2 + 2e^-$
Fe^{2+}		$Fe^{3+} + e^-$

In another example, we look at a single replacement reaction between zinc and copper(II) sulfate. (See Figure 6.7.)

$$Zn(s) + CuSO_4(aq) \longrightarrow ZnSO_4(aq) + Cu(s)$$

We can rewrite the equation to show the atoms and ions:

$$Zn(s) + Cu^{2+}(aq) + SO_4^{2-}(aq) \longrightarrow Zn^{2+}(aq) + SO_4^{2-}(aq) + Cu(s)$$

In this reaction, Zn atoms lose two electrons to form Zn^{2+}; $Zn(s)$ is oxidized. At the same time, Cu^{2+} gains two electrons to form $Cu(s)$; Cu^{2+} is reduced. The SO_4^{2-} ions are spectator ions and do not change.

$$Zn(s) \longrightarrow Zn^{2+}(aq) + 2e^- \qquad \text{Oxidation of Zn}$$

$$Cu^{2+}(aq) + 2e^- \longrightarrow Cu(s) \qquad \text{Reduction of } Cu^{2+}$$

FIGURE 6.7 In this single replacement reaction, $Zn(s)$ is oxidized to Zn^{2+} when it provides two electrons to reduce Cu^{2+} to $Cu(s)$: $Zn(s) + Cu^{2+}(aq) \longrightarrow Cu(s) + Zn^{2+}(aq)$

Q In the oxidation, does $Zn(s)$ lose or gain electrons?

CONCEPT CHECK 6.3

■ Oxidation and Reduction

The following unbalanced reaction takes place in a dry-cell battery used in toys and flashlights:

$$Zn(s) \longrightarrow Zn^{2+}(aq)$$

a. Is this reaction an oxidation or a reduction? Why?
b. What substance is oxidized or reduced?

ANSWER
a. $Zn(s)$ loses electrons to form $Zn^{2+}(aq)$, which is oxidation.

$$Zn(s) \longrightarrow Zn^{2+}(aq) + 2e^-$$

b. $Zn(s)$ is oxidized.

SAMPLE PROBLEM 6.3

■ Oxidation–Reduction Reactions

In photographic film, the following decomposition reaction occurs in the presence of light. What is oxidized and what is reduced?

$$2AgBr(s) \xrightarrow{\text{Light}} 2Ag(s) + Br_2(g)$$

SOLUTION

To determine oxidation and reduction, we need to look at the ions and charges in the reactants and products. In AgBr, there is a silver ion (Ag^+) with a 1+ charge and a bromide ion (Br^-) with a charge of 1−. We can write the balanced reaction as follows:

$$2Ag^+(s) + 2Br^-(s) \longrightarrow 2Ag(s) + Br_2(g)$$

Now we can compare Ag^+ with the product Ag atom. In this case, each Ag^+ gained an electron; Ag^+ is reduced.

$$2Ag^+(s) + 2e^- \longrightarrow 2Ag(s) \quad \text{Reduction}$$

Then we compare Br^- with the Br in the product Br_2. In this case, each Br^- lost an electron; Br^- is oxidized.

$$2Br^-(s) \longrightarrow Br_2(g) + 2e^- \quad \text{Oxidation}$$

STUDY CHECK

In the following combination reaction, which reactant is oxidized and which is reduced?

$$2Li(s) + F_2(g) \longrightarrow 2LiF(s)$$

Oxidation and Reduction in Biological Systems

Oxidation may also involve the addition of oxygen or the loss of hydrogen, and reduction may involve the loss of oxygen or the gain of hydrogen. In the cells of the body, oxidation of organic (carbon) compounds involves the transfer of hydrogen atoms (H), which are composed of electrons and protons. For example, the oxidation of a typical biochemical

EXPLORE YOUR WORLD

Oxidation of Fruits and Vegetables

Freshly cut surfaces of fruits and vegetables discolor when exposed to oxygen in the air. Cut three slices of a fruit or vegetable such as apple, potato, avocado, or banana. Leave one piece on the kitchen counter (uncovered). Wrap one piece in plastic wrap and leave on the kitchen counter. Dip one piece in lemon juice and leave uncovered.

QUESTIONS

1. What changes take place in each sample after 1 to 2 hours?
2. Why would wrapping fruits and vegetables slow the rate of discoloration?
3. If lemon juice contains vitamin C (an antioxidant), why would dipping a fruit or vegetable in lemon juice affect the oxidation reaction on the surface of the fruit or vegetable?
4. Other kinds of antioxidants are vitamin E, citric acid, and BHT. Look for these antioxidants on the labels of cereals, potato chips, and other foods in your kitchen. Why are antioxidants added to food products that will be stored on our kitchen shelves?

molecule can involve the transfer of two hydrogen atoms (or $2H^+$ and $2e^-$) to a proton acceptor such as the coenzyme FAD (flavin adenine dinucleotide). The coenzyme is reduced to $FADH_2$.

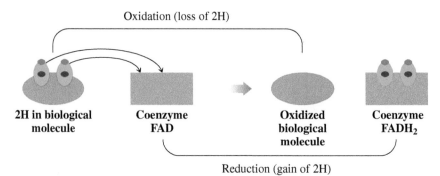

In many biochemical oxidation–reduction reactions, the transfer of hydrogen atoms is necessary for the production of energy in the cells. For example, methyl alcohol (CH_3OH), a poisonous substance, is metabolized in the body by the following reactions:

$$CH_3OH \longrightarrow H_2CO + 2H \qquad \text{Oxidation: loss of H atoms}$$
Methyl alcohol   Formaldehyde

The formaldehyde can be oxidized further, this time by the addition of oxygen, to produce formic acid:

$$2H_2CO + O_2 \longrightarrow 2H_2CO_2 \qquad \text{Oxidation: addition of O atoms}$$
Formaldehyde   Formic acid

Finally, formic acid is oxidized to carbon dioxide and water.

$$2H_2CO_2 + O_2 \longrightarrow 2CO_2 + 2H_2O \qquad \text{Oxidation: addition of O atoms}$$
Formic acid

The intermediate products of the oxidation of methyl alcohol are quite toxic, causing blindness and possibly death as they interfere with key reactions in the cells of the body.

In summary, we find that the particular definition of oxidation and reduction we use depends on the process that occurs in the reaction. All of these definitions are summarized in Table 6.3. Oxidation always involves a loss of electrons, but it may also be seen as an addition of oxygen, or the loss of hydrogen atoms. A reduction always involves a gain of electrons, and it may also be seen as the loss of oxygen, or the gain of hydrogen.

TABLE 6.3 Characteristics of Oxidation and Reduction

Oxidation	
Always Involves	**May Involve**
Loss of electrons	Addition of oxygen
Electrons are a product	Loss of hydrogen

Reduction	
Always Involves	**May Involve**
Gain of electrons	Loss of oxygen
Electrons are a reactant	Gain of hydrogen

QUESTIONS AND PROBLEMS

Oxidation–Reduction Reactions

6.13 Indicate whether each of the following is an oxidation or a reduction reaction:
  a. $Na^+(aq) + e^- \longrightarrow Na(s)$
  b. $Ni(s) \longrightarrow Ni^{2+}(aq) + 2e^-$
  c. $Cr^{3+}(aq) + 3e^- \longrightarrow Cr(s)$
  d. $2H^+(aq) + 2e^- \longrightarrow H_2(g)$

6.14 Indicate whether each of the following is an oxidation or a reduction reaction:
  a. $O_2(g) + 4e^- \longrightarrow 2O^{2-}(aq)$
  b. $Al(s) \longrightarrow Al^{3+}(aq) + 3e^-$
  c. $Fe^{3+}(aq) + e^- \longrightarrow Fe^{2+}(aq)$
  d. $2Br^-(aq) \longrightarrow Br_2(g) + 2e^-$

6.15 In the following reactions, identify which reactant is oxidized and which is reduced:
  a. $Zn(s) + Cl_2(g) \longrightarrow ZnCl_2(s)$
  b. $Cl_2(g) + 2NaBr(aq) \longrightarrow 2NaCl(aq) + Br_2(g)$
  c. $2PbO(s) \longrightarrow 2Pb(s) + O_2(g)$
  d. $2Fe^{3+}(aq) + Sn^{2+}(aq) \longrightarrow 2Fe^{2+}(aq) + Sn^{4+}(aq)$

6.16 In the following reactions, identify which reactant is oxidized and which is reduced:
  a. $2Li(s) + F_2(g) \longrightarrow 2LiF(s)$
  b. $Cl_2(g) + 2KI(aq) \longrightarrow 2KCl(aq) + I_2(g)$
  c. $Zn(s) + Cu^{2+}(aq) \longrightarrow Zn^{2+}(aq) + Cu(s)$
  d. $Fe(s) + CuSO_4(aq) \longrightarrow FeSO_4(aq) + Cu(s)$

6.17 In the mitochondria of human cells, energy for the production of ATP is provided by the oxidation and reduction reactions of the iron ions in the cytochromes of the electron transport chain. Identify each of the following reactions as oxidation or reduction:
  a. $Fe^{3+} + e^- \longrightarrow Fe^{2+}$
  b. $Fe^{2+} \longrightarrow Fe^{3+} + e^-$

6.18 Chlorine (Cl_2) is a strong germicide used to disinfect drinking water and to kill microbes in swimming pools. If the product is Cl^-, was the Cl_2 oxidized or reduced?

6.19 When linoleic acid, an unsaturated fatty acid, reacts with hydrogen, it forms a saturated fatty acid. Is linoleic acid oxidized or reduced in the hydrogenation reaction?

$$C_{18}H_{32}O_2 + 2H_2 \longrightarrow C_{18}H_{36}O_2$$

6.20 In one of the reactions in the citric acid cycle, which provides energy for ATP synthesis, succinic acid is converted to fumaric acid:

$$C_4H_6O_4 \longrightarrow C_4H_4O_4 + 2H$$
Succinic acid   Fumaric acid

The reaction is accompanied by a coenzyme, flavin adenine dinucleotide (FAD):

$$FAD + 2H \longrightarrow FADH_2$$

a. Is succinic acid oxidized or reduced?
b. Is FAD oxidized or reduced?
c. Why would the two reactions occur together?

GREEN CHEMISTRY NOTE

Fuel Cells: Clean Energy for the Future

Fuel cells are of interest to scientists because they provide an alternative source of electrical energy that is more efficient, does not use up oil reserves, and generates products that do not pollute the atmosphere. Fuels cells are considered a clean way to produce energy.

Unlike a battery that runs down, fuel cells are provided continually with new reactants to generate an electrical current. One type of hydrogen–oxygen fuel cell has been used in automobile prototypes. In this hydrogen cell, gas enters the fuel cell, where it comes in contact with platinum embedded in a plastic membrane. The platinum assists in the oxidation of hydrogen atoms to hydrogen ions and electrons:

$$2H_2(g) \xrightarrow{\text{Pt}} 4H^+(aq) + 4e^- \qquad \text{Oxidation}$$

The electrons produce an electric current as they travel through the wire. The hydrogen ions move through the plastic membrane to react with oxygen molecules. The oxygen is reduced to oxide ions that combine with the hydrogen ions to form water:

$$O_2(g) + 4H^+(aq) + 4e^- \longrightarrow 2H_2O(l) \qquad \text{Reduction}$$

The overall hydrogen–oxygen fuel cell reaction can be written as

$$2H_2(g) + O_2(g) \longrightarrow 2H_2O(l)$$

Fuel cells have already been used to power the space shuttle and may soon be available to produce energy for cars and buses.

A major drawback to the practical use of fuel cells is the economic impact of converting cars to fuel cell operation. The storage and cost of producing hydrogen are also problems. Some manufacturers are experimenting with systems that convert gasoline or methanol to hydrogen for immediate use in fuel cells.

In homes, fuel cells may one day replace the batteries currently used to provide electrical power for cell phones, CD and DVD players, and laptop computers. Fuel cell design is still in the prototype phase, although there is much interest in their development. We already know they can work, but modifications must still be made before they become reasonably priced and part of our everyday lives.

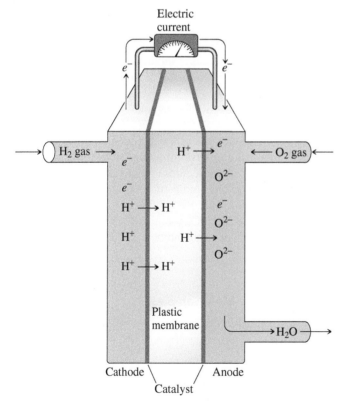

Oxidation
$$2H_2(g) \longrightarrow 4H^+(aq) + 4e^-$$

Reduction
$$O_2(g) + 4H^+(aq) + 4e^- \longrightarrow 2H_2O(l)$$

6.4 The Mole

At the store, you buy eggs by the dozen. In an office, you buy pencils by the gross and paper by the ream. For a restaurant, soda is ordered by the case. In each of these examples, terms such as *dozen, gross, ream*, and *case* count the number of items present. For example, when you buy a dozen eggs, you know you will get 12 eggs in the carton.

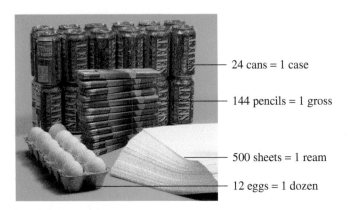

24 cans = 1 case

144 pencils = 1 gross

500 sheets = 1 ream

12 eggs = 1 dozen

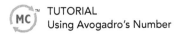
TUTORIAL
Using Avogadro's Number

Avogadro's Number

In chemistry, tiny particles such as atoms, molecules, and ions are counted by the **mole**, a unit that contains 6.02×10^{23} items. This immense number is called **Avogadro's number** after Amedeo Avogadro, an Italian physicist. It looks like this when written with three significant figures:

Avogadro's Number

602 000 000 000 000 000 000 000 = 6.02×10^{23}

One mole of any element always contains Avogadro's number of atoms. For example, 1 mole of carbon contains 6.02×10^{23} carbon atoms; 1 mole of aluminum contains 6.02×10^{23} aluminum atoms; 1 mole of sulfur contains 6.02×10^{23} sulfur atoms.

1 mole of an element = 6.02×10^{23} atoms of that element

Avogadro's number also tells us that one mole of a compound contains 6.02×10^{23} of the particular type of particles that make up that compound. One mole of a covalent compound contains Avogadro's number of molecules. For example, 1 mole of CO_2 contains 6.02×10^{23} molecules of CO_2. One mole of an ionic compound contains Avogadro's number of **formula units**, which are the groups of ions represented by the formula of an ionic compound. One mole of NaCl contains 6.02×10^{23} formula units of NaCl (Na^+, Cl^-). Table 6.4 gives examples of the number of particles in some 1-mole quantities.

TABLE 6.4 Number of Particles in One-Mole Samples

Substance	Number and Type of Particles
1 mole of Al	6.02×10^{23} Al atoms
1 mole of S	6.02×10^{23} S atoms
1 mole of H_2O	6.02×10^{23} H_2O molecules
1 mole of NaCl	6.02×10^{23} NaCl formula units
1 mole of vitamin C ($C_6H_8O_6$)	6.02×10^{23} vitamin C molecules

We can use Avogadro's number as a conversion factor to convert between the moles of a substance and number of particles it contains.

$$\frac{6.02 \times 10^{23} \text{ particles}}{1 \text{ mole}} \quad \text{and} \quad \frac{1 \text{ mole}}{6.02 \times 10^{23} \text{ particles}}$$

For example, we use Avogadro's number to convert 4.00 moles of iron to atoms of iron.

$$4.00 \text{ moles Fe atoms} \times \frac{6.02 \times 10^{23} \text{ Fe atoms}}{1 \text{ mole Fe atoms}} = 2.41 \times 10^{24} \text{ Fe atoms}$$

Avogadro's number as a conversion factor

We can also use Avogadro's number to convert 3.01×10^{24} molecules of CO_2 to moles of CO_2.

$$3.01 \times 10^{24} \text{ CO}_2 \text{ molecules} \times \frac{1 \text{ mole CO}_2 \text{ molecules}}{6.02 \times 10^{23} \text{ CO}_2 \text{ molecules}} = 5.00 \text{ moles of CO}_2 \text{ molecules}$$

Avogadro's number as a conversion factor

Generally, in calculations that convert between moles and particles, the number of moles will be a small number compared to the number of atoms or molecules, which will be a large number.

CONCEPT CHECK 6.4

■ **Moles and Particles**

Explain why 0.20 mole of aluminum is a small number, but the number of atoms in 0.20 mole is a large number: 1.2×10^{23} atoms of aluminum.

ANSWER

The term *mole* is used as a collection term that represents 6.02×10^{23} particles. Because atoms are submicroscopic particles, a large number of atoms are in 1 mole of aluminum.

SAMPLE PROBLEM   6.4

■ **Calculating the Number of Molecules**

How many molecules are present in 1.75 moles of carbon dioxide, CO_2?

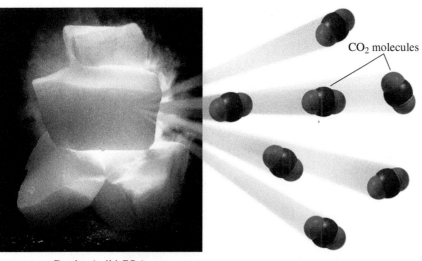

CO_2 molecules

Dry ice (solid CO_2)

Guide to Calculating the Atoms or Molecules of a Substance

STEP 1
Determine the given number of moles.

STEP 2
Write a plan to convert moles to atoms or molecules.

STEP 3
Use Avogadro's number to write conversion factors.

STEP 4
Set up problem to convert given moles to atoms or molecules.

SOLUTION

STEP 1   **Given**   1.75 moles of CO_2 **Need**   molecules of CO_2

STEP 2   **Plan**   moles of CO_2 Avogadro's number   molecules of CO_2

STEP 3   **Equalities/Conversion Factors**

$$1 \text{ mole of } CO_2 = 6.02 \times 10^{23} \text{ molecules of } CO_2$$

$$\frac{6.02 \times 10^{23} \text{ molecules } CO_2}{1 \text{ mole } CO_2} \quad \text{and} \quad \frac{1 \text{ mole } CO_2}{6.02 \times 10^{23} \text{ molecules } CO_2}$$

STEP 4   **Set Up Problem**   Calculate the number of CO_2 molecules:

$$1.75 \text{ moles } CO_2 \times \frac{6.02 \times 10^{23} \text{ molecules } CO_2}{1 \text{ mole } CO_2} = 1.05 \times 10^{24} \text{ molecules of } CO_2$$

STUDY CHECK

How many moles of water, H_2O, contain 2.60×10^{23} molecules of water?

 TUTORIAL
MC Moles and the Chemical Formula

Moles of Elements in a Formula

We have seen that the subscripts in a chemical formula of a compound indicate the number of atoms of each type of element. For example, in a molecule of aspirin, chemical formula $C_9H_8O_4$, there are 9 carbon atoms, 8 hydrogen atoms, and 4 oxygen atoms. The subscripts also state the number of moles of each element in one mole of aspirin: 9 moles of carbon atoms, 8 moles of hydrogen atoms, and 4 moles of oxygen atoms.

$$C_9H_8O_4$$

	Carbon	**Hydrogen**	**Oxygen**
Atoms in 1 molecule	9 atoms C	8 atoms H	4 atoms O
Moles of atoms in 1 mole	9 moles C	8 moles H	4 moles O

Using the subscripts from the aspirin formula, $C_9H_8O_4$, we can write the following conversion factors for each of the elements in 1 mole of aspirin:

$$\frac{9 \text{ moles C}}{1 \text{ mole } C_9H_8O_4} \qquad \frac{8 \text{ moles H}}{1 \text{ mole } C_9H_8O_4} \qquad \frac{4 \text{ moles O}}{1 \text{ mole } C_9H_8O_4}$$

$$\frac{1 \text{ mole } C_9H_8O_4}{9 \text{ moles C}} \qquad \frac{1 \text{ mole } C_9H_8O_4}{8 \text{ moles H}} \qquad \frac{1 \text{ mole } C_9H_8O_4}{4 \text{ moles O}}$$

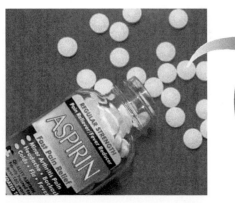

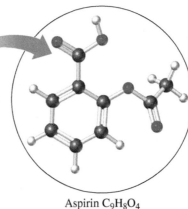

Aspirin $C_9H_8O_4$

Number of atoms in 1 molecule
Carbon (C)   Hydrogen (H)   Oxygen (O)

CONCEPT CHECK 6.5

■ **Using Subscripts of a Formula**

Indicate the moles of C atoms in 1 mole of each of the following:

a. $C_8H_9NO_2$, acetaminophen used in Tylenol
b. $Zn(C_2H_3O_2)_2$, zinc dietary supplement

ANSWER

a. The subscript 8 indicates that there are 8 moles of C atoms in 1 mole of acetaminophen.
b. The subscript 2 within the parentheses indicates there are 2 moles of C in the ion $C_2H_3O_2^-$. The subscript 2 outside the parentheses indicates there are 2 moles of the ion $C_2H_3O_2^-$ in the formula. Thus there is a total of 4 (2 × 2) moles of C atoms in 1 mole of $Zn(C_2H_3O_2)_2$.

SAMPLE PROBLEM   6.5

■ **Calculating the Atoms of an Element**

How many carbon atoms are present in 1.50 moles of aspirin, $C_9H_8O_4$?

SOLUTION

STEP 1   Given 1.50 moles of $C_9H_8O_4$ **Need** carbon atoms

STEP 2   Plan

Moles of $C_9H_8O_4$ Subscript   moles of C atoms   Avogadro's number   C atoms

STEP 3   Equalities/Conversion Factors

$$1 \text{ mole of } C_9H_8O_4 = 9 \text{ moles of C atoms}$$

$$\frac{9 \text{ moles C}}{1 \text{ mole } C_9H_8O_4} \quad \text{and} \quad \frac{1 \text{ mole } C_9H_8O_4}{9 \text{ moles C}}$$

$$1 \text{ mole of C atoms} = 6.02 \times 10^{23} \text{ C atoms}$$

$$\frac{1 \text{ mole C atoms}}{6.02 \times 10^{23} \text{ C atoms}} \quad \text{and} \quad \frac{6.02 \times 10^{23} \text{ C atoms}}{1 \text{ mole C atoms}}$$

STEP 4   Set Up Problem   The conversion factors of the subscript and Avogadro's number can be combined to calculate the number of atoms of C from moles of $C_9H_8O_4$.

$$1.50 \text{ moles } C_9H_8O_4 \times \frac{9 \text{ moles C}}{1 \text{ mole } C_9H_8O_4} \times \frac{6.02 \times 10^{23} \text{ C atoms}}{1 \text{ mole C atoms}} = 8.13 \times 10^{24} \text{ C atoms}$$

STUDY CHECK

How many moles of aspirin, $C_9H_8O_4$, contain 0.480 mole of O atoms?

QUESTIONS AND PROBLEMS

The Mole

6.21 What is a mole?

6.22 What is Avogadro's number?

6.23 Calculate each of the following:
  a. number of Ag atoms in 0.200 mole of Ag
  b. number of C_3H_8O molecules in 0.750 mole of C_3H_8O
  c. moles of Au in 2.88×10^{23} atoms of Au

6.24 Calculate each of the following:
  a. number of Ni atoms in 3.4 moles of Ni
  b. number of $Mg(OH)_2$ formula units in 1.20 moles of $Mg(OH)_2$
  c. moles of Zn in 5.6×10^{24} atoms of Zn

6.25 Consider the formula for quinine, $C_{20}H_{24}N_2O_2$.
  a. How many moles of hydrogen are in 1.0 mole of quinine?
  b. How many moles of carbon are in 5.0 moles of quinine?
  c. How many moles of nitrogen are in 0.020 mole of quinine?

6.26 Consider the formula for $Al_2(SO_4)_3$, which is used in anti-perspirants.
  a. How many moles of sulfur are present in 3.0 moles of $Al_2(SO_4)_3$?
  b. How many moles of aluminum ions are present in 0.40 mole of $Al_2(SO_4)_3$?
  c. How many moles of sulfate ions $\left(SO_4{}^{2-}\right)$ are present in 1.5 moles of $Al_2(SO_4)_3$?

6.27 Calculate each of the following:
  a. number of C atoms in 0.500 mole of C
  b. number of SO_2 molecules in 1.28 moles of SO_2
  c. moles of Fe in 5.22×10^{22} atoms of Fe
  d. moles of C_2H_5OH in 8.50×10^{24} molecules of C_2H_5OH

6.28 Calculate each of the following:
  a. number of Li atoms in 4.5 moles of Li
  b. number of CO_2 molecules in 0.0180 mole of CO_2
  c. moles of Cu in 7.8×10^{21} atoms of Cu
  d. moles of C_2H_6 in 3.754×10^{23} molecules of C_2H_6

6.29 Calculate each of the following quantities in 2.00 moles of H_3PO_4:
  a. moles of H   **b.** moles of O
  c. atoms of P   **d.** atoms of O

6.30 Calculate each of the following quantities in 0.185 mole of $(C_3H_5)_2O$:
  a. moles of C   **b.** moles of O
  c. atoms of H   **d.** atoms of C

6.5 Molar Mass

LEARNING GOAL

Determine the molar mass of a substance and use the molar mass to convert between grams and moles.

 SELF STUDY ACTIVITY
Stoichiometry

A single atom or molecule is much too small to weigh, even on the most accurate balance. In fact, it takes a huge number of atoms or molecules to make a piece of a substance that you can see. An amount of water that contains Avogadro's number of water molecules is only a few sips. In the laboratory, we can use a balance to weigh out Avogadro's number of particles or 1 mole of a substance.

For any element, the quantity called its **molar mass** is the number of grams equal to the atomic mass of that element. For example, carbon has an atomic mass of 12.01 on the periodic table. This means 1 mole of carbon atoms has a mass of 12.01 g. Thus, we can use the periodic table to determine the molar mass of an element.

6.02×10^{23} atoms of C

1 mole of C atoms

12.01 g of C atoms

47
Ag
107.9

1 mole of silver atoms has a mass of 107.9 g

6
C
12.01

1 mole of carbon atoms has a mass of 12.01 g

16
S
32.07

1 mole of sulfur atoms has a mass of 32.07 g

Molar Mass of a Compound

To determine the molar mass of a compound, multiply the molar mass of each element by its subscript in the formula and add the results. For example, the molar mass of sulfur tri-oxide, SO_3, is obtained by adding the molar masses of 1 mole of sulfur and 3 moles of oxygen. In our calculations, we round molar mass to the tenths (0.1 g) place.

STEP 1   Using the periodic table, obtain the molar masses of sulfur and oxygen.

$$\frac{32.1 \text{ g S}}{1 \text{ mole S}} \qquad \frac{16.0 \text{ g O}}{1 \text{ mole O}}$$

STEP 2   Multiply each molar mass by its subscript in the formula.
Grams from 1 mole of S

$$1 \text{ mole S} \times \frac{32.1 \text{ g S}}{1 \text{ mole S}} = 32.1 \text{ g of S}$$

Grams from 3 moles of O

$$3 \text{ moles O} \times \frac{16.0 \text{ g O}}{1 \text{ mole O}} = 48.0 \text{ g of O}$$

STEP 3   Obtain the molar mass of SO_3 by adding the masses of 1 mole of S and 3 moles of O.

1 mole of S	=	32.1 g of S
3 moles of O	=	48.0 g of O
Molar mass of SO_3	=	80.1 g of SO_3

Figure 6.8 shows some 1-mole quantities of substances. Table 6.5 lists the molar mass for several 1-mole samples.

TABLE 6.5 The Molar Mass of Selected Elements and Compounds

Substance	Molar Mass
1 mole of C (carbon)	12.0 g
1 mole of Na (sodium)	23.0 g
1 mole of Fe (iron)	55.9 g
1 mole of NaF (preventative for dental caries)	42.0 g
1 mole of $CaCO_3$ (antacid)	100.1 g
1 mole of $C_6H_{12}O_6$ (glucose)	180.0 g
1 mole of $C_8H_{10}N_4O_2$ (caffeine)	194.0 g

One–Mole Quantities

S   Fe   NaCl $K_2Cr_2O_7$ $C_{12}H_{22}O_{11}$

FIGURE 6.8 One-mole samples: sulfur, S (32.1 g); iron, Fe (55.9 g); salt, NaCl (58.5 g); potassium dichromate, $K_2Cr_2O_7$ (294.2 g); and sugar, sucrose, $C_{12}H_{22}O_{11}$ (342.0 g).
Q How is the molar mass for $K_2Cr_2O_7$ obtained?

SAMPLE PROBLEM   6.6

■ **Calculating Molar Mass of Compounds**

Find the molar mass of Li_2CO_3 used to produce the red color in fireworks.

SOLUTION

STEP 1   Using the periodic table, obtain the molar masses of lithium, carbon, and oxygen.

$$\frac{6.9 \text{ g Li}}{1 \text{ mole Li}} \qquad \frac{12.0 \text{ g C}}{1 \text{ mole C}} \qquad \frac{16.0 \text{ g O}}{1 \text{ mole O}}$$

STEP 2   Multiply each molar mass by its subscript in the formula. Grams from 2 moles of Li

$$2 \text{ moles Li} \times \frac{6.9 \text{ g Li}}{1 \text{ mole Li}} = 13.8 \text{ g of Li}$$

Guide to Calculating Molar Mass

STEP 1
Obtain the molar mass of each element.

STEP 2
Multiply each molar mass by the number of moles (subscript) in the formula.

STEP 3
Calculate the molar mass by adding the masses of the elements.

Grams from 1 mole of C

$$1 \text{ mole C} \times \frac{12.0 \text{ g C}}{1 \text{ mole C}} = 12.0 \text{ g of C}$$

Grams from 3 moles of O

$$3 \text{ moles O} \times \frac{16.0 \text{ g O}}{1 \text{ mole O}} = 48.0 \text{ g of O}$$

STEP 3 **Obtain the molar mass of Li_2CO_3.** Add the masses of 2 moles of Li, 1 mole of C, and 3 moles of O.

2 moles of Li	= 13.8 g of Li
1 mole of C	= 12.0 g of C
3 moles of O	= 48.0 g of O
Molar mass of Li_2CO_3	= 73.8 g

STUDY CHECK

Calculate the molar mass of salicylic acid, $C_7H_6O_3$.

EXPLORE YOUR WORLD

Calculating Moles in the Kitchen

The labels on food products list the components in grams and milligrams. Read the labels of some products in the kitchen and convert the amounts given in grams or milligrams to moles using molar mass.

QUESTIONS

1. How many moles of NaCl are in a box of salt containing 746 g of NaCl?
2. How many moles of sugar are contained in a 5-lb bag of sugar if sugar has the formula $C_{12}H_{22}O_{11}$?
3. A serving of cereal contains 90 mg of potassium. If there are 11 servings of cereal in the box, how many moles of K^+ are present in the cereal in the box?

Calculations Using Molar Mass

The molar mass of an element or a compound is one of the most useful conversion factors in chemistry. Molar mass is used to change from moles of a substance to grams, or from grams to moles. To do these calculations, we use the molar mass as a conversion factor. For example, 1 mole of magnesium has a mass of 24.3 g. To express molar mass as an equality, we can write

1 mole of Mg = 24.3 g of Mg

From this equality, two conversion factors can be written.

$$\frac{24.3 \text{ g Mg}}{1 \text{ mole Mg}} \quad \text{and} \quad \frac{1 \text{ mole Mg}}{24.3 \text{ g Mg}}$$

Conversion factors are written for compounds in the same way. For example, the molar mass of the compound H_2O is 2(1.0 g/mole) + 1(16.0 g/mole) = 18.0 g/mole

1 mole of H_2O = 18.0 g of H_2O

The conversion factors from the molar mass of H_2O are written as

$$\frac{18.0 \text{ g } H_2O}{1 \text{ mole } H_2O} \quad \text{and} \quad \frac{1 \text{ mole } H_2O}{18.0 \text{ g } H_2O}$$

We can now change from moles to grams, or grams to moles, using the conversion factors derived from the molar mass. (Remember, you must determine the molar mass of the substance first.)

SAMPLE PROBLEM 6.7

■ **Converting Moles of an Element to Grams**

Silver metal is used in the manufacture of tableware, mirrors, jewelry, and dental alloys. If the design for a piece of jewelry requires 0.750 mole of silver, how many grams of silver are needed?

TUTORIAL
Converting Between Grams and Moles

SOLUTION

STEP 1 **Given** 0.750 mole of Ag   **Need** grams of Ag

STEP 2 **Plan** moles of Ag   Molar mass factor   grams of Ag

STEP 3 **Equalities/Conversion Factors**

$$1 \text{ mole of Ag} = 107.9 \text{ g of Ag}$$

$$\frac{107.9 \text{ g Ag}}{1 \text{ mole Ag}} \quad \text{and} \quad \frac{1 \text{ mole Ag}}{107.9 \text{ g Ag}}$$

STEP 4 **Set Up Problem** Calculate the grams of silver using the molar mass.

$$0.750 \text{ mole Ag} \times \frac{107.9 \text{ g Ag}}{1 \text{ mole Ag}} = 80.9 \text{ g of Ag}$$

STUDY CHECK

Calculate the number of grams of gold (Au) present in 0.124 mole of gold.

Guide to Calculating the Moles (or Grams) of a Substance from Grams (or Moles)

STEP 1
Determine the given number of moles (or grams).

STEP 2
Write a plan to convert moles to grams (or grams to moles).

STEP 3
Determine the molar mass and write conversion factors.

STEP 4
Set up problem to convert given moles to grams (or grams to moles).

SAMPLE PROBLEM   6.8

■ Converting Mass of a Compound to Moles

A box of salt contains 737 g of NaCl. How many moles of NaCl are present in the box?

SOLUTION

STEP 1 **Given** 737 g of NaCl   **Need** moles of NaCl

STEP 2 **Plan** grams of NaCl   Molar mass factor   moles of NaCl

STEP 3 **Equalities/Conversion Factors** The molar mass of NaCl is the sum of the masses of one mole Na^+ and one mole Cl^-:

$$(1 \times 23.0 \text{ g/mole}) + (1 \times 35.5 \text{ g/mole}) = 58.5 \text{ g/mole}$$

$$1 \text{ mole of NaCl} = 58.5 \text{ g of NaCl}$$

$$\frac{58.5 \text{ g NaCl}}{1 \text{ mole NaCl}} \quad \text{and} \quad \frac{1 \text{ mole NaCl}}{58.5 \text{ g NaCl}}$$

STEP 4 **Set Up Problem** We calculate the moles of NaCl using the molar mass.

$$737 \text{ g NaCl} \times \frac{1 \text{ mole NaCl}}{58.5 \text{ g NaCl}} = 12.6 \text{ moles of NaCl}$$

STUDY CHECK

One gel cap of an antacid contains 311 mg of $CaCO_3$ and 232 mg of $MgCO_3$. In a recommended dosage of two gel caps, how many moles each of $CaCO_3$ and $MgCO_3$ are present?

Figure 6.9 shows the connections between the moles of a compound, mass, and number of molecules, and the moles and atoms of each element in that compound.

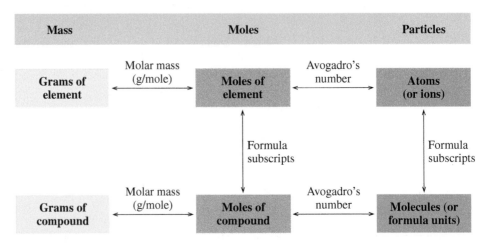

FIGURE 6.9 The moles of a compound are related to its mass in grams by molar mass, to the number of molecules (or formula units) by Avogadro's number, and to the moles of each element by the subscripts in the formula.

Q What steps are needed to calculate the number of H atoms in 5.00 g of CH_4?

QUESTIONS AND PROBLEMS

Molar Mass

6.31 Calculate the molar mass for each of the following:
  a. KCl (salt substitute)
  b. Fe_2O_3 (rust)
  c. Li_2CO_3 (antidepressant)
  d. $Al_2(SO_4)_3$ (antiperspirant)
  e. $Mg(OH)_2$ (antacid)
  f. $C_{16}H_{19}N_3O_5S$ (amoxicillin, an antibiotic)

6.32 Calculate the molar mass for each of the following:
  a. $FeSO_4$ (iron supplement)
  b. Al_2O_3 (absorbent and abrasive)
  c. $C_7H_5NO_3S$ (saccharin)
  d. C_3H_8O (rubbing alcohol)
  e. $(NH_4)_2CO_3$ (baking powder)
  f. $Zn(C_2H_3O_2)_2$ (dietary supplement)

6.33 Calculate the mass in grams in each of the following:
  a. 2.00 moles of Na   **b.** 2.80 moles of Ca
  c. 0.125 mole of Sn   **d.** 1.76 moles of Cu

6.34 Calculate the mass in grams in each of the following:
  a. 1.50 moles of K   **b.** 2.5 moles of C
  c. 0.25 mole of P   **d.** 12.5 moles of He

6.35 Calculate the mass in grams in each of the following:
  a. 0.500 mole of NaCl   **b.** 1.75 moles of Na_2O
  c. 0.225 mole of H_2O **d.** 4.42 moles of CO_2

6.36 Calculate the mass in grams in each of the following:
  a. 2.0 moles of $MgCl_2$ **b.** 3.5 moles of C_3H_8
  c. 5.00 moles of C_2H_6O **d.** 0.488 mole of $C_3H_6O_3$

6.37 a. The compound $MgSO_4$ is called Epsom salts. How many grams will you need to prepare a bath containing 5.00 moles of Epsom salts?
  b. In a bottle of soda, there is 0.25 mole of CO_2. How many grams of CO_2 are in the bottle?

6.38 a. Cyclopropane, C_3H_6, is an anesthetic given by inhalation. How many grams are in 0.25 mole of cyclopropane?
  b. The sedative Demerol hydrochloride has the formula $C_{15}H_{22}ClNO_2$. How many grams are in 0.025 mole of Demerol hydrochloride?

6.39 How many moles are contained in each of the following?
  a. 50.0 g of Ag
  b. 0.200 g of C
  c. 15.0 g of NH_3
  d. 75.0 g of SO_2

6.40 How many moles are contained in each of the following?
  a. 25.0 g of Ca
  b. 5.00 g of S
  c. 40.0 g of H_2O
  d. 12.2 g of O_2

6.41 How many moles of S are in each of the following quantities?
  a. 25 g of S
  b. 125 g of SO_2
  c. 2.0 moles of Al_2S_3

6.42 How many moles of C are in each of the following quantities?
  a. 75 g of C
  b. 0.25 mole of C_2H_6
  c. 88 g of CO_2

6.43 How many atoms of N are in each of the following quantities?
  a. 40.0 g of N
  b. 1.5 moles of N_2O_4
  c. 2.0 moles of N_2

6.44 How many atoms of Ag are in each of the following quantities?
  a. 5.0 g of Ag
  b. 0.40 mole of Ag_2S
  c. 0.75 g of AgCl

6.6 Mole Relationships in Chemical Equations

LEARNING GOAL

Given a quantity in moles of reactant or product, use a mole–mole factor from the balanced equation to calculate the moles of another substance in the reaction.

In an earlier section, we saw that equations are balanced in terms of the numbers of each type of atom in the reactants and products. However, when experiments are done in the laboratory or medications are prepared in the pharmacy, samples contain billions of atoms and molecules, so it is impossible to count them individually. What can be measured conveniently is mass; this is done by using a balance. Because mass is related to the number of particles through the molar mass, measuring the mass is equivalent to counting the number of particles or moles.

Conservation of Mass

In any chemical reaction, the total amount of matter in the reactants is equal to the total amount of matter in the products. If all of the reactants were weighed, they would have a total mass equal to the total mass of the products. This is known as the *law of conservation of mass*, which says that there is no change in the total mass of the substances reacting in a balanced chemical reaction. Thus, no material is lost or gained as original substances are changed to new substances.

TUTORIAL
Moles of Reactants and Products

For example, tarnish forms when silver reacts with sulfur to form silver sulfide.

$$2Ag(s) + S(s) \longrightarrow Ag_2S(s)$$

| 2Ag(s) | + | S(s) | $\longrightarrow$ | Ag$_2$S(s) |
| Mass of reactants | | | = | Mass of products |

In this reaction, the number of silver atoms that react is two times the number of sulfur atoms. When 200 silver atoms react, 100 sulfur atoms are required. However, many more atoms would actually be present in this reaction. If we are dealing with molar amounts, then the coefficients in the equation can be interpreted in terms of moles. Thus, 2 moles of Ag react with 1 mole of sulfur to produce 1 mole of Ag_2S. Because the molar mass of each can be determined, the quantities of silver and sulfur can also be stated in terms of mass in grams of each. Thus, 215.8 g of Ag and 32.1 g of S react to form 247.9 g of Ag_2S. The total mass of the reactants (247.9 g) is equal to the 247.9 g of product. The various ways in which a chemical equation can be interpreted are seen in Table 6.6.

TABLE 6.6 Information Available from a Balanced Equation

	Reactants		Products
Equation	2Ag(s)	+ S(s)	$\longrightarrow$ Ag$_2$S(s)
Atoms	2 Ag atoms	+ 1 S atom	$\longrightarrow$ 1 Ag$_2$S formula unit
	200 Ag atoms	+ 100 S atoms	$\longrightarrow$ 100 Ag$_2$S formula units
Avogadro's number of atoms	$2(6.02 \times 10^{23})$ Ag atoms	+ $1(6.02 \times 10^{23})$ S atoms	$\longrightarrow$ $1(6.02 \times 10^{23})$ Ag$_2$S formula units
Moles	2 moles of Ag	+ 1 mole of S	$\longrightarrow$ 1 mole of Ag$_2$S
Mass (g)	2(107.9 g) of Ag	+ 1(32.1 g) of S	$\longrightarrow$ 1(247.9 g) of Ag$_2$S
Total mass (g)	247.9 g		$\longrightarrow$ 247.9 g

Mole–Mole Factors from an Equation

When iron reacts with sulfur, the product is iron(III) sulfide:

$$2Fe(s) + 3S(s) \longrightarrow Fe_2S_3(s)$$

Iron (Fe)	Sulfur (S)	Iron(III) sulfide (Fe$_2$S$_3$)
$2Fe(s)$ +	$3S(s)$ $\longrightarrow$	$Fe_2S_3(s)$

Because the equation is balanced, we know the proportions of iron and sulfur in the reaction. For this reaction, we see that 2 moles of iron reacts with 3 moles of sulfur to form 1 mole of iron(III) sulfide. From the coefficients, we can write **mole–mole factors** between reactants and between reactants and products. The coefficients used in the mole–mole factors are exact numbers; they do not limit the number of significant figures.

$$\text{Fe and S:} \quad \frac{2 \text{ moles Fe}}{3 \text{ moles S}} \quad \text{and} \quad \frac{3 \text{ moles S}}{2 \text{ moles Fe}}$$

$$\text{Fe and Fe}_2\text{S}_3\text{:} \quad \frac{2 \text{ moles Fe}}{1 \text{ mole Fe}_2\text{S}_3} \quad \text{and} \quad \frac{1 \text{ mole Fe}_2\text{S}_3}{2 \text{ moles Fe}}$$

$$\text{S and Fe}_2\text{S}_3\text{:} \quad \frac{3 \text{ moles S}}{1 \text{ mole Fe}_2\text{S}_3} \quad \text{and} \quad \frac{1 \text{ mole Fe}_2\text{S}_3}{3 \text{ moles S}}$$

Using Mole–Mole Factors in Calculations

Whenever you prepare a recipe, adjust an engine for the proper mixture of fuel and air, or prepare medicines in a pharmaceutical laboratory, you need to know the proper amounts of reactants to use and how much of the product will form. Earlier we wrote all the possible conversion factors that can be obtained from this balanced equation: $2Fe(s) + 3S(s) \longrightarrow Fe_2S_3(s)$. Now we will show how mole–mole factors are used in chemical calculations.

**Guide to Using
Mole–Mole Factors**

STEP 1
Write the given and needed moles.

STEP 2
Write a plan to convert the given to the needed moles.

STEP 3
Use coefficients to write relationships and mole–mole factors.

STEP 4
Set up problem using the mole–mole factor that cancels given moles.

SAMPLE PROBLEM   6.9

■ Using Mole–Mole Factors

In the reaction of iron and sulfur, how many moles of sulfur are needed to react with 6.0 moles of iron?

$$2Fe(s) + 3S(s) \longrightarrow Fe_2S_3(s)$$

SOLUTION

STEP 1   Write the given and needed number of moles.   In this problem, we need to find the number of moles of S that reacts with 6.0 moles of Fe.

Given moles of Fe   **Need** moles of S

STEP 2   **Write the plan to convert the given to the needed moles.**

$$\text{moles of Fe} \quad \boxed{\begin{array}{c}\text{Mole–mole}\\\text{factor}\end{array}} \quad \text{moles of S}$$

STEP 3   **Use coefficients to write relationships and mole–mole factors.**   Use coefficients to write the mole–mole factors for the given and needed substances.

$$2 \text{ moles of Fe} = 3 \text{ moles of S}$$

$$\frac{2 \text{ moles Fe}}{3 \text{ moles S}} \quad \text{and} \quad \frac{3 \text{ moles S}}{2 \text{ moles Fe}}$$

STEP 4   **Set up problem using the mole–mole factor that cancels given moles.**   Use a mole–mole factor to cancel the given moles and provide needed moles.

$$6.0 \ \cancel{\text{moles Fe}} \quad \times \quad \frac{3 \text{ moles S}}{2 \ \cancel{\text{moles Fe}}} \quad = \quad 9.0 \text{ moles of S}$$

The answer is given with 2 significant figures because the given quantity 6.0 moles of Fe has 2 SFs. The values in the mole–mole factor are exact.

STUDY CHECK

Using the equation in Sample Problem 6.9, calculate the number of moles of iron(III) sulfide produced from 2.7 moles of sulfur.

QUESTIONS AND PROBLEMS

Mole Relationships in Chemical Equations

6.45 Write all of the mole–mole factors for each of the following equations:
 a. $2SO_2(g) + O_2(g) \longrightarrow 2SO_3(g)$
 b. $4P(s) + 5O_2(s) \longrightarrow 2P_2O_5(s)$

6.46 Write all of the mole–mole factors for each of the following equations:
 a. $2Al(s) + 3Cl_2(g) \longrightarrow 2AlCl_3(s)$
 b. $4HCl(g) + O_2(g) \longrightarrow 2Cl_2(g) + 2H_2O(g)$

6.47 The reaction of hydrogen with oxygen produces water:

$$2H_2(g) + O_2(g) \longrightarrow 2H_2O(g)$$

 a. How many moles of O_2 are required to react with 2.0 moles of H_2?
 b. If you have 5.0 moles of O_2, how many moles of H_2 are needed for the reaction?
 c. How many moles of H_2O form when 2.5 moles of O_2 react?

6.48 Ammonia is produced by the reaction of hydrogen and nitrogen:

$$N_2(g) + 3H_2(g) \longrightarrow 2NH_3(g)$$
Ammonia

 a. How many moles of H_2 are needed to react with 1.0 mole of N_2?
 b. How many moles of N_2 reacted if 0.60 mole of NH_3 is produced?

 c. How many moles of NH_3 are produced when 1.4 moles of H_2 react?

6.49 Carbon disulfide and carbon monoxide are produced when carbon is heated with sulfur dioxide:

$$5C(s) + 2SO_2(g) \longrightarrow CS_2(l) + 4CO(g)$$

 a. How many moles of C are needed to react with 0.500 mole of SO_2?
 b. How many moles of CO are produced when 1.2 moles of C react?
 c. How many moles of SO_2 are required to produce 0.50 mole of CS_2?
 d. How many moles of CS_2 are produced when 2.5 moles of C react?

6.50 In the acetylene torch, acetylene gas (C_2H_2) burns in oxygen to produce carbon dioxide and water:

$$2C_2H_2(g) + 5O_2(g) \longrightarrow 4CO_2(g) + 2H_2O(g)$$

 a. How many moles of O_2 are needed to react with 2.00 moles of C_2H_2?
 b. How many moles of CO_2 are produced when 3.5 moles of C_2H_2 react?
 c. How many moles of C_2H_2 are required to produce 0.50 mole of H_2O?
 d. How many moles of CO_2 are produced from 0.100 mole of O_2?

6.7 Mass Calculations for Reactions

When you perform a chemistry experiment in the laboratory, you use a laboratory balance to obtain a certain mass of reactant. From the mass in grams, you can determine the number of moles of reactant. By using mole–mole factors, you can predict the moles of product that can be produced. Then the molar mass of the product is used to convert the moles back into mass in grams. The following procedure can be used to set up and solve problems that involve calculations of quantities for substances in a chemical reaction.

LEARNING GOAL

Given the mass in grams of a substance in a reaction, calculate the mass in grams of another substance in the reaction.

Guide to Calculating the Masses of Reactants and Products in a Chemical Reaction

STEP 1
Use molar mass to convert grams of given to moles (if necessary).

STEP 2
Write a mole–mole factor from the coefficients in the equation.

STEP 3
Convert moles of given to moles of needed substance using mole–mole factor.

STEP 4
Convert moles of needed substance to grams using molar mass.

 TUTORIAL
Masses of Reactants and Products

SAMPLE PROBLEM 6.10

■ Mass of Products from Moles of Reactant

In the formation of smog, nitrogen reacts with oxygen to produce nitrogen oxide. Calculate the grams of NO produced when 1.50 moles of O_2 reacts.

$$N_2(g) + O_2(g) \longrightarrow 2NO(g)$$

SOLUTION

STEP 1   Given 1.50 moles of O_2 **Need** grams of NO

STEP 2   Plan

moles of O_2 → Mole–mole factor → moles of NO → Molar mass → grams of NO

STEP 3   Equalities/Conversion Factors   The mole–mole factor that converts moles of O_2 to moles of NO is derived from the coefficients in the balanced equation:

$$1 \text{ mole of } O_2 = 2 \text{ moles of NO}$$

$$\frac{2 \text{ moles NO}}{1 \text{ mole } O_2} \quad \text{and} \quad \frac{1 \text{ mole } O_2}{2 \text{ moles NO}}$$

$$1 \text{ mole of NO} = 30.0 \text{ g of NO}$$

$$\frac{30.0 \text{ g NO}}{1 \text{ mole NO}} \quad \text{and} \quad \frac{1 \text{ mole NO}}{30.0 \text{ g NO}}$$

STEP 4   Set Up Problem   First, we change the given, 1.50 moles of O_2, to moles of NO:

$$1.50 \text{ moles } O_2 \times \frac{2 \text{ moles NO}}{1 \text{ mole } O_2} = 3.00 \text{ moles of NO}$$

Now, the moles of NO are converted to grams of NO using its molar mass.

$$3.00 \text{ moles NO} \times \frac{30.0 \text{ g NO}}{1 \text{ mole NO}} = 90.0 \text{ g of NO}$$

These two steps can also be written as a sequence of conversion factors that lead to the mass in grams of NO.

$$1.50 \text{ moles } O_2 \times \frac{2 \text{ moles NO}}{1 \text{ mole } O_2} \times \frac{30.0 \text{ g NO}}{1 \text{ mole NO}} = 90.0 \text{ g of NO}$$

STUDY CHECK

Using the equation in Sample Problem 6.10, calculate the grams of NO that can be produced when 0.734 mole of N_2 reacts.

SAMPLE PROBLEM 6.11

■ Mass of Product from Mass of Reactant

Acetylene (C_2H_2), used in welding, burns with oxygen.

$$2C_2H_2(g) + 5O_2(g) \longrightarrow 4CO_2(g) + 2H_2O(g)$$

How many grams of carbon dioxide are produced when 54.6 g of C_2H_2 are burned?

SOLUTION

STEP 1 **Given** grams of C_2H_2 **Need** grams of CO_2

STEP 2 **Plan** Once we convert grams of C_2H_2 to moles of C_2H_2 using its molar mass, we can use a mole–mole factor to find the moles of CO_2. Then the molar mass of CO_2 will give us the grams of CO_2.

grams of C_2H_2 → Molar mass → moles of C_2H_2 → Mole–mole factor → moles of CO_2 → Molar mass → grams of CO_2

STEP 3 **Equalities/Conversion Factors** We need the molar mass of C_2H_2 and CO_2. The mole–mole factor that converts moles of C_2H_2 to moles of CO_2 is derived from the coefficients in the balanced equation.

1 mole of C_2H_2 = 26.0 g of C_2H_2

$$\frac{26.0 \text{ g } C_2H_2}{1 \text{ mole } C_2H_2} \quad \text{and} \quad \frac{1 \text{ mole } C_2H_2}{26.0 \text{ g } C_2H_2}$$

2 moles of C_2H_2 = 4 moles of CO_2

$$\frac{2 \text{ moles } C_2H_2}{4 \text{ moles } CO_2} \quad \text{and} \quad \frac{4 \text{ moles } CO_2}{2 \text{ moles } C_2H_2}$$

1 mole of CO_2 = 44.0 g of CO_2

$$\frac{44.0 \text{ g } CO_2}{1 \text{ mole } CO_2} \quad \text{and} \quad \frac{1 \text{ mole } CO_2}{44.0 \text{ g } CO_2}$$

STEP 4 **Set Up Problem** Using our plan, we first convert grams of C_2H_2 to moles of C_2H_2.

$$54.6 \text{ g } C_2H_2 \times \frac{1 \text{ mole } C_2H_2}{26.0 \text{ g } C_2H_2} = 2.10 \text{ moles of } C_2H_2$$

Then we change moles of C_2H_2 to moles of CO_2 by using the mole–mole factor.

$$2.10 \text{ moles } C_2H_2 \times \frac{4 \text{ moles } CO_2}{2 \text{ moles } C_2H_2} = 4.20 \text{ moles of } CO_2$$

Finally, we can convert moles of CO_2 to grams of CO_2.

$$4.20 \text{ moles } CO_2 \times \frac{44.0 \text{ g } CO_2}{1 \text{ mole } CO_2} = 185 \text{ g of } CO_2$$

The solution can be obtained using the conversion factors in sequence.

$$54.6 \text{ g } C_2H_2 \times \frac{1 \text{ mole } C_2H_2}{26.0 \text{ g } C_2H_2} \times \frac{4 \text{ moles } CO_2}{2 \text{ moles } C_2H_2} \times \frac{44.0 \text{ g } CO_2}{1 \text{ mole } CO_2} = 185 \text{ g of } CO_2$$

STUDY CHECK

Using the equation in Sample Problem 6.11, calculate the grams of CO_2 that can be produced when 25.0 g of O_2 reacts.

QUESTIONS AND PROBLEMS

Mass Calculations for Reactions

6.51 Sodium reacts with oxygen to produce sodium oxide.

$$4Na(s) + O_2(g) \longrightarrow 2Na_2O(s)$$

a. How many grams of Na_2O are produced when 2.50 moles of Na react?
b. If you have 18.0 g of Na, how many grams of O_2 are required for reaction?
c. How many grams of O_2 are needed in a reaction that produces 75.0 g of Na_2O?

6.52 Nitrogen gas reacts with hydrogen gas to produce ammonia by the following equation:

$$N_2(g) + 3H_2(g) \longrightarrow 2NH_3(g)$$

a. If you have 1.80 moles of H_2, how many grams of NH_3 can be produced?
b. How many grams of H_2 are needed to react with 2.80 g of N_2?
c. How many grams of NH_3 can be produced from 12.0 g of H_2?

6.53 Ammonia and oxygen react to form nitrogen and water.

$$4NH_3(g) + 3O_2(g) \longrightarrow 2N_2(g) + 6H_2O(g)$$
Ammonia

a. How many grams of O_2 are needed to react with 8.00 moles of NH_3?

b. How many grams of N_2 can be produced when 6.50 g of O_2 reacts?

c. How many grams of water are formed from the reaction of 34.0 g of NH_3?

6.54 Iron(III) oxide reacts with carbon to give iron and carbon monoxide.

$$Fe_2O_3(s) + 3C(s) \longrightarrow 2Fe(s) + 3CO(g)$$

a. How many grams of C are required to react with 2.50 moles of Fe_2O_3?

b. How many grams of CO are produced when 36.0 g of C reacts?

c. How many grams of Fe can be produced when 6.00 g of Fe_2O_3 reacts?

6.55 Nitrogen dioxide and water react to produce nitric acid, HNO_3, and nitrogen oxide:

$$3NO_2(g) + H_2O(l) \longrightarrow 2HNO_3(aq) + NO(g)$$

a. How many grams of H_2O are required to react with 28.0 g of NO_2?

b. How many grams of NO are obtained from 15.8 g of NO_2?

c. How many grams of HNO_3 are produced from 8.25 g of NO_2?

6.56 Calcium cyanamide reacts with water to form calcium carbonate and ammonia:

$$CaCN_2(s) + 3H_2O(l) \longrightarrow CaCO_3(s) + 2NH_3(g)$$

a. How many grams of water are needed to react with 75.0 g of $CaCN_2$?

b. How many grams of NH_3 are produced from 5.24 g of $CaCN_2$?

c. How many grams of $CaCO_3$ form if 155 g of water reacts?

6.57 When the ore lead(II) sulfide burns in oxygen, the products are lead(II) oxide and sulfur dioxide.

a. Write the balanced equation for the reaction.

b. How many grams of oxygen are required to react with 0.125 mole of lead(II) sulfide?

c. How many grams of sulfur dioxide can be produced when 65.0 g of lead(II) sulfide reacts?

d. How many grams of lead(II) sulfide are used to produce 128 g of lead(II) oxide?

6.58 When the gases dihydrogen sulfide and oxygen react, they form the gases sulfur dioxide and water.

a. Write the balanced equation for the reaction.

b. How many grams of oxygen are required to react with 2.50 g of dihydrogen sulfide?

c. How many grams of sulfur dioxide can be produced when 38.5 g of oxygen reacts?

d. How many grams of oxygen are required to produce 55.8 g of water vapor?

6.8 Percent Yield and Limiting Reactants

LEARNING GOAL

Given the actual quantity of product, determine the percent yield for a reaction. Identify a limiting reactant when given the quantities of two or more reactants; calculate the amount of product formed from the limiting reactant.

Up to this point, we have done calculations as though the amount of product were the maximum quantity possible, or 100%. In other words, we assumed that all of the reactants were changed completely to product. Although this would be an ideal situation, it does not usually happen. As we run a reaction and transfer products from one container to another, some product is lost. There may also be side reactions that use up some of the reactants to give a different product. Thus, in a real experiment, the predicted amount of the desired product is never really obtained.

Suppose we are running a chemical reaction in the laboratory. We first measure out specific quantities of the reactants and place them in a reaction flask. Then we calculate the **theoretical yield** for the reaction, which is the amount of product we could expect if all the reactants were converted to product according to the mole ratios of the equation. The **actual yield** is the amount of product we collect when the reaction ends. Because some product is lost, the actual yield is always less than the theoretical yield. If we know the actual yield and the theoretical yield for a product, then we can express the actual yield as a **percent yield**:

$$\text{Percent yield } (\%) = \frac{\text{actual yield}}{\text{theoretical yield}} \times 100\%$$

Guide to Calculations for Percent Yield

STEP 1
Write the given and needed quantities.

STEP 2
Write a plan to calculate the theoretical yield and the percent yield.

STEP 3
Write the molar mass for the reactant and the mole–mole factor from the balanced equation.

STEP 4
Solve for the percent yield ratio by dividing the actual yield (given) by the theoretical yield and multiplying the result by 100%.

SAMPLE PROBLEM 6.12

■ **Calculating Percent Yield**

On a spaceship, LiOH is used to absorb exhaled CO_2 from breathing air.

$$LiOH(s) + CO_2(g) \longrightarrow LiHCO_3(s)$$

What is the percent yield of the reaction if 50.0 g of LiOH gives 72.8 g of $LiHCO_3$?

SOLUTION

STEP 1 **Given** 50.0 g of LiOH and 72.8 g of $LiHCO_3$ (actually produced)
            Need % yield of $LiHCO_3$

STEP 2   **Plan   Calculation of theoretical yield:**

grams of LiOH | Molar mass | moles of LiOH | Mole–mole factor | moles of LiHCO$_3$ | Molar mass | grams of LiHCO$_3$

Calculation of percent yield:

$$\frac{\text{Actual yield}}{\text{Theoretical yield}} \times 100\%$$

STEP 3   **Equalities/Conversion Factors**

1 mole of LiOH = 24.0 g of LiOH

$$\frac{1 \text{ mole LiOH}}{24.0 \text{ g LiOH}} \quad \text{and} \quad \frac{24.0 \text{ g LiOH}}{1 \text{ mole LiOH}}$$

1 mole of LiHCO$_3$ = 1 mole of LiOH

$$\frac{1 \text{ mole LiHCO}_3}{1 \text{ mole LiOH}} \quad \text{and} \quad \frac{1 \text{ mole LiOH}}{1 \text{ mole LiHCO}_3}$$

1 mole of LiHCO$_3$ = 68.0 g of LiHCO$_3$

$$\frac{68.0 \text{ g LiHCO}_3}{1 \text{ mole LiHCO}_3} \quad \text{and} \quad \frac{1 \text{ mole LiHCO}_3}{68.0 \text{ g LiHCO}_3}$$

STEP 4   **Set Up Problem**
Calculation of theoretical yield:

$$50.0 \text{ g LiOH} \times \frac{1 \text{ mole LiOH}}{24.0 \text{ g LiOH}} \times \frac{1 \text{ mole LiHCO}_3}{1 \text{ mole LiOH}}$$

$$\times \frac{68.0 \text{ g LiHCO}_3}{1 \text{ mole LiHCO}_3} = 142 \text{ g of LiHCO}_3$$

Calculation of percent yield:

$$\frac{\text{Actual yield (given)}}{\text{Theoretical yield (calculated)}} \times 100\% = \frac{72.8 \text{ g LiHCO}_3}{142 \text{ g LiHCO}_3} \times 100\% = 51.3\%$$

A percent yield of 51.3% means that 72.8 g of the theoretical amount of 142 g of LiHCO$_3$ was actually produced by the reaction.

STUDY CHECK

For the reaction in Sample Problem 6.12, what is the percent yield if 8.00 g of CO$_2$ produces 10.5 g of LiHCO$_3$?

Limiting Reactants

When you make peanut butter sandwiches for lunch, you need 2 slices of bread and 1 tablespoon of peanut butter for each sandwich. As an equation, we could write:

TUTORIAL
What Will Run Out First?

2 slices of bread + 1 tablespoon of peanut butter $\longrightarrow$ 1 peanut butter sandwich

If you have 8 slices of bread and a full jar of peanut butter, you will run out of bread after you make 4 peanut butter sandwiches. You cannot make any more sandwiches once the bread is used up, even though there is a lot of peanut butter left in the jar. The number of slices of bread has limited the number of sandwiches you can make. On a different day, you might have 8 slices of bread but only a tablespoon of peanut butter left in the peanut butter jar. You will run out of peanut butter after you make just 1 peanut butter sandwich with 6 slices of bread left over. The small amount of peanut butter available has limited the number of sandwiches you can make. This time the amount of peanut butter is limiting.

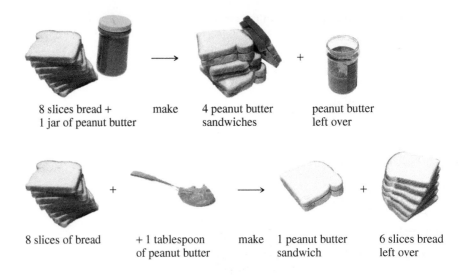

8 slices bread +   make   4 peanut butter   peanut butter
1 jar of peanut butter   sandwiches   left over

8 slices of bread   + 1 tablespoon   make   1 peanut butter   6 slices bread
                of peanut butter   sandwich   left over

Calculating Moles of Product from a Limiting Reactant

In a similar way, the availability of reactants in a chemical reaction can limit the amount of product that forms. In many reactions, the reactants are not combined in quantities that allow each to be used up at exactly the same time. Then one reactant is used up before the other. The reactant that is completely used up is called the **limiting reactant**. The other reactant, called the **excess reactant**, is left over. In the last analogy, the bread was the limiting reactant and the jar of peanut butter was the excess reactant.

Bread	Peanut Butter	Sandwiches	Limiting Reactant	Excess Reactant
1 loaf (20 slices)	1 tablespoon	1	Peanut butter	Bread
4 slices	1 full jar	2	Bread	Peanut butter
8 slices	1 full jar	4	Bread	Peanut butter

CONCEPT CHECK 6.6

■ Limiting Reactants

You are going to plan a picnic. You have 10 spoons, 8 forks, and 6 knives. If each person requires 1 spoon, 1 fork, and 1 knife, how many people can be served lunch at your picnic?

ANSWER

The relationship of utensils required by each person can be written:

   1 person = 1 spoon, 1 fork, and 1 knife

The number of people can be calculated for each utensil as:

$$10 \; \text{spoons} \times \frac{1 \; \text{person}}{1 \; \text{spoon}} = 10 \; \text{people}$$

$$8 \; \text{forks} \times \frac{1 \; \text{person}}{1 \; \text{fork}} = 8 \; \text{people}$$

$$6 \; \text{knives} \times \frac{1 \; \text{person}}{1 \; \text{knife}} = 6 \; \text{people} \quad \text{(smallest number of people)}$$

The limiting utensil is 6 knives, which means that 6 people (including yourself) can be at your picnic.

Consider the reaction in which hydrogen and chlorine form hydrogen chloride:

$$H_2(g) + Cl_2(g) \longrightarrow 2HCl(g)$$

Suppose the reaction mixture contains 2 moles of H_2 and 5 moles of Cl_2. From the equation, we see that 1 mole of hydrogen reacts with 1 mole of chlorine to produce 2 moles of hydrogen chloride. Now we need to calculate the amount of product that is possible from each of the reactants. We are looking for the limiting reactant, which is the one that produces the smaller amount of product.

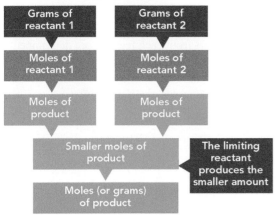

Guide to Calculating Product from a Limiting Reactant

Moles of HCl from H_2:

$$2 \text{ moles } H_2 \times \frac{2 \text{ moles HCl}}{1 \text{ mole } H_2} = 4 \text{ moles of HCl (smaller amount of product)}$$

Moles of HCl from Cl_2:

$$5 \text{ moles } Cl_2 \times \frac{2 \text{ moles HCl}}{1 \text{ mole } Cl_2} = 10 \text{ moles of HCl (not possible)}$$

In this reaction mixture, H_2 is the limiting reactant. When 2 moles of H_2 are used up, the reaction stops. The excess reactant is the 3 moles of Cl_2 left over when the reaction is complete. We can show the changes in each reactant and the product as follows:

	Reactants			Product
Equation	H_2	+	Cl_2 ⟶	2HCl
Initial moles	2 moles		5 moles	0 mole
Moles used/formed	−2 moles		−2 moles	+4 moles
Moles left	0 mole (2 − 2)		3 moles (5 − 2)	4 moles (0 + 4)
Identify as	Limiting reactant		Excess reactant	Product possible

---

CONCEPT CHECK 6.7

■ Moles of Product from Limiting Reactant

Consider the reaction for the synthesis of methanol (CH_3OH):

$$CO(g) + 2H_2(g) \longrightarrow CH_3OH(g)$$

In the laboratory, 3.00 moles of CO and 5.00 moles of H_2 are combined. Calculate the number of moles of CH_3OH that can form and identify the limiting reactant.

ANSWER

STEP 1 **Given** 3.00 moles of CO and 5.00 moles of H_2 **Need** moles of CH_3OH

STEP 2 **Plan** We can determine the limiting reactant and the excess reactant by calculating the moles of methanol that each reactant would produce if it were all used up. The actual number of moles of CH_3OH produced is from the reactant that produces the smaller number of moles.

Moles of CO Mole–mole factor moles of CH_3OH

Moles of H_2 Mole–mole factor moles of CH_3OH

STEP 3   **Equalities/Conversion Factors**   The mole–mole factors needed are obtained from the equation.

$$1 \text{ mole of CO} = 1 \text{ mole of CH}_3\text{OH} \quad 2 \text{ moles of H}_2 = 1 \text{ mole of CH}_3\text{OH}$$

$$\frac{1 \text{ mole CH}_3\text{OH}}{1 \text{ mole CO}} \text{ and } \frac{1 \text{ mole CO}}{1 \text{ mole CH}_3\text{OH}} \qquad \frac{1 \text{ mole CH}_3\text{OH}}{2 \text{ moles H}_2} \text{ and } \frac{2 \text{ moles H}_2}{1 \text{ mole CH}_3\text{OH}}$$

STEP 4   **Set Up Problem**   The moles of CH_3OH from each reactant are determined in separate calculations.

$$3.00 \text{ moles CO} \times \frac{1 \text{ mole CH}_3\text{OH}}{1 \text{ mole CO}} = 3.00 \text{ moles of CH}_3\text{OH}$$

$$5.00 \text{ moles H}_2 \times \frac{1 \text{ mole CH}_3\text{OH}}{2 \text{ moles H}_2} = 2.50 \text{ moles of CH}_3\text{OH (smaller amount)}$$

The smaller amount (2.5 moles of CH_3OH) is all the methanol that can be produced. Thus, H_2 is the limiting reagent and CO is in excess.

	Reactants			Product
	CO	+	$2H_2$ $\longrightarrow$	CH_3OH
Equation				
Initial moles	3.0 moles		5.0 moles	0 mole
Moles used/formed	−2.5 moles		−5.0 moles	+2.5 moles
Moles left	0.5 mole		0 mole	2.5 moles
Identify as	Excess reactant		Limiting reactant	Product possible

Calculating Mass of Product from a Limiting Reactant

When the quantities of the reactants are given in grams, they must first be converted to moles. Once the limiting reactant is determined, the smaller number of moles of product is converted to grams using molar mass. This calculation is shown in Sample Problem 6.13.

■ **Mass of Product from a Limiting Reactant**

Carbon monoxide and hydrogen gas react to form methanol, CH_3OH.

$$CO(g) + 2H_2(g) \longrightarrow CH_3OH(l)$$

If 48.0 g of CO and 10.0 g of H_2 react, how many grams of methanol can be produced?

SOLUTION

STEP 1   **Given**   48.0 g of CO and 10.0 g of H_2 **Need**   grams of CH_3OH

STEP 2   **Plan**   Convert the grams of each reactant to moles and calculate the moles of CH_3OH that each reactant can produce. Then convert the number of moles of CH_3OH from the limiting reactant to grams of CH_3OH using molar mass.

48.0 g of CO → Molar mass → moles of CO → Mole–mole factor → moles of CH_3OH (if smaller) → Molar mass → g of CH_3OH

or

10.0 g of H_2 → Molar mass → moles of H_2 → Mole–mole factor → moles of CH_3OH (if smaller) → Molar mass → g of CH_3OH

STEP 3   **Equalities/Conversion Factors**

1 mole of CO = 28.0 g of CO

$$\frac{1 \text{ mole CO}}{28.0 \text{ g CO}} \quad \text{and} \quad \frac{28.0 \text{ g CO}}{1 \text{ mole CO}}$$

1 mole of CO = 1 mole of CH_3OH

$$\frac{1 \text{ mole CO}}{1 \text{ mole CH}_3\text{OH}} \quad \text{and} \quad \frac{1 \text{ mole CH}_3\text{OH}}{1 \text{ mole CO}}$$

1 mole of H_2 = 2.0 g of H_2

$$\frac{1 \text{ mole H}_2}{2.0 \text{ g H}_2} \quad \text{and} \quad \frac{2.0 \text{ g H}_2}{1 \text{ mole H}_2}$$

2 moles of H_2 = 1 mole of CH_3OH

$$\frac{2 \text{ moles H}_2}{1 \text{ mole CH}_3\text{OH}} \quad \text{and} \quad \frac{1 \text{ mole CH}_3\text{OH}}{2 \text{ moles H}_2}$$

1 mole of CH_3OH = 32.0 g of CH_3OH

$$\frac{1 \text{ mole CH}_3\text{OH}}{32.0 \text{ g CH}_3\text{OH}} \quad \text{and} \quad \frac{32.0 \text{ g CH}_3\text{OH}}{1 \text{ mole CH}_3\text{OH}}$$

STEP 4   **Set Up Problem**   The moles of CH_3OH from each reactant can now be determined in separate calculations.

Moles of CH_3OH produced from CO:

$$48.0 \text{ g CO} \times \frac{1 \text{ mole CO}}{28.0 \text{ g CO}} \times \frac{1 \text{ mole CH}_3\text{OH}}{1 \text{ mole CO}} = 1.71 \text{ moles of CH}_3\text{OH}$$
(smaller number of moles)

Moles of CH_3OH produced from H_2:

$$10.0 \text{ g H}_2 \times \frac{1 \text{ mole H}_2}{2.0 \text{ g H}_2} \times \frac{1 \text{ mole CH}_3\text{OH}}{2 \text{ moles H}_2} = 2.5 \text{ moles of CH}_3\text{OH}$$

Because CO produces the smaller number of moles of CH_3OH, CO is the limiting reactant. Now the grams of product CH_3OH from these reactants is calculated by converting the moles of CH_3OH obtained from CO to grams using molar mass.

$$1.71 \text{ moles CH}_3\text{OH} \times \frac{32.0 \text{ g CH}_3\text{OH}}{1 \text{ mole CH}_3\text{OH}} = 54.7 \text{ g of CH}_3\text{OH}$$

STUDY CHECK

When silicon dioxide (sand) and carbon are heated, the ceramic material silicon carbide (SiC) and carbon monoxide are produced. How many grams of SiC are formed from 20.0 g of SiO_2 and 50.0 g of C?

$$SiO_2(s) + 3C(s) \xrightarrow{\text{Heat}} SiC(s) + 2CO(g)$$

QUESTIONS AND PROBLEMS

Percent Yield and Limiting Reactants

6.59 Carbon disulfide is produced by the reaction of carbon and sulfur dioxide:

$$5C(s) + 2SO_2(g) \longrightarrow CS_2(g) + 4CO(g)$$

a. What is the percent yield for the reaction if 40.0 g of carbon produces 36.0 g of carbon disulfide?

b. What is the percent yield for the reaction if 32.0 g of sulfur dioxide produces 12.0 g of carbon disulfide?

6.60 Iron(III) oxide reacts with carbon monoxide to produce iron and carbon dioxide:

$$Fe_2O_3(s) + 3CO(g) \longrightarrow 2Fe(s) + 3CO_2(g)$$

a. What is the percent yield for the reaction if 65.0 g of iron(III) oxide produces 15.0 g of iron?

b. What is the percent yield for the reaction if 75.0 g of carbon monoxide produces 15.0 g of carbon dioxide?

6.61 Aluminum reacts with oxygen to produce aluminum oxide:

$$4Al(s) + 3O_2(g) \longrightarrow 2Al_2O_3(s)$$

The reaction of 50.0 g of aluminum and sufficient oxygen has a 75.0% yield. How many grams of aluminum oxide are produced?

6.62 Propane (C_3H_8) burns in oxygen to produce carbon dioxide and water:

$$C_3H_8(g) + 5O_2(g) \longrightarrow 3CO_2(g) + 4H_2O(g)$$

Calculate the mass of CO_2 that can be produced if the reaction of 45.0 g of propane and sufficient oxygen has a 60.0% yield.

6.63 When 30.0 g of carbon are heated with silicon dioxide, 28.2 g of carbon monoxide are produced. What is the percent yield of this reaction?

$$SiO_2(s) + 3C(s) \longrightarrow SiC(s) + 2CO(g)$$

6.64 Calcium and nitrogen react to form calcium nitride:

$$3Ca(s) + N_2(g) \longrightarrow Ca_3N_2(s)$$

If 56.6 g of calcium are mixed with nitrogen gas and 32.4 g of calcium nitride are produced, what is the percent yield of the reaction?

6.65 A taxi company has 10 taxis.
   a. On a certain day, only 8 taxi drivers show up for work. How many taxis can be used to pick up passengers?
   b. On another day, 10 taxi drivers show up for work but 3 taxis are in the repair shop. How many taxis can be driven?

6.66 A clock maker has 15 clock faces. Each clock requires 1 face and 2 hands.
   a. If the clock maker has 42 hands, how many clocks can be produced?
   b. If the clock maker has only 8 hands, how many clocks can be produced?

6.67 Nitrogen and hydrogen react to form ammonia:

$$N_2(g) + 3H_2(g) \longrightarrow 2NH_3(g)$$

Determine the limiting reactant in each of the following mixtures of reactants:
   a. 3.0 moles of N_2 and 5.0 moles of H_2
   b. 8.0 moles of N_2 and 4.0 moles of H_2
   c. 3.0 moles of N_2 and 12.0 moles of H_2

6.68 Iron and oxygen react to form iron(III) oxide:

$$4Fe(s) + 3O_2(g) \longrightarrow 2Fe_2O_3(s)$$

Determine the limiting reactant in each of the following mixtures of reactants:
   a. 2.0 moles of Fe and 6.0 moles of O_2
   b. 5.0 moles of Fe and 4.0 moles of O_2
   c. 16.0 moles of Fe and 20.0 moles of O_2

6.69 For each reaction, calculate the moles of product (in parentheses) when 2.00 moles of each reactant is used.
   a. $2SO_2(g) + O_2(g) \longrightarrow 2SO_3(g)$ (SO_3)
   b. $3Fe(s) + 4H_2O(l) \longrightarrow Fe_3O_4(s) + 4H_2(g)$ (Fe_3O_4)
   c. $C_7H_{16}(g) + 11O_2(g) \longrightarrow 7CO_2(g) + 8H_2O(g)$ (CO_2)

6.70 In each reaction, calculate the moles of product (in parentheses) when 3.00 moles of each reactant is used.
   a. $4Li(s) + O_2(g) \longrightarrow 2Li_2O(s)$ (Li_2O)
   b. $Fe_2O_3(s) + 3H_2(g) \longrightarrow 2Fe(s) + 3H_2O(l)$ (Fe)
   c. $Al_2S_3(s) + 6H_2O(l) \longrightarrow 2Al(OH)_3(aq) + 3H_2S(g)$ (H_2S)

6.71 In each reaction, calculate the moles of product (in parentheses) produced when 20.0 g of each reactant is used:
   a. $2Al(s) + 3Cl_2(g) \longrightarrow 2AlCl_3(s)$ ($AlCl_3$)
   b. $4NH_3(g) + 5O_2(g) \longrightarrow 4NO(g) + 6H_2O(g)$ (H_2O)
   c. $CS_2(g) + 3O_2(g) \longrightarrow CO_2(g) + 2SO_2(g)$ (SO_2)

6.72 For each of the following reactions, calculate the moles of product (in parentheses) when 20.0 g of each reactant is used:
   a. $4Al(s) + 3O_2(g) \longrightarrow 2Al_2O_3(s)$ (Al_2O_3)
   b. $3NO_2(g) + H_2O(l) \longrightarrow 2HNO_3(aq) + NO(g)$ (HNO_3)
   c. $4NH_3(g) + 5O_2(g) \longrightarrow 4NO(g) + 6H_2O(g)$ (H_2O)

6.9 Energy Changes in Chemical Reactions

Heat is energy that is lost or gained when a chemical reaction takes place. The *system* is the particular group of reactants and products we are looking at. The *surroundings* are all the things that contain and interact with the system such as the reaction flask, the laboratory room, and the air in the room. In any reaction system, there is a change in energy as reactants break apart and products form. The direction of heat flow depends on whether the products in the reaction have more or less energy than the reactants.

For a chemical reaction to take place, the molecules of the reactants must collide with each other and have the proper orientation and energy. When the molecules collide, bonds between atoms are broken and new bonds can form. The amount of energy needed to break apart those bonds is called the **activation energy**. If the energy of a collision is less than the activation energy, then the molecules bounce apart without reacting.

The concept of activation energy is analogous to climbing over a hill. To reach a destination on the other side, we must expend energy to climb to the top of the hill. Once we are at the top, we can easily run down the other side. The energy needed to get us from our starting point to the top of the hill would be the activation energy.

Heat of Reaction

The **heat of reaction** is the amount of heat absorbed or released during a reaction that takes place at constant pressure. We determine a heat of reaction, symbol ΔH, as the difference in the energy of the products and the reactants.

$$\Delta H = H_{\text{products}} - H_{\text{reactants}}$$

In the energy diagram for an **endothermic reaction** (*endo* means within), the energy of the products is greater than that of the reactants. In these reactions, heat flows out of the surroundings into the system, where it is used to convert the reactants to products. For an endothermic reaction, the heat of reaction can be written as one of the reactants. It can also be written as a ΔH value with a positive sign (+). Let us look at the equation and ΔH for the endothermic reaction in which 137 kcal of heat is needed to break down 2 moles of water into hydrogen and oxygen:

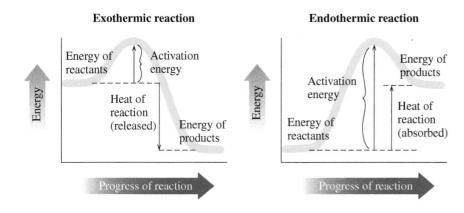

Endothermic, Heat Required

$$2H_2O(l) + 137 \text{ kcal} \longrightarrow 2H_2(g) + O_2(g)$$

$$2H_2O(l) \longrightarrow 2H_2(g) + O_2(g)$$

Heat Is a Reactant

$$\Delta H = +137 \text{ kcal}$$
positive sign

In an **exothermic reaction** (*exo* means out), the products have less energy than the reactants. In these reactions, heat flows out of the system into the surroundings. For an exothermic reaction, the heat of reaction can be written as one of products. It can also be written as a ΔH value with a negative sign (−). The reaction for the formation of ammonia (NH_3) from 3 moles of hydrogen (H_2) and 1 mole of nitrogen (N_2) is exothermic.

Exothermic, Heat Evolved

$$3H_2(g) + N_2(g) \longrightarrow 2NH_3(g) + 22.0 \text{ kcal}$$

$$3H_2(g) + N_2(g) \longrightarrow 2NH_3(g)$$

Heat Is a Product

$$\Delta H = -22.0 \text{ kcal}$$
negative sign

Reaction	Energy Change	Heat in the Equation	Sign of ΔH
Endothermic	Heat absorbed	Reactant side	Positive sign (+)
Exothermic	Heat released	Product side	Negative sign (−)

CONCEPT CHECK 6.8

■ Exothermic and Endothermic Reactions

In the reaction of 1 mole of carbon with oxygen gas, the energy of the carbon dioxide produced is 93.9 kcal lower than the energy of the reactants.
a. Is the reaction exothermic or endothermic?
b. Write the equation for the reaction including the heat of the reaction.
c. Write the value of ΔH for this reaction.

ANSWER
a. When the products have a lower energy than the reactants, the reaction is exothermic.
b. $C(s) + O_2(g) \longrightarrow CO_2(g) + 93.9 \text{ kcal}$
c. $\Delta H = -93.9 \text{ kcal}$

Calculations of Heat in Reactions

The value of ΔH refers to the heat change for the number of moles of each substance in the balanced equation for the reaction. Consider the following decomposition reaction:

$$2H_2O(l) \longrightarrow 2H_2(g) + O_2(g) \qquad \Delta H = 137 \text{ kcal}$$

$$2H_2O(l) + 137 \text{ kcal} \longrightarrow 2H_2(g) + O_2(g)$$

For this reaction, 137 kcal are absorbed by 2 moles of H_2O to produce 2 moles of H_2 and 1 mole of O_2. We can write heat conversion factors for each substance in this reaction:

$$\frac{137 \text{ kcal}}{2 \text{ moles } H_2O} \qquad \frac{137 \text{ kcal}}{2 \text{ moles } H_2} \qquad \frac{137 \text{ kcal}}{1 \text{ mole } O_2}$$

 **TUTORIAL**
Heat of Reaction

Suppose in this reaction that 12.0 g of H_2O undergoes reaction. We can calculate the heat absorbed as

$$12.0 \text{ g } H_2O \times \frac{1 \text{ mole } H_2O}{18.0 \text{ g } H_2O} \times \frac{137 \text{ kcal}}{2 \text{ moles } H_2O} = 45.7 \text{ kcal}$$

**Guide to Calculations Using
Heat of Reaction (ΔH)**

STEP 1
List given and needed
data for the equation.

STEP 2
Write a plan using heat of reaction
and any molar mass needed.

STEP 3
Write the conversion factors
including heat of reaction.

STEP 4
Set up the problem.

SAMPLE PROBLEM 6.14

■ Calculating Heat in a Reaction

The heat of reaction for the formation of ammonia from hydrogen and nitrogen is -92.2 kJ:

$$N_2(g) + 3H_2(g) \longrightarrow 2NH_3(g) \qquad \Delta H = -92.2 \text{ kJ}$$

How much heat, in kilojoules, is released when 50.0 g of ammonia forms?

SOLUTION

STEP 1 **Given** 50.0 g of NH_3, $\Delta H = -92.2$ kJ   **Need** heat in kJ to form NH_3

STEP 2 **Plan** Use conversion factors that relate the heat released to the moles of NH_3.

Grams of NH_3 Molar mass   moles of NH_3 Heat of reaction   kilojoules

STEP 3 **Equalities/Conversion Factors**

1 mole of NH_3 = 17.0 g of NH_3

$$\frac{17.0 \text{ g } NH_3}{1 \text{ mole } NH_3} \quad \text{and} \quad \frac{17.0 \text{ g of } NH_3}{1 \text{ mole } NH_3}$$

2 moles of NH_3 = 92.2 kJ

$$\frac{92.2 \text{ kJ}}{2 \text{ moles } NH_3} \quad \text{and} \quad \frac{2 \text{ moles } NH_3}{92.2 \text{ kJ}}$$

STEP 4 **Set Up Problem**

$$50.0 \text{ g } NH_3 \times \frac{1 \text{ mole } NH_3}{17.0 \text{ g } NH_3} \times \frac{92.2 \text{ kJ}}{2 \text{ moles } NH_3} = 136 \text{ kJ}$$

STUDY CHECK

Mercury(II) oxide decomposes to mercury and oxygen:

$$2HgO(s) \longrightarrow 2Hg(l) + O_2(g) \qquad \Delta H = 182 \text{ kJ}$$

a. Is the reaction exothermic or endothermic?
b. How many kJ are needed to react 25.0 g of mercury(II) oxide?

QUESTIONS AND PROBLEMS

Energy in Chemical Reactions

6.73 a. Why do chemical reactions require activation energy?
    b. In an exothermic reaction, is the energy of the products higher or lower than the reactants?
    c. Draw an energy diagram for an exothermic reaction.

6.74 a. What is measured by the heat of reaction?
    b. In an endothermic reaction, is the energy of the products higher or lower than the reactants?
    c. Draw an energy diagram for an endothermic reaction.

6.75 Classify the following as exothermic or endothermic reactions:
    a. 55 kcal is released.
    b. The energy level of the products is higher than the reactants.
    c. The metabolism of glucose in the body provides energy.

6.76 Classify the following as exothermic or endothermic reactions:
    a. The energy level of the products is lower than the reactants.
    b. In the body, the synthesis of proteins requires energy.
    c. 12 kcal is absorbed.

6.77 Classify the following as exothermic or endothermic reactions and give ΔH for each:
    a. gas burning in a Bunsen burner:

$$CH_4(g) + 2O_2(g) \longrightarrow CO_2(g) + 2H_2O(g) + 210 \text{ kcal}$$

    b. dehydrating limestone:

$$Ca(OH)_2(s) + 65.3 \text{ kJ} \longrightarrow CaO(s) + H_2O(l)$$

    c. formation of aluminum oxide and iron from aluminum and iron(III) oxide:

$$2Al(s) + Fe_2O_3(s) \longrightarrow Al_2O_3(s) + 2Fe(s) + 205 \text{ kcal}$$

6.78 Classify the following as exothermic or endothermic reactions and give ΔH for each of the following:
    a. combustion of propane:

$$C_3H_8(g) + 5O_2(g) \longrightarrow 3CO_2(g) + 4H_2O(g) + 530 \text{ kcal}$$

    b. formation of "table" salt:

$$2Na(s) + Cl_2(g) \longrightarrow 2NaCl(s) + 196 \text{ kcal}$$

    c. decomposition of phosphorus pentachloride:

$$PCl_5(g) + 67 \text{ kJ} \longrightarrow PCl_3(g) + Cl_2(g)$$

6.79 The equation for the formation of silicon tetrachloride from silicon and chlorine is

$$Si(s) + 2Cl_2(g) \longrightarrow SiCl_4(g) \quad \Delta H = -157 \text{ kcal}$$

How many kilocalories are released when 125 g of Cl_2 reacts with silicon?

6.80 Methanol (CH_3OH), which is used as a cooking fuel, undergoes combustion to produce carbon dioxide and water:

$$2CH_3OH(l) + 3O_2(g) \longrightarrow$$
$$2CO_2(g) + 4H_2O(l) \; \Delta H = -726 \text{ kJ}$$

How many kilojoules are released when 75.0 g of methanol is burned?

HEALTH NOTE

Hot Packs and Cold Packs

In a hospital, at a first-aid station, or at an athletic event, an instant *cold pack* may be used to reduce swelling from an injury, remove heat from inflammation, or decrease capillary size to lessen the effect of hemorrhaging. Inside the plastic container of a cold pack, there is a compartment containing solid ammonium nitrate (NH_4NO_3) that is separated from a compartment containing water. The pack is activated when it is hit or squeezed hard enough to break the walls between the compartments and cause the ammonium nitrate to mix with the

water (shown as H_2O over the reaction arrow). In an endothermic process, each gram of NH_4NO_3 that dissolves absorbs 79 cal of heat from the water. The temperature drops and the pack becomes cold and ready to use.

Endothermic Reaction in a Cold Pack

$$6.2 \text{ kcal} + NH_4NO_3(s) \xrightarrow{H_2O} NH_4NO_3(aq)$$

Hot packs are used to relax muscles, lessen aches and cramps, and increase circulation by expanding capillary size. Constructed in the same way as cold packs, a hot pack may contain the salt $CaCl_2$. The dissolving of the salt in water is exothermic and releases 160 cal per gram of salt. The temperature rises and the pack becomes hot and ready to use.

Exothermic Reaction in a Hot Pack

$$CaCl_2(s) \xrightarrow{H_2O} CaCl_2(aq) + 18 \text{ kcal}$$

CONCEPT MAP

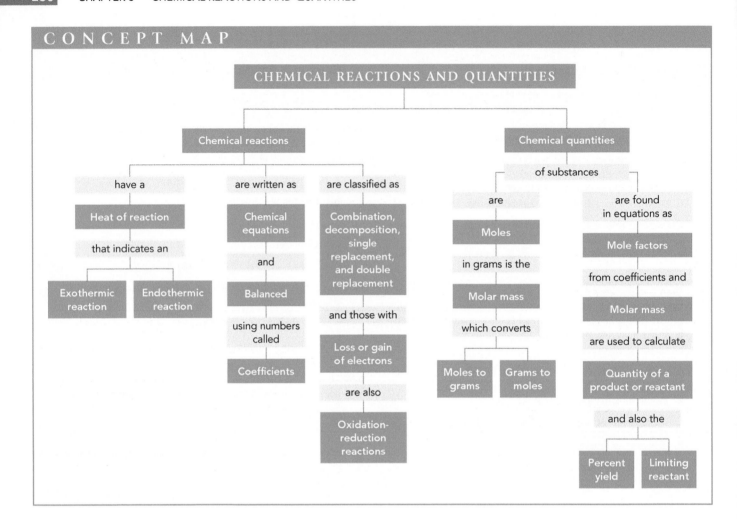

CHAPTER REVIEW

6.1 Chemical Reactions
LEARNING GOAL: *Write a balanced chemical equation from the formulas of the reactants and products for a chemical reaction.*
A chemical reaction occurs when the atoms of the initial substances rearrange to form new substances. A chemical equation shows the formulas of the substances that react on the left side of a reaction arrow and the products that form on the right side of the reaction arrow. An equation is balanced by writing the smallest whole numbers (coefficients) in front of formulas to equalize the atoms of each element in the reactants and the products.

6.2 Types of Reactions
LEARNING GOAL: *Identify a chemical reaction as a combination, decomposition, single replacement, or double replacement reaction.*
Many chemical reactions can be organized by reaction type: combination, decomposition, single replacement, or double replacement.

6.3 Oxidation–Reduction Reactions
LEARNING GOAL: *Define the terms oxidation and reduction.*
When electrons are transferred in a reaction, it is an oxidation–reduction reaction. One reactant loses electrons, and another reactant gains electrons. Overall, the number of electrons lost and gained is equal.

6.4 The Mole
LEARNING GOAL: *Use Avogadro's number to determine the number of particles in a given amount of moles.*

One mole of an element contains 6.02×10^{23} atoms; a mole of a compound contains 6.02×10^{23} molecules or formula units.

6.5 Molar Mass
LEARNING GOAL: *Determine the molar mass of a substance and use the molar mass to convert between grams and moles.*
The molar mass (g/mole) of any substance is the mass in grams equal numerically to its atomic mass, or the sum of the atomic masses, which have been multiplied by their subscripts in a formula. It becomes a conversion factor when it is used to change a quantity in grams to moles, or to change a given number of moles to grams.

6.6 Mole Relationships in Chemical Equations
LEARNING GOAL: *Given a quantity in moles of reactant or product, use a mole–mole factor from the balanced equation to calculate the moles of another substance in the reaction.*
In a balanced equation, the total mass of the reactants is equal to the total mass of the products. The coefficients in an equation that describes the relationship between the moles of any two components are used to write mole–mole factors. When the number of moles for one substance is known, a mole–mole factor is used to find the moles of a different substance in the reaction.

6.7 Mass Calculations for Reactions
LEARNING GOAL: *Given the mass in grams of a substance in a reaction, calculate the mass in grams of another substance in the reaction.*

In calculations using equations, the molar masses of the substances and their mole factors are used to change the number of grams of one substance to the corresponding grams of a different substance.

6.8 Percent Yield and Limiting Reactants

LEARNING GOAL: *Given the actual quantity of product, determine the percent yield for a reaction. Identify a limiting reactant when given the quantities of two or more reactants; calculate the amount of product formed from the limiting reactant.*

The percent yield of a reaction indicates the percent of product actually produced during a reaction. The percent yield is calculated by dividing the actual yield in grams of a product by the theoretical yield in grams. A limiting reactant is the reactant that produces the smaller amount of product while some excess reactant is left over. When the mass of two or more reactants is given, the mass of a product is calculated from the product produced by the limiting reactant.

6.9 Energy Changes in Chemical Reactions

LEARNING GOAL: *Describe the energy changes in exothermic and endothermic reactions.*

In chemical reactions, the heat of reaction (ΔH) is the energy difference between the reactants and the products. In an exothermic reaction, the energy of the products is lower than the reactants. Heat is released and ΔH is negative. In an endothermic reaction, the energy of the products is higher than the reactants. Heat is absorbed and the ΔH is positive.

■ KEY TERMS

activation energy The energy needed to break the bonds of reacting molecules.

actual yield The actual amount of product produced by a reaction.

Avogadro's number The number of items in a mole; equal to 6.02×10^{23}.

balanced equation The final form of a chemical equation that shows the same number of atoms of each element in the reactants and products.

chemical equation A shorthand way to represent a chemical reaction using chemical formulas to indicate the reactants and products and coefficients to show reacting ratios.

chemical reaction The process by which a chemical change takes place.

coefficients Whole numbers placed in front of the formulas to balance the number of atoms or moles of atoms of each element on both sides of an equation.

combination reaction A reaction in which reactants combine to form a single product.

decomposition reaction A reaction in which a single reactant splits into two or more simpler substances.

double replacement reaction A reaction in which parts of two different reactants exchange places.

endothermic reaction A reaction in which the energy of the products is greater than that of the reactants.

excess reactant The reactant that remains when the limiting reactant is used up in a reaction.

exothermic reaction A reaction in which the energy of the reactants is greater than that of the products.

formula unit The group of ions represented by the formula of an ionic compound.

heat of reaction The heat (symbol ΔH) absorbed or released when a reaction takes place at constant pressure.

limiting reactant The reactant used up during a chemical reaction; it limits the amount of product that can form.

molar mass The mass in grams of 1 mole of an element equal numerically to its atomic mass. The molar mass of a compound is equal to the sum of the masses of the elements in the formula.

mole A group of atoms, molecules, or formula units that contains 6.02×10^{23} of these items.

mole–mole factor A conversion factor that relates the number of moles of two compounds derived from the coefficients in an equation.

oxidation The loss of electrons by a substance. Biological oxidation may involve the addition of oxygen or the loss of hydrogen.

oxidation–reduction reaction A reaction in which the oxidation of one reactant is always accompanied by the reduction of another reactant.

percent yield The ratio of the actual yield of a reaction to the theoretical yield possible for the reaction that is multiplied by 100%.

products The substances formed as a result of a chemical reaction.

reactants The initial substances that undergo change in a chemical reaction.

reduction The gain of electrons by a substance. Biological reduction may involve the loss of oxygen or the gain of hydrogen.

single replacement reaction A reaction in which an element replaces a different element in a compound.

theoretical yield The maximum amount of product that a reaction can produce from a given amount of reactant.

■ UNDERSTANDING THE CONCEPTS

6.81 Balance each of the following by adding coefficients and identify the type of reaction for each:

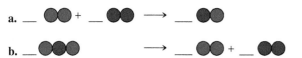

6.82 Balance each of the following by adding coefficients and identify the type of reaction for each:

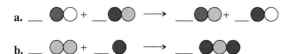

6.83 If red spheres represent oxygen atoms and blue spheres represent nitrogen atoms:

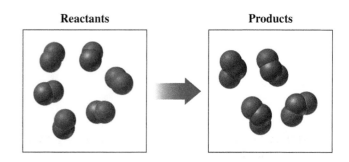

| Reactants | Products |

a. Write a balanced equation for the reaction.
b. Indicate the type of reaction as decomposition, combination, single replacement, or double replacement.

6.84 If purple spheres represent iodine atoms and light blue spheres represent hydrogen atoms:

Reactants   Products

a. Write a balanced equation for the reaction.
b. Indicate the type of reaction as decomposition, combination, single replacement, or double replacement.

6.85 If blue spheres represent nitrogen atoms and purple spheres represent iodine atoms:

Reactants   Products

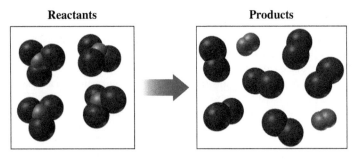

a. Write a balanced equation for the reaction.
b. Indicate the type of reaction as decomposition, combination, single replacement, or double replacement.

6.86 If green spheres represent chlorine atoms, yellow-green spheres represent fluorine atoms, and light blue spheres represent hydrogen atoms:

Reactants   Products

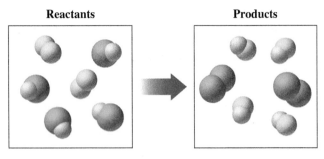

a. Write a balanced equation for the reaction.
b. Indicate the type of reaction as decomposition, combination, single replacement, or double replacement.

6.87 If green spheres represent chlorine atoms and red spheres represent oxygen atoms:

Reactants   Products

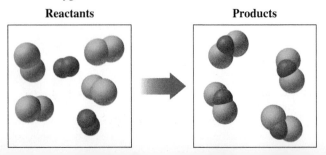

a. Write a balanced equation for the reaction.
b. Indicate the type of reaction as decomposition, combination, single replacement, or double replacement.

6.88 If blue spheres represent nitrogen atoms and purple spheres represent iodine atoms:

Reactants   Products

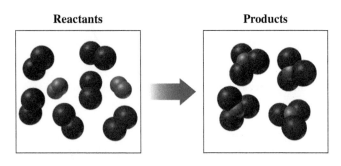

a. Write a balanced equation for the reaction.
b. Indicate the type of reaction as decomposition, combination, single replacement, or double replacement.

6.89 Using the following models of the molecules, determine (black = C, light blue = H, yellow = S, green = Cl):

1.   **2.**

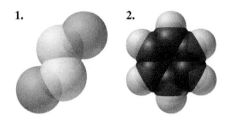

a. formula
b. molar mass
c. number of moles in 10.0 g

6.90 Using the following models of the molecules, determine (black = C, light blue = H, yellow = S, red = O):

1.   **2.**

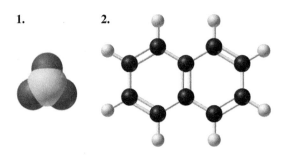

a. formula
b. molar mass
c. number of moles in 10.0 g

6.91 A dandruff shampoo contains pyrithion, $C_{10}H_8N_2O_2S_2$, an antibacterial and antifungal agent.

a. What is the molar mass of pyrithion?
b. How many moles of pyrithion are in 25.0 g?
c. How many moles of carbon are in 25.0 g of pyrithion?

6.92 Ammonium sulfate $(NH_4)_2SO_4$ is used in fertilizers to provide nitrogen for the soil.

a. How many formula units are in 0.200 mole of ammonium sulfate?

b. How many H atoms are in 0.100 mole of ammonium sulfate?

c. How many moles of ammonium sulfate contain 7.4×10^{25} atoms of N?

d What is the molar mass of ammonium sulfate?

6.93 In an experiment, a piece of copper is weighed on a balance and then allowed to react with oxygen:

$$2Cu(s) + O_2(g) \longrightarrow 2CuO(s)$$

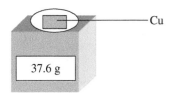

a. How many grams of CuO could be produced according to the equation?

b. How many moles of O_2 are required to completely react the Cu?

6.94 Allyl sulfide $(C_3H_5)_2S$ is the substance that gives garlic its characteristic odor.

a. How many moles of sulfur are in 23.2 g of $(C_3H_5)_2S$?

b. How many hydrogen atoms are in 0.75 mole of $(C_3H_5)_2S$?

c. How many grams of carbon are in 4.20×10^{23} molecules of $(C_3H_5)_2S$?

d. How many carbon atoms are in 15.0 g of $(C_3H_5)_2S$?

ADDITIONAL QUESTIONS AND PROBLEMS

For instructor-assigned homework, go to www.masteringchemistry.com.

6.95 Balance each of the following unbalanced equations and identify the type of reaction:

a. $NH_3(g) + HCl(g) \longrightarrow NH_4Cl(s)$

b. $Fe_3O_4(s) + H_2(g) \longrightarrow Fe(s) + H_2O(g)$

c. $Sb(s) + Cl_2(g) \longrightarrow SbCl_3(s)$

d. $NI_3(s) \longrightarrow N_2(g) + I_2(g)$

e. $KBr(aq) + Cl_2(aq) \longrightarrow KCl(aq) + Br_2(l)$

f. $Al_2(SO_4)_3(aq) + NaOH(aq) \longrightarrow Na_2SO_4(aq) + Al(OH)_3(s)$

6.96 Balance each of the following unbalanced equations and identify the type of reaction:

a. $Li_3N(s) \longrightarrow Li(s) + N_2(g)$

b. $Mg(s) + N_2(g) \longrightarrow Mg_3N_2(s)$

c. $Mg(s) + H_3PO_4(aq) \longrightarrow Mg_3(PO_4)_2(s) + H_2(g)$

d. $Cr_2O_3(s) + H_2(g) \longrightarrow Cr(s) + H_2O(g)$

e. $Al(s) + Cl_2(g) \longrightarrow AlCl_3(s)$

f. $MgCl_2(aq) + AgNO_3(aq) \longrightarrow Mg(NO_3)_2(aq) + AgCl(s)$

6.97 Identify each of the following as an oxidation or a reduction reaction:

a. $Zn^{2+} + 2e^- \longrightarrow Zn$

b. $Al \longrightarrow Al^{3+} + 3e^-$

c. $Pb \longrightarrow Pb^{2+} + 2e^-$

d. $Cl_2 + 2e^- \longrightarrow 2Cl^-$

6.98 Write a balanced chemical equation for each of the following oxidation–reduction reactions:

a. Sulfur reacts with molecular chlorine to form sulfur dichloride.

b. Molecular chlorine and sodium bromide react to form molecular bromine and sodium chloride.

c. Aluminum metal and iron(III) oxide react to produce aluminum oxide and elemental iron.

d. Copper(II) oxide reacts with elemental C to form elemental copper and carbon dioxide.

6.99 During heavy exercise and workouts, lactic acid, $C_3H_6O_3$, accumulates in the muscles, where it can cause pain and soreness.

a. What is the molar mass of lactic acid?

b. How many molecules are in 0.500 mole of lactic acid?

c. How many C atoms are in 1.50 moles of lactic acid?

d. How many grams of lactic acid contain 4.5×10^{24} atoms of O?

6.100 Ibuprofen, the anti-inflammatory ingredient in Advil, has the formula $C_{13}H_{18}O_2$.

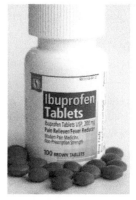

a. What is the molar mass of ibuprofen?

b. How many molecules are in 0.200 mole of ibuprofen?

c. How many H atoms are in 0.100 mole of ibuprofen?

d. How many grams of ibuprofen contain 7.4×10^{25} atoms of C?

6.101 Calculate the molar mass of each of the following:

a. $FeSO_4$, iron(II) sulfate, iron supplement

b. $Ca(IO_3)_2$, calcium iodate, iodine source in table salt

c. $C_5H_8NNaO_4$, monosodium glutamate, flavor enhancer

6.102 Calculate the molar mass of each of the following:

a. $Mg(HCO_3)_2$, magnesium hydrogen carbonate

b. $Au(OH)_3$, gold(III) hydroxide, used in gold plating

c. $C_{18}H_{34}O_2$, oleic acid from olive oil

6.103 How many grams are in 0.150 mole of each of the following?

    a. K   **b.** Cl_2 **c.** Na_2CO_3

6.104 How many grams are in 2.25 moles of each of the following?

    a. N_2 **b.** NaBr   **c.** C_6H_{14}

6.105 How many moles are in 25.0 g of each of the following compounds?

    a. CO_2 **b.** $Al(OH)_3$ **c.** $MgCl_2$

6.106 How many moles are in 4.00 g of each of the following compounds?

    a. NH_3 **b.** $Ca(NO_3)_2$ **c.** SO_3

6.107 At a winery, glucose ($C_6H_{12}O_6$) in grapes undergoes fermentation to produce ethanol (C_2H_6O) and carbon dioxide:

$$C_6H_{12}O_6(aq) \longrightarrow 2C_2H_6O(l) + 2CO_2(g)$$
$$\text{Glucose} \qquad\qquad \text{Ethanol}$$

a. How many moles of glucose are required to form 124 g of ethanol?

b. How many grams of ethanol would be formed from the reaction of 0.240 kg of glucose?

6.108 Gasohol is a fuel that contains ethanol (C_2H_6O), which burns in oxygen (O_2) to give carbon dioxide and water.

a. State the reactants and products for this reaction in the form of a balanced equation.

b. How many moles of O_2 are needed to completely react with 4.0 moles of C_2H_6O?

c. If a car produces 88 g of CO_2, how many grams of O_2 are used up in the reaction?

d. If you add 125 g of C_2H_6O to your fuel, how many grams of CO_2 and H_2O can be produced from the ethanol?

6.109 Balance the following equation:

$$NH_3(g) + F_2(g) \longrightarrow N_2F_4(g) + HF(g)$$

a. How many moles of each reactant are needed to produce 4.00 moles of HF?

b. How many grams of F_2 are required to react with 1.50 moles of NH_3?

c. How many grams of N_2F_4 can be produced when 3.40 g of NH_3 reacts?

6.110 When peroxide (H_2O_2) is used in rocket fuels, it produces water, oxygen, and heat:

$$2H_2O_2(l) \longrightarrow 2H_2O(l) + O_2(g)$$

a. If 2.00 g of H_2O_2 releases 5.76 kJ, what is the heat of reaction?

b. How many kilojoules are released when 275 g of peroxide are allowed to react?

6.111 Ethane, C_2H_6, reacts with chlorine to form hexachloroethane and hydrogen chloride:

$$C_2H_6(g) + 6Cl_2(g) \longrightarrow C_2Cl_6(g) + 6HCl(g)$$
$$\text{Ethane}$$

a. How many grams of chlorine gas must react to produce 1.60 moles of hexachloroethane?

b. How many grams of hydrogen chloride are produced from 50.0 g of ethane and excess chlorine gas?

6.112 Propane gas, C_3H_8, a fuel for many barbecues, reacts with oxygen to produce water and carbon dioxide. Propane has a density of 2.02 g/L at room temperature.

$$C_3H_8(g) + 5O_2(g) \longrightarrow 3CO_2(g) + 4H_2O(l)$$
$$\text{Propane}$$

a. How many moles of water form when 5.00 L of propane gas (C_3H_8) completely react?

b. How many grams of CO_2 are produced from 18.5 g of oxygen gas and excess propane?

c. How many grams of H_2O can be produced from the reaction of 8.50×10^{22} molecules of propane gas, C_3H_8?

6.113 Acetylene gas, C_2H_2, burns in oxygen to produce carbon dioxide and water. If 62.0 g of CO_2 are produced when 22.5 g of C_2H_2 react with sufficient oxygen, what is the percent yield for the reaction?

6.114 When 50.0 g of iron(III) oxide reacts with carbon monoxide, 32.8 g of iron is produced. What is the percent yield of the reaction?

$$Fe_2O_3(s) + 3CO(g) \longrightarrow 2Fe(s) + 3CO_2(g)$$

6.115 Pentane gas, C_5H_{12}, reacts with oxygen to produce carbon dioxide and water:

$$C_5H_{12}(g) + 8O_2(g) \longrightarrow 5CO_2(g) + 6H_2O(g)$$
$$\text{Pentane}$$

a. How many grams of pentane must react to produce 4.0 moles of water?

b. How many grams of CO_2 are produced from 32.0 g of oxygen and excess pentane?

c. How many grams of CO_2 are formed if 44.5 g of C_5H_{12} is mixed with 108 g of O_2?

6.116 When nitrogen dioxide (NO_2) from car exhaust combines with water in the air it forms nitric acid (HNO_3), which causes acid rain, and nitrogen oxide.

$$3NO_2(g) + H_2O(l) \longrightarrow 2HNO_3(aq) + NO(g)$$

a. How many molecules of NO_2 are needed to react with 0.250 mole of H_2O?

b. How many grams of HNO_3 are produced when 60.0 g of NO_2 completely reacts?

c. How many grams of HNO_3 can be produced if 225 g of NO_2 is mixed with 55.2 g of H_2O?

6.117 When a mixture of 12.8 g of Na and 10.2 g of Cl_2 reacts, what is the mass of NaCl that is produced?

$$2Na(s) + Cl_2(g) \longrightarrow 2NaCl(s)$$

6.118 If a mixture of 35.8 g of CH_4 and 75.5 g of S reacts, how many grams of H_2S are produced?

$$CH_4(g) + 4S(g) \longrightarrow CS_2(g) + 2H_2S(g)$$

6.119 The formation of nitrogen oxide, NO, from $N_2(g)$ and $O_2(g)$, requires 21.6 kcal of heat:

$$N_2(g) + O_2(g) \longrightarrow 2NO(g) \qquad \Delta H = 21.6 \text{ kcal}$$

a. How many kcal are required to form 3.00 g of NO?

b. What is the complete equation (including heat) for the decomposition of NO?

c. How many kcal are released when 5.00 g of NO decomposes to N_2 and O_2?

6.120 The formation of rust (Fe_2O_3) from solid iron and oxygen gas releases 1.7×10^3 kJ:

$$4Fe(s) + 3O_2(g) \longrightarrow 2Fe_2O_3(s) \; \Delta H = -1.7 \times 10^3 \text{ kJ}$$

a. How many kJ are released when 2.00 g of Fe of react?

b. How many grams of rust form when 150 kcal are released?

CHALLENGE QUESTIONS

6.121 Write a balanced equation for each of the following reaction descriptions and identify each type of reaction:
  a. An aqueous solution of lead(II) nitrate is mixed with aqueous sodium phosphate to produce solid lead(II) phosphate and aqueous sodium nitrate.
  b. Gallium metal heated in oxygen gas forms solid gallium(III) oxide.
  c. When solid sodium nitrate is heated, solid sodium nitrite and oxygen gas are produced.
  d. Solid bismuth(III) oxide and solid carbon react to form bismuth metal and carbon monoxide gas.

6.122 A toothpaste contains 0.24% by mass sodium fluoride (NaF) used to prevent dental caries and 0.30% by mass triclosan, $C_{12}H_7Cl_3O_2$, a preservative and antigingivitis agent. One tube contains 119 g of toothpaste.
  a. How many moles of NaF are in the tube of toothpaste?
  b. How many fluoride ions (F^-) are in the tube of toothpaste?
  c. How many grams of sodium ion (Na^+) are in 1.50 g of toothpaste?
  d. How many molecules of triclosan are in the tube of toothpaste?

6.123 A gold bar is 2.31 cm long, 1.48 cm wide, and 0.0758 cm thick.
  a. If gold has a density of 19.3 g/mL, what is the mass of the gold bar?
  b. How many atoms of gold are in the bar?
  c. When the same mass of gold combines with oxygen, the oxide product has a mass of 5.61 g. How many moles of O are combined with the gold?
  d. What is the formula of the oxide product?

6.124 The gaseous hydrocarbon acetylene, C_2H_2, used in welders' torches, releases a large amount of heat when it burns according to the following equation:

$$2C_2H_2(g) + 5O_2(g) \longrightarrow 4CO_2(g) + 2H_2O(g)$$

  a. How many moles of water are produced from the complete reaction of 64.0 g of oxygen?
  b. How many moles of oxygen are needed to react completely with 2.25×10^{24} molecules of acetylene?

  c. How many grams of carbon dioxide are produced from the complete reaction of 78.0 g of acetylene?
  d. If the reaction in part **c** produces 186 g of CO_2, what is the percent yield for the reaction?

6.125 Acetylene, C_2H_2, used in welders' torches, burns according to the following equation:

$$2C_2H_2(g) + 5O_2(g) \longrightarrow 4CO_2(g) + 2H_2O(g)$$

  a. How many molecules of oxygen are needed to react with 22.0 g of acetylene?
  b. How many grams of carbon dioxide could be produced from the complete reaction of the acetylene in part **a.**?
  c. If the reaction in part **a.** produces 64.0 g of CO_2, what is the percent yield for the reaction?

6.126 Consider the equation for the reaction of sodium and nitrogen to form sodium nitride:

$$Na(s) + N_2(g) \longrightarrow Na_3N(s)$$

  a. Balance the equation.
  b. If 80.0 g of sodium is mixed with 20.0 g of nitrogen gas, what mass of sodium nitride forms?
  c. If the reaction in part **b.** has a percent yield of 75.0%, how much sodium nitride is actually produced?

6.127 Consider the following equation:

$$Al(s) + O_2(g) \longrightarrow Al_2O_3(s)$$

  a. Balance the equation.
  b. Identify the type of reaction.
  c. How many moles of oxygen must react with 4.50 moles of Al?
  d. How many grams of aluminum oxide are produced when 50.2 g of aluminum reacts?
  e. When 0.500 mole of aluminum is reacted in a closed container with 8.00 g of oxygen, how many grams of aluminum oxide can form?
  f. If 45.0 g of aluminum and 62.0 g of oxygen undergo a reaction that has a 70.0% yield, what mass of aluminum oxide forms?

ANSWERS

ANSWERS TO STUDY CHECKS

6.1 $3Fe(s) + 2O_2(g) \longrightarrow Fe_3O_4(s)$

6.2 $2NO(g) + O_2(g) \longrightarrow 2NO_2(g)$ Combination reaction

6.3 Lithium is oxidized: $2Li(s) \longrightarrow 2Li^+(s) + 2e^-(s)$
Fluorine is reduced: $F_2(g) + 2e^- \longrightarrow 2F^-(s)$

6.4 0.432 mole of H_2O

6.5 0.120 mole of aspirin

6.6 138.0 g of salicylic acid

6.7 24.4 g of Au

6.8 0.00621 mole of $CaCO_3$, 0.00550 mole of $MgCO_3$

6.9 0.90 mole of Fe_2S_3

6.10 44.0 g of NO

6.11 27.5 g of CO_2

6.12 84.7%

6.13 13.4 g of SiC

6.14 **a.** endothermic
  b. 10.5 kJ

ANSWERS TO SELECTED QUESTIONS AND PROBLEMS

6.1 **a.** not balanced
  b. balanced
  c. not balanced
  d. balanced

6.3 **a.** $N_2(g) + O_2(g) \longrightarrow 2NO(g)$
  b. $2HgO(s) \longrightarrow 2Hg(l) + O_2(g)$
  c. $4Fe(s) + 3O_2(g) \longrightarrow 2Fe_2O_3(s)$
  d. $2Na(s) + Cl_2(g) \longrightarrow 2NaCl(s)$

6.5 **a.** $Mg(s) + 2AgNO_3(aq) \longrightarrow Mg(NO_3)_2(aq) + 2Ag(s)$
b. $2Al(s) + 3CuSO_4(aq) \longrightarrow 3Cu(s) + Al_2(SO_4)_3(aq)$
c. $Pb(NO_3)_2(aq) + 2NaCl(aq) \longrightarrow PbCl_2(s) + 2NaNO_3(aq)$
d. $2Al(s) + 6HCl(aq) \longrightarrow 2AlCl_3(aq) + 3H_2(g)$

6.7 **a.** A single reactant breaks into two simpler substances (elements).
b. One element in the reacting compound is replaced by the other reactant.

6.9 **a.** combination reaction
b. single replacement reaction
c. decomposition reaction
d. double replacement reaction
e. double replacement reaction

6.11 **a.** $Mg(s) + Cl_2(g) \longrightarrow MgCl_2(s)$
b. $2HBr(g) \longrightarrow H_2(g) + Br_2(g)$
c. $Mg(s) + Zn(NO_3)_2(aq) \longrightarrow Zn(s) + Mg(NO_3)_2(aq)$
d. $K_2S(aq) + Pb(NO_3)_2(aq) \longrightarrow 2KNO_3(aq) + PbS(s)$

6.13 **a.** reduction   **b.** oxidation
c. reduction   **d.** reduction

6.15 **a.** Zn is oxidized; Cl_2 is reduced.
b. Br^- in NaBr is oxidized; Cl_2 is reduced.
c. The O^{2-} in PbO is oxidized; the Pb^{2+} is reduced.
d. Sn^{2+} is oxidized; Fe^{3+} is reduced.

6.17 **a.** reduction
b. oxidation

6.19 Linoleic acid gains hydrogen atoms and is reduced.

6.21 1.00 mole contains 6.02×10^{23} atoms of an element, molecules of a covalent substance, or formula units of an ionic substance.

6.23 **a.** 1.20×10^{23} atoms of Ag
b. 4.52×10^{23} molecules of C_3H_8O
c. 0.478 mole of Au

6.25 **a.** 24 moles of H
b. 1.0×10^2 moles of C
c. 0.040 mole of N

6.27 **a.** 3.01×10^{23} atoms of C
b. 7.71×10^{23} molecules of SO_2
c. 0.0867 mole of Fe
d. 14.1 moles of C_2H_5OH

6.29 **a.** 6.00 moles of H
b. 8.00 moles of O
c. 1.20×10^{24} atoms of P
d. 4.82×10^{24} atoms of O

6.31 **a.** 74.6 g/mole   **b.** 159.8 g/mole
c. 73.8 g/mole   **d.** 342.3 g/mole
e. 58.3 g/mole   **f.** 365.1 g/mole

6.33 **a.** 46.0 g   **b.** 112 g
c. 14.8 g   **d.** 112 g

6.35 **a.** 29.3 g   **b.** 109 g
c. 4.05 g   **d.** 194 g

6.37 **a.** 602 g   **b.** 11 g

6.39 **a.** 0.463 mole   **b.** 0.0167 mole
c. 0.882 mole   **d.** 1.17 moles

6.41 **a.** 0.78 mole of S
b. 1.95 moles of S
c. 6.0 moles of S

6.43 **a.** 1.72×10^{24} atoms of N
b. 1.8×10^{24} atoms of N
c. 2.4×10^{24} atoms of N

6.45 **a.** $\dfrac{2 \text{ moles } SO_2}{1 \text{ mole } O_2}$ and $\dfrac{1 \text{ mole } O_2}{2 \text{ moles } SO_2}$

$\dfrac{2 \text{ moles } SO_2}{2 \text{ moles } SO_3}$ and $\dfrac{2 \text{ moles } SO_3}{2 \text{ moles } SO_2}$

$\dfrac{2 \text{ moles } SO_3}{1 \text{ mole } O_2}$ and $\dfrac{1 \text{ mole } O_2}{2 \text{ moles } SO_3}$

b. $\dfrac{4 \text{ moles } P}{5 \text{ moles } O_2}$ and $\dfrac{5 \text{ moles } O_2}{4 \text{ moles } P}$

$\dfrac{4 \text{ moles } P}{2 \text{ moles } P_2O_5}$ and $\dfrac{2 \text{ moles } P_2O_5}{4 \text{ moles } P}$

$\dfrac{5 \text{ moles } O_2}{2 \text{ moles } P_2O_5}$ and $\dfrac{2 \text{ moles } P_2O_5}{5 \text{ moles } O_2}$

6.47 **a.** 1.0 mole of O_2 **b.** 10. moles of H_2
c. 5.0 moles of H_2O

6.49 **a.** 1.25 moles of C   **b.** 0.96 mole of CO
c. 1.0 mole of SO_2 **d.** 0.50 mole of CS_2

6.51 **a.** 77.5 g of Na_2O **b.** 6.26 g of O_2
c. 19.4 g of O_2

6.53 **a.** 192 g of O_2 **b.** 3.79 g of N_2
c. 54.0 g of H_2O

6.55 **a.** 3.65 g of H_2O **b.** 3.43 g of NO
c. 7.53 g of HNO_3

6.57 **a.** $2PbS(s) + 3O_2(g) \longrightarrow 2PbO(s) + 2SO_2(g)$
b. 6.00 g of O_2
c. 17.4 g of SO_2
d. 137 g of PbS

6.59 **a.** 70.9%   **b.** 63.2%

6.61 70.8 g of Al_2O_3

6.63 60.4%

6.65 **a.** 8 taxis can be used to pick up passengers.
b. 7 taxis can be driven.

6.67 **a.** 5.0 moles of H_2 **b.** 4.0 moles of H_2
c. 3.0 moles of N_2

6.69 **a.** 2.00 moles of SO_3 **b.** 0.500 mole of Fe_3O_4
c. 1.27 moles of CO_2

6.71 **a.** 0.188 mole of $AlCl_3$ **b.** 0.750 mole of H_2O
c. 0.417 mole of SO_2

6.73 **a.** The activation energy is the energy required to break the bonds of the reacting molecules.
b. In exothermic reactions, the energy of the products is lower than the reactants.
c.

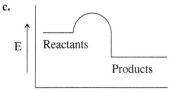

6.75 **a.** exothermic   **b.** endothermic
c. exothermic

6.77 **a.** exothermic $\Delta H = -210$ kcal
b. endothermic $\Delta H = 65.3$ kJ
c. exothermic $\Delta H = -205$ kcal

6.79 138 kcal

6.81 **a.** 1, 1, 2 combination reaction
 b. 2, 2, 1 decomposition reaction

6.83 **a.** $2NO(g) + O_2(g) \longrightarrow 2NO_2(g)$
 b. combination reaction

6.85 **a.** $2NI_3(s) \longrightarrow N_2(g) + 3I_2(g)$
 b. decomposition reaction

6.87 **a.** $2Cl_2(g) + O_2(g) \longrightarrow 2OCl_2(g)$
 b. combination reaction

6.89 (1) **a.** S_2Cl_2 **b.** 135.2 g/mole   **c.** 0.0740 mole
 (2) **a.** C_6H_6 **b.** 78.0 g/mole   **c.** 0.128 mole

6.91 **a.** 252.2 g/mole   **b.** 0.0991 mole
 c. 0.991 mole of C

6.93 **a.** 47.1 g of CuO   **b.** 0.296 mole of O_2

6.95 **a.** $NH_3(g) + HCl(g) \longrightarrow NH_4Cl(s)$ Combination
 b. $Fe_3O_4(s) + 4H_2(g) \longrightarrow 3Fe(s) + 4H_2O(g)$
     Single replacement
 c. $2Sb(s) + 3Cl_2(g)_3(s)$ Combination
 d. $2NI_3(s) \longrightarrow N_2(g) + 3I_2(g)$ Decomposition
 e. $2KBr(aq) + Cl_2(aq) \longrightarrow 2KCl(aq) + Br_2(l)$
     Single replacement
 f. $Al_2(SO_4)_3(aq) + 6NaOH(aq) \longrightarrow$
     $3Na_2SO_4(aq) + 2Al(OH)_3(s)$ Double replacement

6.97 **a.** reduction   **b.** oxidation
 c. oxidation   **d.** reduction

6.99 **a.** 90.0 g/mole
 b. 3.01×10^{23} molecules
 c. 2.71×10^{24} atoms of C
 d. 220 g of lactic acid

6.101 **a.** 152.0 g/mole   **b.** 389.9 g/mole
 c. 169.0 g/mole

6.103 **a.** 5.87 g   **b.** 10.7 g   **c.** 15.9 g

6.105 **a.** 0.568 mole   **b.** 0.321 mole
 c. 0.262 mole

6.107 **a.** 1.35 moles of glucose
 b. 123 g of ethanol

6.109 $2NH_3(g) + 5F_2(g) \longrightarrow N_2F_4(g) + 6HF(g)$
 a. 1.33 moles of NH_3 and 3.33 moles of F_2
 b. 143 g of F_2
 c. 10.4 g of N_2F_4

6.111 **a.** 682 g of Cl_2
 b. 365 g of HCl

6.113 81.4%

6.115 **a.** 48 g of C_5H_{12}
 b. 27.5 g of CO_2
 c. 92.8 g of CO_2

6.117 16.8 g of NaCl

6.119 **a.** 1.08 kcal
 b. $2NO(g) \longrightarrow N_2(g) + O_2(g) + 21.6$ kcal
 c. 1.80 kcal

6.121 **a.** $3Pb(NO_3)_2(aq) + 2Na_3PO_4(aq) \longrightarrow$
      $Pb_3(PO_4)_2(s) + 6NaNO_3(aq)$ Double replacement
 b. $4Ga(s) + 3O_2(g) \longrightarrow 2Ga_2O_3(s)$ Combination
 c. $2NaNO_3(s) \longrightarrow 2NaNO_2(s) + O_2(g)$
      Decomposition
 d. $Bi_2O_3(s) + 3C(s) \longrightarrow 2Bi(s) + 3CO(g)$
      Single replacement

6.123 **a.** 5.00 g of gold
 b. 1.53×10^{22} Au atoms
 c. 0.038 mole of oxygen
 d. Au_2O_3

6.125 **a.** 1.27×10^{24} molecules of O_2
 b. 74.5 g of CO_2
 c. 85.9% yield

6.127 **a.** $4Al(s) + 3O_2(g) \longrightarrow 2Al_2O_3(s)$
 b. This is a combination reaction.
 c. 3.38 moles of oxygen
 d. 94.8 g of aluminum oxide
 e. 17.0 g of aluminum oxide
 f. 59.5 g of aluminum oxide

COMBINING IDEAS FROM CHAPTERS 3 TO 6

CI.7 Some of the isotopes of silicon are listed in the following table:

Isotope	% Natural Abundance	Atomic Mass	Half-Life	Radiation Emitted
$^{27}_{14}Si$		26.99	4.2 s	Positron
$^{28}_{14}Si$	92.23	27.99	Stable	None
$^{29}_{14}Si$	4.67	28.99	Stable	None
$^{30}_{14}Si$	3.10	29.98	Stable	None
$^{31}_{14}Si$		30.99	2.6 h	Beta

a. In the following table, indicate the number of protons, neutrons, and electrons for each isotope listed:

Isotope	Number of Protons	Number of Neutrons	Number of Electrons
$^{27}_{14}Si$			
$^{28}_{14}Si$			
$^{29}_{14}Si$			
$^{30}_{14}Si$			
$^{31}_{14}Si$			

b. What is the electron configuration of silicon?
c. Calculate the atomic mass for silicon using the isotopes that have a natural abundance.
d. Write the nuclear equations for $^{27}_{14}Si$ and $^{31}_{14}Si$.
e. Write the electron-dot formula and predict the shape of $SiCl_4$.
f. How many hours are needed for a sample of $^{31}_{14}Si$ with an activity of 16 μCi to decay to 2.0 μCi?

CI.8 K^+ is an electrolyte required by the human body and is found in many foods as well as salt substitutes. One of the isotopes of potassium is $^{40}_{19}K$ which has a natural abundance of 0.012% and a half-life of 1.30×10^9 years. The isotope $^{40}_{19}K$ decays to $^{40}_{20}Ca$ or to $^{40}_{18}Ar$. A typical activity for $^{40}_{19}K$ is 7.0 μCi per gram.

a. Write a nuclear equation for each type of decay.
b. Identify the particle emitted for each type of decay.
c. How many K^+ ions are in 3.5 oz of KCl?
d. What is the activity of 25 g of KCl, in becquerels?

CI.9 Of much concern to environmentalists is the radioactive noble gas radon-222, which can seep from the ground into basements of homes and buildings. Radon-222 is a product of the decay of radium-226 that occurs naturally in rocks and soil in much of the United States. Radon-222, which has a half-life of 3.8 days, decays by emitting an alpha particle. Radon-222, which is a gas, can be inhaled; because of that, it is strongly associated with lung cancer. Radon levels in a home can be measured with a home radon-detection kit. Environmental agencies have set the maximum level of radon-222 in a home at 4 picocuries per liter (pCi/L) of air in a home.

a. Write the equation for the decay of Ra-226.
b. Write the equation for the decay of Rn-222.
c. If a room contains 24 000 atoms of radon-222, how many atoms of radon-222 remain after 15.2 days?
d. Suppose a room in a home has a volume of 72 000 liters (7.2×10^4 L). If the radon level is 2.5 picocuries/liter, how many alpha particles are emitted in one day? (1 Ci $= 3.7 \times 10^{10}$ disintegrations per second.)

CI.10 A gold bar has a volume of 728 cm^3 and a density of 19.3 g/cm^3.
a. What is the mass in kilograms of the gold bar?
b. How many atoms of gold are in the bar?
c. Give the number of protons and neutrons in each of the following isotopes of gold:
$^{185}_{79}Au \quad ^{197}_{79}Au \quad ^{198}_{79}Au$

CI.11 The following reaction occurs between a metal in Group 1A (1) or Group 2A (2) and a nonmetal:

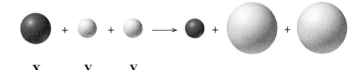

X Y Y

a. Which spheres represent a metal? A nonmetal?
b. Which reactant has the higher electronegativity?
c. What are the ionic charges of X and Y in the product?
d. If these elements are both in period 3:
   1. Write the electron configurations of the atoms.
   2. Write the electron configurations of their ions.
   3. Give the names of the noble gases with the same electron configurations as these ions.
   4. Write the formula and name of the product.
e. Match the spheres below with atoms of Li, Na, K, and Rb.

A.   B.   C.   D.

CI.12 The active ingredient in Tums is calcium carbonate. One Tums tablet contains 500. mg of calcium carbonate.

a. What is the formula for calcium carbonate?
b. What is the molar mass of calcium carbonate?
c. How many moles of calcium carbonate are in one roll of Tums that contains 12 tablets?
d. If a person takes two Tums tablets a day, how many grams of calcium are obtained?
e. If the daily recommended quantity of Ca^{2+} to maintain bone strength in older women is 1500 mg, how many Tums tablets are needed each day?

CI.13 Ethanol, C_2H_5OH, is obtained from renewable crops such as corn, which use the sun as their source of energy. In the United States, automobiles can now use a fuel known as E10 that contains 10.0% ethanol and 90.0% unleaded gasoline by volume (%v/v). Ethanol has a melting point of -115 °C, a boiling point of 78 °C, a heat of fusion of 23.6 cal/g, and a heat of vaporization of 201 cal/g. Liquid ethanol has a density of 0.796 g/mL and a specific heat of 0.588 cal/g °C.

a. Draw a heating curve for ethanol from -150 °C to 100 °C.

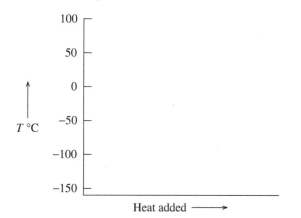

T °C

Heat added ⟶

b. When 20.0 g of ethanol at -55 °C is heated to 37 °C, how much energy, in calories, is required?
c. How many kilojoules are needed to vaporize 1.00 L of ethanol at 78 °C?
d. If a 15-gallon gas tank is filled with E10, how many liters of ethanol are in the gas tank?
e. Write the balanced chemical equation for the reaction of ethanol with oxygen gas to produce carbon dioxide and water vapor.
f. How many kilograms of carbon dioxide, CO_2, are produced from the complete reaction of the ethanol in a full 15-gallon gas tank?

CI.14 Butyric acid contributes to the characteristic odor of Parmesan cheese.

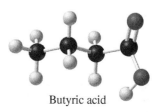

Butyric acid

a. If black spheres are carbon atoms, light blue spheres are hydrogen atoms, and red spheres are oxygen atoms, what is the formula of butyric acid?
b. What is the molar mass of butyric acid?
c. How many grams of butyric acid contain 3.28×10^{23} oxygen atoms?
d. How many grams of carbon are in 5.28 g of butyric acid?
e. If butyric acid has a density of 0.959 g/mL at 20 °C, how many moles of butyric acid are in 1.56 mL of butyric acid?
f. Write a balanced equation for the reaction of butyric acid with oxygen gas to form carbon dioxide and water.
g. How many grams of oxygen are needed to completely react 1.58 g of butyric acid?
h. What mass of carbon dioxide is formed when 100. g of butyric acid and 100. g of oxygen react?

CI.15 Oseltamivir, $C_{16}H_{28}N_2O_4$, is the active ingredient in Tamiflu, an antiviral drug used to treat influenza. The preparation of oseltamivir begins with the extraction of shikimic acid from the seedpods of the spice Chinese star anise. From 2.6 g of star anise, 0.13 g of shikimic acid can be obtained and used to produce one Tamiflu capsule containing 75 mg of oseltamivir. The usual adult dosage for treatment of influenza is two capsules of Tamiflu twice daily for 5 days.

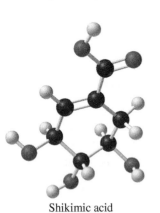

Shikimic acid

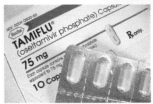

a. What is the formula of shikimic acid? (Black spheres are carbon, light blue spheres are hydrogen, and red spheres are oxygen.)

b. What is the molar mass of shikimic acid?

c. How many moles of shikimic acid are contained in 1.3 g of shikimic acid?

d. How many capsules of Tamiflu could be produced from 154 g of star anise?

e. What is the molar mass of oseltamivir?

f. How many grams of carbon are in 75 mg of oseltamivir?

g. How many kilograms of oseltamivir would be needed to treat all the people in a city with a population of 500 000 people if each person takes 2 Tamiflu capsules a day for 5 days?

CI.16 When clothes have stains, bleach is often added to the wash to react with the soil and make the stains colorless. One brand of bleach contains 5.25% sodium hypochlorite by mass (active ingredient) with a density of 1.08 g/mL. The liquid bleach solution is prepared by bubbling chlorine gas into a solution of sodium hydroxide to produce sodium hypochlorite, sodium chloride, and water.

a. What is the formula and molar mass of sodium hypochlorite?

b. How many hypochlorite ions are present in 1 gallon of bleach solution?

c. Write the equation for the preparation of bleach.

d. How many grams of NaOH are required to produce the mass of sodium hypochlorite in 1 gallon of bleach?

e. If 165 g of Cl_2 is passed through a solution containing 275 g of NaOH and 162 g of sodium hypochlorite is produced, what is the percent yield for the reaction?

■ ANSWERS

CI.7 a.

Isotope	Number of Protons	Number of Neutrons	Number of Electrons
$^{27}_{14}Si$	14	13	14
$^{28}_{14}Si$	14	14	14
$^{29}_{14}Si$	14	15	14
$^{30}_{14}Si$	14	16	14
$^{31}_{14}Si$	14	17	14

b. $1s^2 2s^2 2p^6 3s^2 3p^2$

c. Atomic mass calculated from the three stable isotopes is 28.10 amu.

d. $^{27}_{14}Si \longrightarrow ^{27}_{13}Al + ^{0}_{+1}e$ and $^{31}_{14}Si \longrightarrow ^{31}_{15}P + ^{0}_{-1}e$

e.

$$:\ddot{C}l:$$
$$|$$
$$:\ddot{C}l—Si—\ddot{C}l: \quad \text{Tetrahedral}$$
$$|$$
$$:\ddot{C}l:$$

f. 7.8 h

CI.9 a. $^{226}_{88}Ra \longrightarrow ^{222}_{86}Rn + ^{4}_{2}He$ **b.** $^{222}_{86}Rn \longrightarrow ^{218}_{84}Po + ^{4}_{2}He$

c. 1500 atoms of radon-222 remain

d. 5.8×10^8 alpha particles

CI.11 a. X is a metal; Y is a nonmetal.

b. Y has the higher electronegativity.

c. X^{2+}, Y^-

d. 1. $X = 1s^2 2s^2 2p^6 3s^2$ $Y = 1s^2 2s^2 2p^6 3s^2 3p^5$

2. $X^{2+} = 1s^2 2s^2 2p^6$ $Y^- = 1s^2 2s^2 2p^6 3s^2 3p^6$

3. X^{2+} has the same electron configuration as Ne. Y^- has the same electron configuration as Ar.

4. $MgCl_2$, magnesium chloride

e. Li is D, Na is A, K is C, and Rb is B.

CI.13 a.

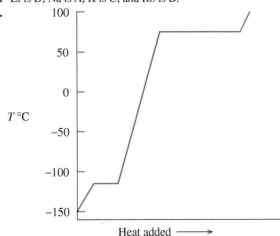

b. 1100 cal   **c.** 669 kJ   **d.** 57 L

e. $C_2H_5OH(l) + 3O_2(g) \longrightarrow 2CO_2(g) + 3H_2O(g)$

f. 86 kg of CO_2

CI.15 a. $C_7H_{10}O_5$ **b.** 174 g/mole   **c.** 0.0075 mole

d. 59 capsules   **e.** 312.0 g/mole   **f.** 0.046 g of carbon

g. 380 kg

Gases

7

"When oxygen levels in the blood are low, the cells in the body don't get enough oxygen," says Sunanda Tripathi, registered nurse, Santa Clara Valley Medical Center. "We use an oxygen mask to give supplemental oxygen to a patient. At a flow rate of 2 liters per minute, a patient breathes in a gaseous mixture that is about 28% oxygen, compared to 21% in ambient air."

When a patient has a breathing disorder, the flow and volume of oxygen into and out of the lungs are measured. A ventilator may be used if a patient has difficulty breathing. When the pressure is increased, the lungs expand. When the pressure of the incoming gas is reduced, the lung volume contracts to expel carbon dioxide. These relationships—known as gas laws—are an important part of ventilation and breathing.

Visit **www.masteringchemistry.com** for self-study materials and instructor-assigned homework.

We all live at the bottom of a sea of gases called the atmosphere. The most important of these gases is oxygen, which constitutes about 21% of the atmosphere. Without oxygen, life on this planet would be impossible—oxygen is vital to all life processes of plants and animals. Ozone (O_3), formed in the upper atmosphere by the interaction of oxygen with ultraviolet light, absorbs some of the harmful radiation before it can strike Earth's surface. The other gases in the atmosphere include nitrogen (78%), argon, carbon dioxide (CO_2), and water vapor. Carbon dioxide gas, a product of combustion and metabolism, is used by plants in photosynthesis, a process that produces the oxygen that is essential for humans and animals.

The atmosphere has become a dumping ground for other gases, such as methane, chlorofluorocarbons (CFCs), and nitrogen oxides, as well as volatile organic compounds (VOCs), which are gases from paints, paint thinners, and cleaning supplies. The chemical reactions of these gases with sunlight and oxygen in the air are contributing to air pollution, ozone depletion, global warming, and acid rain. Such chemical changes can seriously affect our health and our lifestyle. An understanding of gases and the laws that govern gas behavior can help us understand the nature of matter and allow us to make decisions concerning important environmental and health issues.

7.1 Properties of Gases

LEARNING GOAL

Describe the kinetic molecular theory of gases and the properties of gases.

 SELF STUDY ACTIVITY
Properties of Gases

The behavior of gases is quite different from that of liquids and solids. Gas particles are far apart, whereas particles of both liquids and solids are held close together because strong attractive forces become more important at lower temperatures. This means that a gas has no definite shape or volume and will completely fill any container. Because there are great distances between its particles, a gas is less dense than a solid or liquid and can be compressed. A model for the behavior of a gas, called the **kinetic molecular theory of gases**, helps us understand gas behavior.

Kinetic Molecular Theory of Gases

1. **A gas consists of small particles (atoms or molecules) that move randomly with rapid velocities.** Gas molecules moving in all directions at high speeds cause a gas to fill the entire volume of a container.

2. **The attractive forces between the particles of a gas can be neglected.** Gas particles are far apart and fill a container of any size and shape.

3. **The actual volume occupied by gas molecules is extremely small compared to the volume that the gas occupies.** The volume of the container is considered equal to the volume of the gas. Most of the volume of a gas is empty space, which allows gases to be easily compressed.

4. **Gas particles are in constant motion, moving rapidly in straight paths.** When gas particles collide, they rebound and travel in new directions. Every time they hit the walls of the container, they exert pressure. An increase in the number or force of collisions against the walls of the container causes an increase in the pressure of the gas.

5. **The average kinetic energy of gas molecules is proportional to the Kelvin temperature.** Gas particles move faster as the temperature increases. At higher temperatures, gas particles hit the walls of the container with more force, producing higher pressures.

The kinetic molecular theory helps explain some of the characteristics of gases. For example, we can quickly smell perfume from a bottle that is opened on the other side of a room because its particles move rapidly in all directions. At room temperatures, the molecules of air are moving at about 1000 miles per hour. They move faster at higher temperatures and more slowly at lower temperatures. Sometimes tires and gas-filled containers explode when temperatures are too high. From the kinetic molecular theory, we know that gas particles move faster when heated, hit the walls of a container with more force, and cause a buildup of pressure inside a container.

When we talk about a gas, we describe it in terms of four properties: pressure, volume, temperature, and the amount of gas.

Pressure (P) Gas particles are extremely small and move rapidly. When they hit the walls of a container, they exert a force known as *pressure*. (See Figure 7.1.) If we heat the container, the molecules move faster and smash into the walls more often and with increased force, thus increasing the pressure. The gas particles in the air, mostly oxygen and nitrogen, exert a pressure on us called **atmospheric pressure**. (See Figure 7.2.) As altitude increases, the atmospheric pressure decreases because there are fewer particles in the air. The most common units used for gas measurement are *atmospheres* (atm) and *millimeters of mercury* (mmHg). On the TV weather report, you may hear or see the atmospheric pressure given in inches of mercury or, in countries other than the United States, kilopascals. In a chemistry lab, the unit *torr* may be used.

Volume (V) The volume of gas equals the size of the container in which the gas is placed. When you inflate a tire or a basketball, you are adding more gas particles. The increase in the number of particles hitting the walls of the tire or basketball increases the volume. Sometimes, on a cool morning, a tire looks flat. The volume of the tire has decreased because a lower temperature decreases the speed of the molecules, which in turn reduces the force of their impacts on the walls of the tire. The most common units for volume measurement are liters (L) and milliliters (mL).

Temperature (T) The temperature of a gas is related to the kinetic energy of its particles. For example, if we have a gas at 200 K in a rigid container and heat it to a temperature of 400 K, the gas particles will have twice the kinetic energy that they did at 200 K.

FIGURE 7.1 Gas particles move in straight lines within a container. The gas particles exert pressure when they collide with the walls of the container.

Q Why does heating the container increase the pressure of the gas within it?

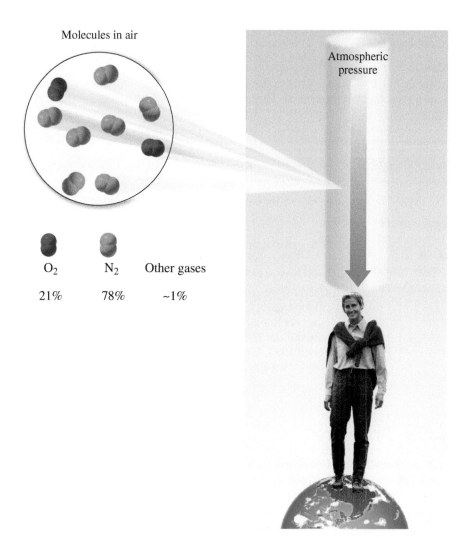

Molecules in air

O$_2$ N$_2$ Other gases

21% 78% ~1%

Atmospheric pressure

FIGURE 7.2 A column of air extending from the upper atmosphere to the surface of the Earth produces a pressure on each of us of about 1 atmosphere. While there is a lot of pressure on the body, it is balanced by the pressure inside the body.

Q Why is there less pressure at higher altitudes?

This also means that the gas at 400 K exerts twice the pressure of the gas at 200 K. Although you measure gas temperature using a Celsius thermometer, all comparisons of gas behavior and all calculations related to temperature must use the Kelvin temperature scale. No one has yet achieved the conditions for absolute zero (0 K), but we predict that the particles will have zero kinetic energy and exert zero pressure at absolute zero.

Amount of Gas (n) When you add air to a bicycle tire, you increase the amount of gas, which results in a higher pressure in the tire. Usually we measure the amount of gas by its mass (grams). In gas law calculations, we need to change the grams of gas to moles.

A summary of the four properties of a gas is given in Table 7.1.

EXPLORE YOUR WORLD

Forming a Gas

Obtain baking soda and a jar or a plastic bottle. You will also need an elastic glove that fits over the mouth of the jar or a balloon that fits snugly over the top of the plastic bottle. Place a cup of vinegar in the jar or bottle. Sprinkle some baking soda into the fingertips of the glove or into the balloon. Carefully fit the glove or balloon over the top of the jar or bottle. Slowly lift the fingers of the glove or the balloon so that the baking soda falls into the vinegar. Watch what happens. Squeeze the glove or balloon.

QUESTION

1. Describe the properties of gas that you observe as the reaction takes place between vinegar and baking soda.
2. How do you know that a gas was formed?

TABLE 7.1 Properties That Describe a Gas

Property	Description	Unit(s) of Measurement
Pressure (P)	The force exerted by gas against the walls of the container	atmosphere (atm); millimeters of mercury (mmHg); torr; pascal (Pa)
Volume (V)	The space occupied by the gas	liter (L); milliliter (mL); cubic meter (m^3)
Temperature (T)	Determines the kinetic energy and rate of motion of the gas particles	Celsius (°C); kelvin (K) *is required in calculations*
Amount (n)	The quantity of gas present in a container	grams (g); moles (n) *is required in calculations*

CONCEPT CHECK 7.1

■ **Properties of Gases**

Use the kinetic molecular theory to explain why a gas completely fills a container of any size and shape.

ANSWER
Gas particles move at high speeds in all directions, moving as far apart as possible until they hit the walls of a container. Thus, they completely fill a container of any size and shape.

QUESTIONS AND PROBLEMS

Properties of Gases

7.1 Use the kinetic molecular theory of gases to explain each of the following:
   a. Gas particles move faster at higher temperatures.
   b. Gases can be compressed much more than liquids or solids.

7.2 Use the kinetic molecular theory of gases to explain each of the following:
   a. A container of nonstick cooking spray explodes when thrown into a fire.
   b. The air in a hot-air balloon is heated to make the balloon rise.

7.3 Identify the property of a gas that is measured in each of the following:
   a. 350 K
   b. space occupied by a gas
   c. 2.00 g of O_2
   d. force of gas particles striking the walls of the container

7.4 Identify the property of a gas that is measured in each of the following:
   a. 425 K
   b. 1.0 atm
   c. 10.0 L
   d. 0.50 mole of He

7.2 Gas Pressure

LEARNING GOAL
Describe the units of measurement used for pressure, and change from one unit to another.

When billions and billions of gas particles hit against the walls of a container, they exert **pressure**, which is defined as a force acting on a certain area.

$$\text{Pressure } (P) = \frac{\text{force}}{\text{area}}$$

The *atmospheric pressure* can be measured using a barometer. (See Figure 7.3.) At a pressure of *exactly* 1 atmosphere (atm), the mercury column would be *exactly* 760 mm high. One **atmosphere (atm)** is defined as *exactly* 760 mmHg (millimeters of mercury). One atmosphere is also 760 *torr*, a pressure unit named to honor Evangelista Torricelli, the inventor of the barometer. Because they are equal, units of torr and mmHg are used interchangeably.

1 atm = 760 mmHg = 760 torr (exact)

1 mmHg = 1 torr (exact)

In SI units, pressure is measured in pascals (Pa); 1 atm is equal to 101 325 Pa. Because a pascal is a very small unit, pressures can be reported in kilopascals.

1 atm = 101 325 Pa = 101.325 kPa

The U.S. equivalent of 1 atm is 14.7 pounds per square inch (psi). When you use a pressure gauge to check the air pressure in the tires of a car, it may read 30–35 psi. This measurement is actually 30–35 psi above the pressure that the atmosphere exerts on the outside of the tire. Table 7.2 summarizes the various units used in the measurement of pressure.

TABLE 7.2 Units for Measuring Pressure

Unit	Abbreviation	Unit Equivalent to 1 atm
Atmosphere	atm	1 atm (exact)
Millimeters of Hg	mmHg	760 mmHg (exact)
Torr	torr	760 torr (exact)
Inches of Hg	in. Hg	29.9 in. Hg
Pounds per square inch	lb/in.^{2} (psi)	14.7 lb/in.^{2}
Pascal	Pa	101 325 Pa
Kilopascal	kPa	101.325 kPa

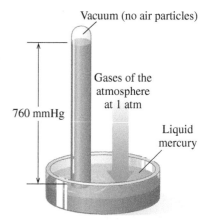

FIGURE 7.3 A barometer: The pressure exerted by the gases in the atmosphere is equal to the downward pressure of a mercury column in a closed glass tube. The height of the mercury column measured in mmHg is called atmospheric pressure.

Q Why does the height of the mercury column change from day to day?

(MC) TUTORIAL
Converting Between
Units of Pressure

(MC) CASE STUDY
Scuba Diving and Blood Gases

If you have a barometer in your home, it probably measures pressure in inches of mercury. Atmospheric pressure changes with variations in weather and altitude. On a hot, sunny day, a column of air has more particles, which increases the pressure on the surface of the mercury. The mercury column rises, indicating a higher atmospheric pressure. On a rainy day, the atmosphere exerts less pressure, which causes the mercury column to fall. In meteorological terms, this type of weather is called a *low-pressure system*. Above sea level, the density of the gases in the air decreases, which causes lower atmospheric pressures; the atmospheric pressure is greater than 760 mmHg at the Dead Sea because it is below sea level. (See Table 7.3.)

Divers must be concerned about increasing pressures on their ears and lungs when they dive below the surface of the ocean. Because water is more dense than air, the pressure on a diver increases rapidly as the diver descends. At a depth of 33 ft below the surface of the ocean, an additional 1 atmosphere of pressure is exerted by the water on a diver, for a total of 2 atm. At 100 ft down, there is a total pressure of 4 atm on a diver. The air tanks a diver carries continuously adjust the pressure of the breathing mixture to match the increase in pressure.

TABLE 7.3 Altitude and Atmospheric Pressure

Location	Altitude (km)	Atmospheric Pressure (mmHg)
Dead Sea	−0.40	800
Sea level	0	760
Los Angeles	0.09	752
Las Vegas	0.70	700
Denver	1.60	630
Mount Whitney	4.50	440
Mount Everest	8.90	253

$P = 0.70$ atm

$P = 1.0$ atm

Sea level

■ **Units of Pressure**

A sample of neon gas has a pressure of 0.50 atm. Give the pressure of the neon in mmHg.

SOLUTION

The equality 1 atm = 760 mmHg can be written as conversion factors:

$$\frac{760 \text{ mmHg}}{1 \text{ atm}} \quad \text{and} \quad \frac{1 \text{ atm}}{760 \text{ mmHg}}$$

Using the appropriate conversion factor, the problem is set up as

$$0.50 \text{ atm} \times \frac{760 \text{ mmHg}}{1 \text{ atm}} = 380 \text{ mmHg}$$

STUDY CHECK

What is the pressure, in atmospheres, for a gas that has a pressure of 655 torr?

HEALTH NOTE

Measuring Blood Pressure

Your blood pressure is one of the vital signs a doctor or nurse checks during a physical examination. It actually consists of two separate measurements. Acting as a pump, the heart contracts to create the pressure that pushes blood through the circulatory system. During contraction, the blood pressure is at its highest; this is your *systolic* pressure. When the heart muscles relax, the blood pressure falls; this is your *diastolic* pressure. The normal range for systolic pressure is 100–120 mmHg. For diastolic pressure, it is 60–80 mmHg. These two measurements are usually expressed as a ratio such as 100/80. These values are somewhat higher in older people. When blood pressures are elevated, say, 140/90, there is a greater risk of stroke, heart attack, or kidney damage. Low blood pressure prevents the brain from receiving adequate oxygen, causing dizziness and fainting.

The blood pressures are measured by a sphygmomanometer, an instrument consisting of a stethoscope and an inflatable cuff connected to a tube of mercury called a manometer. After the cuff is wrapped around the upper arm, it is pumped up with air until it cuts off the flow of blood through the arm. With the stethoscope over the artery, the air is slowly released from the cuff. When the pressure equals the systolic pressure, blood starts to flow again, and the noise it makes is heard through the stethoscope. As air continues to be released, the cuff deflates until no sound is heard in the artery.

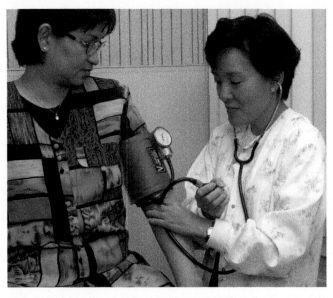

That second pressure reading is noted as the diastolic pressure, the pressure when the heart is not contracting.

The use of digital blood pressure monitors is becoming more common. However, they have not been validated for use in all situations and can sometimes give inaccurate readings.

QUESTIONS AND PROBLEMS

Gas Pressure

7.5 What units are used to measure the pressure of a gas?

7.6 Which of the following statement(s) describes the pressure of a gas?
   a. the force of the gas particles on the walls of the container
   b. the number of gas particles in a container
   c. the volume of the container
   d. 3.00 atm   **e.** 750 torr

7.7 An oxygen tank contains oxygen (O_2) at a pressure of 2.00 atm. What is the pressure in the tank in terms of the following units?
   a. torr   **b.** mmHg

7.8 On a climb up Mt. Whitney, the atmospheric pressure is 467 mmHg. What is the pressure in terms of the following units?
   a. atm   **b.** torr

7.3 Pressure and Volume (Boyle's Law)

LEARNING GOAL

Use the pressure–volume relationship (Boyle's law) to determine the new pressure or volume of a certain amount of gas at a constant temperature.

Imagine that you can see air particles hitting the walls inside a bicycle tire pump. What happens to the pressure inside the pump as you push down on the handle? As the volume decreases, there is a decrease in the surface area of the container. The air particles are crowded together, more collisions occur, and the pressure increases within the container.

When a change in one property (in this case, volume) causes a change in another property (in this case, pressure), the two properties are related. If the changes occur in opposite directions, the properties have an **inverse relationship**. The inverse relationship between the pressure and volume of a gas is known as **Boyle's law**. The law states that the volume (V) of a sample of gas changes inversely with the pressure (P) of the gas as long as there has been no change in the temperature (T) or amount of gas (n), as illustrated in Figure 7.4.

If the volume or pressure of a gas sample changes without any change in the temperature or in the amount of the gas, then the new pressure and volume will give the same PV product as the initial pressure and volume. Therefore, we can set the initial and final PV products equal to each other.

Boyle's Law

$$P_1V_1 = P_2V_2 \quad \text{No change in number of moles and temperature}$$

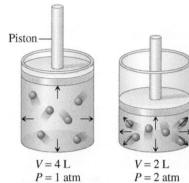

$$V = 4 \text{ L} \qquad V = 2 \text{ L}$$
$$P = 1 \text{ atm} \qquad P = 2 \text{ atm}$$

FIGURE 7.4 Boyle's law: As volume decreases, gas molecules become more crowded, which causes the pressure to increase. Pressure (P) and volume (V) are inversely related.

Q If the volume of a gas increases, what will happen to its pressure?

CONCEPT CHECK 7.2

■ **Boyle's Law**

State and explain the reason for the change (*increases, decreases*) in a gas that occurs for the following when n and T do not change:

	Pressure	Volume
a.		Decreases
b.	Decreases	

ANSWER

a. Increases. When the volume of a gas decreases (at constant n and T), the gas particles are closer together, which increases the number of collisions with the container walls.
b. Increases. When the pressure of a gas decreases (at constant n and T), there are fewer collisions with the container walls, which indicates that the volume has increased.

SAMPLE PROBLEM   7.2

■ **Calculating Pressure When Volume Changes**

A sample of hydrogen gas (H_2) has a volume of 5.0 L and a pressure of 1.0 atm. What is the new pressure if the volume is decreased to 2.0 L at constant temperature?

TUTORIAL
Pressure and Volume

SOLUTION

STEP 1   **Organize the data in a table.**   In this problem, we want to know the final pressure (P_2) for the change in volume. In calculations with gas laws, it is helpful to organize the data in a table. Because we know that the volume decreases, we can predict that the pressure will increase.

Conditions 1	Conditions 2	Know	Predict
$V_1 = 5.0 \text{ L}$	$V_2 = 2.0 \text{ L}$	V decreases	
$P_1 = 1.0 \text{ atm}$	$P_2 = ?$		P increases

Guide to Using the Gas Laws

STEP 1
Organize the data in a table of initial and final conditions.

STEP 2
Rearrange the gas law to solve for the unknown quantity.

STEP 3
Substitute values into the gas law equation to solve for the unknown.

STEP 2   **Rearrange the gas law for the unknown.**   For a PV relationship, we use Boyle's law and solve for P_2 by dividing both sides by V_2:

$$P_1V_1 = P_2V_2$$

$$\frac{P_1V_1}{V_2} = \frac{P_2\cancel{V_2}}{\cancel{V_2}}$$

$$P_2 = P_1 \times \frac{V_1}{V_2}$$

STEP 3   **Substitute values into the gas law to solve for the unknown.**   When we substitute in the values, we see that the ratio of the volumes (volume factor) is greater than 1, which increases the pressure. The final pressure (P_2) has increased as we predicted in Step 1. Note that the units of volume (L) cancel to give the final pressure in atmospheres.

$$P_2 = 1.0 \text{ atm} \times \frac{5.0 \, L}{2.0 \, L} = 2.5 \text{ atm}$$

Volume factor increases pressure

STUDY CHECK

A sample of helium gas has a volume of 150 mL at 750 torr. If the volume expands to 450 mL at constant temperature, what is the new pressure in torr?

■ Calculating Volume When Pressure Changes

The gauge on a 12-L tank of compressed oxygen reads 3800 mmHg. How many liters would this same gas occupy at a pressure of 0.75 atm at constant temperature?

SOLUTION

STEP 1   **Organize the data in a table.**   To match the units for pressure, we can convert atm to mmHg, or mmHg to atm.

$$0.75 \text{ atm} \times \frac{760 \text{ mmHg}}{1 \text{ atm}} = 570 \text{ mmHg}$$

$$3800 \text{ mmHg} \times \frac{1 \text{ atm}}{1 \text{ mmHg}} = 5.0 \text{ atm}$$

Placing our information using units of mmHg for pressure in a table, we know that pressure decreases. We can predict that the volume should increase. (We could have both pressures in units of atm as well.)

Conditions 1	Conditions 2	Know	Predict
$P_1 = 3800$ mmHg	$P_2 = 570$ mmHg	P decreases	
$V_1 = 12$ L	$V_2 = ?$		V increases

STEP 2   **Rearrange the gas law for the unknown.**   Using Boyle's law, we solve for V_2. According to Boyle's law, a decrease in the pressure will cause an increase in the volume.

$$P_1V_1 = P_2V_2$$

$$\frac{P_1V_1}{P_2} = \frac{P_2V_2}{P_2}$$

$$V_2 = V_1 \times \frac{P_1}{P_2}$$

STEP 3   **Substitute values into the gas law to solve for the unknown.**   When we substitute in the values with pressures in units of mmHg or atm, the ratio of pressures (pressure factor) is greater than 1, which increases the volume.

$$V_2 = 12 \text{ L} \times \frac{3800 \text{ mmHg}}{570 \text{ mmHg}} = 80. \text{ L}$$

Pressure factor increases volume

Or:

$$V_2 = 12 \text{ L} \times \frac{5.0 \text{ atm}}{0.75 \text{ atm}} = 80. \text{ L}$$

Pressure factor increases volume

STUDY CHECK

A sample of methane gas (CH_4) has a volume of 125 mL at 0.600 atm pressure. How many milliliters will it occupy at a pressure of 1.50 atm at constant temperature?

HEALTH NOTE

Pressure–Volume Relationship in Breathing

The importance of Boyle's law becomes more apparent when you consider the mechanics of breathing. Our lungs are elastic, balloonlike structures contained within an airtight chamber called the thoracic cavity. The diaphragm, a muscle, forms the flexible floor of the cavity.

Inspiration

The process of taking a breath of air begins when the diaphragm contracts and the rib cage expands, causing an increase in the volume of the thoracic cavity. The elasticity of the lungs allows them to expand when the thoracic cavity expands. According to Boyle's law, the pressure inside the lungs will decrease when their volume increases, causing the pressure inside the lungs to fall below the pressure of the atmosphere. This difference in pressures produces a *pressure gradient* between the lungs and the atmosphere. In a pressure gradient, molecules flow from an area of greater pressure to an area of lower pressure. Thus, we inhale as air flows into the lungs (*inspiration*), until the pressure within the lungs becomes equal to the pressure of the atmosphere.

Expiration

Expiration, or the exhalation phase of breathing, occurs when the diaphragm relaxes and moves back up into the thoracic cavity

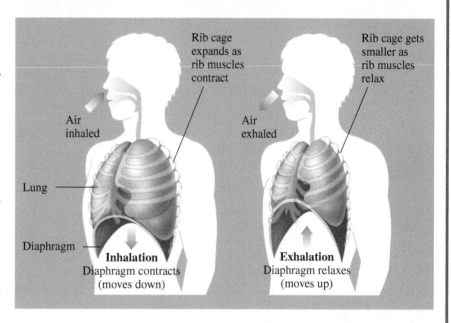

to its resting position. This reduces the volume of the thoracic cavity, which squeezes the lungs and decreases their volume. Now the pressure in the lungs is greater than the pressure of the atmosphere, so air flows out of the lungs. Thus, breathing is a process in which pressure gradients are continuously created between the lungs and the environment because of the changes in the volume.

QUESTIONS AND PROBLEMS

Pressure and Volume (Boyle's Law)

7.9 Why do scuba divers need to exhale air when they ascend to the surface of the water?

7.10 Why does a sealed bag of chips expand when you take it to a higher altitude?

7.11 The air in a cylinder with a piston has a volume of 220 mL and a pressure of 650 mmHg.
   a. To obtain a higher pressure inside the cylinder at constant temperature, should the cylinder change as shown in A or B? Explain your choice.

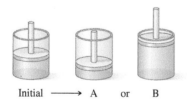

   b. If the pressure inside the cylinder increases to 1.2 atm, what is the final volume of the cylinder? Complete the following data table:

Property	Conditions 1	Conditions 2	Know	Predict
Pressure (P)				
Volume (V)				

7.12 A balloon is filled with helium gas. When the following changes are made at constant temperature, which of these diagrams (A, B, or C) shows the new volume of the balloon?

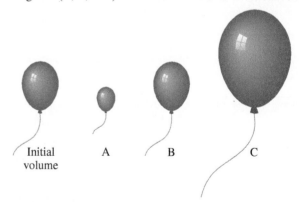

   a. The balloon floats to a higher altitude where the outside pressure is lower.
   b. The balloon is taken inside the house, but the atmospheric pressure remains the same.
   c. The balloon is put in a hyperbaric chamber in which the pressure is increased.

7.13 A gas with a volume of 4.0 L is in a closed container. Indicate what changes in pressure must have occurred if the volume undergoes the following changes at constant temperature:
   a. The volume is compressed to 2 L.
   b. The volume is allowed to expand to 12 L.
   c. The volume is compressed to 0.40 L.

7.14 A gas at a pressure of 2.0 atm is in a closed container. Indicate the changes in its volume when the pressure undergoes the following changes at constant temperature:
   a. The pressure increases to 6.0 atm.
   b. The pressure drops to 1.0 atm.
   c. The pressure drops to 0.40 atm.

7.15 A 10.0-L balloon contains helium gas at a pressure of 655 mmHg. What is the new pressure of the helium gas at each of the following volumes if there is no change in temperature?
   a. 20.0 L   **b.** 2.50 L   **c.** 1500 mL

7.16 The air in a 5.00-L tank has a pressure of 1.20 atm. What is the new pressure of the air when the air is placed in tanks that have the following volumes if there is no change in temperature?
   a. 1.00 L   **b.** 2500. mL   **c.** 750. mL

7.17 A sample of nitrogen (N_2) has a volume of 50.0 L at a pressure of 760 mmHg. What is the volume of the gas at each of the following pressures if there is no change in temperature?
   a. 1500 mmHg   **b.** 2.0 atm   **c.** 0.500 atm

7.18 A sample of methane (CH_4) has a volume of 25 mL at a pressure of 0.80 atm. What is the volume of the gas at each of the following pressures if there is no change in temperature?
   a. 0.40 atm   **b.** 2.00 atm   **c.** 2500 mmHg

7.19 Cyclopropane, C_3H_6, is a general anesthetic. A 5.0-L sample has a pressure of 5.0 atm. What is the volume of the anesthetic given to a patient at a pressure of 1.0 atm?

7.20 The volume of air in a person's lungs is 615 mL at a pressure of 760 mmHg. Inhalation occurs as the pressure in the lungs drops to 752 mmHg. To what volume did the lungs expand?

7.21 Use the words *inspiration* and *expiration* to describe the part of the breathing cycle that occurs because of each of the following:
   a. The diaphragm contracts (flattens out).
   b. The volume of the lungs decreases.
   c. The pressure within the lungs is less than the atmosphere.

7.22 Use the words *inspiration* and *expiration* to describe the part of the breathing cycle that occurs because of each of the following:
   a. The diaphragm relaxes, moving up into the thoracic cavity.
   b. The volume of the lungs expands.
   c. The pressure within the lungs is greater than the atmosphere.

7.4 Temperature and Volume (Charles's Law)

Suppose that you are going to take a ride in a hot-air balloon. The captain turns on a propane burner to heat the air inside the balloon. As the temperature rises, the air particles move faster and spread out, causing the volume of the balloon to increase. As the air is heated, it becomes less dense than the air outside, causing the balloon and its passengers to lift off. In 1787, Jacques Charles, a balloonist as well as a physicist, proposed that the volume of a gas is related to the temperature. This proposal became **Charles's law**, which states that the volume (V) of a gas is directly related to the temperature (T) when there is no change in the pressure (P) or amount (n) of gas. (See Figure 7.5.) A **direct relationship** is one in which the related properties increase or decrease together. For two conditions, we can write Charles's law as follows:

Charles's Law

$$\frac{V_1}{T_1} = \frac{V_2}{T_2} \quad \text{No change in number of moles and pressure}$$

All temperatures used in gas law calculations must be converted to their corresponding Kelvin (K) temperatures.

	CONCEPT CHECK 7.3

■ **Charles's Law**

State and explain the reason for the change (*increases, decreases*) in a gas that occurs for the following when P and n do not change:

	Temperature	Volume
a.	Increases	
b.	Decreases	

ANSWER
   a. Increases. When the temperature of a gas increases (at constant P and n), the gas particles move faster. To keep the pressure constant, the volume of the container must increase.
   b. Decreases. When the temperature of a gas decreases (at constant P and n), the gas particles move slower. To keep the pressure constant, the volume of the container must decrease.

SAMPLE PROBLEM   7.4

■ **Calculating Volume When Temperature Changes**

A sample of neon gas has a volume of 5.40 L and a temperature of 15 °C. Find the new volume of the gas after the temperature has been increased to 42 °C at constant pressure.

SOLUTION

STEP 1   Organize the data in a table.   When the temperatures are given in degrees Celsius, they must be changed to kelvins.

$$T_1 = 15\,°C + 273 = 288\ K$$
$$T_2 = 42\,°C + 273 = 315\ K$$

Conditions 1	Conditions 2	Know	Predict
$T_1 = 288\ K$	$T_2 = 315\ K$	T increases	
$V_1 = 5.40\ L$	$V_2 = ?$		V increases

STEP 2   Rearrange the gas law for the unknown.   In this problem, we want to know the final volume (V_2) when the temperature increases. Using Charles's law, we solve for V_2 by multiplying both sides by T_2:

$$\frac{V_1}{T_1} = \frac{V_2}{T_2}$$

$$\frac{V_1}{T_1} \times T_2 = \frac{V_2}{\cancel{T_2}} \times \cancel{T_2}$$

$$V_2 = V_1 \times \frac{T_2}{T_1}$$

STEP 3   Substitute values into the gas law to solve for the unknown.   From the table, we see that the temperature has increased. Because temperature is directly related to volume, the volume must increase. When we substitute in the values, we see that the ratio of the temperatures (temperature factor) is greater than 1, which increases the volume, as predicted:

$$V_2 = 5.40\ L \times \frac{315\ \cancel{K}}{288\ \cancel{K}} = 5.91\ L$$

Temperature factor
increases volume

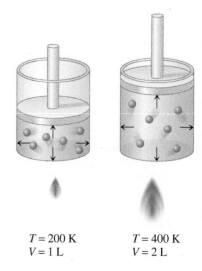

FIGURE 7.5 Charles's law: The Kelvin temperature of a gas is directly related to the volume of the gas when there is no change in the pressure. When the temperature increases, making the molecules move faster, the volume must increase to maintain constant pressure.

$T = 200\ K$ $T = 400\ K$
$V = 1\ L$ $V = 2\ L$

Q If the temperature of a gas decreases at constant pressure, how will the volume change?

STUDY CHECK

A mountain climber inhales 486 mL of air at a temperature of −8 °C. What volume, in mL, will the air occupy in the lungs if the climber's body temperature is 37 °C?

QUESTIONS AND PROBLEMS

Temperature and Volume (Charles's Law)

7.23 Select the diagram that shows the new volume of a balloon when the following changes are made at constant pressure:
  a. The temperature is changed from 100 K to 300 K.
  b. The balloon is placed in a freezer.
  c. The balloon is first warmed, and then returned to its starting temperature.

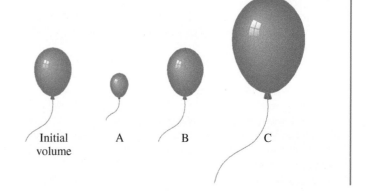

Initial volume   A   B   C

7.24 Indicate whether the final volume of gas in each of the following is the same, larger, or smaller than the initial volume:
  a. A volume of 500 mL of air on a cold winter day at 5 °C is breathed into the lungs, where body temperature is 37 °C.
  b. The heater used to heat 1400 L of air in a hot-air balloon is turned off.
  c. A balloon filled with helium at the amusement park is left in a car on a hot day.

7.25 A sample of neon initially has a volume of 2.50 L at 15 °C. What is the new temperature, in °C, when the volume of the sample is changed at constant pressure to each of the following?
  a. 5.00 L   **b.** 1250 mL
  c. 7.50 L   **d.** 3550 mL

7.26 A gas has a volume of 4.00 L at 0 °C. What final temperature, in degrees Celsius, is needed to cause the volume of the gas to change to the following, if n and P are not changed?
  a. 100. L   **b.** 1200 mL
  c. 250 L   **d.** 50.0 mL

7.27 A balloon contains 2500 mL of helium gas at 75 °C. What is the new volume (mL) of the gas when the temperature changes to the following, if n and P are not changed?
  a. 55 °C   **b.** 680. K
  c. −25 °C   **d.** 240. K

7.28 An air bubble has a volume of 0.500 L at 18 °C. If the pressure does not change, what is the volume, in liters, at each of the following temperatures?
  a. 0 °C   **b.** 425 K
  c. −12 °C   **d.** 575 K

GREEN CHEMISTRY NOTE

Greenhouse Gases

The term "greenhouse gases" was first used during the early 1800s for the gases in the atmosphere that trap heat. Among the greenhouse gases are carbon dioxide (CO_2), methane (CH_4), dinitrogen oxide (N_2O), and chlorofluorocarbons (CFCs). The molecules of greenhouse gases consist of more than two atoms that vibrate when heat is absorbed. By contrast, oxygen and nitrogen are not greenhouse gases. Because the two atoms in their molecules are so tightly bonded, they do not absorb heat.

Greenhouses gases are beneficial in keeping the average surface temperature for Earth at 15 °C. Without greenhouse gases, it is estimated that the average surface temperature of Earth would be −18 °C. Most scientists say that the concentration of greenhouse gases in the atmosphere and the surface temperature of Earth are increasing because of human activities. As we discussed in Chapter 2, the increase in atmospheric carbon dioxide is mostly a result of the burning of fossil fuels and wood.

Methane (CH_4) is a colorless, odorless gas that is released by livestock, rice farming, the decomposition of organic plant material in landfills, and the mining, drilling, and transport of coal and oil. The contribution from livestock comes from the breakdown of organic material in the digestive tracts of cows, sheep, and camels. The level of methane in the atmosphere has increased about 150% since industrialization. In one year, as much as 5×10^{11} kg of methane are added to the atmosphere. Livestock produce about 20% of the greenhouse gases. In one day, one cow emits about 200 g of methane. For a global population of 1.5 billion livestock, a total of 3×10^8 kg of methane is produced every day. In the past few years, methane levels have stabilized due to improvements in the recovery of methane. Methane remains in the atmosphere for about ten years, but its molecular structure causes it to trap 20 times more heat than does carbon dioxide.

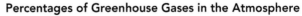

Percentages of Greenhouse Gases in the Atmosphere

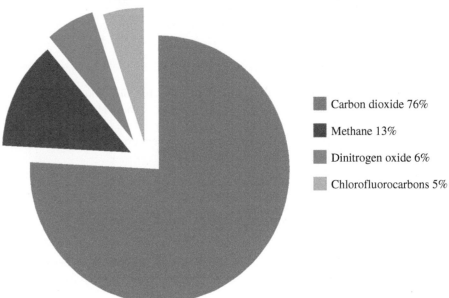

Carbon dioxide 76%

Methane 13%

Dinitrogen oxide 6%

Chlorofluorocarbons 5%

Dinitrogen oxide (N_2O), commonly called nitrous oxide, is a colorless greenhouse gas that has a sweet odor. Most people recognize it as an anesthetic used in dentistry called "laughing gas." Although some dinitrogen oxide is released naturally from soil bacteria, its primary increases are from agricultural and industrial processes. Atmospheric dinitrogen oxide has increased by about 15% since industrialization, caused by the extensive use of fertilizers, sewage treatment plants, and car exhaust. Each year, 1×10^{10} kg of dinitrogen oxide is added to the atmosphere. Dinitrogen oxide released today will remain in the atmosphere for about 150–180 years, where it has a greenhouse effect that is 300 times greater than that of carbon dioxide.

Chlorofluorinated gases (CFCs) are synthetic compounds containing chlorine, fluorine, and carbon. Chlorofluorocarbons were used as propellants in aerosol cans and as refrigerants in refrigerators and air conditioners. During the 1970s, scientists determined that CFCs in the atmosphere were destroying the protective ozone layer. Since then, many countries have banned the production and use of CFCs, and their levels in the atmosphere have declined slightly. Hydrofluorocarbons (HFCs), in which hydrogen atoms replace chlorine atoms, are now used as refrigerants. Although HFCs do not destroy the ozone layer, they are greenhouse gases because they trap heat in the atmosphere.

Based on current trends and climate models, scientists estimate that levels of atmospheric carbon dioxide will increase by about 2% each year up through 2025. As long as the greenhouse gases trap more heat than is reflected back into space, average surface temperatures on Earth will continue to rise. Efforts are taking place around the world to slow or decrease the emissions of greenhouse gases into the atmosphere. It is anticipated that temperatures will stabilize only when the amount of energy that reaches the surface of Earth is equal to the heat that is reflected back into space.

In 2007, former U.S. Vice President Al Gore and the United Nations Panel on Climate Change were awarded the Nobel Peace Prize for increasing global awareness of the relationship between human activities and global warming.

7.5 Temperature and Pressure (Gay–Lussac's Law)

If we could watch the molecules of a gas as the temperature rises, we would notice that they move faster and hit the sides of the container more often and with greater force. If we keep the volume of the container the same, we would observe an increase in the pressure. A temperature–pressure relationship, also known as **Gay–Lussac's law**, states that the pressure of a gas is directly related to its Kelvin temperature. This means that an increase in temperature increases the pressure of a gas, and a decrease in temperature decreases the pressure of the gas, provided the volume and number of moles of the gas remain the same. (See Figure 7.6.) The ratio of pressure (P) to temperature (T) is the same under all conditions as long as volume (V) and amount of gas (n) do not change.

Gay–Lussac's Law

$$\frac{P_1}{T_1} = \frac{P_2}{T_2}$$ No change in number of moles and volume

All temperatures used in gas law calculations must be converted to their corresponding Kelvin (K) temperatures.

LEARNING GOAL

Use the temperature–pressure relationship (Gay–Lussac's law) to determine the new temperature or pressure of a certain amount of gas at a constant volume.

$T = 200$ K $T = 400$ K
$P = 1$ atm $P = 2$ atm

FIGURE 7.6 Gay–Lussac's law: The pressure of a gas is directly related to the temperature of the gas. When the Kelvin temperature of a gas is doubled, the pressure is doubled at constant volume.

Q How does a decrease in the temperature of a gas affect its pressure at constant volume?

	CONCEPT CHECK 7.4

■ Gay–Lussac's Law

State and explain the reason for the change (*increases, decreases*) in a gas that occurs for the following when V and n do not change:

	Temperature	Pressure
a.	Increases	
b.	Decreases	

ANSWER

a. Increases. When the temperature of a gas (at constant V and n) increases, the gas particles move faster. When the volume does not change, the gas particles collide with the walls more often and with more force, which increases the pressure.
b. Decreases. When the temperature of a gas (at constant V and n) decreases, the gas particles move slower. When the volume does not change, the gas particles collide less often with the walls of the container and with less force, which decreases the pressure.

SAMPLE PROBLEM	7.5

■ Calculating Pressure When Temperature Changes

Aerosol containers can be dangerous if they are heated because they can explode. Suppose a container of hair spray with a pressure of 4.0 atm at a room temperature of 25 °C is thrown into a fire. If the temperature of the gas inside the aerosol can reaches 402 °C, what will be its pressure? The aerosol container may explode if the pressure inside exceeds 8.0 atm. Would you expect it to explode?

 TUTORIAL
Temperature and Pressure

SOLUTION

STEP 1   Organize the data in a table.   We must first change the temperatures to kelvins.

$$T_1 = 25\,°C + 273 = 298\ K$$

$$T_2 = 402\,°C + 273 = 675\ K$$

Conditions 1	Conditions 2	Know	Predict
$P_1 = 4.0$ atm	$P_2 = ?$		P increases
$T_1 = 298$ K	$T_2 = 675$ K	T increases	

STEP 2   Rearrange the gas law for the unknown.   Using Gay-Lussac's law, we can solve for P_2.

$$\frac{P_1}{T_1} = \frac{P_2}{T_2}$$

$$\frac{P_1}{T_1} \times T_2 = \frac{P_2}{T_2} \times T_2$$

$$P_2 = P_1 \times \frac{T_2}{T_1}$$

STEP 3   Substitute values into the gas law to solve for the unknown.   From the table, we see that the temperature has increased. Because pressure and temperature are directly related, the pressure must increase. When we substitute in the values, we see the ratio of the temperatures (temperature factor) is greater than 1, which increases pressure.

$$P_2 = 4.0\ \text{atm} \times \frac{675\ K}{298\ K} = 9.1\ \text{atm}$$

Temperature factor
increases volume

Because the calculated pressure of 9.1 atm is greater than 8.0 atm, we expect the can to explode.

STUDY CHECK

In a storage area where the temperature has reached 55 °C, the pressure of oxygen gas in a 15.0-L steel cylinder is 965 torr. To what temperature (°C) would the gas have to be cooled to reduce the pressure to 850. torr?

TABLE 7.4 Vapor Pressure of Water

Temperature (°C)	Vapor Pressure (mmHg)
0	5
10	9
20	18
30	32
37	47[a]
40	55
50	93
60	149
70	234
80	355
90	528
100	760

[a]At body temperature.

TABLE 7.5 Pressure and the Boiling Point of Water

Pressure (mmHg)	Boiling Point (°C)
270	70
467	87
630	95
752	99
760	100
800	100.4
1075	110
1520 (2 atm)	120
2026	130
7600 (10 atm)	180

Vapor Pressure and Boiling Point

In Chapter 2, we learned that liquid molecules with sufficient kinetic energy can break away from the surface of the liquid as they become gas particles or vapor. In an open container, all the liquid will eventually evaporate. In a closed container, the vapor accumulates and creates pressure called **vapor pressure**. Each liquid exerts its own vapor pressure at a given temperature. As temperature increases, more vapor forms, and vapor pressure increases. Table 7.4 lists the vapor pressure of water at various temperatures.

A liquid reaches its boiling point when its vapor pressure becomes equal to the external pressure. As boiling occurs, bubbles of the gas form within the liquid and quickly rise to the surface. For example, at an atmospheric pressure of 760 mmHg, water will boil at 100 °C, the temperature at which its vapor pressure reaches 760 mmHg. (See Table 7.5.)

At higher altitudes, where atmospheric pressures are lower, the boiling point of water is lower than 100 °C. Earlier, we saw that the typical atmospheric pressure in Denver is 630 mmHg. This means that water in Denver needs a vapor pressure of 630 mmHg to boil. Because water has a vapor pressure of 630 mmHg at 95 °C, water boils at 95 °C in Denver.

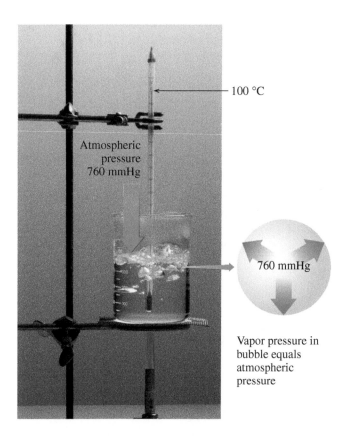

100 °C

Atmospheric
pressure
760 mmHg

760 mmHg

Vapor pressure in
bubble equals
atmospheric
pressure

People who live at high altitudes often use pressure cookers to obtain higher temperatures when preparing food. When the external pressure is greater than 1 atm, a temperature higher than 100 °C is needed to boil water. Laboratories and hospitals use devices called *autoclaves* to sterilize laboratory and surgical equipment. An autoclave, like a pressure cooker, is a closed container that increases the total pressure above the liquid so it will boil at higher temperatures.

MC TUTORIAL
Vapor Pressure and Boiling Point

QUESTIONS AND PROBLEMS

Temperature and Pressure (Gay–Lussac's Law)

7.29 Why do aerosol cans explode if heated?

7.30 Why is there an increased danger of the tires on a car having a blowout when the car is driven on hot pavement in the desert?

7.31 For the following, calculate the new temperature, in degrees Celsius, when pressure is changed, with n and V constant:
  a. A sample of xenon at 25 °C and 745 mmHg is cooled to give a pressure of 625 mmHg.
  b. A tank of argon gas with a pressure of 0.950 atm at −18 °C is heated to give a pressure of 1250 torr.

7.32 For the following, calculate the new temperature, in degrees Celsius, when pressure is changed, with n and V constant:
  a. A tank of helium gas with a pressure of 250 torr at 0 °C is heated to give a pressure of 1500 torr.
  b. A sample of air at 40. °C and 745 mmHg is cooled to give a pressure of 685 mmHg.

7.33 Solve for the new pressure when each of the following temperature changes occurs, with n and V constant:
  a. A gas with an initial pressure of 1200 torr at 155 °C is cooled to 0 °C.
  b. A gas in an aerosol container at an initial pressure of 1.40 atm at 12 °C is heated to 35 °C.

7.34 Solve for the new pressure in each of the following, with n and V constant:
  a. A gas with a pressure of 1.20 atm at 75 °C is cooled to −22 °C.
  b. A sample of N_2 with a pressure of 780 mmHg at −75 °C is heated to 28 °C.

7.35 Match the terms *vapor pressure, atmospheric pressure*, and *boiling point* to the following descriptions:
  a. the temperature at which bubbles of vapor appear within the liquid
  b. the pressure exerted by a gas above the surface of its liquid
  c. the pressure exerted on Earth by the particles in the air
  d. the temperature at which the vapor pressure of a liquid becomes equal to the external pressure

7.36 In which pair(s) would boiling occur?

Atmospheric Pressure	Vapor Pressure
a. 760 mmHg	700 mmHg
b. 480 torr	480 mmHg
c. 1.2 atm	912 mmHg
d. 1020 mmHg	760 mmHg
e. 740 torr	1.0 atm

7.37 Explain the following observations:
  a. Water boils at 87 °C on the top of Mt. Whitney.
  b. Food cooks more quickly in a pressure cooker than in an open pan.

7.38 Explain the following observations:
  a. Boiling water at sea level is hotter than boiling water in the mountains.
  b. Water used to sterilize surgical equipment is heated to 120 °C at 2.0 atm in an autoclave.

7.6 The Combined Gas Law

LEARNING GOAL

Use the combined gas law to find the new pressure, volume, or temperature of a gas when changes in two of these properties are given.

All the pressure–volume–temperature relationships for gases that we have studied may be combined into a single relationship called the **combined gas law**. This expression is useful for studying the effect of changes in two of these variables on the third as long as the amount of gas (number of moles) remains constant.

Combined Gas Law

$$\frac{P_1 V_1}{T_1} = \frac{P_2 V_2}{T_2} \qquad \text{No change in moles of gas}$$

By using the combined gas law, we can derive any of the gas laws by omitting those properties that do not change, as seen in Table 7.6.

TABLE 7.6 Summary of Gas Laws

Combined Gas Law	Properties Held Constant	Relationship	Name of Gas Law
$\dfrac{P_1 V_1}{\cancel{T_1}} = \dfrac{P_2 V_2}{\cancel{T_2}}$	T, n	$P_1 V_1 = P_2 V_2$	Boyle's
$\dfrac{\cancel{P_1} V_1}{T_1} = \dfrac{\cancel{P_2} V_2}{T_2}$	P, n	$\dfrac{V_1}{T_1} = \dfrac{V_2}{T_2}$	Charles's
$\dfrac{P_1 \cancel{V_1}}{T_1} = \dfrac{P_2 \cancel{V_2}}{T_2}$	V, n	$\dfrac{P_1}{T_1} = \dfrac{P_2}{T_2}$	Gay–Lussac's

CONCEPT CHECK 7.5

■ **Combined Gas Law**

State and explain the reason for the change (*increases, decreases, no change*) in a gas that occurs for the following when n does not change:

	Pressure	Volume	Temperature (K)
a.		Twice as large	Half the Kelvin temperature
b.	Twice as large		Twice as large

ANSWER
  a. Decreases. When the volume (at constant n) doubles, the pressure will be halved. If the temperature in Kelvin is halved, the pressure is also halved. The changes in both V and T decrease the pressure to one-fourth its initial value.
  b. No change. When the Kelvin temperature of a gas (at constant n) is doubled, the volume is doubled. But when the pressure is twice as much, the volume must decrease to one-half. The changes offset each other, and no change occurs in the volume.

SAMPLE PROBLEM 7.6

(MC) TUTORIAL
The Combined Gas Law

■ **Using the Combined Gas Law**

A 25.0-mL bubble is released from a diver's air tank at a pressure of 4.00 atm and a temperature of 11 °C. What is the volume (mL) of the bubble when it reaches the ocean surface, where the pressure is 1.00 atm and the temperature is 18 °C?

SOLUTION

STEP 1   **Organize the data in a table.**   We must first change the temperature to kelvins.

$$T_1 = 11\,°C + 273 = 284\text{ K}$$
$$T_2 = 18\,°C + 273 = 291\text{ K}$$

Conditions 1	Conditions 2
$P_1 = 4.00$ atm	$P_2 = 1.00$ atm
$V_1 = 25.0$ mL	$V_2 = ?$
$T_1 = 284$ K	$T_2 = 291$ K

STEP 2   **Rearrange the gas law for the unknown.**   Because the pressure and temperature are both changing, we must use the combined gas law to solve for V_2.

$$\frac{P_1V_1}{T_1} = \frac{P_2V_2}{T_2}$$

$$\frac{P_1V_1}{T_1} \times \frac{T_2}{P_2} = \frac{P_2V_2 \times T_2}{T_2 \times P_2}$$

$$V_2 = V_1 \times \frac{P_1}{P_2} \times \frac{T_2}{T_1}$$

STEP 3   **Substitute the values into the gas law to solve for the unknown.**   From the data table, we determine that both the pressure decrease and the temperature increase will increase the volume.

$$V_2 = 25.0\text{ mL} \times \frac{4.00\text{ atm}}{1.00\text{ atm}} \times \frac{291\text{ K}}{284\text{ K}} = 102\text{ mL}$$

Pressure factor increases volume   Temperature factor increases volume

STUDY CHECK

A weather balloon is filled with 15.0 L of helium at a temperature of 25 °C and a pressure of 685 mmHg. What is the pressure (mmHg) of the helium in the balloon in the upper atmosphere when the temperature is −35 °C and the volume becomes 34.0 L?

QUESTIONS AND PROBLEMS

The Combined Gas Law

7.39 A sample of helium gas has a volume of 6.50 L at a pressure of 845 mmHg and a temperature of 25 °C. What is the pressure of the gas, in atm, when the volume and temperature of the gas sample are changed to the following?
 a. 1850 mL and 325 K   **b.** 2.25 L and 12 °C
 c. 12.8 L and 47 °C

7.40 A sample of argon gas has a volume of 735 mL at a pressure of 1.20 atm and a temperature of 112 °C. What is the volume of the gas, in milliliters, when the pressure and temperature of the gas sample are changed to the following?

 a. 658 mmHg and 281 K   **b.** 0.55 atm and 75 °C
 c. 15.4 atm and −15 °C

7.41 A 124-mL bubble of hot gases at 212 °C and 1.80 atm escapes from an active volcano. What is the temperature, in °C, of the gas in the bubble outside the volcano if the new volume of the bubble is 138 mL and the pressure is 0.800 atm?

7.42 A scuba diver 40 ft below the ocean surface inhales 50.0 mL of compressed air in a scuba tank at a pressure of 3.00 atm and a temperature of 8 °C. What is the pressure of air in the lungs if the gas expands to 150.0 mL at a body temperature of 37 °C?

7.7   Volume and Moles (Avogadro's Law)

In our study of the gas laws, we have looked at changes in properties for a specified amount (n) of gas. Now we will consider how the properties of a gas change when there is a change in the amount (number of moles or grams) of gas itself.

   When you blow up a balloon, its volume increases because you are adding more air molecules. If a basketball gets a hole in it, and some of the air leaks out, its volume

LEARNING GOAL

Use Avogadro's law to describe the relationship between the amount of a gas and its volume, and use this relationship in calculations.

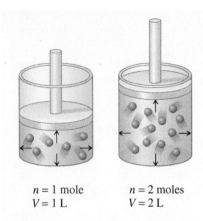

$n = 1$ mole $n = 2$ moles
$V = 1$ L $V = 2$ L

FIGURE 7.7 Avogadro's law: The volume of a gas is directly related to the number of moles of the gas. If the number of moles is doubled, the volume must double at constant temperature and pressure.

Q If a balloon has a leak, what happens to its volume?

TUTORIAL
Volume and Moles

decreases. **Avogadro's law** states that the volume of a gas is directly related to the number of moles of a gas when temperature and pressure are not changed. If the number of moles of a gas is doubled, then the volume will double as long as we do not change the pressure or the temperature. (See Figure 7.7.) Under conditions of constant pressure and temperature, we can write Avogadro's law as follows:

Avogadro's Law

$$\frac{V_1}{n_1} = \frac{V_2}{n_2}$$ No change in pressure or temperature

---

SAMPLE PROBLEM   7.7

■ Calculating Volume for a Change in Moles

A weather balloon with a volume of 44 L is filled with 2.0 moles of helium. To what volume will the balloon expand if 3.0 moles of helium are added, to give a total of 5.0 moles of helium (the pressure and temperature do not change)?

SOLUTION

STEP 1   **Organize the data in a table.**   A data table for our given information can be set up as follows:

Conditions 1	Conditions 2	Know	Predict
$V_1 = 44$ L	$V_2 = ?$		V increases
$n_1 = 2.0$ moles	$n_2 = 5.0$ moles	n increases	

STEP 2   **Rearrange the gas law for the unknown.**   Using Avogadro's law, we can solve for V_2.

$$\frac{V_1}{n_1} = \frac{V_2}{n_2}$$

$$n_2 \times \frac{V_1}{n_1} = \frac{V_2}{n_2} \times n_2$$

$$V_2 = V_1 \times \frac{n_2}{n_1}$$

STEP 3   **Substitute the values into the gas law to solve for the unknown.**   From the table, we see that the number of moles has increased. Because the number of moles and volume are directly related, the volume must increase at constant pressure and temperature. When we substitute in the values, we see the ratio of the moles (mole factor) is greater than 1, which increases volume.

$$V_2 = 44 \text{ L} \times \frac{5.0 \text{ moles}}{2.0 \text{ moles}} = 110 \text{ L}$$

New   Initial   Mole factor
volume   volume   increases volume

STUDY CHECK

A sample containing 8.00 g of oxygen gas has a volume of 5.00 L. What is the volume after 4.00 g of oxygen gas is added to the balloon, if temperature and pressure do not change?

STP and Molar Volume

Using Avogadro's law, we can say that any two gases will have equal volumes if they contain the same number of moles of gas at the same temperature and pressure. To help us make comparisons between different gases, arbitrary conditions called *standard temperature* (273 K) and *standard pressure* (1 atm), together abbreviated **STP**, were selected by scientists:

STP Conditions

Standard temperature is *exactly* 0 °C (273 K).
Standard pressure is *exactly* 1 atm (760 mmHg).

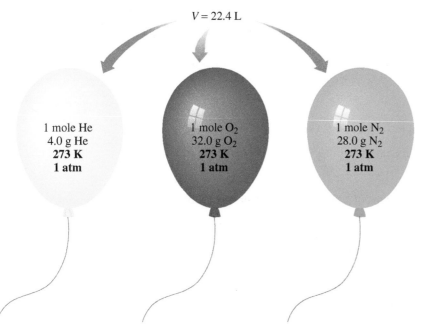

$V = 22.4\,\text{L}$

1 mole He	1 mole O_2	1 mole N_2
4.0 g He	32.0 g O_2	28.0 g N_2
273 K	**273 K**	**273 K**
1 atm	**1 atm**	**1 atm**

FIGURE 7.8 Avogadro's law indicates that 1 mole of any gas at STP has a molar volume of 22.4 L.

Q What volume of gas is occupied by 16.0 g of methane gas, CH_4, at STP?

At STP, 1 mole of any gas has a volume of 22.4 L. (A volume of 22.4 L is about the same as the volume of three basketballs.) This volume is called a gas's **molar volume**. (See Figure 7.8.)

When a gas is at STP conditions (0 °C and 1 atm), its molar volume can be used as a conversion factor to convert between the number of moles of gas and its volume.

Molar Volume Conversion Factors

$$\frac{1\text{ mole gas (STP)}}{22.4\text{ L}} \quad \text{and} \quad \frac{22.4\text{ L}}{1\text{ mole gas (STP)}}$$

Moles of gas ⟷ Molar volume 22.4 L/mole ⟷ Volume (L) of gas

SAMPLE PROBLEM 7.8

■ Using Molar Volume to Find Volume at STP

What is the volume, in liters, of 64.0 g of O_2 gas at STP?

SOLUTION

Once we convert the mass of O_2 to moles of O_2, the molar volume of a gas at STP can be used to calculate the volume (L) of O_2.

STEP 1 **Given** 64.0 g of $O_2(g)$ at STP   **Need** volume in liters (L)

STEP 2 **Write a plan.**

grams of O_2 Molar mass   moles of O_2 Molar volume   liters of O_2

STEP 3 **Write conversion factors.**

1 mole of O_2 = 32.0 g of O_2 1 mole of O_2 (STP) = 22.4 L of O_2 (STP)

$$\frac{32.0\text{ g }O_2}{1\text{ mole }O_2} \quad \text{and} \quad \frac{1\text{ mole }O_2}{32.0\text{ g }O_2} \qquad \frac{22.4\text{ L }O_2}{1\text{ mole }O_2} \quad \text{and} \quad \frac{1\text{ mole }O_2}{22.4\text{ L }O_2}$$

STEP 4 **Set up problem with factors to cancel units.**

$$64.0\text{ g }O_2 \times \frac{1\text{ mole }O_2}{32.0\text{ g }O_2} \times \frac{22.4\text{ L }O_2}{1\text{ mole }O_2} = 44.8\text{ L of }O_2\text{ (STP)}$$

STUDY CHECK

How many grams of $N_2(g)$ are in 5.6 L of $N_2(g)$ at STP?

Guide to Using Molar Volume

STEP 1
Identify given and needed.

STEP 2
Write a plan.

STEP 3
Write conversion factors including 22.4 L/mole at STP.

STEP 4
Set up problem with factors to cancel units.

Gases in Reactions at STP

We can use the molar volume at STP to determine the moles of a gas in a reaction. Once we know the moles of gas in a reaction, we can use a mole factor to determine the moles of any other substance as we have done before.

■ Gases in Chemical Reactions at STP

When potassium metal reacts with chlorine gas, the product is solid potassium chloride.

$$2K(s) + Cl_2(g) \longrightarrow 2KCl(s)$$

How many grams of potassium chloride are produced when 7.25 L of chlorine gas at STP reacts with excess potassium?

SOLUTION

STEP 1 **Find moles of Cl_2 using molar volume.** At STP, we can use molar volume (22.4 L/mole) to determine moles of Cl_2 gas.

$$7.25 \text{ L } Cl_2 \times \frac{1 \text{ mole } Cl_2}{22.4 \text{ L } Cl_2} = 0.324 \text{ mole of } Cl_2$$

STEP 2 **Determine moles of KCl using the mole–mole factor from the balanced equation.**

$$1 \text{ mole of } Cl_2 = 2 \text{ moles of KCl}$$

$$\frac{2 \text{ moles KCl}}{1 \text{ mole } Cl_2} \quad \text{and} \quad \frac{1 \text{ mole } Cl_2}{2 \text{ moles KCl}}$$

$$0.324 \text{ mole } Cl_2 \times \frac{2 \text{ moles KCl}}{1 \text{ mole } Cl_2} = 0.648 \text{ mole of KCl}$$

STEP 3 **Convert moles of KCl to grams.** Using the molar mass of KCl, we can determine the grams of KCl.

$$1 \text{ mole of KCl} = 74.6 \text{ g of KCl}$$

$$\frac{1 \text{ mole KCl}}{74.6 \text{ g KCl}} \quad \text{and} \quad \frac{74.6 \text{ g KCl}}{1 \text{ mole KCl}}$$

$$0.648 \text{ mole KCl} \times \frac{74.6 \text{ g KCl}}{1 \text{ mole KCl}} = 48.3 \text{ g of KCl}$$

These steps can also be set up as a continuous solution.

$$7.25 \text{ L } Cl_2 \times \frac{1 \text{ mole } Cl_2}{22.4 \text{ L } Cl_2} \times \frac{2 \text{ moles KCl}}{1 \text{ mole } Cl_2} \times \frac{74.6 \text{ g KCl}}{1 \text{ mole KCl}} = 48.3 \text{ g of KCl}$$

STUDY CHECK

H_2 gas forms when zinc metal reacts with aqueous HCl according to the following equation:

$$Zn(s) + 2HCl(aq) \longrightarrow ZnCl_2(aq) + H_2(g)$$

How many liters of H_2 gas at STP are produced when 15.8 g of zinc reacts?

Guide to Problem Solving
Reactions Involving Gases

STEP 1
Find moles of gas A using molar volume or ideal gas law.

STEP 2
Determine moles of substance B using mole–mole factor.

STEP 3
Convert moles of substance B to grams or volume.

QUESTIONS AND PROBLEMS

Volume and Moles (Avogadro's Law)

7.43 What happens to the volume of a bicycle tire or a basketball when you use an air pump to add air?

7.44 Sometimes when you blow up a balloon and release it, it flies around the room. What is happening to the air that was in the balloon and its volume?

7.45 A sample containing 1.50 moles of neon gas has a volume of 8.00 L. What is the new volume of gas, in liters, when the following changes occur in the quantity of the gas at constant pressure and temperature?
   a. A leak allows one-half of the neon atoms to escape.
   b. A sample of 25.0 g of neon is added to the 1.50 moles of neon gas in the container.

c. A sample of 3.50 moles of O_2 is added to the 1.50 moles of neon gas in the container.

7.46 A sample containing 4.80 g of O_2 gas has a volume of 15.0 L. Pressure and temperature remain constant.
  a. What is the new volume if 0.500 mole of O_2 gas is added?
  b. Oxygen is released until the volume is 10.0 L. How many moles of O_2 are removed?
  c. What is the volume after 4.00 g of He is added to the 4.80 g of O_2 gas in the container?

7.47 Use the molar volume of a gas to solve the following at STP:
  a. the number of moles of O_2 in 44.8 L of O_2 gas
  b. the number of moles of CO_2 in 4.00 L of CO_2 gas
  c. the volume (L) of 6.40 g of O_2
  d. the volume (mL) occupied by 50.0 g of neon

7.48 Use molar volume to solve the following problems at STP:
  a. the volume (L) occupied by 2.50 moles of N_2
  b. the volume (mL) occupied by 0.420 mole of He
  c. the number of grams of neon contained in 11.2 L of Ne gas
  d. the number of moles of H_2 in 1620 mL of H_2 gas

7.49 Mg metal reacts with HCl to produce hydrogen gas:

$$Mg(s) + 2HCl(aq) \longrightarrow MgCl_2(aq) + H_2(g)$$

What volume of H_2 at STP is released when 8.25 g of Mg reacts?

7.50 Aluminum oxide is formed from its elements:

$$4Al(s) + 3O_2(g) \longrightarrow 2Al_2O_3(s)$$

How many grams of Al will react with 12.0 L of O_2 at STP?

7.8 The Ideal Gas Law

The four properties used in the measurement of a gas—pressure (P), volume (V), temperature (T), and amount (n)—can be combined to give a single expression called the **ideal gas law**, which is written as follows:

Ideal Gas Law

$$PV = nRT$$

Rearranging the ideal gas law shows that the four gas properties equal a constant, R:

$$\frac{PV}{nT} = R$$

To calculate the value of R, we substitute the STP conditions for molar volume into the expression: 1 mole of any gas occupies 22.4 L at STP (273 K and 1 atm).

$$R = \frac{(1.00 \text{ atm})(22.4 \text{ L})}{(1.00 \text{ mole})(273 \text{ K})} = \frac{0.0821 \text{ L} \cdot \text{atm}}{\text{mole} \cdot \text{K}}$$

The value for R, the **ideal gas constant**, is 0.0821 L · atm per mole · K. If we use 760 mmHg for the pressure, we obtain another useful value for R: 62.4 L · mmHg per mole · K.

$$R = \frac{(760 \text{ mmHg})(22.4 \text{ L})}{(1.00 \text{ mole})(273 \text{ K})} = \frac{62.4 \text{ L} \cdot \text{mmHg}}{\text{mole} \cdot \text{K}}$$

The ideal gas law is a useful expression when you are given the values for any three of the four properties of a gas. In working problems using the ideal gas law, the units of each variable must match the units in the R you select:

Ideal Gas Constant (R)	$\dfrac{0.0821 \text{ L} \cdot \text{atm}}{\text{mole} \cdot \text{K}}$	$\dfrac{62.4 \text{ L} \cdot \text{mmHg}}{\text{mole} \cdot \text{K}}$
Pressure (P)	atm	mmHg
Volume (V)	L	L
Amount (n)	moles	moles
Temperature (T)	K	K

LEARNING GOAL

Use the ideal gas law to solve for P, V, T, or n of a gas when given three of the four values in the ideal gas law.

TUTORIAL
Introduction to the Ideal Gas Law

MC **SELF STUDY ACTIVITY**
The Ideal Gas Law

SAMPLE PROBLEM 7.10

■ **Using the Ideal Gas Law**

Dinitrogen oxide, N_2O, which is used in dentistry, is an anesthetic also called "laughing gas." What is the pressure, in atmospheres, of 0.350 mole of N_2O at 22 °C in a 5.00 L container?

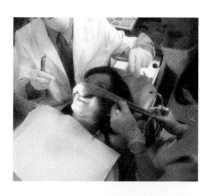

**Guide to Using
the Ideal Gas Law**

STEP 1
Organize data given for the gas.

STEP 2
Solve the ideal gas law for the unknown.

STEP 3
Substitute gas data and calculate unknown value.

SOLUTION

STEP 1   **Organize the data, including R.**   When three of the four quantities (P, V, n, and T) are known, we use the ideal gas law to solve for the unknown quantity. The temperature is converted from degrees Celsius to kelvins so that the units of V, n, and T match the units of the gas constant R:

$$P = ?   V = 5.00\,L   n = 0.350\,mole   R = 0.0821\frac{L \cdot atm}{mole \cdot K}   T = 22\,°C + 273 = 295\,K$$

STEP 2   **Rearrange the ideal gas law to solve for the unknown.**   By dividing both sides of the ideal gas law by V, we solve for pressure, P:

$$PV = nRT   \text{Ideal gas law}$$

$$P\frac{\cancel{V}}{\cancel{V}} = \frac{nRT}{V}$$

$$P = \frac{nRT}{V}$$

STEP 3   **Substitute values to calculate unknown.**

$$P = \frac{0.350\,\cancel{mole} \times 0.0821\,\dfrac{\cancel{L} \cdot atm}{\cancel{mole} \cdot \cancel{K}} \times 295\,\cancel{K}}{5.00\,\cancel{L}} = 1.70\,atm$$

STUDY CHECK

Chlorine gas, Cl_2, is used to purify water. How many moles of chlorine gas are in a 7.00 L tank if the gas has a pressure of 865 mmHg and a temperature of 24 °C?

SAMPLE PROBLEM 7.11

■ **Calculating Mass Using the Ideal Gas Law**

Butane, C_4H_{10}, is used as a fuel for barbecues and as an aerosol propellant. If you have 108 mL of butane at 715 mmHg and 25 °C, what is the mass (g) of the butane?

SOLUTION

STEP 1   **Organize the data, including R.**   When three of the four quantities (P, V, n, and T) are known, we use the ideal gas law to solve for the unknown quantity. Because the pressure is given in mmHg, we will use the R in mmHg. The volume given in milliliters (mL) is converted to a volume in liters (L). The temperature is converted from degrees Celsius to kelvins.

Initial values	Adjusted for units in ideal gas constant R
$P = 715\,mmHg$	$715\,mmHg$
$V = 108\,mL$	$108\,\cancel{mL} \times \dfrac{1\,L}{1000\,\cancel{mL}} = 0.108\,L$
$n = ?$ moles of C_4H_{10}	? moles of C_4H_{10}
$R = \dfrac{62.4\,L \cdot mmHg}{mole \cdot K}$	$\dfrac{62.4\,L \cdot mmHg}{mole \cdot K}$
$T = 25\,°C$	$25\,°C + 273 = 298\,K$

STEP 2   **Rearrange the ideal gas law to solve for the unknown.**   By dividing both sides of the ideal gas law by RT, we solve for moles, n:

$$PV = n\,RT   \text{Ideal gas law}$$

$$\frac{PV}{RT} = n\,\frac{\cancel{RT}}{\cancel{RT}}$$

$$n = \frac{PV}{RT}$$

STEP 3   **Substitute the known values to calculate the unknown.**

$$n = \frac{715 \text{ mmHg} \times 0.108 \text{ L}}{\dfrac{62.4 \text{ L} \cdot \text{mmHg}}{\text{mole} \cdot \text{K}} \times 298 \text{ K}} = 0.00415 \text{ mole } (4.15 \times 10^{-3} \text{ mole})$$

Now we convert the moles of butane to grams using its molar mass (58.0 g/mole).

$$0.00415 \text{ mole C}_4\text{H}_{10} \times \frac{58.0 \text{ g C}_4\text{H}_{10}}{1 \text{ mole C}_4\text{H}_{10}} = 0.241 \text{ g of C}_4\text{H}_{10}$$

STUDY CHECK

What is the volume of 1.20 g of carbon monoxide at 8 °C if it has a pressure of 724 mmHg?

SAMPLE PROBLEM 7.12

Molar Mass of a Gas Using the Ideal Gas Law

What is the molar mass of a gas if a 3.16-g sample at 0.750 atm at 45 °C occupies a volume of 2.05 L?

SOLUTION

STEP 1   **Given**   3.16 g of a gas, $P = 0.750$ atm, $V = 2.05$ L, $T = 45 \,°\text{C} + 273 = 318$ K   **Need**   molar mass (g/mole)

STEP 2   **Write a plan.**   The molar mass is the grams of the gas divided by the moles. In this problem, we need to use the ideal gas law to determine the moles of the gas.

$$P, V, T \boxed{\text{Ideal gas law}} > \text{moles } (n) \text{ of gas}$$

$$\frac{3.16 \text{ g}}{\text{moles } (n) \text{ gas}} = \text{molar mass (g/mole)}$$

STEP 3   **Write conversion factors.**

$$PV = n\,RT \qquad \text{Ideal gas law}$$

$$\frac{PV}{RT} = \frac{n\,RT}{RT}$$

$$n = \frac{PV}{RT}$$

The moles of the gas are calculated as

$$n = \frac{0.750 \text{ atm} \times 2.05 \text{ L}}{\dfrac{0.0821 \text{ L} \cdot \text{atm}}{\text{mole} \cdot \text{K}} \times 318 \text{ K}} = 0.0589 \text{ mole}$$

Set up calculation for molar mass (g/mole).   The molar mass of the gas is obtained by dividing the mass by the moles of gas.

$$\text{Molar mass} = \frac{\text{mass}}{\text{moles}} = \frac{3.16 \text{ g}}{0.0589 \text{ mole}} = 53.7 \text{ g/mole}$$

STUDY CHECK

What is the molar mass of an unknown gas in a 1.50-L container if 0.488 g of the gas has a pressure of 0.0750 atm at 19.0 °C?

Ideal Gas Law and Chemical Reactions

If a gas is not at STP, we use its pressure (P), volume (V), and temperature (T) to determine the moles of that gas involved in a reaction. Then we can determine the moles of any other substance by using the mole factors as we did in Chapter 6.

SAMPLE PROBLEM 7.13

▪ Ideal Gas Law and Chemical Equations

Limestone ($CaCO_3$) reacts with HCl to produce aqueous calcium chloride and carbon dioxide gas:

$$CaCO_3(s) + 2HCl(aq) \longrightarrow CaCl_2(aq) + CO_2(g) + H_2O(l)$$

How many liters of CO_2 are produced at 752 mmHg and 24 °C from a 25.0-g sample of limestone?

SOLUTION

STEP 1   Find the moles of $CaCO_3$ using molar mass.   The moles of limestone require the molar mass of limestone.

$$1 \text{ mole of } CaCO_3 = 100.1 \text{ g of } CaCO_3$$

$$\frac{100.1 \text{ g } CaCO_3}{1 \text{ mole } CaCO_3} \quad \text{and} \quad \frac{1 \text{ mole } CaCO_3}{100.1 \text{ g } CaCO_3}$$

$$25.0 \text{ g } CaCO_3 \times \frac{1 \text{ mole } CaCO_3}{100.1 \text{ g } CaCO_3} = 0.250 \text{ mole of } CaCO_3$$

STEP 2   Determine moles of CO_2 using the mole–mole factor from the balanced equation.

$$1 \text{ mole of } CaCO_3 = 1 \text{ mole of } CO_2$$

$$\frac{1 \text{ mole } CaCO_3}{1 \text{ mole } CO_2} \quad \text{and} \quad \frac{1 \text{ mole } CO_2}{1 \text{ mole } CaCO_3}$$

$$0.250 \text{ mole } CaCO_3 \times \frac{1 \text{ mole } CO_2}{1 \text{ mole } CaCO_3} = 0.250 \text{ mole of } CO_2$$

STEP 3   Convert moles of CO_2 to volume.   Now the moles of CO_2 can be placed in the ideal gas law to solve for the volume (L) of gas. The ideal gas law solved for volume is

$$V = \frac{nRT}{P}$$

$$V = \frac{0.250 \text{ mole} \times \dfrac{62.4 \text{ L} \cdot mmHg}{K \cdot mole} \times 297 \text{ K}}{752 \text{ mmHg}} = 6.16 \text{ L of } CO_2$$

STUDY CHECK

If 12.8 g of aluminum reacts with HCl, how many liters of H_2 would be formed at 715 mmHg and 19 °C?

$$2Al(s) + 6HCl(aq) \longrightarrow 2AlCl_3(aq) + 3H_2(g)$$

QUESTIONS AND PROBLEMS

The Ideal Gas Law

7.51 Calculate the pressure, in atmospheres, of 2.00 moles of helium gas in a 10.0-L container at 27 °C.

7.52 What is the volume, in liters, of 4.0 moles of methane gas, CH_4, at 18 °C and 1.40 atm?

7.53 An oxygen gas container has a volume of 20.0 L. How many grams of oxygen are in the container if the gas has a pressure of 845 mmHg at 22 °C?

7.54 A 10.0-g sample of krypton has a temperature of 25 °C at 575 mmHg. What is the volume, in milliliters, of the krypton gas?

7.55 A 25.0-g sample of nitrogen, N_2, has a volume of 50.0 L and a pressure of 630. mmHg. What is the temperature of the gas?

7.56 A 0.226-g sample of carbon dioxide, CO_2, has a volume of 525 mL and a pressure of 455 mmHg. What is the temperature of the gas?

7.57 Determine the molar mass of each of the following gases:
   a. 0.84 g of a gas that occupies 450 mL at STP
   b. 1.48 g of a gas that occupies 1.00 L at 685 mmHg and 22 °C
   c. 2.96 g of a gas that occupies 2.30 L at 0.95 atm and 24 °C

7.58 Determine the molar mass of each of the following gases:
   a. 11.6 g of a gas that occupies 2.00 L at STP
   b. 0.726 g of a gas that occupies 855 mL at 1.20 atm and 18 °C
   c. 2.32 g of a gas that occupies 1.23 L at 685 mmHg and 25 °C

7.59 Butane is used to fill gas tanks for heating. The following equation describes its combustion:

$$2C_4H_{10}(g) + 13O_2(g) \longrightarrow 8CO_2(g) + 10H_2O(g)$$

If a tank contains 55.2 g of butane, what volume, in liters, of oxygen is needed to burn all the butane at 0.850 atm and 25 °C?

7.60 When heated to 350. °C at 0.950 atm, ammonium nitrate decomposes to produce nitrogen, water, and oxygen gases:

$$2NH_4NO_3(s) \longrightarrow 2N_2(g) + 4H_2O(g) + O_2(g)$$

   a. How many liters of water vapor are produced when 25.8 g of NH_4NO_3 decomposes?
   b. How many grams of NH_4NO_3 are needed to produce 10.0 L of oxygen?

7.61 What volume, in liters, of O_2 at 35 °C and 1.19 atm can be produced from the decomposition of 50.0 g of KNO_3?

$$2KNO_3(s) \longrightarrow 2KNO_2(s) + O_2(g)$$

7.62 Nitrogen dioxide reacts with water to produce oxygen and ammonia:

$$4NO_2(g) + 6H_2O(g) \longrightarrow 7O_2(g) + 4NH_3(g)$$

At a temperature of 415 °C and a pressure of 725 mmHg, how many grams of NH_3 can be produced when 4.00 L of NO_2 react?

7.9 Partial Pressures (Dalton's Law)

Many gas samples are a mixture of gases. For example, the air you breathe is a mixture of mostly oxygen and nitrogen gases. Scientists have observed that all gas particles in ideal gas mixtures behave in the same way. Therefore, the total pressure of the gases in a mixture is a result of the collisions of the gas particles regardless of what type of gas they are.

In a gas mixture, each gas exerts its **partial pressure**, which is the pressure it would exert if it were the only gas in the container. **Dalton's law** states that the total pressure of a gas mixture is the sum of the partial pressures of the gases in the mixture.

LEARNING GOAL

Use Dalton's law of partial pressures to calculate the total pressure of a mixture of gases.

 TUTORIAL
Mixture of Gases

Dalton's Law

$$P_{total} = P_1 + P_2 + P_3 + \cdots$$
Total pressure = sum of the partial pressures
of a gas mixture   of the gases in the mixture

Suppose we have two separate tanks, one filled with helium at 2.0 atm and the other filled with argon at 4.0 atm. When the gases are combined in a single tank with the same volume and temperature, the number of gas molecules, not the type of gas, determines the pressure in a container. The pressure of the combined gas mixture in the single tank would be 6.0 atm, which is the sum of their individual or partial pressures.

$$P_{total} = P_{He} + P_{Ar}$$
$$= 2.0 \text{ atm} + 4.0 \text{ atm}$$
$$= 6.0 \text{ atm}$$

$P_{He} = 2.0$ atm $P_{Ar} = 4.0$ atm

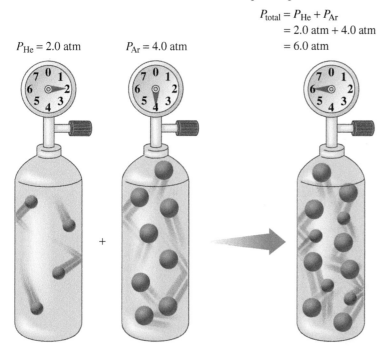

Pressure of a Gas Mixture

One 10-L gas tank contains propane (C_3H_8) gas at 300. torr, and a second 10-L gas tank contains methane (CH_4) gas at 500. torr. After the gases from both tanks are combined in a 10-L container with no change in temperature, what is the pressure of the gas mixture?

ANSWER

Using Dalton's law of partial pressures, we find that the total pressure of the gas mixture is the sum of the partial pressures of the gases in the mixture.

$$P_{total} = P_{propane} + P_{methane}$$
$$= 300.\ torr + 500.\ torr$$
$$= 800.\ torr$$

Therefore, when both propane and methane are placed in the same container, the total pressure of the mixture is 800. torr.

TABLE 7.7 Typical Composition of Air

Gas	Partial Pressure (mmHg)	Percentage (%)
Nitrogen, N_2	594	78
Oxygen, O_2	160	21
Carbon dioxide, CO_2		
Argon, Ar	6	1
Water vapor, H_2O (variable)		
Total air	760	100

Air Is a Gas Mixture

The air you breathe is a mixture of gases. What we call the *atmospheric pressure* is actually the sum of the partial pressures of all the gases in the air. Table 7.7 lists partial pressures for the gases in air on a typical day.

SAMPLE PROBLEM 7.14

Partial Pressure of a Gas in a Mixture

A mixture of oxygen and helium is prepared for a scuba diver who is going to descend 200 ft below the ocean surface. At that depth, the diver breathes a gas mixture that has a total pressure of 7.00 atm. If the partial pressure of the oxygen in the tank at that depth is 1140 mmHg, what is the partial pressure of the helium?

SOLUTION

Guide to Solving for Partial Pressure

STEP 1 Write the equation for sum of partial pressures.

STEP 2 Solve for the unknown pressure.

STEP 3 Substitute known pressures and calculate unknown.

STEP 1　**Write the equation for the sum of the partial pressures.** From Dalton's law of partial pressures, we know that the total pressure is equal to the sum of the partial pressures:

$$P_{total} = P_{O_2} + P_{He}$$

STEP 2　**Solve for the unknown pressure.** To solve for the partial pressure of helium (P_{He}), we rearrange the expression to give the following:

$$P_{total} = P_{He} + P_{O_2}$$
$$P_{He} = P_{total} - P_{O_2}$$

Convert units to match.

$$P_{O_2} = 1140\ mmHg \times \frac{1\ atm}{760\ mmHg} = 1.50\ atm$$

STEP 3　**Substitute known pressures and calculate the unknown.**

$$P_{He} = P_{total} - P_{O_2}$$
$$P_{He} = 7.00\ atm - 1.50\ atm$$
$$= 5.50\ atm$$

STUDY CHECK

An anesthetic consists of a mixture of cyclopropane gas, C_3H_6, and oxygen gas, O_2. If the mixture has a total pressure of 1.09 atm, and the partial pressure of the cyclopropane is 73 torr, what is the partial pressure (torr) of the oxygen in the anesthetic?

HEALTH NOTE

Blood Gases

Our cells continuously use oxygen and produce carbon dioxide. Both gases move in and out of the lungs through the membranes of the alveoli, the tiny air sacs at the ends of the airways in the lungs. An exchange of gases occurs in which oxygen from the air diffuses into the lungs and into the blood, while carbon dioxide produced in the cells is carried to the lungs to be exhaled. In Table 7.8, partial pressures are given for the gases in the air that we inhale (inspired air), the air in the alveoli, and the air that we exhale (expired air).

At sea level, oxygen normally has a partial pressure of 100 mmHg in the alveoli of the lungs. Because the partial pressure of oxygen in venous blood is 40 mmHg, oxygen diffuses from the alveoli into the bloodstream. The oxygen combines with hemoglobin, which carries

it to the tissues of the body, where the partial pressure of oxygen can be very low, less than 30 mmHg. Oxygen diffuses from the blood where the partial pressure of O_2 is high into the tissues where O_2 pressure is low.

As oxygen is used in the cells of the body during metabolic processes, carbon dioxide is produced, so the partial pressure of CO_2 may be as high as 50 mmHg or more. Carbon dioxide diffuses from the tissues into the bloodstream and is carried to the lungs. There it diffuses out of the blood, where CO_2 has a partial pressure of 46 mmHg, into the alveoli, where the CO_2 is at 40 mmHg, and is exhaled. Table 7.9 gives the partial pressures of blood gases in the tissues and in oxygenated and deoxygenated blood.

TABLE 7.8 Partial Pressures of Gases During Breathing

| Gas | Partial Pressure (mmHg) | | |
	Inspired Air	Alveolar Air	Expired Air
Nitrogen, N_2	594	573	569
Oxygen, O_2	160	100	116
Carbon dioxide, CO_2	0.3	40	28
Water vapor, H_2O	5.7	47	47
Total	760	760	760

TABLE 7.9 Partial Pressures of Oxygen and Carbon Dioxide in Blood and Tissues

| Gas | Partial Pressure (mmHg) | | |
	Oxygenated Blood	Deoxygenated Blood	Tissues
O_2	100	40	30 or less
CO_2	40	46	50 or greater

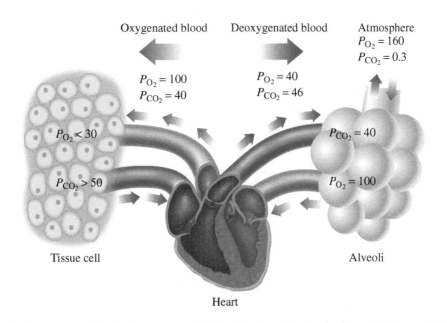

QUESTIONS AND PROBLEMS

Partial Pressures (Dalton's Law)

7.63 A typical air sample in the lungs contains oxygen at 100 mmHg, nitrogen at 573 mmHg, carbon dioxide at 40 mmHg, and water vapor at 47 mmHg. Why are these pressures called partial pressures?

7.64 Suppose a mixture contains helium and oxygen gases. If the partial pressure of helium is the same as the partial pressure of oxygen, what do you know about the number of helium atoms compared to the number of oxygen molecules? Explain.

7.65 In a gas mixture, the partial pressures are nitrogen 425 torr, oxygen 115 torr, and helium 225 torr. What is the total pressure (torr) exerted by the gas mixture?

7.66 In a gas mixture, the partial pressures are argon 415 mmHg, neon 75 mmHg, and nitrogen 125 mmHg. What is the total pressure (atm) exerted by the gas mixture?

7.67 A gas mixture containing oxygen, nitrogen, and helium exerts a total pressure of 925 torr. If the partial pressures are oxygen 425 torr and helium 75 torr, what is the partial pressure (torr) of the nitrogen in the mixture?

7.68 A gas mixture containing oxygen, nitrogen, and neon exerts a total pressure of 1.20 atm. If helium added to the mixture increases the pressure to 1.50 atm, what is the partial pressure (atm) of the helium?

7.69 In certain lung ailments such as emphysema, there is a decrease in the ability of oxygen to diffuse into the blood.
a. How would the partial pressure of oxygen in the blood change?
b. Why does a person with severe emphysema sometimes use a portable oxygen tank?

7.70 An injury to the head can affect the ability of a person to ventilate (breathe in and out), and so can certain drugs.
a. What would happen to the partial pressures of oxygen and carbon dioxide in the blood if a person cannot properly ventilate?
b. When a person with hypoventilation is placed on a ventilator, an air mixture is delivered at pressures that are alternately above and below the air pressure in the person's lung. How will this move oxygen gas into the lungs, and carbon dioxide out?

HEALTH NOTE

Hyperbaric Chambers

A burn patient may undergo treatment for burns and infections in a hyperbaric chamber, a device in which pressures can be obtained that are two to three times greater than atmospheric pressure. A greater oxygen pressure increases the level of dissolved oxygen in the blood and tissues. Because high levels of oxygen are toxic to many strains of bacteria, this helps fight bacterial infections. The hyperbaric chamber may also be used to counteract carbon monoxide (CO) poisoning and to treat some cancers.

The blood is normally capable of dissolving up to 95% of the oxygen available to it. Thus, if the partial pressure of the oxygen is 2280 mmHg (3 atm), 95% of that—2160 mmHg—can dissolve in the blood, saturating the tissues. In the case of carbon monoxide poisoning, this oxygen can replace the carbon monoxide that has attached to the hemoglobin.

A patient undergoing treatment in a hyperbaric chamber must also undergo decompression (reduction of pressure) at a rate that slowly reduces the concentration of dissolved oxygen in the blood. If decompression is too rapid, the oxygen dissolved in the blood may form gas bubbles in the circulatory system.

If scuba divers do not decompress slowly, they suffer a similar condition called *the bends*. While below the surface of the ocean, divers breathe air at higher pressures. At such high pressures, nitrogen gas will dissolve in their blood. If they ascend to the surface too quickly, the dissolved nitrogen forms bubbles in the blood that can produce life-threatening blood clots. The gas bubbles can also appear in the joints and tissues of the body and be quite painful. A diver suffering from the bends is placed immediately into a hyperbaric chamber, where pressure is first increased and then slowly decreased. The dissolved nitrogen can then diffuse through the lungs until atmospheric pressure is reached.

CONCEPT MAP

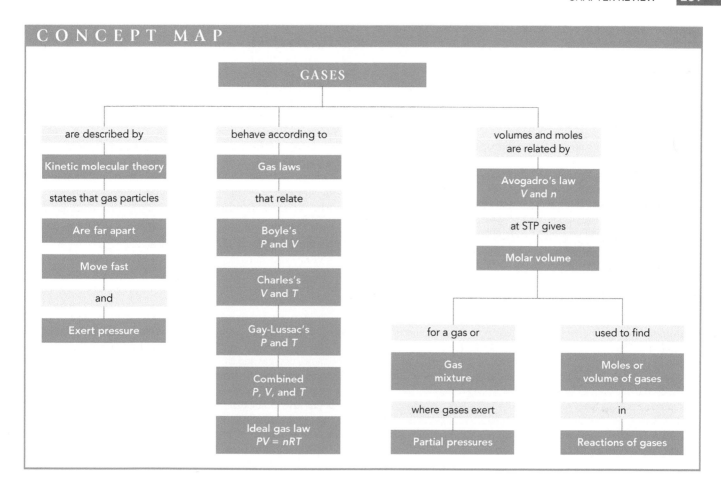

CHAPTER REVIEW

7.1 Properties of Gases
LEARNING GOAL: *Describe the kinetic molecular theory of gases and the properties of gases.*

In a gas, particles are so far apart and moving so fast that their attractions are unimportant. A gas is described by the physical properties of pressure (P), volume (V), temperature (T), and amount in moles (n).

7.2 Gas Pressure
LEARNING GOAL: *Describe the units of measurement used for pressure, and change from one unit to another.*

A gas exerts pressure, the force of the gas particles striking the surface of a container. Gas pressure is measured in units of torr, mmHg, and atm.

7.3 Pressure and Volume (Boyle's Law)
LEARNING GOAL: *Use the pressure–volume relationship (Boyle's law) to determine the new pressure or volume of a certain amount of gas at a constant temperature.*

The volume (V) of a gas changes inversely with the pressure (P) of the gas if there is no change in the amount and temperature: $P_1V_1 = P_2V_2$. This means that the pressure increases if volume decreases; pressure decreases if volume increases.

7.4 Temperature and Volume (Charles's Law)
LEARNING GOAL: *Use the temperature–volume relationship (Charles's law) to determine the new temperature or volume of a certain amount of gas at a constant pressure.*

The volume (V) of a gas is directly related to its Kelvin temperature (T) when there is no change in the amount and pressure of the gas:

$$\frac{V_1}{T_1} = \frac{V_2}{T_2}$$

Therefore, if temperature increases, the volume of the gas increases; if temperature decreases, volume decreases.

7.5 Temperature and Pressure (Gay–Lussac's Law)
LEARNING GOAL: *Use the temperature–pressure relationship (Gay–Lussac's law) to determine the new temperature or pressure of a certain amount of gas at a constant volume.*

The pressure (P) of a gas is directly related to its Kelvin temperature (T):

$$\frac{P_1}{T_1} = \frac{P_2}{T_2}$$

This relationship means that an increase in temperature increases the pressure of a gas, and a decrease in temperature decreases the pressure, as long as the amount and volume stay constant.

7.6 The Combined Gas Law
LEARNING GOAL: *Use the combined gas law to find the new pressure, volume, or temperature of a gas when changes in two of these properties are given.*

Gas laws combine into a relationship of pressure (P), volume (V), and temperature (T):

$$\frac{P_1V_1}{T_1} = \frac{P_2V_2}{T_2}$$

This expression is used to determine the effect of changes in two of the variables on the third.

7.7 Volume and Moles (Avogadro's Law)

LEARNING GOAL: *Use Avogadro's law to describe the relationship between the amount of a gas and its volume, and use this relationship in calculations.*

The volume (V) of a gas is directly related to the number of moles (n) of the gas when the pressure and temperature of the gas do not change:

$$\frac{V_1}{n_1} = \frac{V_2}{n_2}$$

If the moles of gas are increased, the volume must increase; if the moles of gas are decreased, the volume must decrease. At standard temperature (273 K) and pressure (1 atm), abbreviated STP, 1 mole of any gas has a volume of 22.4 L.

7.8 The Ideal Gas Law

LEARNING GOAL: *Use the ideal gas law to solve for P, V, T, or n of a gas when given three of the four values in the ideal gas law.*

The ideal gas law gives the relationship of all the quantities P, V, n, and T that describe and measure a gas: $PV = nRT$. Any of the four variables can be calculated if the other three are known.

7.9 Partial Pressures (Dalton's Law)

LEARNING GOAL: *Use Dalton's law of partial pressures to calculate the total pressure of a mixture of gases.*

In a mixture of two or more gases, the total pressure is the sum of the partial pressures of the individual gases:

$$P_{total} = P_1 + P_2 + P_3 + \cdots$$

The partial pressure of a gas in a mixture is the pressure it would exert if it were the only gas in the container.

▮ KEY TERMS

atmosphere (atm) The pressure exerted by a column of mercury 760 mm high.

atmospheric pressure The pressure exerted by the atmosphere.

Avogadro's law A gas law that states that the volume of gas is directly related to the number of moles of gas when pressure and temperature do not change.

Boyle's law A gas law stating that the pressure of a gas is inversely related to the volume when temperature (K) and amount (moles) of the gas do not change.

Charles's law A gas law stating that the volume of a gas changes directly with a change in Kelvin temperature when pressure and amount (moles) of the gas do not change.

combined gas law A relationship that combines several gas laws relating pressure, volume, and temperature:

$$\frac{P_1 V_1}{T_1} = \frac{P_2 V_2}{T_2}$$

Dalton's law A gas law stating that the total pressure exerted by a mixture of gases in a container is the sum of the partial pressures that each gas would exert alone.

direct relationship A relationship in which two properties increase or decrease together.

Gay–Lussac's law A gas law stating that the pressure of a gas changes directly with a change in Kelvin temperature when the number of moles of a gas and its volume do not change.

ideal gas constant, R A numerical value that relates the quantities P, V, n, and T in the ideal gas law, $PV = nRT$.

ideal gas law A law that combines the four measured properties of a gas in the equation $PV = nRT$.

inverse relationship A relationship in which two properties change in opposite directions.

kinetic molecular theory of gases A model used to explain the behavior of gases.

molar volume A volume of 22.4 L occupied by 1 mole of a gas at STP conditions of 0 °C (273 K) and 1 atm.

partial pressure The pressure exerted by a single gas in a gas mixture.

pressure The force exerted by gas particles that hit the walls of a container.

STP Standard conditions of exactly 0 °C (273 K) temperature and 1 atm pressure used for the comparison of gases.

vapor pressure The pressure exerted by the particles of vapor above a liquid.

▮ UNDERSTANDING THE CONCEPTS

7.71 At 100 °C, which of the following gases exerts
  a. the lowest pressure?
  b. the highest pressure?

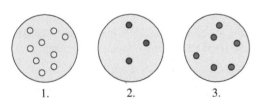

7.72 Indicate which diagram represents the volume of the gas sample in a flexible container when each of the following changes takes place:
  a. The temperature increases at constant pressure.
  b. The temperature decreases at constant pressure.

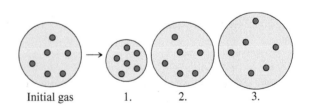

Initial gas   1.   2.   3.

  c. The pressure increases at constant temperature.
  d. The pressure decreases at constant temperature.
  e. Both the pressure and the Kelvin temperature are doubled.

7.73 A balloon is filled with helium gas with a pressure of 1.00 atm and neon gas with a pressure of 0.50 atm. For each of the following changes of the initial balloon, select the diagram (A, B, or C) that shows the final (new) volume of the balloon:

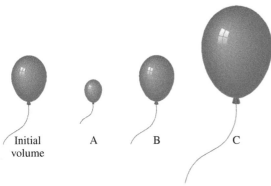

a. The balloon is put in a cold storage unit (*P* and *n* constant).
b. The balloon floats to a higher altitude where the pressure is less (*n* and *T* constant).
c. All of the neon gas is removed (*T* and *P* constant).
d. The Kelvin temperature doubles and one-half of the gas atoms leak out (*P* constant).
e. 2.0 moles of O_2 gas are added at constant *T* and *P*.

7.74 Indicate if pressure increases, decreases, or stays the same in each of the following:

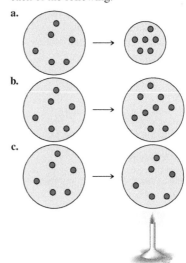

ADDITIONAL QUESTIONS AND PROBLEMS

For instructor-assigned homework, go to www.masteringchemistry.com.

7.75 At a restaurant, a customer chokes on a piece of food. You put your arms around the person's waist and use your fists to push up on the person's abdomen, an action called the *Heimlich maneuver*.
a. How would this action change the volume of the chest and lungs?
b. Why does it cause the person to expel the food item from the airway?

7.76 An airplane is pressurized to 650. mmHg, which is the atmospheric pressure at a ski resort at an altitude of 13 000 ft.
a. If air is 21% oxygen, what is the partial pressure of oxygen on the plane?
b. If the partial pressure of oxygen drops below 100. mmHg, passengers become drowsy. If this happens, oxygen masks are released. What is the total cabin pressure at which oxygen masks are dropped?

7.77 In 1783, Jacques Charles launched his first balloon filled with hydrogen gas, which he chose because it was lighter than air. If the balloon has a volume of 31 000 L, how many grams of hydrogen would be needed to fill the balloon at STP?

The AEROSTATIC GLOBE
Exhibited at Paris by Messrs Charles & Robert.
Decr 1 1783.

7.78 In problem 7.77, the balloon reached an altitude of 1000 m, where the pressure was 658 mmHg and the temperature was −8 °C. What was the volume, in liters, of the balloon at these conditions?

7.79 A fire extinguisher has a pressure of 10. atm at 25 °C. What is the pressure, in atmospheres, if the fire extinguisher is used at a temperature of 75 °C?

7.80 A weather balloon has a volume of 750 L when filled with helium at 8 °C at a pressure of 380 torr. What is the new volume of the balloon when the pressure is 0.20 atm and the temperature is −45 °C?

7.81 A sample of hydrogen (H_2) gas at 127 °C has a pressure of 2.00 atm. At what temperature (°C) will the pressure of the H_2 decrease to 0.25 atm?

7.82 A sample of nitrogen (N_2) gas has a volume of 250. mL at 30. °C and a pressure of 745 mmHg. What is the volume of the nitrogen at STP?

7.83 A 2.00-L container is filled with methane gas (CH_4) at a pressure of 2500 mmHg and a temperature of 18 °C. How many grams of methane are in the container?

7.84 A steel cylinder with a volume of 15.0 L is filled with 50.0 g of nitrogen gas at 25 °C. What is the pressure of the N_2 gas in the cylinder?

7.85 How many molecules of CO_2 are in 35.0 L of $CO_2(g)$ at 1.2 atm and 5 °C?

7.86 A container is filled with 4.0×10^{22} O_2 molecules at 5 °C and 845 mmHg. What is the volume, in mL, of the container?

7.87 When heated, calcium carbonate decomposes to give calcium oxide and carbon dioxide gas:

$$CaCO_3(s) \longrightarrow CaO(s) + CO_2(g)$$

If 2.00 moles of $CaCO_3$ react, how many liters of CO_2 gas are produced at STP?

7.88 Magnesium reacts with oxygen to form magnesium oxide:

$$2Mg(s) + O_2(g) \longrightarrow 2MgO(s)$$

How many liters of oxygen gas at STP are needed to react completely with 8.0 g of magnesium?

7.89 Your space ship has docked at a space station above Mars. The temperature inside the space station is a carefully controlled 24 °C at a pressure of 745 mmHg. A balloon with a volume of 425 mL drifts into the airlock, where the temperature is −95 °C and the pressure is 0.115 atm. What is the new volume of the balloon? Assume that the balloon is very elastic.

7.90 How many liters of H_2 gas can be produced at STP from 25.0 g of Zn?

$$Zn(s) + 2HCl(aq) \longrightarrow ZnCl_2(aq) + H_2(g)$$

7.91 Aluminum oxide can be formed from its elements:

$$4Al(s) + 3O_2(g) \longrightarrow 2Al_2O_3(s)$$

What volume of oxygen is needed at STP to completely react 5.4 g of aluminum?

7.92 Glucose, $C_6H_{12}O_6$, is metabolized in living systems according to the reaction

$$C_6H_{12}O_6(s) + 6O_2(g) \longrightarrow 6CO_2(g) + 6H_2O(l)$$

How many grams of water can be produced when 12.5 L of O_2 reacts at STP?

7.93 A sample of gas with a mass of 1.62 g occupies a volume of 941 mL at a pressure of 748 torr and a temperature of 20 °C. What is the molar mass of the gas?

7.94 What is the molar mass of a gas if 1.15 g of the gas has a volume of 225 mL at STP?

7.95 Nitrogen dioxide reacts with water to produce oxygen and ammonia:

$$4NO_2(g) + 6H_2O(g) \longrightarrow 7O_2(g) + 4NH_3(g)$$

a. How many liters of O_2 at STP are produced when 2.5×10^{23} molecules of NO_2 react?

b. A 5.00-L sample of $H_2O(g)$ reacts at a temperature of 375 °C and a pressure of 725 mmHg. How many grams of NH_3 can be produced?

7.96 Hydrogen gas can be produced in the laboratory through the reaction of aluminum metal with hydrochloric acid:

$$2Al(s) + 6HCl(aq) \longrightarrow 2AlCl_3(aq) + 3H_2(g)$$

What is the volume, in liters, of H_2 gas produced at STP from the reaction of 25.0 g of Al?

7.97 A weather balloon is partially filled with helium to allow for expansion at high altitudes. At STP, a weather balloon is filled with enough helium to give a volume of 25.0 L. At an altitude of 30.0 km, where the temperature is −35 °C, it has expanded to 2460 L. The increase in volume causes it to burst, and a small parachute returns the instruments to Earth.
a. How many grams of helium were added to the balloon?
b. What was the pressure, in mmHg, of the helium inside the balloon when it burst?

7.98 What is the total pressure, in mmHg, of a gas mixture containing argon gas at 0.25 atm, helium gas at 350 mmHg, and nitrogen gas at 360 torr?

7.99 A gas mixture contains oxygen and argon at partial pressures of 0.60 atm and 425 mmHg. If nitrogen gas added to the sample increases the total pressure to 1250 torr, what is the partial pressure, in torr, of the nitrogen added?

7.100 A gas mixture contains helium and oxygen at partial pressures of 255 torr and 0.450 atm. What is the total pressure, in mmHg, of the mixture after it is placed in a container one-half the volume of the original container?

CHALLENGE QUESTIONS

7.101 A gas sample has a volume of 4250 mL at 15 °C and 745 mmHg. What is the new temperature (°C) after the sample is transferred to a new container with a volume of 2.50 L and a pressure of 1.20 atm?

7.102 In the fermentation of glucose (wine making), a volume of 780 mL of CO_2 gas was produced at 37 °C and 1.00 atm. What is the volume (L) of the gas when measured at 22 °C and 675 mmHg?

7.103 When sensors in a car detect a collision, they cause the reaction of sodium azide, NaN_3:

$$2NaN_3(s) \longrightarrow 2Na(s) + 3N_2(g)$$

This generates nitrogen gas, which fills the air bags within 0.03 second.
    How many liters of N_2 are produced at STP if the air bag contains 132 g of NaN_3?

7.104 Nitrogen dioxide reacts with water to produce oxygen and ammonia:

$$4NO_2(g) + 6H_2O(g) \longrightarrow 7O_2(g) + 4NH_3(g)$$

How many liters of O_2 at STP are produced when 2.5×10^{23} molecules of NO_2 react?

7.105 A 1.00-g sample of dry ice (CO_2) is placed in a container that has a volume of 4.60 L and a temperature of 24.0 °C. Calculate

the pressure of CO_2, in mmHg, inside the container after all the dry ice changes to a gas.

$$CO_2(s) \longrightarrow CO_2(g)$$

7.106 A 250-mL sample of nitrogen (N_2) has a pressure of 745 mmHg at 30 °C. What is the mass of nitrogen?

7.107 Hydrogen gas can be produced in the laboratory through the reaction of magnesium metal with hydrochloric acid:

$$Mg(s) + 2HCl(aq) \longrightarrow MgCl_2(aq) + H_2(g)$$

What is the volume, in liters, of H_2 gas produced at 24 °C and 835 mmHg, from the reaction of 12.0 g of Mg?

7.108 In the formation of smog, nitrogen and oxygen gas react to form nitrogen dioxide. How many grams of NO_2 will be produced when 2.0 L of nitrogen at 840 mmHg and 24 °C are completely reacted?

$$N_2(g) + 2O_2(g) \longrightarrow 2NO_2(g)$$

7.109 Solid aluminum reacts with aqueous H_2SO_4 to form H_2 gas and aluminum sulfate. When a sample of Al reacts, 415 mL of H_2 gas is produced at 23 °C at a pressure of 734 mmHg. How many grams of Al reacted?

$$2Al(s) + 3H_2SO_4(aq) \longrightarrow 3H_2(g) + Al_2(SO_4)_3(aq)$$

7.110 When heated, solid $KClO_3$ forms solid KCl and O_2 gas. When a sample of $KClO_3$ is heated, 226 mL of O_2 gas is produced with a pressure of 719 mmHg and a temperature of 26 °C. How many grams of $KClO_3$ reacted?

$$2KClO_3(s) \longrightarrow 2KCl(s) + 3O_2(g)$$

7.111 We saw in Chapter 1 that 1 teragram (Tg) is equal to 10^{12} g. In 2000, CO_2 emissions from the generation of electricity for use in homes in the United States were 780 Tg. In 2020, it is estimated that CO_2 emissions from the generation of electricity for use in homes will be 990 Tg.

   a. Calculate the number of kilograms of CO_2 emitted for the years 2000 and 2020.
   b. Calculate the number of moles of CO_2 emitted for the years 2000 and 2020.

   c. What is the increase, in megagrams, for the CO_2 emissions between the years 2000 and 2020?

7.112 We saw in Chapter 1 that 1 teragram (Tg) is equal to 10^{12} g. In 2000, CO_2 emissions from fuels used for transportation in the United States was 1990 Tg. In 2020, it is estimated that CO_2 emissions from the fuels used for transportation in the United States will be 2760 Tg.

   a. Calculate the number of kilograms of CO_2 emitted for the years 2000 and 2020.
   b. Calculate the number of moles of CO_2 emitted for the years 2000 and 2020.
   c. What is the increase, in megagrams, for the CO_2 emitted between the years 2000 and 2020?

ANSWERS

ANSWERS TO STUDY CHECKS

7.1 0.862 atm

7.2 250 torr

7.3 50.0 mL

7.4 569 mL

7.5 16 °C

7.6 241 mmHg

7.7 7.50 L

7.8 7.0 g of N_2

7.9 5.41 L of H_2

7.10 0.327 mole of Cl_2

7.11 1.04 L of CO

7.12 104 g/mole

7.13 18.1 L of H_2

7.14 755 torr

ANSWERS TO SELECTED QUESTIONS AND PROBLEMS

7.1 **a.** At a higher temperature, gas particles have greater kinetic energy, which makes them move faster.
   b. Because there are great distances between the particles of a gas, they can be pushed closer together and still remain a gas.

7.3 **a.** temperature   **b.** volume   **c.** amount   **d.** pressure

7.5 atmospheres (atm), mmHg, torr, lb/in.^{2}, kPa

7.7 **a.** 1520 torr   **b.** 1520 mmHg

7.9 As a diver ascends to the surface, external pressure decreases. If the air in the lungs were not exhaled, its volume would expand and severely damage the lungs. The pressure in the lungs must adjust to changes in the external pressure.

7.11 **a.** The pressure is greater in cylinder A. According to Boyle's law, a decrease in volume pushes the gas particles closer together, which will cause an increase in the pressure.
   b.

Property	Conditions 1	Conditions 2	Know	Predict
Pressure (P)	650 mmHg	1.2 atm (910 mmHg)	P increases	
Volume (V)	220 mL	160 mL		V decreases

7.13 **a.** The pressure doubles.
   b. The pressure falls to one-third the initial pressure.
   c. The pressure increases to ten times the original pressure.

7.15 **a.** 328 mmHg   **b.** 2620 mmHg   **c.** 4400 mmHg

7.17 **a.** 25 L   **b.** 25 L   **c.** 100. L

7.19 25 L

7.21 **a.** inspiration   **b.** expiration   **c.** inspiration

7.23 **a.** C   **b.** A   **c.** B

7.25 **a.** 303 °C   **b.** −129 °C   **c.** 591 °C   **d.** 136 °C

7.27 **a.** 2400 mL   **b.** 4900 mL   **c.** 1800 mL   **d.** 1700 mL

7.29 An increase in temperature increases the pressure inside the can. When the pressure exceeds the pressure limit of the can, it explodes.

7.31 **a.** −23 °C   **b.** 168 °C

7.33 **a.** 770 torr   **b.** 1.51 atm

7.35 **a.** boiling point   **b.** vapor pressure
   c. atmospheric pressure   **d.** boiling point

7.37 **a.** On top of a mountain, water boils below 100 °C because the atmospheric (external) pressure is less than 1 atm.
   b. Because the pressure inside a pressure cooker is greater than 1 atm, water boils above 100 °C. At a higher temperature, food cooks faster.

7.39 **a.** 4.26 atm   **b.** 3.07 atm   **c.** 0.605 atm

7.41 −33 °C

7.43 The volume increases because the number of gas particles is increased.

7.45 **a.** 4.00 L   **b.** 14.6 L   **c.** 26.7 L

7.47 **a.** 2.00 moles of O_2 **b.** 0.179 mole of CO_2
   c. 4.48 L   **d.** 55 400 mL

7.49 7.60 L of H_2

7.51 4.93 atm

7.53 29.4 g of O_2

7.55 565 K (292 °C)

7.57 **a.** 42 g/mole **b.** 39.8 g/mole **c.** 33 g/mole

7.59 178 L of O_2

7.61 5.25 L of O_2

7.63 In a gas mixture, the pressure that each gas exerts as part of the total pressure is called the *partial pressure* of that gas. Because the air sample is a mixture of gases, the total pressure is the sum of the partial pressures of each gas in the sample.

7.65 765 torr

7.67 425 torr

7.69 **a.** The partial pressure of oxygen will be lower than normal.
b. Breathing a higher concentration of oxygen will help to increase the supply of oxygen in the lungs and blood and raise the partial pressure of oxygen in the blood.

7.71 **a.** 2 **b.** 1

7.73 **a.** A **b.** C **c.** A **d.** B **e.** C

7.75 **a.** The volume of the chest and lungs is decreased.
b. The decrease in volume increases the pressure, which can dislodge the food in the trachea.

7.77 2.8×10^3 g of H_2

7.79 12 atm

7.81 −223 °C

7.83 4.5 g

7.85 1.1×10^{24} molecules of CO_2

7.87 44.8 L of CO_2

7.89 2170 mL

7.91 3.4 L of O_2

7.93 42.1 g/mole

7.95 **a.** 16 L of O_2 **b.** 1.02 g of NH_3

7.97 **a.** 4.46 g of helium **b.** 6.73 mmHg

7.99 370 torr

7.101 −66 °C

7.103 68.2 L of N_2

7.105 91.5 mmHg

7.107 11.0 L of H_2

7.109 0.297 g of Al

7.111 **a.** 7.8×10^{11} kg of CO_2 (2000), 9.9×10^{11} kg of CO_2 (2020)
b. 1.8×10^{13} moles of CO_2 (2000), 2.3×10^{13} moles of CO_2 (2020)
c. 2.1×10^8 Mg of CO_2 increase

Solutions

8

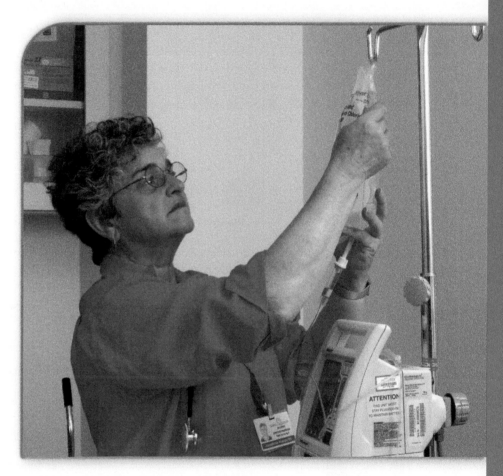

"There is a lot of chemistry going on in the body, including drug interactions," says Josephine Firenze, registered nurse, Kaiser Hospital.

Normally, the body maintains a homeostasis of fluids and electrolytes. Conditions that alter the composition of body fluids can lead to convulsions, coma, or death. To halt the disease process and to establish homeostasis, a patient may be given intravenous fluid therapy. Solutions that are compatible with body fluids, such as a 5% glucose or a 0.9% saline solution, are used. An infusion pump delivers the desired number of milliliters per hour to the patient. During IV therapy, a patient is checked for fluid overload as indicated by edema (swelling) or a greater fluid input than output.

Mastering**CHEMISTRY**™

Visit **www.masteringchemistry.com** for self-study materials and instructor-assigned homework.

Solutions are everywhere around us. Most consist of one substance dissolved in another. The air we breathe is a solution of primarily oxygen and nitrogen gases. Carbon dioxide gas dissolved in water makes carbonated drinks. When we make solutions of coffee or tea, we use hot water to dissolve substances from coffee beans or tea leaves. The ocean is also a solution, consisting of many salts, such as sodium chloride, dissolved in water. In a hospital, the antiseptic tincture of iodine is a solution of iodine dissolved in ethanol.

Our body fluids contain water and dissolved substances, such as glucose and urea, and ions called electrolytes, such as K^+, Na^+, Cl^-, Mg^{2+}, HCO_3^-, and HPO_4^{2-}. Proper amounts of each of these dissolved substances and water must be maintained in the body fluids. Small changes in electrolyte levels can seriously disrupt cellular processes, endangering our health. Therefore, the measurement of their concentrations is a valuable diagnostic tool.

Through the processes of osmosis and dialysis, water, essential nutrients, and waste products enter and leave the cells of the body. In osmosis, water flows in and out of the cells of the body. In dialysis, small particles in solution as well as water diffuse through semipermeable membranes. The kidneys utilize osmosis and dialysis to regulate the amount of water and electrolytes that are excreted.

8.1 Solutions

LEARNING GOAL

Identify the solute and solvent in a solution. Describe the formation of a solution.

A **solution** is a homogeneous mixture in which one substance called the **solute** is uniformly dispersed in another substance called the **solvent**. Because the solute and the solvent do not react with each other, they can be mixed in varying proportions. A little salt dissolved in water tastes slightly salty. When more salt dissolves, the water tastes very salty. Usually, the solute (in this case, salt) is the substance present in the smaller amount, whereas the solvent (in this case, water) is present in the larger amount. In a solution, the particles of the solute are evenly dispersed within the solvent. (See Figure 8.1.)

Solute: The substance present in lesser amount

Salt

Water

Solvent: The substance present in greater amount

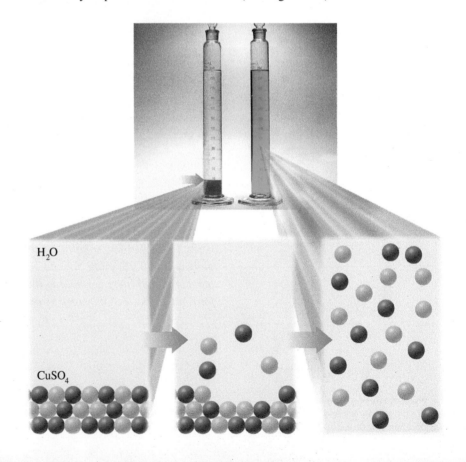

H₂O

CuSO₄

FIGURE 8.1 A solution of copper(II) sulfate (CuSO₄) forms as particles of solute dissolve, move away from the crystals, and become evenly dispersed among the solvent (water) molecules.

Q What does the uniform blue color indicate about the CuSO₄ solution?

TABLE 8.1 Some Examples of Solutions

Type	Example	Primary Solute	Solvent
Gas Solutions			
Gas in a gas	Air	Oxygen (gas)	Nitrogen (gas)
Liquid Solutions			
Gas in a liquid	Soda water	Carbon dioxide (gas)	Water (liquid)
	Household ammonia	Ammonia (gas)	Water (liquid)
Liquid in a liquid	Vinegar	Acetic acid (liquid)	Water (liquid)
Solid in a liquid	Seawater	Sodium chloride (solid)	Water (liquid)
	Tincture of iodine	Iodine (solid)	Ethanol (liquid)
Solid Solutions			
Liquid in a solid	Dental amalgam	Mercury (liquid)	Silver (solid)
Solid in a solid	Brass	Zinc (solid)	Copper (solid)
	Steel	Carbon (solid)	Iron (solid)

Types of Solutes and Solvents

Solutes and solvents may be solids, liquids, or gases. The solution that forms has the same physical state as the solvent. When sugar crystals are dissolved in water, the resulting sugar solution is liquid. Sugar is the solute, and water is the solvent. Soda water and soft drinks are prepared by dissolving carbon dioxide gas in water. The carbon dioxide gas is the solute, and water is the solvent. Table 8.1 lists some solutes and solvents and their solutions.

Water as a Solvent

Water is one of the most common solvents in nature. In the H_2O molecule, an oxygen atom shares electrons with two hydrogen atoms. Because the oxygen atom is much more electronegative, the O—H bonds are polar. In each of the polar bonds, the oxygen atom has a partial negative (δ^-) charge, and the hydrogen atom has a partial positive (δ^+) charge. Because of the arrangement of the polar bonds, water is a *polar solvent*.

Hydrogen bonds occur between molecules where a partially positive hydrogen is attracted to the strongly electronegative atoms of O, N, or F in other molecules. In water, hydrogen bonds are formed by the attraction between the oxygen atom of one water molecule and a hydrogen atom in another water molecule. In the diagram, hydrogen bonds are shown as dots between the water molecules. Although hydrogen bonds are much weaker than covalent or ionic bonds, there are many of them linking molecules together. As a result, hydrogen bonding plays an important role in the properties of water and biological compounds such as proteins, carbohydrates, and DNA.

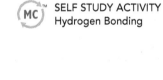

SELF STUDY ACTIVITY
Hydrogen Bonding

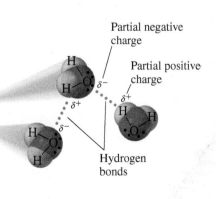

Partial negative charge

Partial positive charge

Hydrogen bonds

HEALTH NOTE

Water in the Body

The average adult body contains about 60% water by mass, and the average infant about 75%. About 60% of the body's water is contained

24 Hours

Water gain	
Liquid	1000 mL
Food	1200 mL
Metabolism	300 mL
Total	2500 mL

Water loss	
Urine	1500 mL
Perspiration	300 mL
Breath	600 mL
Feces	100 mL
Total	2500 mL

within the cells as intracellular fluids; the other 40% makes up extracellular fluids, which include the interstitial fluid in tissue and the plasma in the blood. These external fluids carry nutrients and waste materials between the cells and the circulatory system.

Every day you lose between 1500 and 3000 mL of water from the kidneys as urine, from the skin as perspiration, from the lungs as you exhale, and from the gastrointestinal tract. Serious dehydration can occur in an adult if there is a 10% loss in total body fluid. A 20% loss of fluid can be fatal. An infant suffers severe dehydration with a 5–10% loss in body fluid.

Water loss is continually replaced by the liquids and foods in the diet and from metabolic processes that produce water in the cells of the body. Table 8.2 lists the percentage by mass of water contained in some foods.

TABLE 8.2 Percentage of Water in Some Foods

Food	Water (% by mass)	Food	Water (% by mass)
Vegetables		**Meats/Fish**	
Carrot	88	Chicken, cooked	71
Celery	94	Hamburger, broiled	60
Cucumber	96	Salmon	71
Tomato	94	**Grains**	
Fruits		Cake	34
Apple	85	French bread	31
Banana	76	Noodles, cooked	70
Cantaloupe	91	**Milk Products**	
Orange	86	Cottage cheese	78
Strawberry	90	Milk, whole	87
Watermelon	93	Yogurt	88

Formation of Solutions

The interactions between solute and solvent will determine whether a solution will form. Initially, energy is needed to separate the particles in the solute and to move the solvent particles apart. Then energy is released as solute particles move between the solvent particles to form a solution. However, attractive forces between the solute and the solvent particles must be strong enough to provide the energy for the initial separation. These attractive forces only occur when the solute and the solvent have similar polarities. If there is no attraction between a solute and a solvent, there is not sufficient energy to form a solution. (See Table 8.3.)

TABLE 8.3 Possible Combinations of Solutes and Solvents

Solutions Will Form		Solutions Will Not Form	
Solute	**Solvent**	**Solute**	**Solvent**
Polar	Polar	Polar	Nonpolar
Nonpolar	Nonpolar	Nonpolar	Polar

Solutions with Ionic and Polar Solutes

In ionic solutes such as sodium chloride, NaCl, there are strong solute-solute attractions between positively charged Na^+ ions and negatively charged Cl^- ions. In water, a polar solvent, the hydrogen bonds provide strong solvent-solvent attractions. When a NaCl crystal is placed in water, negatively charged oxygen atoms of water molecules attract positive Na^+ ions, and the positively charged hydrogen atoms of other water molecules attract negative Cl^- ions. (See Figure 8.2.) As soon as the Na^+ and Cl^- ions form a solution, they undergo **hydration** as water molecules surround each ion. The strong solute-solvent attractions between the Na^+ and Cl^- ions and the polar water molecules release the energy needed to form the solution. In the equation for the formation of the NaCl solution, the solid and aqueous NaCl are shown with the formula H_2O over the arrow, which indicates that water is needed for the dissociation process but is not a reactant.

$$NaCl(s) \xrightarrow{H_2O} Na^+(aq) + Cl^-(aq)$$

In another example, we find that a polar covalent compound such as methanol, CH_3OH, dissolves in water because methanol has a polar —OH group that forms hydrogen bonds with water.

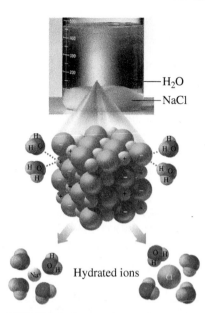

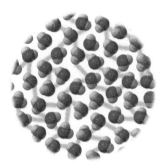

Methanol (CH_3OH) solute   Water solvent   Methanol-water solution with hydrogen bonding

FIGURE 8.2 Ions on the surface of a crystal of NaCl dissolve in water as they are attracted to the polar water molecules that pull the ions into solution and surround them.

Q What helps keep the Na^+ and Cl^- ions in solution?

Solutions with Nonpolar Solutes

Compounds containing nonpolar molecules such as iodine (I_2), oil, or grease do not dissolve in water, because there is little or no interaction between the particles of a nonpolar solute and the polar solvent. Nonpolar solutes require nonpolar solvents for a solution to form. The expression *"like dissolves like"* is a way of saying that the polarities of a solute and a solvent must be similar to form a solution. Figure 8.3 illustrates the formation of some polar and nonpolar solutions.

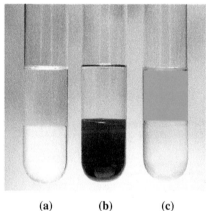

(a)   (b)   (c)

FIGURE 8.3 Like dissolves like. **(a)** The test tubes contain an upper layer of water (polar) and a lower layer of CH_2Cl_2 (nonpolar). **(b)** The nonpolar solute I_2 dissolves in the nonpolar layer. **(c)** The ionic solute $Ni(NO_3)_2$ dissolves in the water.

Q Which layer would dissolve polar molecules of sugar?

CONCEPT CHECK 8.1

■ Polar and Nonpolar Solutes

Indicate whether each of the following substances will form solutions with water. Explain.
a. KCl
b. octane, C_8H_{18}, in gasoline
c. ethanol, C_2H_5OH, in mouthwash

ANSWER

a. KCl is an ionic compound. The solute-solvent attractions between K^+ and Cl^- and polar water will release the energy needed to break solute-solute and solvent-solvent bonds. Thus, a KCl solution will form.

b. C_8H_{18} is a nonpolar substance that will not form a solution with water. The nonpolar solute-polar solvent attractions will not occur and no energy is released to form a solution.

c. C_2H_5OH is a polar solute. Because attractions between a polar solute and polar water release energy to break solute-solute and solvent-solvent bonds, a C_2H_5OH solution will form.

QUESTIONS AND PROBLEMS

Solutions

8.1 Identify the solute and the solvent in each solution composed of the following:
   a. 10.0 g of NaCl and 100.0 g of H_2O
   b. 50.0 mL of ethanol, C_2H_5OH, and 10.0 mL of H_2O
   c. 0.20 L of O_2 and 0.80 L of N_2 at STP

8.2 Identify the solute and the solvent in each solution composed of the following:
   a. 50.0 g of silver and 4.0 g of mercury
   b. 100.0 mL of water and 5.0 g of sugar
   c. 1.0 g of I_2 and 50.0 mL of alcohol

8.3 Describe the formation of an aqueous KI solution.

8.4 Describe the formation of an aqueous LiBr solution.

8.5 Water is a polar solvent; CCl_4 is a nonpolar solvent. In which solvent is each of the following more likely to be soluble?
   a. KCl, ionic
   b. I_2, nonpolar
   c. sucrose (table sugar), polar
   d. gasoline, nonpolar

8.6 Water is a polar solvent; hexane is a nonpolar solvent. In which solvent is each of the following more likely to be soluble?
   a. vegetable oil, nonpolar
   b. benzene, nonpolar
   c. $LiNO_3$, ionic
   d. Na_2SO_4, ionic

8.2 Electrolytes and Nonelectrolytes

LEARNING GOAL

Identify solutes as electrolytes or nonelectrolytes.

Solutes can be classified by their ability to conduct an electrical current. When **electrolytes** dissolve in water, they separate into ions that conduct electricity. When **nonelectrolytes** dissolve in water, they do not separate into ions, and their solutions do not conduct electricity.

To test solutions for ions, we can use an apparatus that consists of a battery and a pair of electrodes connected by wires to a light bulb. The light bulb glows when electricity flows, which happens only when the solution contains ions that move to each of the electrodes to complete the circuit.

Electrolytes

EXPLORE YOUR WORLD

Like Dissolves Like

Mix together small amounts of the following substances:
a. oil and water
b. water and vinegar
c. salt and water
d. sugar and water
e. salt and oil

QUESTIONS

1. Which of the mixtures formed a solution? Which did not?
2. Why do some mixtures form solutions, but others do not?

Electrolytes can be further classified as *strong electrolytes* and *weak electrolytes*. For all electrolytes, some or all of the solute that dissolves produces ions, a process called *dissociation*. For a **strong electrolyte**, such as sodium chloride (NaCl), 100% of the solute dissociates into ions. When the electrodes from the light bulb apparatus are placed in the NaCl solution, the light bulb is very bright.

In an equation for dissociation, the electrical charges must balance. For example, the strong electrolyte magnesium nitrate dissociates to give one magnesium ion for every two nitrate ions. However, only the ionic bonds between Mg^{2+} and NO_3^- are broken, not the covalent bonds within the polyatomic ion. The equation for the dissociation for $Mg(NO_3)_2$ is written as follows:

$$Mg(NO_3)_2(s) \xrightarrow{\text{H}_2\text{O}} Mg^{2+}(aq) + 2NO_3^-(aq)$$

For a **weak electrolyte** such as HF, only a small percentage of the dissolved solute dissociates into ions. Most of a weak electrolyte is present in a solution as undissociated molecules. When the electrodes are placed in a solution of a weak electrolyte, the glow of the light bulb is very dim. Thus, an aqueous solution of the weak electrolyte HF consists of mostly HF molecules and only a few H^+ and F^- ions. As HF molecules dissociate into ions, some of H^+ and F^- ions recombine to form HF molecules. These forward and reverse reactions of molecules to ions and back again are indicated by two arrows that point in opposite directions, as shown in the following equation:

$$HF(aq) \underset{\text{Recombination}}{\overset{\text{Dissociation}}{\rightleftharpoons}} H^+(aq) + F^-(aq)$$

Nonelectrolytes

A nonelectrolyte such as sucrose (sugar) dissolves in water as molecules, which do not dissociate into ions. When electrodes are placed in a solution of a nonelectrolyte, the light bulb does not glow, because the solution does not conduct electricity.

$$C_{12}H_{22}O_{11}(s) \xrightarrow{H_2O} C_{12}H_{22}O_{11}(aq)$$

Sucrose   Solution of sucrose molecules

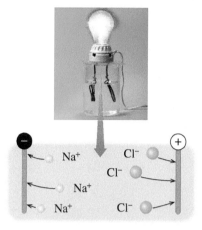

Strong electrolyte

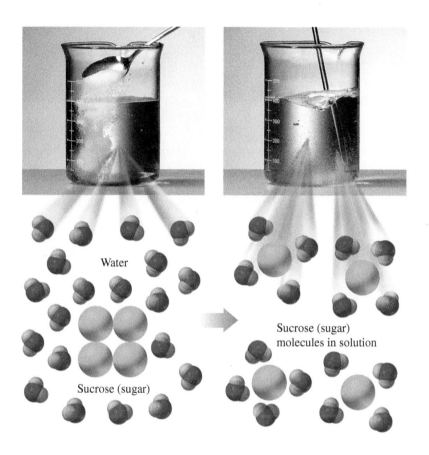

Water

Sucrose (sugar)

Sucrose (sugar) molecules in solution

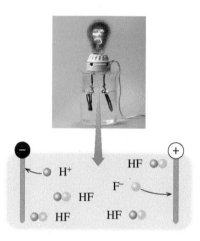

Weak electrolyte

Table 8.4 summarizes the classification of solutes in aqueous solutions.

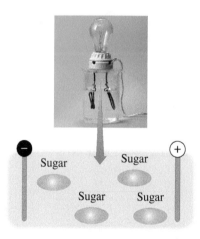

Nonelectrolyte

TABLE 8.4 Classification of Solutes in Aqueous Solutions

Type of Solute	Dissociation	Particles in Solution	Conducts Electricity?	Examples
Strong electrolyte	Complete	Ions only	Yes	Ionic compounds such as NaCl, KBr, MgCl$_2$, NaNO$_3$; NaOH, KOH; HCl, HBr, HI, HNO$_3$, HClO$_4$, H$_2$SO$_4$
Weak electrolyte	Partial	Mostly molecules and a few ions	Yes, but poorly	HF, H$_2$O, NH$_3$, HC$_2$H$_3$O$_2$ (acetic acid)
Nonelectrolyte	None	Molecules only	No	Carbon compounds such as CH$_3$OH (methanol), C$_2$H$_5$OH (ethanol), C$_{12}$H$_{22}$O$_{11}$ (sucrose), CH$_4$N$_2$O (urea)

CONCEPT CHECK 8.2

■ **Electrolytes and Nonelectrolytes**

Identify the components in each of the following aqueous solutions, and write the equation for the formation of a solution:

a. ammonium bromide, a strong electrolyte
b. urea, CH_4N_2O, a nonelectrolyte
c. hypochlorous acid, $HClO$, a weak electrolyte

ANSWER

a. An aqueous solution of the strong electrolyte, NH_4Br, contains NH_4^+ and Br^- ions and the solvent H_2O molecules:

$$NH_4Br(s) \xrightarrow{H_2O} NH_4^+(aq) + Br^-(aq)$$

b. An aqueous solution of the nonelectrolyte, CH_4N_2O, contains only molecules of urea, CH_4N_2O, and the solvent H_2O molecules:

$$CH_4N_2O(s) \xrightarrow{H_2O} CH_4N_2O(aq)$$

c. An aqueous solution of the weak electrolyte, $HClO$, contains mostly $HClO$ molecules, a few H^+ and ClO^- ions, and the solvent H_2O molecules:

$$HClO(aq) \xrightleftharpoons{H_2O} H^+(aq) + ClO^-(aq)$$

SAMPLE PROBLEM   8.1

■ **Solutions of Electrolytes and Nonelectrolytes**

Indicate whether solutions of each of the following contain only ions, only molecules, or mostly molecules and a few ions:

a. Na_2SO_4, a strong electrolyte   **b.** CH_3OH, a nonelectrolyte

SOLUTION

a. A solution of Na_2SO_4 contains only the ions Na^+ and SO_4^{2-}.
b. A nonelectrolyte such as CH_3OH dissolves only as molecules.

STUDY CHECK

Boric acid, H_3BO_3, is a weak electrolyte. Would you expect a boric acid solution to contain only ions, only molecules, or mostly molecules and a few ions?

Equivalents

Body fluids typically contain a mixture of several electrolytes, such as Na^+, Cl^-, K^+, and Ca^{2+}. We measure each individual ion in terms of an **equivalent (Eq)**, which is the amount of that ion equal to 1 mole of positive or negative electrical charge. For example, 1 mole of Na^+ ions and 1 mole of Cl^- ions are each 1 equivalent or 1000 milliequivalents (mEq) because they each contain 1 mole of charge. For an ion with a charge of $2+$ or $2-$, there are 2 equivalents for each mole. Some examples of ions and equivalents are shown in Table 8.5.

TABLE 8.5 Equivalents of Electrolytes

Ion	Electrical Charge	Number of Equivalents in 1 Mole
Na^+	$1+$	1 Eq
Ca^{2+}	$2+$	2 Eq
Fe^{3+}	$3+$	3 Eq
Cl^-	$1-$	1 Eq
SO_4^{2-}	$2-$	2 Eq

In a solution, the charge of the positive ions is always balanced by the charge of the negative ions. For example, a solution containing 25 mEq/L of Na^+ and 4 mEq/L of K^+ has a total positive charge of 29 mEq/L. If Cl^- is the only anion, its concentration must be 29 mEq/L.

SAMPLE PROBLEM 8.2

■ Electrolyte Concentration

In body fluids, concentrations of electrolytes are often expressed as milliequivalents (mEq) per liter. A typical concentration for Ca^{2+} in the blood is 8.8 mEq/L.

a. How many moles of calcium ion are in 0.50 L of blood?
b. If chloride ion is the only other ion present, what is its concentration in mEq/L?

SOLUTION

a. Using the volume and the electrolyte concentration (in mEq/L), we can find the number of equivalents in 0.50 L of blood:

$$0.50 \ \cancel{L} \times \frac{8.8 \ \cancel{mEq \ Ca^{2+}}}{1 \ \cancel{L}} \times \frac{1 \ Eq \ Ca^{2+}}{1000 \ \cancel{mEq \ Ca^{2+}}} = 0044 \ Eq \ of \ Ca^{2+}$$

We can then convert equivalents to moles (for Ca^{2+} there are 2 Eq per mole):

$$0.0044 \ \cancel{Eq \ Ca^{2+}} \times \frac{1 \ mole \ Ca^{2+}}{2 \ \cancel{Eq \ Ca^{2+}}} = 0.0022 \ mole \ of \ Ca^{2+}$$

b. If the concentration of Ca^{2+} is 8.8 mEq/L, then the concentration of Cl^- must be 8.8 mEq/L to balance the charge.

STUDY CHECK

A Ringer's solution for intravenous fluid replacement contains 155 mEq Cl^- per liter of solution. If a patient receives 1250 mL of Ringer's solution, how many moles of chloride were given?

QUESTIONS AND PROBLEMS

Electrolytes and Nonelectrolytes

8.7 KF is a strong electrolyte, and HF is a weak electrolyte. How are they different?

8.8 NaOH is a strong electrolyte, and CH_3OH is a nonelectrolyte. How are they different?

8.9 The following soluble salts are strong electrolytes. For each, write a balanced equation for their dissociation in water.
    a. KCl   **b.** $CaCl_2$ **c.** K_3PO_4 **d.** $Fe(NO_3)_3$

8.10 The following soluble salts are strong electrolytes. For each, write a balanced equation for their dissociation in water.
    a. LiBr   **b.** $NaNO_3$ **c.** $FeCl_3$ **d.** $Mg(NO_3)_2$

8.11 Indicate whether aqueous solutions of the following will contain only ions, only molecules, or mostly molecules and a few ions:
    a. acetic acid ($HC_2H_3O_2$), found in vinegar, a weak electrolyte
    b. NaBr, a strong electrolyte
    c. fructose ($C_6H_{12}O_6$), a nonelectrolyte

8.12 Indicate whether aqueous solutions of the following will contain only ions, only molecules, or mostly molecules and a few ions:
    a. Na_2SO_4, a strong electrolyte
    b. ethanol, C_2H_5OH, a nonelectrolyte
    c. HCN, hydrocyanic acid, a weak electrolyte

8.13 Indicate the type of electrolyte represented in the following equations:

    a. $K_2SO_4(s) \xrightarrow{H_2O} 2K^+(aq) + SO_4^{2-}(aq)$

    b. $NH_4OH(aq) \overset{H_2O}{\rightleftharpoons} NH_4^+(aq) + OH^-(aq)$

    c. $C_6H_{12}O_6(s) \xrightarrow{H_2O} C_6H_{12}O_6(aq)$

8.14 Indicate the type of electrolyte represented in the following equations:

a. $CH_3OH(l) \xrightarrow{H_2O} CH_3OH(aq)$

b. $MgCl_2(s) \xrightarrow{H_2O} Mg^{2+}(aq) + 2Cl^-(aq)$

c. $HClO(aq) \underset{}{\overset{H_2O}{\rightleftharpoons}} H^+(aq) + ClO^-(aq)$

8.15 Indicate the number of equivalents in each of the following:
a. 1 mole of K^+ b. 2 moles of OH^-
c. 1 mole of Ca^{2+} d. 3 moles of $CO_3{}^{2-}$

8.16 Indicate the number of equivalents in each of the following:
a. 1 mole of Mg^{2+} b. 0.5 mole of H^+
c. 4 moles of Cl^- d. 2 moles of Fe^{3+}

8.17 A physiological saline solution contains 154 mEq/L each of Na^+ and Cl^-. How many moles each of Na^+ and Cl^- are in 1.00 L of the saline solution?

8.18 A solution to replace potassium loss contains 40. mEq/L each of K^+ and Cl^-. How many moles each of K^+ and Cl^- are in 1.5 L of the solution?

8.19 A solution contains 40. mEq/L of Cl^- and 15 mEq/L of $HPO_4{}^{2-}$. If Na^+ is the only cation in the solution, what is the Na^+ concentration in milliequivalents per liter?

8.20 A sample of Ringer's solution contains the following concentrations (mEq/L) of cations: Na^+ 147, K^+ 4, and Ca^{2+} 4. If Cl^- is the only anion in the solution, what is the Cl^- concentration in milliequivalents per liter?

HEALTH NOTE

Electrolytes in Body Fluids

The concentrations of electrolytes present in body fluids and in intravenous fluids given to a patient are often expressed in milliequivalents per liter (mEq/L) of solution:

$$1 \text{ Eq} = 1000 \text{ mEq}$$

Table 8.6 gives the concentrations of some typical electrolytes in blood plasma. There is a charge balance because the total number of positive charges is equal to the total number of negative charges. The use of a specific intravenous solution depends on the nutritional, electrolyte, and fluid needs of the individual patient. Examples of various types of solutions are given in Table 8.7.

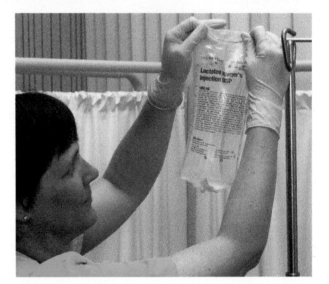

TABLE 8.6 Some Typical Concentrations of Electrolytes in Blood Plasma

Electrolyte	Concentration (mEq/L)
Cations	
Na^+	138
K^+	5
Mg^{2+}	3
Ca^{2+}	4
Total	150
Anions	
Cl^-	110
$HCO_3{}^-$	30
$HPO_4{}^{2-}$	4
Proteins	6
Total	150

TABLE 8.7 Electrolyte Concentrations in Intravenous Replacement Solutions

Solution	Electrolytes (mEq/L)	Use
Sodium chloride (0.9%)	Na^+ 154, Cl^- 154	Replacement of fluid loss
Potassium chloride with 5% dextrose	K^+ 40, Cl^- 40	Treatment of malnutrition (low potassium levels)
Ringer's solution	Na^+ 147, K^+ 4, Ca^{2+} 4, Cl^- 155	Replacement of fluids and electrolytes lost through dehydration
Maintenance solution with 5% dextrose	Na^+ 40, K^+ 35, Cl^- 40, lactate$^-$ 20, $HPO_4{}^{2-}$ 15	Maintenance of fluid and electrolyte levels
Replacement solution (extracellular)	Na^+ 140, K^+ 10, Ca^{2+} 5, Mg^{2+} 3, Cl^- 103, acetate$^-$ 47, citrate^{3-} 8	Replacement of electrolytes in extracellular fluids

8.3 Solubility

The term **solubility** describes the amount of a solute that can dissolve in a given amount of solvent. Many factors, such as the type of solute, the type of solvent, and the temperature, affect solubility. Solubility is usually expressed in grams of solute in 100 grams of solvent and is the maximum amount of solute that can be dissolved at a certain temperature. If a solute readily dissolves when added to the solvent, the solution does not contain the maximum amount of solute. We call the solution an **unsaturated solution**.

A solution that contains all the solute that can dissolve is a **saturated solution**.

When a solution is saturated, the rate of the reaction that dissolves the solute becomes equal to the rate of recrystallization. Then there is no further change in the amount of dissolved solute in solution.

$$\text{Solid solute} \underset{\text{Crystallizes}}{\overset{\text{Dissolves}}{\rightleftharpoons}} \text{saturated solution}$$

We can prepare a saturated solution by adding solute greater than needed for solubility. Stirring the solution will dissolve the maximum amount of solute and leave the excess on the bottom of the container. Once we have a saturated solution, the addition of more solute will increase only the amount of undissolved solute.

LEARNING GOAL

Define solubility; distinguish between an unsaturated and a saturated solution.

 SELF STUDY ACTIVITY
Solubility

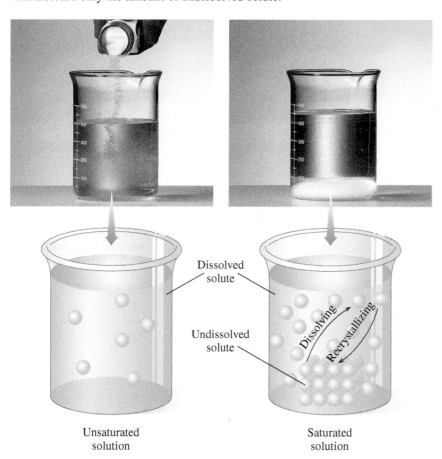

Unsaturated solution

Saturated solution

SAMPLE PROBLEM 8.3

■ Saturated Solutions

At 20 °C, the solubility of KCl is 34 g/100 g of water. In the laboratory, a student mixes 75 g of KCl with 200. g of water at a temperature of 20 °C.

a. How much of the KCl can dissolve?

b. Is the solution saturated or unsaturated?

c. What is the mass of any solid KCl in the bottom of the container?

a. KCl has a solubility of 34 g of KCl in 100 g of water. Using solubility as a conversion factor, the maximum amount of KCl that can dissolve in 200. g of water is calculated as follows:

$$200. \, \cancel{\text{g H}_2\text{O}} \times \frac{34 \text{ g KCl}}{100 \, \cancel{\text{g H}_2\text{O}}} = 68 \text{ g of KCl}$$

b. Because 75 g of KCl exceeds the amount that can dissolve in 200. g of water, the KCl solution is saturated.

c. If we add 75 g of KCl to 200. g of water and only 68 g of KCl can dissolve, there is 7 g of solid (undissolved) KCl on the bottom of the container.

CASE STUDY
Kidney Stones and Saturated Solutions

STUDY CHECK

At 50 °C, the solubility of $NaNO_3$ is 110 g/100 g of water. How many grams of $NaNO_3$ are needed to make a saturated $NaNO_3$ solution with 50. g of water at 50 °C?

HEALTH NOTE

Gout and Kidney Stones: A Problem of Saturation in Body Fluids

The conditions of gout and kidney stones involve compounds in the body that exceed their solubility levels and form solid products. Gout affects adults, primarily men, over the age of 40. Attacks of gout may occur when the concentration of uric acid in blood plasma exceeds its solubility, which is 7 mg/100 mL of plasma at 37 °C. Insoluble deposits of needle-like crystals of uric acid can form in the cartilage, tendons, and soft tissues, where they cause painful gout attacks. They may also form in the tissues of the kidneys, where they can cause renal damage. High levels of uric acid in the body can be caused by an increase in uric acid production, failure of the kidneys to remove uric acid, or by a diet with an overabundance of foods containing purines, which are metabolized to uric acid in the body. Foods in the diet that contribute to high levels of uric acid include certain meats, sardines, mushrooms, asparagus, and beans.

Drinking alcoholic beverages may also significantly increase uric acid levels and bring about gout attacks.

Treatment for gout involves diet changes and drugs. Depending on the levels of uric acid, a medication such as probenecid can be used to help the kidneys eliminate uric acid, or allopurinol can be administered to block the production of uric acid by the body.

Kidney stones are solid materials that form in the urinary tract. Most kidney stones are composed of calcium phosphate and calcium oxalate, although they can be solid uric acid. The excessive ingestion of minerals and insufficient water intake can cause the concentration of mineral salts to exceed their solubility and lead to the formation of kidney stones. When a kidney stone passes through the urinary tract, it causes considerable pain and discomfort, necessitating the use of painkillers and possibly surgery. Sometimes ultrasound is used to break up kidney stones. Persons prone to kidney stones are advised to drink six to eight glasses of water every day to prevent saturation levels of minerals in the urine.

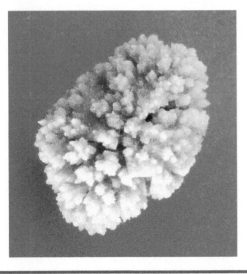

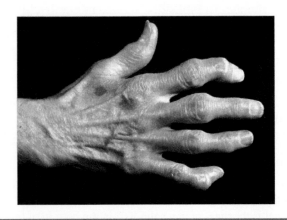

EXPLORE YOUR WORLD

Preparing Solutions

Place $\frac{1}{2}$ cup of cold water in a glass. Begin adding 1 tablespoon of sugar at a time and stir thoroughly. Count the number of tablespoons of sugar you add. As the sugar solution becomes more concentrated, you may need to stir for a few minutes until all the sugar dissolves. Each time observe the solution after several minutes to determine when it is saturated.

Repeat the above activity with $\frac{1}{2}$ cup of warm water. Count the number of tablespoons of sugar you need to form a saturated solution.

QUESTIONS

1. How did you know when you obtained a saturated solution?
2. How much sugar dissolved in the warm water compared to the cold water?

Effect of Temperature on Solubility

The solubility of most solids becomes greater as temperature increases, which means that solutions usually can contain more dissolved solute at higher temperatures. A few substances show little change in solubility at higher temperatures, and a few are less soluble. (See Figure 8.4.) For example, when you add sugar to iced tea, some undissolved sugar may quickly form on the bottom of the glass. But if you add sugar to hot tea, many teaspoons of sugar are needed before solid sugar appears. Hot tea dissolves more sugar than does cold tea because the solubility of sugar is much greater at a higher temperature. When a saturated solution is carefully cooled, it becomes a *supersaturated solution* because it contains more solute than the solubility allows. Such a solution is unstable, and if the solution is agitated or if a solute crystal is added, the excess solute will crystallize once again to give a saturated solution.

The solubility of a gas in water decreases as the temperature increases. At higher temperatures, more gas molecules have the energy to escape from the solution. Perhaps you have observed the bubbles escaping from a cold carbonated soft drink as it warms. At high temperatures, bottles containing carbonated solutions may burst as more gas molecules leave the solution and increase the gas pressure inside the bottle. Biologists have found that increased temperatures in rivers and lakes cause the amount of dissolved oxygen to decrease until the warm water can no longer support a biological community. Electricity-generating plants are required to have their own ponds to use with their cooling towers to lessen the threat of thermal pollution to surrounding waterways.

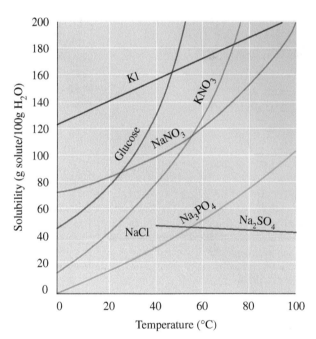

FIGURE 8.4 In water, most common solids are more soluble as the temperature increases.

Q Compare the solubility of $NaNO_3$ at 20 °C and 60 °C.

Henry's Law

Henry's law states that the solubility of gas in a liquid is directly related to the pressure of that gas above the liquid. At higher pressures, there are more gas molecules available to enter and dissolve in the liquid. A can of soda is carbonated by using CO_2 gas at high pressure to increase the solubility of the CO_2 in the beverage. When you open the can at atmospheric pressure, the pressure on the CO_2 drops, which decreases the solubility of CO_2. As a result, bubbles of CO_2 rapidly escape from the solution. The burst of bubbles is even more noticeable when you open a warm can of soda.

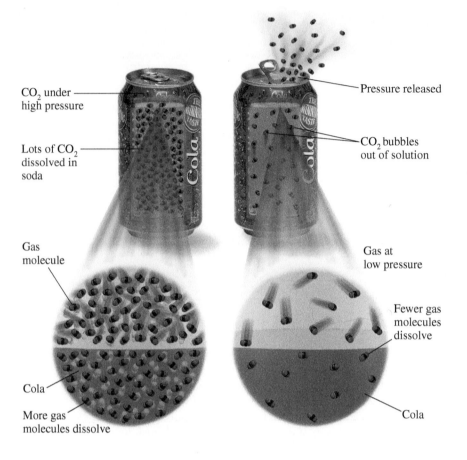

CO$_2$ under high pressure

Lots of CO$_2$ dissolved in soda

Gas molecule

Cola

More gas molecules dissolve

Pressure released

CO$_2$ bubbles out of solution

Gas at low pressure

Fewer gas molecules dissolve

Cola

SAMPLE PROBLEM   8.4

■ Factors Affecting Solubility

Indicate whether the solubility of the solute will increase or decrease in each of the following situations:

a. dissolving sugar using 80 °C water instead of 25 °C water
b. effect on the dissolved O$_2$ in a lake as it warms

SOLUTION

a. An increase in the temperature increases the solubility of the sugar.
b. An increase in the temperature decreases the solubility of O$_2$ gas.

STUDY CHECK

At 10 °C, the solubility of KNO$_3$ is 30 g/100 g H$_2$O. Would you expect the solubility of KNO$_3$ to be higher or lower at 40 °C? Explain.

Soluble and Insoluble Salts

TUTORIAL
Solubility

Up to now, we have considered ionic compounds called **soluble salts** that dissolve in water. However, some ionic compounds do not separate into ions in water. They are **insoluble salts** that remain as solids even in contact with water.

Salts that are soluble in water typically contain at least one of the following ions: Li$^+$, Na$^+$, K$^+$, NH$_4{}^+$, NO$_3{}^-$, or C$_2$H$_3$O$_2{}^-$. Most salts containing Cl$^-$ are soluble, but AgCl, PbCl$_2$, or Hg$_2$Cl$_2$ are not; they are insoluble chloride salts. Similarly, most salts containing SO$_4{}^{2-}$ are soluble, but a few are insoluble (See Table 8.8). Most other salts are insoluble

TABLE 8.8 Solubility Rules for Ionic Solids in Water

Soluble if Salt Contains		Insoluble if Salt Contains
NH_4^+, Li^+, Na^+, K^+ NO_3^-, $C_2H_3O_2^-$ (acetate)	but are soluble with	CO_3^{2-}, S^{2-} PO_4^{3-}, OH^-
Cl^-, Br^-, I^-	but are not soluble with	Ag^+, Pb^{2+}, or Hg_2^{2+}
SO_4^{2-}	but are not soluble with	Ba^{2+}, Pb^{2+}, Ca^{2+}, Sr^{2+}

and do not dissolve in water. (See Figure 8.5.) In an insoluble salt, attractions between its positive and negative ions are too strong for the polar water molecules to break. We can use the solubility rules to predict whether a salt (a solid ionic compound) would be expected to dissolve in water. Table 8.9 illustrates the use of these rules.

In medicine, the insoluble salt $BaSO_4$ is used as an opaque substance to enhance X-rays of the gastrointestinal tract. $BaSO_4$ is so insoluble that it does not dissolve in gastric fluids.

CdS

FeS

$PbCrO_4$

$Ni(OH)_2$

FIGURE 8.5 Mixing certain aqueous solutions produces insoluble salts.

Q What makes each of these salts insoluble in water?

TABLE 8.9 Using Solubility Rules

Ionic Compound	Solubility in Water	Reasoning
K_2S	Soluble	Contains K^+
$Ca(NO_3)_2$	Soluble	Contains NO_3^-
$PbCl_2$	Insoluble	Is an insoluble chloride
$NaOH$	Soluble	Contains Na^+
$AlPO_4$	Insoluble	Contains no soluble ions

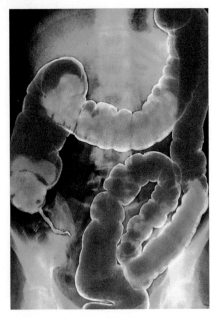

FIGURE 8.6 A barium sulfate enhanced X-ray of the abdomen shows the large intestine.

Q Is $BaSO_4$ a soluble or an insoluble substance?

(See Figure 8.6.) Other barium salts cannot be used; they would dissolve in water, releasing Ba^{2+}, which is poisonous.

CONCEPT CHECK 8.3

■ Soluble and Insoluble Salts

Predict whether each of the following salts is soluble in water and explain why:

a. Na_3PO_4 **b.** $CaCO_3$

ANSWER

a. The salt Na_3PO_4 is soluble in water because a compound that contains Na^+ is soluble.

b. The salt $CaCO_3$ is not soluble. The compound does not contain a soluble positive ion, which means that a calcium salt containing CO_3^{2-} is not soluble.

Formation of a Solid

We can use solubility rules to predict whether a solid, called a *precipitate*, forms when two solutions of ionic compounds are mixed. A solid forms when two ions of an insoluble salt come in contact with one another. For example, when a solution of $AgNO_3$ (Ag^+ and NO_3^-) is mixed with a solution of NaCl (Na^+ and Cl^-), the white insoluble salt AgCl is produced. We can write the equation for a double replacement reaction. However, the chemical equation does not show the individual ions to help us decide which, if any, insoluble salt would form. To help us determine any insoluble salt, we can first write the reactants to show all the ions present when the two solutions are mixed:

$$Ag^+(aq) + NO_3^-(aq) + Na^+(aq) + Cl^-(aq) \longrightarrow$$

Then we look at the cations and anions to see if any of the combinations would be an insoluble salt. The new combination AgCl forms an insoluble salt.

STEP 1   **Write the reactant ions.**   **STEP 2**   **Write the product combinations.**

Reactants **(initial combinations)**	**Mixture** **(new combinations)**	**Product**
$Ag^+(aq) + NO_3^-(aq)$	$Ag^+(aq) + Cl^-(aq) \longrightarrow AgCl(s)$	
$Na^+(aq) + Cl^-(aq)$	$Na^+(aq) + NO_3^-(aq)$	

STEP 3   **Write the ionic equation including the solid.**   Show that a precipitate forms, while the ions Na^+ and NO_3^- are in solution:

$$Ag^+(aq) + NO_3^-(aq) + Na^+(aq) + Cl^-(aq) \longrightarrow$$
$$AgCl(s) + Na^+(aq) + NO_3^-(aq)$$

STEP 4   **Write the net ionic equation.**   Now we can remove the Na^+ and NO_3^- ions known as *spectator ions* because they are unchanged during the reaction:

$$Ag^+(aq) + \underbrace{NO_3^-(aq) + Na^+(aq)}_{\text{Spectator ions}} + Cl^-(aq) \longrightarrow AgCl(s) + \underbrace{Na^+(aq) + NO_3^-(aq)}_{\text{Spectator ions}}$$

Finally, a **net ionic equation** can be written that gives the chemical reaction that occurred. The Na^+ and NO_3^- ions, the spectator ions, are removed from the ionic equation we wrote above:

$$Ag^+(aq) + Cl^-(aq) \longrightarrow AgCl(s)$$

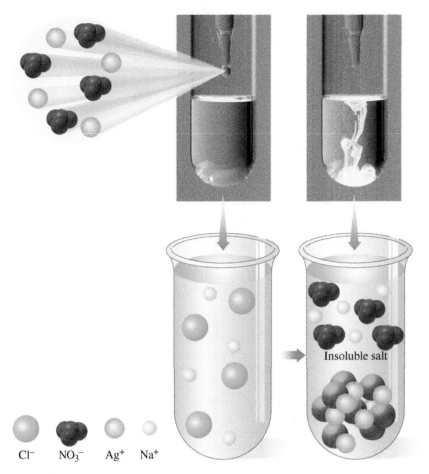

Cl⁻   NO₃⁻   Ag⁺   Na⁺

Insoluble salt

Type of Equation

Chemical	$AgNO_3(aq)$ + $NaCl(aq)$ ⟶	$AgCl(s)$ + $NaNO_3(aq)$
Ionic	$Ag^+(aq)$ + $Na^+(aq) + Cl^-(aq)$ ⟶	$AgCl(s)$ + $Na^+(aq)$
Net ionic	$Ag^+(aq)$ + $Cl^-(aq)$ ⟶	$AgCl(s)$

SAMPLE PROBLEM   8.5

■ Formation of an Insoluble Salt

Solutions of $BaCl_2$ and K_2SO_4 are mixed and a white solid forms.

a. Write the net ionic equation.
b. What is the white solid that forms?

SOLUTION

a. STEP 1 $Ba^{2+}(aq) + Cl^-(aq) + K^+(aq) + SO_4{}^{2-}(aq)$

   STEP 2 $BaSO_4(s)$ is insoluble.

   STEP 3 $Ba^{2+}(aq) + 2Cl^-(aq) + 2K^+(aq) + SO_4{}^{2-}(aq) \longrightarrow$
   $$BaSO_4(s) + 2Cl^-(aq) + 2K^+(aq)$$

   STEP 4 $Ba^{2+}(aq) + SO_4{}^{2-}(aq) \longrightarrow BaSO_4(s)$

b. $BaSO_4$ is the white solid.

STUDY CHECK

Predict whether a solid might form in each of the following mixtures of solutions. If so, write the net ionic equation for the reaction.

a. $NH_4Cl(aq) + Ca(NO_3)_2(aq)$ **b.** $Pb(NO_3)_2(aq) + KCl(aq)$

Guide to Writing Net Ionic Equations for an Insoluble Salt

STEP 1
Write the ions of the reactants.

STEP 2
Write the new combinations of ions and determine if any are insoluble.

STEP 3
Write the ionic equation including the solid.

STEP 4
Write the net ionic equation by removing spectator ions.

QUESTIONS AND PROBLEMS

Solubility

8.21 State whether each of the following refers to a saturated or unsaturated solution:
    a. A crystal added to a solution does not change in size.
    b. A sugar cube completely dissolves when added to a cup of coffee.

8.22 State whether each of the following refers to a saturated or unsaturated solution:
    a. A spoonful of salt added to boiling water dissolves.
    b. A layer of sugar forms on the bottom of a glass of tea as ice is added.

Use this table for problems 8.23–8.26.

Solubility (g/100 g H_2O)		
Substance	**20 °C**	**50 °C**
KCl	34	43
$NaNO_3$	88	110
$C_{12}H_{22}O_{11}$ (sugar)	204	260

8.23 Using the above table, determine whether each of the following solutions will be saturated or unsaturated at 20 °C:
    a. adding 25 g of KCl to 100. g of H_2O
    b. adding 11 g of $NaNO_3$ to 25 g of H_2O
    c. adding 400. g of sugar to 125 g of H_2O

8.24 Using the above table, determine whether each of the following solutions will be saturated or unsaturated at 50 °C:
    a. adding 25 g of KCl to 50. g of H_2O
    b. adding 150. g of $NaNO_3$ to 75 g of H_2O
    c. adding 80. g of sugar to 25 g of H_2O

8.25 A solution containing 80. g of KCl in 200. g of H_2O at 50 °C is cooled to 20 °C.
    a. How many grams of KCl remain in solution at 20 °C?
    b. How many grams of solid KCl crystallized after cooling?

8.26 A solution containing 80. g of $NaNO_3$ in 75 g of H_2O at 50 °C is cooled to 20 °C.
    a. How many grams of $NaNO_3$ remain in solution at 20 °C?
    b. How many grams of solid $NaNO_3$ crystallized after cooling?

8.27 Explain the following observations:
    a. More sugar dissolves in hot tea than in iced tea.
    b. Champagne in a warm room goes flat.
    c. A warm can of soda has more spray when opened than a cold one.

8.28 Explain the following observations:
    a. An open can of soda loses its "fizz" quicker at room temperature than in the refrigerator.
    b. Chlorine gas in tap water escapes as the water warms to room temperature.
    c. Less sugar dissolves in iced coffee than in hot coffee.

8.29 Predict whether each of the following ionic compounds is soluble in water:
    a. LiCl   **b.** AgCl   **c.** $BaCO_3$
    d. K_2O **e.** $Fe(NO_3)_3$

8.30 Predict whether each of the following ionic compounds is soluble in water:
    a. PbS   **b.** NaI   **c.** Na_2S
    d. Ag_2O **e.** $CaSO_4$

8.31 Determine whether a solid forms when solutions containing the following salts are mixed. If so, write the ionic equation and the net ionic equation.
    a. KCl and Na_2S **b.** $AgNO_3$ and K_2S
    c. $CaCl_2$ and Na_2SO_4 **d.** $CuCl_2$ and Li_3PO_4

8.32 Determine whether a solid forms when solutions containing the following salts are mixed. If so, write the ionic equation and the net ionic equation.
    a. Na_3PO_4 and $AgNO_3$ **b.** K_2SO_4 and Na_2CO_3
    c. $Pb(NO_3)_2$ and Na_2CO_3 **d.** $BaCl_2$ and KOH

8.4 Percent Concentration

LEARNING GOAL

Calculate the percent concentration of a solute in a solution; use percent concentration to calculate the amount of solute or solution.

The amount of solute dissolved in a certain amount of solution is called the **concentration** of the solution. We will look at the concentrations that are a ratio of a certain amount of solute in a given amount of solution:

$$\text{Concentration of a solution} = \frac{\text{amount of solute}}{\text{amount of solution}}$$

Mass Percent

In the mass percent (% m/m) of a solution, the units of mass of the solute and solution must be the same. Typically, a mass percent (% m/m) describes the mass of the solute in grams for exactly 100 g of solution. If the mass of the solute is given as kilograms, then the mass of the solution must also be kilograms. The mass of the solution is the sum of the mass of the solute and the mass of the solvent:

$$\text{Mass percent (m/m)} = \frac{\text{mass of solute(g)}}{\text{mass of solute(g) + mass of solvent(g)}} \times 100\%$$

$$= \frac{\text{mass of solute(g)}}{\text{mass of solution(g)}} \times 100\%$$

Suppose we prepared a solution by mixing 8.00 g of KCl (solute) with 42.00 g of water (solvent). Together the mass of the solute and mass of solvent give the mass of the solution (8.00 g + 42.00 g = 50.00 g). The mass percent is calculated by substituting in the values into the mass percent expression:

$$\underbrace{\frac{8.00 \text{ g KCl}}{50.00 \text{ g solution}} \times 100\% = 16.0\% \text{ (m/m)}}$$

$$\overbrace{8.00 \text{ g KCl} + 42.00 \text{ g H}_2\text{O}}$$
$$\text{(Solute} \quad + \quad \text{Solvent)}$$

Add 8.00 g of KCl.

CONCEPT CHECK 8.4

■ Mass Percent Concentration

A NaBr solution is prepared by adding 10.0 g of NaBr to 100. g of H_2O. Is the final concentration of the NaBr solution equal to 9.09% (m/m), 10.0% (m/m), or 90.0% (m/m)? Explain your reasoning.

ANSWER

The final concentration of the NaBr is equal to 9.09% (m/m). The mass of the solute is 10.0 g of NaBr, and the mass of the solution is 110.0 g (10.0 g of NaBr + 100.0 g of H_2O):

$$\frac{10.0 \text{ g NaBr}}{110.0 \text{ g of solution}} \times 100\% = 9.09\% \text{ (m/m) NaBr}$$

Add water until the mass of the solution is 50.00 g.

SAMPLE PROBLEM   8.6

■ Calculating Mass Percent

What is the mass percent of a solution prepared by dissolving 30.0 g of NaOH in 120.0 g of H_2O?

SOLUTION

STEP 1 **Given** 30.0 g of NaOH and 120.0 g of H_2O
 Need mass percent (m/m) of NaOH

STEP 2 **Plan** The mass percent is calculated by using the mass in grams of the solute and solution in the definition of mass percent.

STEP 3 **Equalities/Conversion Factors**

$$\text{Mass percent (m/m)} = \frac{\text{mass of solute}}{\text{mass of solute} + \text{mass of solvent}} \times 100\%$$

$$\text{Mass percent (m/m)} = \frac{\text{grams of solute}}{\text{grams of solution}} \times 100\%$$

STEP 4 **Set Up Problem** The mass of the solute and the solution are obtained from the data:

$$\begin{array}{ll} \text{Mass of solute} = & 30.0 \text{ g NaOH} \\ \text{Mass of solvent} = & +120.0 \text{ g H}_2\text{O} \\ \hline \text{Mass of solution} = & 150.0 \text{ g solution} \end{array}$$

$$\text{Mass percent (m/m)} = \frac{30.0 \text{ g NaOH}}{150.0 \text{ g solution}} \times 100\%$$

$$= 20.0\% \text{ (m/m) NaOH}$$

Guide to Calculating Solution Concentrations

STEP 1
State the given and needed concentration.

STEP 2
Write a plan to calculate needed concentration.

STEP 3
Write equalities and conversion factors.

STEP 4
Set up problem to calculate answer.

STUDY CHECK

What is the mass percent (m/m) of NaCl in a solution made by dissolving 2.0 g of NaCl in 56.0 g of H_2O?

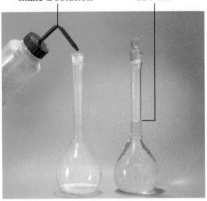

Water added to make a solution   250 mL

5.0 g of KI   2.0% (m/v)
KI solution

TUTORIAL
MC™ Calculating Percent Concentration

Volume Percent

Because the volumes of liquids or gases are easily measured, the concentrations of their solutions are often expressed as **volume percent** (v/v). The units of volume used in the ratio must be the same, for example, both in milliliters or both in liters.

$$\text{Volume percent } (v/v) = \frac{\text{volume of solute}}{\text{volume of solution}} \times 100\%$$

We interpret a volume/volume percent as the volume of solute in 100 mL of solution. In the wine industry, a label that reads 12% (v/v) means 12 mL of alcohol in 100 mL of wine.

Mass/Volume Percent

A **mass/volume percent** (m/v), or weight/volume percent (w/v), is calculated by dividing the grams of the solute by the volume (mL) of solution and multiplying by 100%. The mass/volume percent is widely used in hospitals and pharmacies for the preparation of intravenous solutions and medicines.

$$\text{Mass/volume percent } (m/v) = \frac{\text{grams of solute}}{\text{milliliters of solution}} \times 100\%$$

SAMPLE PROBLEM | 8.7

■ Calculating Percent Concentration

A student prepared a solution by dissolving 5.0 g of KI in enough water to give a final volume of 250 mL. What is the mass/volume percent (m/v) of the KI solution?

SOLUTION

STEP 1   Given   5.0 g of KI and 250 mL of solution
             Need   mass/volume percent (m/v) of KI
STEP 2   Plan   The mass/volume percent is calculated by using the mass in grams of the solute and the volume in mL of the solution in the definition of mass/ volume percent.
STEP 3   Equalities/Conversion Factors   Write the mass/volume percent expression.

$$\text{Mass/volume percent } (m/v) = \frac{\text{grams of solute}}{\text{milliliters of solution}} \times 100\%$$

STEP 4   Set Up Problem   Substitute solute and solution quantities into the mass/volume percent expression.

$$\text{Mass/volume percent } (\% \ m/v) = \frac{\overset{\text{Mass of solute}}{5.0 \text{ g KI}}}{\underset{\text{Volume of solution}}{250 \text{ mL solution}}} \times 100\% = 2.0\% \ (m/v) \ KI$$

STUDY CHECK

What is the mass/volume percent (m/v) of Br_2 in a solution prepared by dissolving 12 g of bromine (Br_2) in enough carbon tetrachloride to make 250 mL of solution?

TUTORIAL
MC™ Percent Concentration as a Conversion Factor

Percent Concentrations as Conversion Factors

In the preparation of solutions, we often need to calculate the amount of solute or solution. Then the percent concentration is useful as a conversion factor. The value of 100 in the denominator of a percent expression is an *exact* number. Some examples of percent concentrations, their meanings, and possible conversion factors are given in Table 8.10.

TABLE 8.10 Conversion Factors from Percent Concentrations

Percent Concentration	Meaning	Conversion Factors	
15% (m/m) KCl	There are 15 g of KCl in 100 g of solution.	$\dfrac{15 \text{ g KCl}}{100 \text{ g solution}}$ and	$\dfrac{100 \text{ g solution}}{15 \text{ g KCl}}$
5% (m/v) glucose	There are 5 g of glucose in 100 mL of solution.	$\dfrac{5 \text{ g glucose}}{100 \text{ mL solution}}$ and	$\dfrac{100 \text{ mL solution}}{5 \text{ g glucose}}$
12% (v/v) ethanol	There are 12 mL of ethanol in 100 mL of solution.	$\dfrac{12 \text{ mL ethanol}}{100 \text{ mL solution}}$ and	$\dfrac{100 \text{ mL solution}}{12 \text{ mL ethanol}}$

SAMPLE PROBLEM   8.8

■ Using Mass/Volume Percent to Find Mass of Solute

A topical antibiotic is 1.0% (m/v) Clindamycin. How many grams of Clindamycin are in 60. mL of the 1.0% (m/v) solution?

SOLUTION

STEP 1   **Given**   1.0% (m/v) Clindamycin
Need   grams of Clindamycin

STEP 2   **Plan**   milliliters of solution   → % (m/v) factor →   grams of Clindamycin

STEP 3   **Equalities/Conversion Factors**   The percent (m/v) indicates the grams of a solute in every 100 mL of a solution. The 1.0% (m/v) can be written as two conversion factors:

$$100 \text{ mL of solution} = 1.0 \text{ g of Clindamycin}$$

$$\frac{1.0 \text{ g Clindamycin}}{100 \text{ mL solution}} \quad \text{and} \quad \frac{100 \text{ mL solution}}{1.0 \text{ g Clindamycin}}$$

STEP 4   **Set Up Problem**   The volume of the solution is converted to mass of solute using the conversion factor:

$$60. \text{ mL solution} \times \frac{1.0 \text{ g Clindamycin}}{100 \text{ mL solution}} = 0.60 \text{ g of Clindamycin}$$

Guide to Using Concentration to Calculate Mass or Volume

STEP 1
State the given and needed quantities.

STEP 2
Write a plan to calculate mass or volume.

STEP 3
Write equalities and conversion factors including concentration.

STEP 4
Set up problem to calculate mass or volume.

STUDY CHECK

Calculate the grams of KCl in 225 g of an 8.00% (m/m) KCl solution.

QUESTIONS AND PROBLEMS

Percent Concentration

8.33 What is the difference between a 5% (m/m) glucose solution and a 5% (m/v) glucose solution?

8.34 What is the difference between a 10.% (v/v) methyl alcohol (CH$_3$OH) solution and a 10.% (m/m) methyl alcohol solution?

8.35 Calculate the mass percent (m/m) for the solute in each of the following solutions:
   a. 25 g of KCl and 125 g of H$_2$O
   b. 12 g of sugar in 225 g of tea solution with sugar

8.36 Calculate the mass percent (m/m) for the solute in each of the following solutions:
   a. 75 g of NaOH in 325 g of NaOH solution
   b. 2.0 g of KOH in 20.0 g of H$_2$O

8.37 Calculate the mass/volume percent (m/v) for the solute in each of the following solutions:
   a. 75 g of Na$_2$SO$_4$ in 250 mL of a Na$_2$SO$_4$ solution
   b. 39 g of sucrose in 355 mL of a carbonated drink

8.38 Calculate the mass/volume percent (m/v) for the solute in each of the following solutions:
   a. 2.50 g of KCl in 50.0 mL of solution
   b. 7.5 g of casein in 120 mL of low-fat milk

8.39 Calculate the amount of solute needed to prepare the following solutions:
  a. 50.0 mL of a 5.0% (m/v) KCl solution
  b. 1250 mL of a 4.0% (m/v) NH_4Cl solution

8.40 Calculate the amount of solute needed to prepare the following solutions:
  a. 150 mL of a 40.0% (m/v) $LiNO_3$ solution
  b. 450 mL of a 2.0% (m/v) KCl solution

8.41 A mouthwash contains 22.5% alcohol by volume. If the bottle of mouthwash contains 355 mL, what is the volume, in milliliters, of the alcohol?

8.42 A bottle of champagne is 11% alcohol by volume. If there are 750 mL of champagne in the bottle, how many milliliters of alcohol are present?

8.43 A patient receives 100. mL of 20.% (m/v) mannitol solution every hour.
  a. How many grams of mannitol are given in 1 hour?
  b. How many grams of mannitol does the patient receive in 15 hours?

8.44 A patient receives 250 mL of a 4.0% (m/v) amino acid solution twice a day.
  a. How many grams of amino acids are in 250 mL of solution?
  b. How many grams of amino acids does the patient receive in 1 day?

8.45 A patient needs 100. g of glucose in the next 12 hours. How many liters of a 5% (m/v) glucose solution must be given?

8.46 A patient received 2.0 g of NaCl in 8 hours. How many milliliters of a 0.90% (m/v) NaCl (saline) solution were delivered?

8.5 Molarity and Dilution

LEARNING GOAL

Calculate the molarity of a solution; use molarity to calculate the moles of solute or the volume of a solution. Describe the dilution of a solution.

When the solutes of solutions take part in reactions, chemists are often interested in the number of reacting particles. For this purpose, chemists use **molarity (M)**, a concentration that states the number of moles of solute in exactly 1 liter of solution. The molarity of a solution can be calculated knowing the moles of solute and the volume of solution in liters.

$$\text{Molarity}(M) = \frac{\text{moles of solute}}{\text{liters of solution}}$$

For example, if 1.0 mole of NaCl were dissolved in enough water to prepare 1.0 L of solution, the resulting NaCl solution has a molarity of 1.0 M. The abbreviation M indicates the units of moles per liter (moles/L):

$$M = \frac{\text{moles of solute}}{\text{liters of solution}} = \frac{1.0 \text{ mole NaCl}}{1.0 \text{ L}} = 1.0 \text{ M NaCl}$$

SAMPLE PROBLEM 8.9

■ Calculating Molarity

What is the molarity (M) of 60.0 g of NaOH in 0.250 L of solution?

SOLUTION

STEP 1 **Given** 60.0 g of NaOH in 0.250 L of solution
  Need molarity (moles/L)

STEP 2 **Plan** The calculation of molarity requires the moles of NaOH and the volume of the solution in liters.

$$\text{Molarity}(M) = \frac{\text{moles of solute}}{\text{liters of solution}}$$

grams of NaOH Molar mass $\dfrac{\text{moles NaOH}}{\text{volume (L)}}$ = M NaOH solution

STEP 3 **Equalities/Conversion Factors**

$$1 \text{ mole of NaOH} = 40.0 \text{ g of NaOH}$$

$$\frac{1 \text{ mole NaOH}}{40.0 \text{ g NaOH}} \quad \text{and} \quad \frac{40.0 \text{ g NaOH}}{1 \text{ mole NaOH}}$$

Guide to Calculating Molarity

STEP 1
State the given quantities.

STEP 2
Write a plan to calculate molarity.

STEP 3
Write equalities and conversion factors needed.

STEP 4
Set up problem to calculate molarity.

STEP 4   **Set Up Problem**

$$\text{Moles of NaOH} = 60.0 \; \cancel{\text{g NaOH}} \times \frac{1 \text{ mole NaOH}}{40.0 \; \cancel{\text{g NaOH}}} = 1.50 \text{ moles of NaOH}$$

The molarity is calculated by dividing the moles of NaOH by the volume in liters.

$$\frac{1.50 \text{ moles NaOH}}{0.250 \text{ L}} = \frac{6.00 \text{ moles NaOH}}{1 \text{ L}} = 6.00 \text{ M NaOH}$$

STUDY CHECK

What is the molarity of a solution that contains 75.0 g of KNO_3 dissolved in 0.350 L of solution?

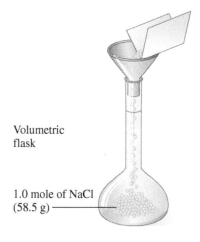

Volumetric flask

1.0 mole of NaCl (58.5 g)

Add water until the 1.0 liter mark is reached

Mix

A 1.0 molar NaCl solution

Molarity as a Conversion Factor

When we need to calculate the moles of solute or the volume of solution, the molarity is used as a conversion factor. The volume (1 L) is an exact number. Examples of conversion factors from molarity are given in Table 8.11.

Using the molarity of the solution with the molar mass of the solute, we can calculate the volume of solution needed as illustrated in Sample Problem 8.10.

TABLE 8.11 Some Examples of Molar Solutions

Molarity	Meaning	Conversion Factors		
6.0 M HCl	6.0 moles of HCl in 1 liter of solution	$\dfrac{6.0 \text{ moles HCl}}{1 \text{ L}}$	and	$\dfrac{1 \text{ L}}{6.0 \text{ moles HCl}}$
0.20 M NaOH	0.20 mole of NaOH in 1 liter of solution	$\dfrac{0.20 \text{ mole NaOH}}{1 \text{ L}}$	and	$\dfrac{1 \text{ L}}{0.20 \text{ mole NaOH}}$

SAMPLE PROBLEM 8.10

■ Using Molarity to Find Volume

How many liters of a 2.00 M NaCl solution are needed to provide 67.3 g of NaCl?

SOLUTION

STEP 1   **Given**   67.3 g of NaCl from a 2.00 M NaCl solution
          Need   liters of NaCl solution

STEP 2   **Plan**   The volume of the NaCl solution is calculated using the moles of NaCl and molarity of the NaCl solution:

   Grams of NaCl   Molar mass   moles of NaCl   Molarity   liters of NaCl solution

STEP 3   **Equalities/Conversion Factors**

$$1 \text{ mole of NaCl} = 58.5 \text{ g of NaCl}$$
$$\frac{1 \text{ mole NaCl}}{58.5 \text{ g NaCl}} \quad \text{and} \quad \frac{58.5 \text{ g NaCl}}{1 \text{ mole NaCl}}$$

The molarity of any solution can be written as two conversion factors:

$$1 \text{ L of NaCl} = 2.00 \text{ moles of NaCl}$$
$$\frac{1 \text{ L NaCl}}{2.00 \text{ moles NaCl}} \quad \text{and} \quad \frac{2.00 \text{ moles NaCl}}{1 \text{ L NaCl}}$$

STEP 4   Set Up Problem

$$\text{Liters of NaCl} = 67.3 \ \cancel{\text{g NaCl}} \times \frac{1 \ \cancel{\text{mole NaCl}}}{58.5 \ \cancel{\text{g NaCl}}} \times \frac{1 \ \text{L NaCl}}{2.00 \ \cancel{\text{moles NaCl}}}$$

$$= 0.575 \ \text{L of NaCl solution}$$

STUDY CHECK

How many moles of HCl are present in 750 mL of a 6.0 M HCl solution?

Dilution

TUTORIAL
Dilution

In chemistry and biology, we often prepare dilute solutions from more concentrated (stock) solutions. In a process called **dilution**, a solvent, usually water, is added to a solution, which increases the volume. In an everyday example, you are making a dilution when you add three cans of water to a can of concentrated orange juice.

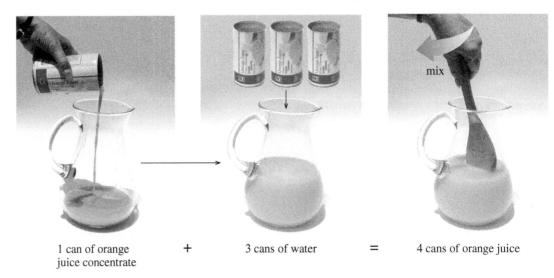

mix

1 can of orange   +   3 cans of water   =   4 cans of orange juice
juice concentrate

When a solution is diluted, the amount of solute before dilution is equal to the amount of solute in the diluted solution. (See Figure 8.7.)

Grams or moles of solute = grams or moles of solute
Concentrated solution   Diluted solution

We can write this equality in terms of the concentration, C, and the volume, V.

C_1V_1 = C_2V_2
Concentrated   Diluted
solution   solution

FIGURE 8.7 When water is added to a concentrated solution, there is no change in the number of particles, but the solute particles spread out as the volume of the diluted solution increases.

Q What is the concentration of the diluted solution after an equal volume of water is added to a sample of 6 M HCl solution?

We know from the discussion of percent concentration that the grams of solute are obtained from the volume and the percent concentration.

Grams of solute = percent (grams/100 mL) × volume (mL)

We can express the number of grams for the concentrated solution as $\%_1 V_1$ and the number of grams in the diluted solution as $\%_2 V_2$.

Grams of solute = grams of solute
Concentrated solution = Diluted solution
$$\%_1 V_1 = \%_2 V_2$$

When the concentration is given as molarity (M), the moles of solute are obtained from the volume (liters) and the molarity.

Moles of solute = molarity (moles/L) × volume (L)

Expressing the number of moles in the concentrated solution as $M_1 V_1$ and the number of moles in the diluted solution as $M_2 V_2$, the equality is written as follows:

Moles of solute = moles of solute
Concentrated solution = Diluted solution
$$M_1 V_1 = M_2 V_2$$

If we are given any 3 of the 4 variables, we can rearrange the dilution expression to solve for the unknown quantity as seen in Sample Problem 8.11.

SAMPLE PROBLEM 8.11

■ **Molarity of a Diluted Solution**

What is the molarity of a solution prepared when 75.0 mL of a 4.00 M KCl solution is diluted to a volume of 0.500 L?

SOLUTION

STEP 1   Give Data in a Table   We make a table of the molar concentrations and volumes of the initial and diluted solutions. For the calculation, units must be the same.

Initial: M_1 = 4.00 M KCl solution V_1 = 75.0 mL = 0.0750 L

Diluted: M_2 = ? M KCl solution V_2 = 0.500 L

STEP 2   Plan   The unknown molarity can be calculated by solving the dilution expression for M_2:

$$M_1 V_1 = M_2 V_2$$

Divide both sides by V_2 $$\frac{M_1 V_1}{V_2} = M_2 \frac{\cancel{V_2}}{\cancel{V_2}}$$

$$M_2 = M_1 \times \frac{V_1}{V_2}$$

STEP 3   Set Up Problem   The values from the table are placed into the dilution expression:

$$M_2 = 4.00 \text{ M} \times \frac{0.075 \cancel{L}}{0.500 \cancel{L}} = 0.600 \text{ M KCl solution (diluted)}$$

STUDY CHECK

You need to prepare 600. mL of 2.00 M NaOH solution from a 10.0 M NaOH solution. What volume of the 10.0 M NaOH solution do you use?

Guide to Calculating Dilution Quantities

STEP 1
Prepare a table of the initial and diluted volumes and concentrations.

STEP 2
Write a plan that solves the dilution expression for the unknown quantity.

STEP 3
Set up problem by placing known quantities in dilution expression.

Solutions and Chemical Reactions

When chemical reactions involve aqueous solutions, we use molarity and volume to determine the moles of the substances required or produced. Using the balanced chemical equation, we can determine the volume of a solution from the molarity and moles of a solute as seen in Sample Problem 8.12.

■ Volume of a Solution in a Reaction

Zinc reacts with HCl to produce $ZnCl_2$ and hydrogen gas H_2:

$$Zn(s) + 2HCl(aq) \longrightarrow ZnCl_2(aq) + H_2(g)$$

How many liters of a 1.50 M HCl solution completely react with 5.32 g of zinc?

SOLUTION

STEP 1 **Given** 5.32 g of Zn and a 1.50 M HCl solution
Need liters of HCl solution

STEP 2 **Plan** We start the problem with the grams of Zn given and use its molar mass to calculate moles. Then we can use the mole–mole factor from the equation and the molarity of the HCl as conversion factors:

Grams of Zn | Molar mass | moles of Zn | Mole–mole factor | moles of HCl | Molarity | L of HCl solution

Guide to Calculations Involving Solutions in Chemical Reactions

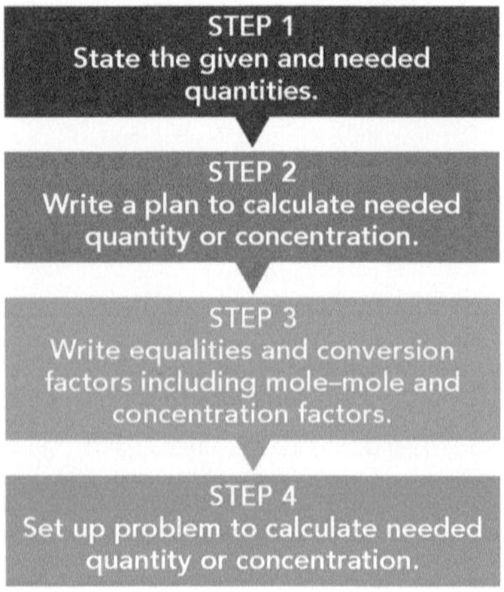

STEP 1
State the given and needed quantities.

STEP 2
Write a plan to calculate needed quantity or concentration.

STEP 3
Write equalities and conversion factors including mole–mole and concentration factors.

STEP 4
Set up problem to calculate needed quantity or concentration.

STEP 3 **Equalities/Conversion Factors**

Molar mass of Zn
1 mole of Zn = 65.4 g of Zn

$$\dfrac{1 \text{ mole Zn}}{65.4 \text{ g Zn}} \quad \text{and} \quad \dfrac{65.4 \text{ g Zn}}{1 \text{ mole Zn}}$$

Mole-mole factor
1 mole of Zn = 2 moles of HCl

$$\dfrac{1 \text{ mole Zn}}{2 \text{ moles HCl}} \quad \text{and} \quad \dfrac{2 \text{ moles HCl}}{1 \text{ mole Zn}}$$

Molarity of HCl solution
1 L of HCl solution = 1.50 moles of HCl

$$\dfrac{1 \text{ L HCl}}{1.50 \text{ moles HCl}} \quad \text{and} \quad \dfrac{1.50 \text{ moles HCl}}{1 \text{ L HCl}}$$

STEP 4 **Set Up Problem** We can write the problem setup as seen in our plan:

$$5.32 \text{ g Zn} \times \dfrac{1 \text{ mole Zn}}{65.4 \text{ g Zn}} \times \dfrac{2 \text{ moles HCl}}{1 \text{ mole Zn}} \times \dfrac{1 \text{ L HCl}}{1.50 \text{ moles HCl}} = 0.108 \text{ L of HCl solution}$$

STUDY CHECK

Using the reaction in Sample Problem 8.12, how many grams of zinc can react with 225 mL of 0.200 M HCl solution?

Figure 8.8 gives a summary of the pathways and conversion factors needed for substances, including solutions, involved in chemical reactions.

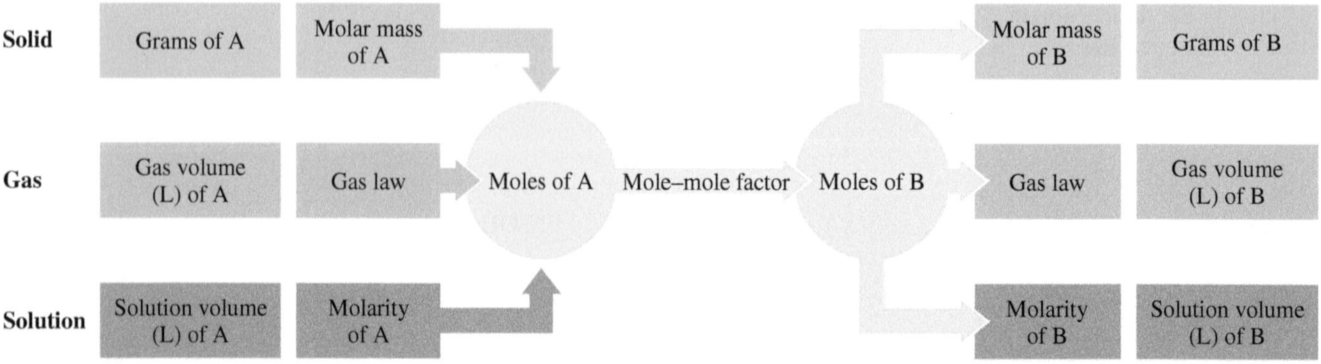

Solid	Grams of A	Molar mass of A					Molar mass of B	Grams of B
Gas	Gas volume (L) of A	Gas law	Moles of A	Mole–mole factor	Moles of B	Gas law	Gas volume (L) of B
Solution	Solution volume (L) of A	Molarity of A					Molarity of B	Solution volume (L) of B

FIGURE 8.8 In calculations involving chemical reactions, substance A is converted to moles of A using molar mass (if solid), gas laws (if gas), or molarity (if solution). Then moles of A are converted to moles of substance B, which are converted to grams of solid, liters of gas, or liters of solution, as needed.

Q What sequence of conversion factors would you use to calculate the number of grams of $CaCO_3$ needed to react with 1.50 L of a 2.00 M HCl solution in the reaction: $2HCl(aq) + CaCO_3(s) \longrightarrow CaCl_2(aq) + CO_2(g) + H_2O(l)$?

QUESTIONS AND PROBLEMS

Molarity and Dilution

8.47 Calculate the molarity (M) of the following solutions:
  a. 2.0 moles of glucose in 4.0 L of glucose solution
  b. 4.0 g of KOH in 2.0 L of KOH solution
  c. 5.85 g of NaCl in 400. mL of NaCl solution

8.48 Calculate the molarity (M) of the following solutions:
  a. 0.50 mole of glucose in 0.200 L of glucose solution
  b. 36.5 g of HCl in 1.0 L of HCl solution
  c. 30.0 g of NaOH in 350. mL of NaOH solution

8.49 Calculate the moles of solute needed to prepare each of the following:
  a. 1.0 L of a 3.0 M NaCl solution
  b. 0.40 L of a 1.0 M KBr solution
  c. 125 mL of a 2.0 M $MgCl_2$ solution

8.50 Calculate the moles of solute needed to prepare each of the following:
  a. 5.0 L of a 2.0 M $CaCl_2$ solution
  b. 4.0 L of a 0.10 M NaOH solution
  c. 215 mL of a 4.0 M HNO_3 solution

8.51 Calculate the grams of solute needed to prepare each of the following:
  a. 2.0 L of a 1.5 M NaOH solution
  b. 4.0 L of a 0.20 M KCl solution
  c. 25.0 mL of 6.0 M HCl solution

8.52 Calculate the grams of solute needed to prepare each of the following:
  a. 2.0 L of a 6.0 M NaOH solution
  b. 5.0 L of a 0.10 M $CaCl_2$ solution
  c. 175 mL of a 3.00 M $NaNO_3$ solution

8.53 What volume is needed for each of the following:
  a. liters of a 2.0 M NaOH solution to obtain 3.0 moles of NaOH
  b. liters of a 1.5 M NaCl solution to obtain 15 moles of NaCl
  c. milliliters of a 0.800 M $Ca(NO_3)_2$ solution to obtain 0.0500 moles of $Ca(NO_3)_2$

8.54 What volume is needed for each of the following:
  a. liters of 4.0 M KCl solution to obtain 0.100 mole of KCl
  b. liters of a 6.0 M HCl solution to obtain 5.0 moles of HCl
  c. milliliters of a 2.5 M K_2SO_4 solution to obtain 1.2 moles of K_2SO_4

8.55 Calculate the final concentration of each of the following diluted solutions:
  a. 2.0 L of a 6.0 M HCl solution is added to water so that the final volume is 6.0 L.
  b. Water is added to 0.50 L of a 12 M NaOH solution to make 3.0 L of a diluted NaOH solution.
  c. A 10.0-mL sample of 25% (m/v) KOH solution is diluted with water so that the final volume is 100.0 mL.
  d. A 50.0-mL sample of 15% (m/v) H_2SO_4 solution is added to water to give a final volume of 250 mL.

8.56 Calculate the final concentration of each of the following diluted solutions:
  a. 1.0 L of a 4.0 M HNO_3 solution is added to water so that the final volume is 8.0 L.
  b. Water is added to 0.25 L of a 6.0 M KOH solution to make 2.0 L of a diluted KOH solution.

  c. A 50.0-mL sample of 8.0% (m/v) NaOH is diluted with water so that the final volume is 200.0 mL.
  d. A 5.0-mL sample of 50.0% (m/v) acetic acid ($HC_2H_3O_2$) solution is added to water to give a final volume of 25 mL.

8.57 What is the final volume of each of the following diluted solutions?
  a. liters of a 0.20 M HCl solution prepared from 20.0 mL of a 6.0 M HCl solution
  b. milliliters of a 2.0% (m/v) NaOH solution prepared from 50.0 mL of a 10.0% (m/v) NaOH solution
  c. liters of a 0.50 M H_3PO_4 solution prepared from 0.500 L of a 6.0 M H_3PO_4 solution
  d. milliliters of a 5.0% (m/v) glucose solution prepared from 75 mL of a 12% (m/v) glucose solution

8.58 What is the final volume (mL) of each of the following diluted solutions?
  a. a 1.0% (m/v) KOH solution prepared from 10.0 mL of a 20.0% KOH solution
  b. a 0.10 M HCl solution prepared from 25 mL of a 6.0 M HCl solution
  c. a 1.0 M NaOH solution prepared from 50.0 mL of a 12 M NaOH solution
  d. a 1.0% (m/v) NaCl solution prepared from 18 mL of a 4.0% (m/v) NaCl solution

8.59 Answer the following for the reaction
$$Pb(NO_3)_2(aq) + 2KCl(aq) \longrightarrow$$
$$PbCl_2(s) + 2KNO_3(aq)$$
  a. How many grams of $PbCl_2$ will be formed from 50.0 mL of 1.50 M KCl solution?
  b. How many milliliters of 2.00 M $Pb(NO_3)_2$ solution will react with 50.0 mL of 1.50 M KCl solution?

8.60 Answer the following for the reaction
$$NiCl_2(aq) + 2NaOH(aq) \longrightarrow$$
$$Ni(OH)_2(s) + 2NaCl(aq)$$
  a. How many milliliters of 0.200 M NaOH solution are needed to react with 18.0 mL of 0.500 M $NiCl_2$ solution?
  b. How many grams of $Ni(OH)_2$ are produced from the reaction of 35.0 mL of 1.75 M NaOH solution?

8.61 Answer the following for the reaction
$$Mg(s) + 2HCl(aq) \longrightarrow MgCl_2(aq) + H_2(g)$$
  a. How many milliliters of a 6.00 M HCl solution are required to react with 15.0 g of magnesium?
  b. How many moles of hydrogen gas form when 0.500 L of 2.00 M HCl solution reacts?

8.62 The calcium carbonate in limestone reacts with HCl to produce a calcium chloride solution and carbon dioxide gas:
$$CaCO_3(s) + 2HCl(aq) \longrightarrow$$
$$CaCl_2(aq) + H_2O(l) + CO_2(g)$$
  a. How many milliliters of 0.200 M HCl solution can react with 8.25 g of $CaCO_3$?
  b. How many moles of CO_2 form when 15.5 mL of 3.00 M HCl solution react?

8.6 Physical Properties of Solutions

LEARNING GOAL

Identify a mixture as a solution, a colloid, or a suspension. Describe how the particles of a solution affect the physical properties of a solution.

The solute particles in a solution play an important role in determining the properties of that solution. In most of the solutions discussed so far, the solute is dissolved as small particles that are uniformly dispersed throughout the solvent to give a homogeneous solution. When you observe a solution, such as salt water, you cannot visually distinguish the solute from the solvent. The solution appears transparent, although it may have a color. The particles are so small that they go through filters and through semipermeable membranes. A **semipermeable membrane** allows solvent molecules such as water and very small solute particles to pass through but does not allow the passage of large solute molecules.

Colloids

The particles in a colloidal dispersion, or **colloid**, are much larger than solute particles in a solution. Colloidal particles are large molecules, such as proteins, or groups of molecules or ions. Colloids are homogeneous mixtures that do not separate or settle out. Colloidal particles are small enough to pass through filters but too large to pass through semipermeable membranes. Table 8.12 lists several examples of colloids.

HEALTH NOTE

Colloids and Solutions in the Body

In the body, colloids are retained by semipermeable membranes. For example, the intestinal lining allows solution particles to pass into the blood and lymph circulatory systems. However, the colloids from foods are too large to pass through the membrane, and they remain in the intestinal tract. Digestion breaks down large colloidal particles, such as starch and protein, into smaller particles, such as glucose and amino acids, that can pass through the intestinal membrane and enter the circulatory system. Human digestive processes cannot break down certain foods, such as bran, a fiber, and they move through the intestine intact.

Because large proteins, such as enzymes, are colloids, they remain inside cells. However, many of the substances that must be obtained by cells, such as oxygen, amino acids, electrolytes, glucose, and minerals, can pass through cellular membranes. Waste products, such as urea and carbon dioxide, pass out of the cell to be excreted.

TABLE 8.12 Examples of Colloids

	Substance Dispersed	Dispersing Medium
Fog, clouds, sprays	Liquid	Gas
Dust, smoke	Solid	Gas
Shaving cream, whipped cream, soapsuds	Gas	Liquid
Styrofoam, marshmallows	Gas	Solid
Mayonnaise, butter, homogenized milk, hand lotions	Liquid	Liquid
Cheese, butter	Liquid	Solid
Blood plasma, paints (latex), gelatin	Solid	Liquid

Suspensions

Suspensions are heterogeneous, nonuniform mixtures that are very different from solutions or colloids. The particles of a suspension are so large that they can often be seen with the naked eye. These particles are trapped by filters and semipermeable membranes.

The weight of the suspended solute particles causes them to settle out soon after mixing. If you stir muddy water, it mixes but then quickly separates as the suspended particles settle to the bottom and leave clear liquid at the top. You can find suspensions among the medications in a hospital or in your medicine cabinet. These include Kaopectate, calamine lotion, antacid mixtures, and liquid penicillin. It is important to "shake well before using" to suspend all the particles before giving a medication that is a suspension.

Water-treatment plants make use of the properties of suspensions to purify water. When flocculants such as aluminum sulfate or iron(III) sulfate are added to untreated water, they react with small particles of impurities to form large suspended particles called *floc*. In the water-treatment plant, a system of filters traps the suspended particles but allows clean water to pass through.

Table 8.13 compares the different types of mixtures, and Figure 8.9 illustrates some properties of solutions, colloids, and suspensions.

TABLE 8.13 Comparison of Solutions, Colloids, and Suspensions

Type of Mixture	Type of Particle	Settling	Separation
Solution	Small particles such as atoms, ions, or small molecules	Particles do not settle	Particles cannot be separated by filters or semipermeable membranes
Colloid	Larger molecules or groups of molecules or ions	Particles do not settle	Particles can be separated by semipermeable membranes but not by filters
Suspension	Very large particles that may be visible	Particles settle rapidly	Particles can be separated by filters

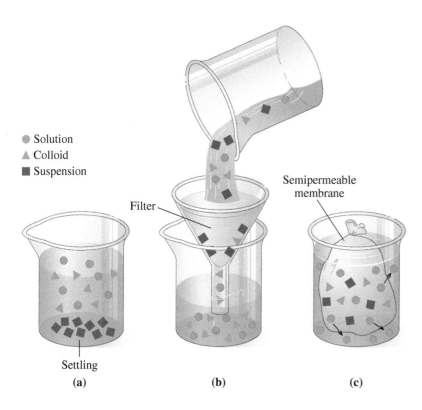

- ● Solution
- ▲ Colloid
- ■ Suspension

Filter

Semipermeable membrane

Settling
(a)   (b)   (c)

FIGURE 8.9 Properties of different types of mixtures: **(a)** suspensions settle out; **(b)** suspensions are separated by a filter; **(c)** solution particles go through a semipermeable membrane, but colloids and suspensions do not.

Q A filter paper can be used to separate suspension particles from a solution, but a semipermeable membrane is needed to separate colloids from a solution. Explain.

CONCEPT CHECK 8.5

■ Classifying Types of Mixtures

Classify each of the following as a solution, colloid, or suspension:

a. a mixture that has particles that settle upon standing
b. a mixture whose solute particles pass through both filters and membranes
c. an enzyme, which is a large protein molecule, that cannot pass through cellular membranes, but does pass through a filter

ANSWER

a. A suspension has very large particles that settle upon standing.
b. A solution contains particles small enough to pass through both filters and membranes.
c. A colloid is a particle that is small enough to pass through a filter but too large to pass through a membrane.

Freezing Point Lowering and Boiling Point Elevation

When a solute is added to water, the physical properties such as freezing point and boiling point change. The freezing point is lowered and boiling point is raised. These types of changes in physical properties known as *colligative properties* depend on the number of solute particles in the solution.

In many cold wintry areas, salt is spread on sidewalks and roads. The salt lowers the freezing point, which causes the ice to melt. In both cold and hot regions, antifreeze is added to the radiator of a car to lower the temperature at which water freezes and to increase the temperature at which water boils. Antifreeze prevents the water in the radiator from forming ice in the cold and from boiling over on a hot desert highway.

The solute particles disrupt the formation of the solid ice structure. Thus, a lower temperature is required to freeze the water in the solution. The greater the solute concentration, the lower the freezing point will be. One mole of particles in 1000 g of water lowers the freezing point from 0 °C to -1.86 °C. If there are 2 moles of particles in 1000 g of water, the freezing point drops to -3.72 °C. A similar change occurs with the boiling point of water. One mole of particles in 1000 g of water raises the boiling point by 0.52 °C, from 100. °C to 100.52 °C.

As we discussed in section 8.2, a solute that is a nonelectrolyte dissolves as molecules, whereas a solute that is a strong electrolyte dissolves entirely as ions. The solute in antifreeze, which is ethylene glycol, $C_2H_6O_2$, dissolves as molecules.

Nonelectrolyte:

1 mole of $C_2H_6O_2(l)$ = 1 mole of $C_2H_6O_2(aq)$

Strong electrolytes:

$$1 \text{ mole of NaCl}(s) = \underbrace{1 \text{ mole of Na}^+(aq) + 1 \text{ mole of Cl}^-(aq)}_{2 \text{ moles of particles }(aq)}$$

$$1 \text{ mole of CaCl}_2(s) = \underbrace{1 \text{ mole of Ca}^{2+}(aq) + 2 \text{ moles of Cl}^-(aq)}_{3 \text{ moles of particles }(aq)}$$

The effect of $CaCl_2$ used to salt icy roads is to produce 3 moles of particles, which will lower the freezing point of water three times more than 1 mole of ethylene glycol. The effect of solute particles on the freezing point and the boiling point is summarized in Table 8.14.

TABLE 8.14 Effect of Solute Concentration on Freezing and Boiling Points of 1000 g of Water

	Type of Solute	Moles of Solute Particles	Freezing Point	Boiling Point
Pure Water	None	0	0 °C	100 °C
Temperature change		1 mole	$\Delta T_f = 1.86$ °C	$\Delta T_b = 0.52$ °C
1 mole of ethylene glycol	Nonelectrolyte	1 mole	-1.86 °C	100.52 °C
1 mole of NaCl	Strong electrolyte	2 moles	-3.72 °C	101.04 °C
1 mole of CaCl₂	Strong electrolyte	3 moles	-5.58 °C	101.56 °C

Osmotic Pressure

The movement of water into and out of the cells of almost all living things is an important biological process that depends on the solute concentration. In a process called **osmosis**, water molecules move through a semipermeable membrane from the solution with the lower concentration of solute into a solution with the higher solute concentration. In an osmosis apparatus, water is placed on one side of a semipermeable membrane and sucrose (sugar) solution on the other side. The semipermeable membrane allows water molecules to flow back and forth but blocks the sucrose molecules because they are too large to pass through the membrane. Because the sucrose solution has a higher solute concentration, there are more water molecules flowing into the sucrose solution and the volume of the sucrose solution increases, while the volume on the other side decreases. The movement of the water dilutes the sucrose solution to equalize (or attempt to equalize) the concentrations on both sides of the membrane.

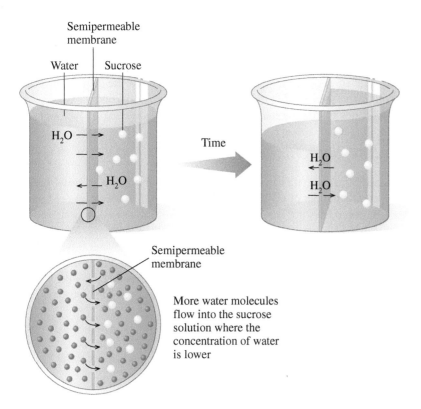

More water molecules flow into the sucrose solution where the concentration of water is lower

Eventually, the height of the sucrose solution creates sufficient pressure to equalize the flow of water between the two compartments. This pressure, called **osmotic pressure**, prevents the flow of additional water into the more concentrated solution. Then there is no further change in the volumes of the two solutions. The osmotic pressure depends on the concentration of solute particles in the solution. The greater the number of particles dissolved, the higher its osmotic pressure. In this example, the sucrose solution has a higher osmotic pressure than pure water, which has an osmotic pressure of zero.

In a process called *reverse osmosis*, a pressure greater than the **osmotic pressure** is applied to a solution. The flow of water is reversed so that water flows out of the solution with the higher solute concentration. This process of reverse osmosis is used in desalination plants to obtain pure water from sea (salt) water.

EXPLORE YOUR WORLD

Everyday Osmosis

1. Place a few pieces of dried fruit such as raisins, prunes, or banana chips in water. Observe them after 1 hour or more. Look at them again the next day.
2. Place some grapes in a concentrated salt-water solution. Observe them after 1 hour or more. Look at them again the next day.
3. Place one potato slice in water and another slice in a concentrated saltwater solution. After 1 or 2 hours observe the shapes and sizes of the slices. Look at them again the next day.

QUESTIONS

1. How did the shape of the dried fruit change after being in water? Explain.
2. How did the appearance of the grapes change after being in a concentrated salt solution? Explain.
3. How does the appearance of the potato slice that was placed in water compare to the appearance of the potato slice placed in salt water? Explain.
4. At the grocery store, why are sprinklers used to spray water on fresh produce such as lettuce, carrots, and cucumbers?

 SELF STUDY ACTIVITY
Diffusion

 TUTORIAL
Osmosis

CONCEPT CHECK 8.6

■ Osmotic Pressure

A 2% (m/v) sucrose solution and an 8% (m/v) sucrose solution are separated by a semipermeable membrane.

a. Which sucrose solution exerts the greater osmotic pressure?
b. In what direction does water flow initially?
c. Which solution will have the higher level of liquid at equilibrium?

ANSWER

a. The 8% (m/v) sucrose solution has the higher solute concentration, more solute particles, and the greater osmotic pressure.
b. Initially, water will flow out of the 2% (m/v) solution into the more concentrated 8% (m/v) solution.
c. The level of the 8% (m/v) solution will be higher.

Isotonic Solutions

Because the cell membranes in biological systems are semipermeable, osmosis is an ongoing process. The solutes in body solutions such as blood, tissue fluids, lymph, and plasma all exert osmotic pressure. Most intravenous solutions are **isotonic solutions**, which exert the same osmotic pressure as body fluids. *Iso* means "equal to," and *tonic* refers to the osmotic pressure of the solution in the cell. In the hospital, isotonic solutions, or **physiological solutions**, include 0.9% (m/v) NaCl solution and 5% (m/v) glucose solution. These physiological solutions exert the same osmotic pressure as the particles in the body fluids, which is 0.3 mole of particles in 1 L. Although they are not the same particles, a 0.9% (m/v) NaCl solution as well as a 5% (m/v) glucose solution each contains 0.3 mole of particles (Na^+ and Cl^- ions or glucose molecules) in 1 L.

Hypotonic and Hypertonic Solutions

A red blood cell placed in an isotonic solution retains its normal volume because there is an equal flow of water into and out of the cell. (See Figure 8.10a.) However, if a red blood cell is placed in a solution that is not isotonic, the differences in osmotic pressure inside and outside the cell can drastically alter the volume of the cell. When a red blood cell is placed in pure water, a **hypotonic solution** (*hypo* means "lower than"), water flows into the cell by osmosis. (See Figure 8.10b.) The increase in fluid causes the cell to swell, and possibly burst—a process called **hemolysis**. A similar process occurs when you place dehydrated food, such as raisins or dried fruit, in water. The water enters the cells, and the food becomes plump and smooth.

If a red blood cell is placed in a **hypertonic solution**, which has a higher solute concentration (*hyper* means "greater than"), water leaves the cell by osmosis. Suppose a red blood cell is placed in a 10% (m/v) NaCl solution. Because the osmotic pressure in the red blood

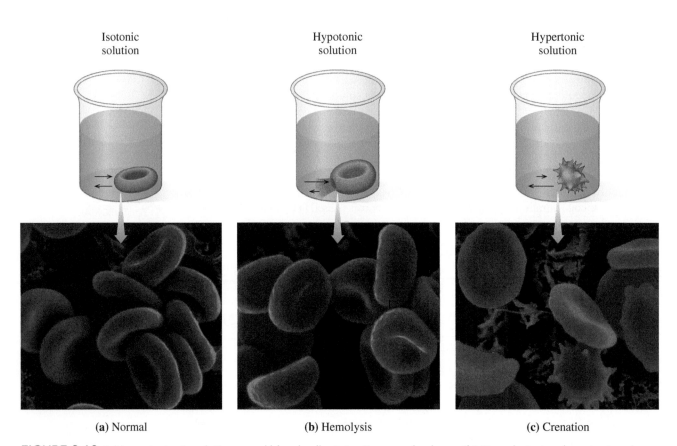

Isotonic solution   Hypotonic solution   Hypertonic solution

(a) Normal   (b) Hemolysis   (c) Crenation

FIGURE 8.10 **(a)** In an isotonic solution, a red blood cell retains its normal volume. **(b)** Hemolysis: In a hypotonic solution, water flows into a red blood cell, causing it to swell and burst. **(c)** Crenation: In a hypertonic solution, water leaves the red blood cell, causing it to shrink.

Q What happens to a red blood cell placed in a 4% NaCl solution?

cell is equal to that of a 0.90% (m/v) NaCl solution, the 10% (m/v) NaCl solution has a much greater osmotic pressure. As water is lost, the cell shrinks—a process called **crenation**. (See Figure 8.10c.) A similar process occurs when making pickles, which uses a hypertonic salt solution that causes the cucumbers to shrivel as they lose water.

SAMPLE PROBLEM 8.13

■ **Isotonic, Hypotonic, and Hypertonic Solutions**

Describe each of the following solutions as isotonic, hypotonic, or hypertonic. Indicate whether a red blood cell placed in each solution will undergo hemolysis, crenation, or no change.

a. a 5.0% (m/v) glucose solution
b. a 0.2% (m/v) NaCl solution

SOLUTION

a. A 5.0% (m/v) glucose solution is isotonic. A red blood cell will not undergo any change.
b. A 0.2% (m/v) NaCl solution is hypotonic. A red blood cell will undergo hemolysis.

STUDY CHECK

What is the effect of a 10% (m/v) glucose solution on a red blood cell?

Dialysis

Dialysis is a process that is similar to osmosis. In dialysis, a semipermeable membrane, called a *dialyzing membrane*, permits small solute molecules and ions as well as solvent water molecules to pass through, but it retains large particles, such as colloids. Dialysis is a way to separate solution particles from colloids.

Suppose we fill a cellophane bag with a solution containing NaCl, glucose, starch, and protein and place it in pure water. Cellophane is a dialyzing membrane, and the sodium ions, chloride ions, and glucose molecules will pass through it into the surrounding water. However, starch and protein remain inside because they are colloids. Water molecules will flow by osmosis into the cellophane bag. Eventually the concentrations of sodium ions, chloride ions, and glucose molecules inside and outside the dialysis bag become equal. To remove more NaCl or glucose, the cellophane bag must be placed in a fresh sample of pure water.

TUTORIAL
Dialysis

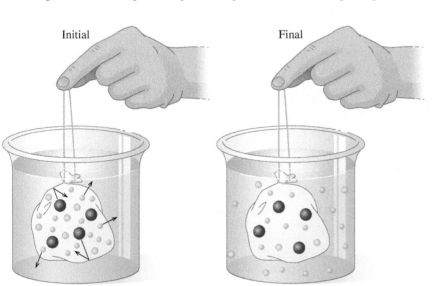

● Solution particles such as Na⁺, Cl⁻, glucose
● Colloidal particles such as protein, starch

HEALTH NOTE

Dialysis by the Kidneys and the Artificial Kidney

The fluids of the body undergo dialysis by the membranes of the kidneys, which remove waste materials, excess salts, and water. In an adult, each kidney contains about 2 million nephrons. At the top of each nephron, there is a network of arterial capillaries called the *glomerulus*.

As blood flows into the glomerulus, small particles, such as amino acids, glucose, urea, water, and certain ions, will move through the capillary membranes into the nephron. As this solution moves through the nephron, substances still of value to the body (such as amino acids, glucose, certain ions, and 99% of the water) are reabsorbed. The major waste product, urea, is excreted in the urine.

Hemodialysis

If the kidneys fail to dialyze waste products, increased levels of urea can become life threatening in a relatively short time. A person with kidney failure must use an artificial kidney, which cleanses the blood by **hemodialysis**.

A typical artificial kidney machine contains a large tank filled with about 100 L of water containing selected electrolytes. In the center of this dialyzing bath (dialysate), there is a dialyzing coil or membrane made of cellulose tubing. As the patient's blood flows through the dialyzing coil, the highly concentrated waste products dialyze out of the blood. No blood is lost, because the membrane is not permeable to large particles such as red blood cells.

Dialysis patients do not produce much urine. As a result, they retain large amounts of water between dialysis treatments, which produces a strain on the heart. The intake of fluids for a dialysis patient may be restricted to as little as a few teaspoons of water a day. In the dialysis procedure, the pressure of the blood is increased as it circulates through the dialyzing coil so water can be squeezed out of the blood. For some dialysis patients, 2–10 L of water may be removed during one treatment. Dialysis patients typically have from two to three treatments a week, each treatment requiring about 5–7 hr. Some of the newer treatments require less time. For many patients, dialysis is done at home with a home dialysis unit.

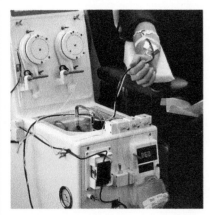

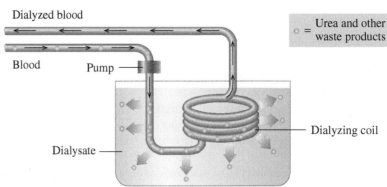

QUESTIONS AND PROBLEMS

Physical Properties of Solutions

8.63 Identify the following as characteristic of a solution, colloid, or suspension:
  a. a mixture that cannot be separated by a semipermeable membrane
  b. a mixture that settles out upon standing

8.64 Identify the following as characteristic of a solution, colloid, or suspension:
  a. Particles of this mixture remain inside a semipermeable membrane but pass through filters.
  b. The particles of solute in this mixture are very large and visible.

8.65 How many moles of each of the following strong electrolytes are needed to give the same freezing point lowering as 0.12 mole of the nonelectrolyte ethylene glycol in 1000 g of water?
  a. NaCl
  b. K_3PO_4

8.66 Two solutions, A and B, are separated by a semipermeable membrane. Indicate the solution that has the greater osmotic pressure and the direction in which water will move.
  a. A is 0.1 M NaCl and B is 0.2 M K_2SO_4
  b. A is 0.3 M LiBr and B is 0.2 M K_3PO_4

8.67 A 10% (m/v) starch solution is separated from pure water by an osmotic membrane.

  a. Which liquid has the higher osmotic pressure?

  b. In which direction will water flow initially?

  c. In which compartment will the volume level rise?

8.68 Two solutions, a 0.1% (m/v) albumin solution and a 2% (m/v) albumin solution, are separated by a semipermeable membrane. (Albumins are colloidal proteins.)

  a. Which compartment has the higher osmotic pressure?

  b. In which direction will water flow initially?

  c. In which compartment will the volume level rise?

8.69 Indicate the compartment (A or B) that will increase in volume for each of the following pairs of solutions separated by semipermeable membranes:

	A	B
a.	5.0% (m/v) starch	10% (m/v) starch
b.	4% (m/v) albumin	8% (m/v) albumin
c.	0.1% (m/v) sucrose	10% (m/v) sucrose

8.70 Indicate the compartment (A or B) that will increase in volume for each of the following pairs of solutions separated by semipermeable membranes:

	A	B
a.	20% (m/v) starch	10% (m/v) starch
b.	10% (m/v) albumin	2% (m/v) albumin
c.	0.5% (m/v) sucrose	5% (m/v) sucrose

8.71 Are the following solutions isotonic, hypotonic, or hypertonic compared with a red blood cell?

  a. distilled H_2O

  b. 1% (m/v) glucose

  c. 0.90% (m/v) NaCl

  d. 5.0% (m/v) glucose

8.72 Will a red blood cell undergo crenation, hemolysis, or no change in each of the following solutions?

  a. 1% (m/v) glucose

  b. 2% (m/v) NaCl

  c. 5% (m/v) NaCl

  d. 0.1% (m/v) NaCl

8.73 Each of the following mixtures is placed in a dialyzing bag and immersed in distilled water. Which substances will be found outside the bag in the distilled water?

  a. NaCl solution

  b. starch (colloid) and alanine (amino acid) solution

  c. NaCl solution and starch (colloid)

  d. urea solution

8.74 Each of the following mixtures is placed in a dialyzing bag and immersed in distilled water. Which substances will be found outside the bag in the distilled water?

  a. KCl solution and glucose solution

  b. an albumin solution (colloid)

  c. an albumin solution (colloid), KCl solution, and glucose solution

  d. urea solution and NaCl solution

CONCEPT MAP

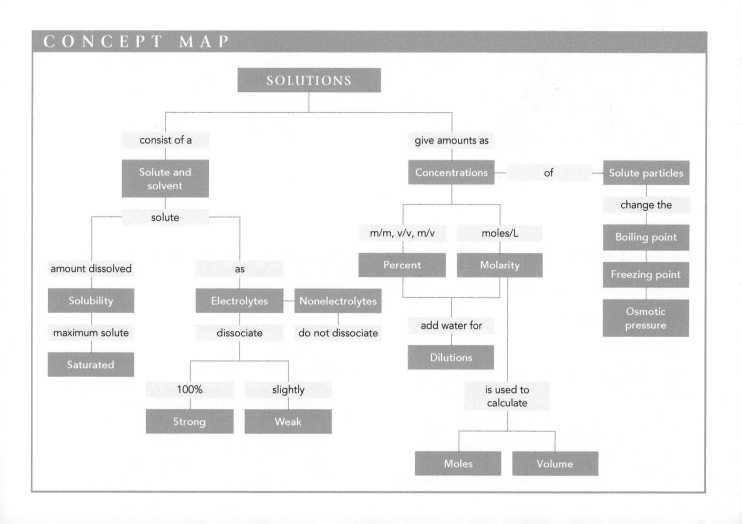

CHAPTER REVIEW

8.1 Solutions

LEARNING GOAL: *Identify the solute and solvent in a solution. Describe the formation of a solution.*

A solution forms when a solute dissolves in a solvent. In a solution, the particles of solute are evenly distributed in the solvent. The solute and solvent may be solid, liquid, or gas. The polar O—H bond leads to hydrogen bonding in water molecules. An ionic solute dissolves in water—a polar solvent—because the polar water molecules attract and pull the ions into solution, where they become hydrated. The expression "like dissolves like" means that a polar or ionic solute dissolves in a polar solvent while a nonpolar solute requires a nonpolar solvent.

8.2 Electrolytes and Nonelectrolytes

LEARNING GOAL: *Identify solutes as electrolytes or nonelectrolytes.*

Substances that release ions in water are called electrolytes because the solution will conduct an electrical current. Strong electrolytes are completely ionized, whereas weak electrolytes are only partially ionized. Nonelectrolytes are substances that dissolve in water to produce molecules and cannot conduct electrical currents. An equivalent is the amount of an electrolyte that carries 1 mole of positive or negative charge. One mole of Na^+ is 1 equivalent. One mole of Ca^{2+} is 2 equivalents. In fluid replacement solutions, the concentrations of electrolytes are expressed as mEq/L of solution.

8.3 Solubility

LEARNING GOAL: *Define solubility; distinguish between an unsaturated and a saturated solution.*

A solution that contains the maximum amount of dissolved solute is a saturated solution. The solubility of a solute is the maximum amount of a solute that can dissolve in 100 g of solvent. A solution containing less than the maximum amount of dissolved solute is unsaturated. An increase in temperature increases the solubility of most solids in water but decreases the solubility of gases in water. Salts that are soluble in water usually contain Li^+, Na^+, K^+, NH_4^+, NO_3^-, or acetate $C_2H_3O_2^-$. An ionic equation consists of writing all the dissolved substances in an equation for the formation of an insoluble salt as individual ions. A net ionic equation is written by removing all the ions not involved in the chemical change (spectator ions) from the ionic equation.

8.4 Percent Concentration

LEARNING GOAL: *Calculate the percent concentration of a solute in a solution; use percent concentration to calculate the amount of solute or solution.*

The concentration of a solution is the amount of solute dissolved in a certain amount of solution. Mass percent expresses the ratio of the mass of solute to the mass of solution multiplied by 100. Percent concentration is also expressed as volume/volume (v/v) and mass/volume (m/v) ratios. In calculations of grams or milliliters of solute or solution, the percent concentration is used as a conversion factor.

8.5 Molarity and Dilution

LEARNING GOAL: *Calculate the molarity of a solution; use molarity to calculate the moles of solute or the volume of a solution. Describe the dilution of a solution.*

Molarity is the moles of solute per liter of solution. Units of molarity, moles/liter, are used in conversion factors to solve for moles of solute or volume of solution. In dilution, the volume of solvent increases and the solute concentration decreases. If the mass or solution volume and molarity of substances in a reaction are given, the balanced equation can be used to determine the quantities or concentrations of any of the other substances in the reaction.

8.6 Physical Properties of Solutions

LEARNING GOAL: *Identify a mixture as a solution, a colloid, or suspension. Describe how the particles of a solution affect the physical properties of a solution.*

Colloids contain particles that do not settle out and which pass through most filters but not semipermeable membranes. Suspensions have very large particles that settle out of solution. Colligative properties are the physical properties that change when solute dissolves in water.

In osmosis, solvent (water) passes through a semipermeable membrane from a solution with a lower osmotic pressure (lower solute concentration) to a solution with a higher osmotic pressure (higher solute concentration). Isotonic solutions have osmotic pressures equal to that of body fluids. A red blood cell maintains its volume in an isotonic solution but swells and may burst (hemolyze) in a hypotonic solution and shrinks (crenates) in a hypertonic solution. In dialysis, water and small solute particles pass through a dialyzing membrane, while larger particles are retained.

KEY TERMS

colloids Mixtures having particles that are moderately large. Colloids pass through filters but cannot pass through semipermeable membranes.

concentration A measure of the amount of solute that is dissolved in a specified amount of solution.

crenation The shriveling of a cell due to water leaving the cell when the cell is placed in a hypertonic solution.

dialysis A process in which water and small solute particles pass through a semipermeable membrane.

dilution A process by which water (solvent) is added to a solution to increase the volume and decrease (dilute) the concentration of the solute.

electrolyte A substance that produces ions when dissolved in water; its solution conducts electricity.

equivalent (Eq) The amount of a positive or negative ion that supplies 1 mole of electrical charge.

hemodialysis A cleansing of the blood by an artificial kidney using the principle of dialysis.

hemolysis A swelling and bursting of red blood cells in a hypotonic solution due to an increase in fluid volume.

Henry's law The solubility of a gas in a liquid is directly related to the pressure of that gas above the liquid.

hydration The process of surrounding dissolved ions by water molecules.

hypertonic solution A solution that has a higher osmotic pressure than the red blood cells of the body.

hypotonic solution A solution that has a lower osmotic pressure than the red blood cells of the body.

insoluble salts Ionic compounds that do not dissolve in water.

ionic equation An equation for a reaction in solution that gives all the individual ions, both reacting ions and spectator ions.

isotonic solution A solution that has the same osmotic pressure as that of the red blood cells of the body.

mass percent (m/m) The grams of solute in exactly 100 grams of solution.

mass/volume percent (m/v) The grams of solute in exactly 100 mL of solution.

molarity (M) The number of moles of solute in exactly 1 L of solution.

net ionic equation An equation for a reaction that gives only the reactants and products involved in a chemical change.

nonelectrolyte A substance that dissolves in water as molecules; its solution will not conduct an electrical current.

osmosis The flow of a solvent, usually water, through a semipermeable membrane into a solution of higher solute concentration.

osmotic pressure The pressure that prevents the flow of water into the more concentrated solution.

physiological solution A solution that exerts the same osmotic pressure as normal body fluids.

saturated solution A solution containing the maximum amount of solute that can dissolve at a given temperature. Any additional solute will remain undissolved in the container.

semipermeable membrane A membrane that permits the passage of certain substances while blocking or retaining others.

solubility The maximum amount of solute that can dissolve in exactly 100 g of solvent, usually water, at a given temperature.

soluble salts Ionic compounds that dissolve in water.

solute The component in a solution that changes state upon dissolving; if no change in state occurs, it is the component present in the smaller quantity.

solution A homogeneous mixture in which the solute is made up of small particles (ions or molecules) that can pass through filters and semipermeable membranes.

solvent The substance in which the solute dissolves; usually the component present in greatest amount.

strong electrolyte A polar or ionic compound that ionizes completely when it dissolves in water. Its solution is a good conductor of electricity.

suspension A mixture in which the solute particles are large enough and heavy enough to settle out and be retained by both filters and semipermeable membranes.

unsaturated solution A solution that contains less solute than can be dissolved.

volume percent (v/v) A percent concentration that relates the volume of the solute to the volume of the solution.

weak electrolyte A substance that produces only a few ions along with many molecules when it dissolves in water. Its solution is a weak conductor of electricity.

■ UNDERSTANDING THE CONCEPTS

8.75 Select the diagram that represents the solution formed by a solute 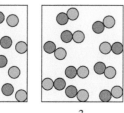 that is a
a. nonelectrolyte
b. weak electrolyte
c. strong electrolyte

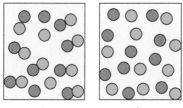

1.   2.   3.

8.76 Match the diagrams with the following:
a. a polar solute and a polar solvent
b. a nonpolar solute and a polar solvent
c. a nonpolar solute and a nonpolar solvent

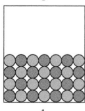 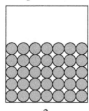

1.   2.

8.77 A pickle is made by soaking a cucumber in brine, a saltwater solution. What makes the smooth cucumber become wrinkled like a prune?

8.78 Do you think solution (1) has undergone heating or cooling to give the solid shown in (2) and (3)?

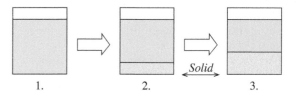

1.   2.   *Solid*   3.

8.79 Select the container that represents the dilution of a 4% (m/v) NaCl solution to each of the following:
a. 2% (m/v) NaCl
b. 1% (m/v) NaCl

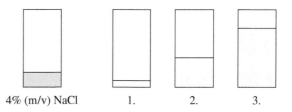

4% (m/v) NaCl   1.   2.   3.

8.80 Why do the lettuce leaves in a salad wilt after a vinaigrette dressing containing salt is added?

Use the following beakers and solutions for questions 8.81 and 8.82:

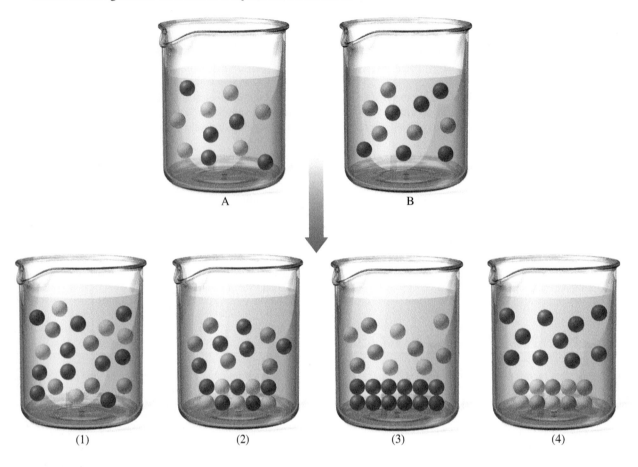

A

B

(1) (2) (3) (4)

8.81 Use the following:

Na⁺   Cl⁻   Ag⁺   NO₃⁻

a. Select the beaker (1, 2, 3, or 4) that contains the products after the solutions in beakers A and B are mixed.
b. If an insoluble salt forms, write the ionic equation.
c. If a reaction occurs, write the net ionic equation.

8.82 Use the following:

K⁺   NO₃⁻   NH₄⁺   Br⁻

a. Select the beaker (1, 2, 3, or 4) that contains the products after the solutions in beakers A and B are mixed.
b. If an insoluble salt forms, write the ionic equation.
c. If a reaction occurs, write the net ionic equation.

8.83 A semipermeable membrane separates two compartments, A and B. If the levels of solutions in A and B are equal initially, select the diagram that illustrates the final levels for each of the following:

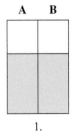

1.   2.   3.

	A	B
a.	2% (m/v) starch	8% (m/v) starch
b.	1% (m/v) starch	1% (m/v) starch
c.	5% (m/v) sucrose	1% (m/v) sucrose
d.	0.1% (m/v) sucrose	1% (m/v) sucrose

8.84 Select the diagram that represents the shape of a red blood cell when placed in each of the following solutions:

1.   2.   3.

Normal red blood cell

a. 0.90% (m/v) NaCl
b. 10% (m/v) glucose
c. 0.01% (m/v) NaCl
d. 5.0% (m/v) glucose
e. 1% (m/v) glucose

ADDITIONAL QUESTIONS AND PROBLEMS

8.85 Why does iodine dissolve in hexane but not in water?

8.86 How do temperature and pressure affect the solubility of solids and gases in water?

8.87 If NaCl has a solubility of 36.0 g in 100 g of H_2O at 20 °C, how many grams of water are needed to prepare a saturated solution containing 80.0 g of NaCl?

8.88 If the solid NaCl in a saturated solution of NaCl continues to dissolve, why is there no change in the concentration of the NaCl solution?

8.89 Potassium nitrate has a solubility of 34 g of KNO_3 in 100 g of H_2O at 20 °C. State if each of the following forms an unsaturated or saturated solution at 20 °C:
 a. 34 g of KNO_3 and 200. g of H_2O
 b. 17 g of KNO_3 and 50. g of H_2O
 c. 68 g of KNO_3 and 150. g of H_2O

8.90 Potassium fluoride has a solubility of 92 g of KF in 100 g of H_2O at 18 °C. State if each of the following forms an unsaturated or saturated solution at 18 °C:
 a. 46 g of KF and 100 g of H_2O
 b. 46 g of KF and 50 g of H_2O
 c. 184 g of KF and 150 g of H_2O

8.91 Calculate the mass percent (m/m) of a solution containing 15.5 g of Na_2SO_4 and 75.5 g of H_2O.

8.92 How many grams of K_2CO_3 are in 750 mL of a 3.5% (m/v) K_2CO_3 solution?

8.93 A patient receives all her nutrition from fluids given through the vena cava. Every 12 hours, 750 mL of a solution that is 4% (m/v) amino acids (protein) and 25% (m/v) glucose (carbohydrate) is given along with 500 mL of a 10% (m/v) lipid (fat).
 a. In 1 day, how many grams of amino acids, glucose, and lipid are given to the patient?
 b. How many kilocalories does she obtain in 1 day?

8.94 An 80-proof brandy is 40.0% (v/v) ethyl alcohol. The "proof" is twice the percent concentration of alcohol in the beverage. How many milliliters of alcohol are present in 750 mL of brandy?

8.95 How many milliliters of a 12% (v/v) propyl alcohol solution would you need to obtain 4.5 mL of propyl alcohol?

8.96 How many liters of a 5.0% (m/v) glucose solution would you need to obtain 75 g of glucose?

8.97 If you were in the laboratory, how would you prepare 0.250 L of a 2.00 M KCl solution?

8.98 What is the molarity of a solution containing 15.6 g of KCl in 274 mL of solution?

8.99 A solution is prepared with 70.0 g of HNO_3 and 130.0 g of H_2O. It has a density of 1.21 g/mL.
 a. What is the mass percent (m/m) of the HNO_3 solution?
 b. What is the total volume of the solution?
 c. What is the mass/volume percent (m/v)?
 d. What is its molarity (M)?

8.100 What is the molarity of a 15% (m/v) NaOH solution?

8.101 How many grams of solute are in each of the following solutions?
 a. 2.5 L of 3.0 M $Al(NO_3)_3$ solution
 b. 75 mL of 0.50 M $C_6H_{12}O_6$ solution

8.102 How many grams of solute are in each of the following solutions?
 a. 428 mL of a 0.450 M Na_2SO_4 solution
 b. 10.5 mL of a 2.50 M $AgNO_3$ solution
 c. 28.4 mL of a 6.00 M H_3PO_4 solution

8.103 Why would a solution made by mixing solutions of $NaNO_3$ and KCl be clear, while a combination of KCl and $Pb(NO_3)_2$ solution produces a solid?

8.104 Indicate whether each of the following is soluble in water:
 a. KCl **b.** $MgSO_4$ **c.** PbS
 d. $AgNO_3$ **e.** $Ca(OH)_2$

8.105 Write the net ionic equation to show the formation of a precipitate (insoluble salt) when the following solutions are mixed. Write *none* if there is no precipitate.
 a. $AgNO_3(aq)$ and $NaCl(aq)$
 b. $NaCl(aq)$ and $KNO_3(aq)$
 c. $Na_2SO_4(aq)$ and $BaCl_2(aq)$

8.106 Write the net ionic equation to show the formation of a precipitate (insoluble salt) when the following solutions are mixed. Write *none* if there is no precipitate.
 a. $Ca(NO_3)_2(aq)$ and $Na_2S(aq)$
 b. $Na_3PO_4(aq)$ and $Pb(NO_3)_2(aq)$
 c. $FeCl_3(aq)$ and $NH_4NO_3(aq)$

8.107 Calculate the molarity of the solution when water is added to prepare each of the following solutions:
 a. 25.0 mL of 0.200 M NaBr solution diluted to 50.0 mL
 b. 15.0 mL of 1.20 M K_2SO_4 solution diluted to 40.0 mL
 c. 75.0 mL of 6.00 M NaOH solution diluted to 255 mL

8.108 Calculate the molarity of the solution when water is added to prepare each of the following solutions:
 a. 25.0 mL of 18.0 M HCl solution diluted to 500. mL
 b. 50.0 mL of 1.50 M NaCl solution diluted to 125 mL
 c. 4.50 mL of 8.50 M KOH solution diluted to 75.0 mL

8.109 What is the final volume, in mL, when 25.0 mL of 5.00 M HCl solution is diluted to each of the following concentrations?
 a. 2.50 M HCl
 b. 1.00 M HCl
 c. 0.500 M HCl

8.110 What is the final volume, in mL, when 5.00 mL of 12.0 M NaOH solution is diluted to each of the following concentrations?
 a. 0.600 M **b.** 1.00 M **c.** 2.50 M

8.111 The antacid Amphogel contains aluminum hydroxide $Al(OH)_3$. How many milliliters of 6.00 M HCl solution are required to react with 60.0 mL of 1.00 M $Al(OH)_3$ solution?

$$Al(OH)_3(s) + 3HCl(aq) \longrightarrow AlCl_3(aq) + 3H_2O(l)$$

8.112 Calcium carbonate, $CaCO_3$, reacts with stomach acid (HCl, hydrochloric acid) according to the following equation:

$$CaCO_3(s) + 2HCl(aq) \longrightarrow CaCl_2(aq) + H_2O(l) + CO_2(g)$$

Tums, an antacid, contains $CaCO_3$. If Tums is added to 20.0 mL of 0.400 M HCl solution, how many grams of CO_2 gas are produced?

8.113 Why would solutions with high salt content be used to prepare dried flowers?

8.114 Why would a dialysis unit (artificial kidney) use isotonic concentrations of NaCl, KCl, $NaHCO_3$, and glucose in the dialysate?

8.115 Why can't you drink seawater even if you are stranded on a desert island?

8.116 A patient on dialysis has a high level of urea, a high level of sodium, and a low level of potassium in the blood. Why is the dialyzing solution prepared with a high level of potassium but no sodium or urea?

CHALLENGE QUESTIONS

8.117 How many grams of NO gas can be produced from 80.0 mL of a 4.00 M HNO_3 solution and excess Cu?

$$3Cu(s) + 8HNO_3(aq) \longrightarrow$$
$$3Cu(NO_3)_2(aq) + 4H_2O(l) + 2NO(g)$$

8.118 Osmolarity (Osm) is the molar concentration of the particles—molecules and/or ions—in a solution. In physiological solutions, 5% (m/v) glucose ($C_6H_{12}O_6$) and 0.9% (m/v) NaCl, the osmolarity must be the same as for the blood, which is 0.3 Osm. Calculate the osmolarity of each solute compound in these two physiological solutions.

8.119 Indicate whether each of the following ionic compounds is soluble (S) or insoluble (I) in water:

    a. Na_3PO_4 **b.** $PbBr_2$ **c.** KCl
    d. $(NH_4)_2S$ **e.** $MgCO_3$ **f.** $FePO_4$

8.120 Write the net ionic equation to show the formation of a precipitate (insoluble salt) when the following solutions are mixed. Write *none* if no insoluble salt forms.

    a. $AgNO_3 + Na_2SO_4$ **b.** $KCl + Pb(NO_3)_2$
    c. $CaCl_2 + Mg_3(PO_4)_2$ **d.** $Na_2SO_4 + BaCl_2$

8.121 In a laboratory experiment, a 10.0-mL sample of NaCl solution is poured into an evaporating dish with a mass of 24.10 g. The combined mass of the evaporating dish and NaCl solution is 36.15 g. After heating, the evaporating dish and dry NaCl have a combined mass of 25.50 g.

    a. What is the % (m/m) of the NaCl solution?
    b. What is the molarity (M) of the NaCl solution?
    c. If water is added to 10.0 mL of the initial NaCl solution to give a final volume of 60.0 mL, what is the molarity of the dilute NaCl solution?

8.122 A solution contains 4.56 g of KCl in 175 mL of solution. If the density of the KCl solution is 1.12 g/mL, what are the % (m/m) and molarity, M, for the potassium chloride solution?

8.123 A solution is prepared by dissolving 22.0 g of NaOH in 118.0 g water. The NaOH solution has a density of 1.15 g/mL.

    a. What is the % (m/m) concentration of the NaOH solution?
    b. What is the total volume (mL) of the solution?
    c. What is the molarity (M) of the solution?

8.124 How many milliliters of a 1.75 M LiCl solution contain 15.2 g of LiCl?

8.125 How many grams of NaBr are contained in 75.0 mL of a 1.50 M NaBr solution?

8.126 Magnesium reacts with HCl to produce magnesium chloride and hydrogen gas:

$$Mg(s) + 2HCl(aq) \longrightarrow MgCl_2(aq) + H_2(g)$$

What is the molarity of the HCl solution if 250. mL of the HCl solution reacts with magnesium to produce 4.20 L of H_2 gas measured at STP?

ANSWERS

ANSWERS TO STUDY CHECKS

8.1 A solution of a weak electrolyte will contain both molecules and ions.

8.2 0.194 mole of Cl^-

8.3 57 g of $NaNO_3$

8.4 A higher solubility is more likely because the solubility of most solids increases when the temperature increases.

8.5 **a.** No solid forms.
    b. $Pb^{2+}(aq) + 2Cl^-(aq) \longrightarrow PbCl_2(s)$

8.6 3.4% (m/m) NaCl solution

8.7 4.8% (m/v) Br_2 in CCl_4

8.8 18 g of KCl

8.9 2.12 M KNO_3 solution

8.10 4.5 moles of HCl

8.11 120. mL

8.12 1.47 g of Zn

8.13 The red blood cell will shrink (crenate).

ANSWERS TO SELECTED QUESTIONS AND PROBLEMS

8.1 **a.** NaCl, solute; water, solvent
    b. water, solute; ethanol, solvent
    c. oxygen, solute; nitrogen, solvent

8.3 The polar water molecules pull the K^+ and I^- ions away from the solid and into solution, where they are hydrated.

8.5 **a.** water   **b.** CCl_4 **c.** water   **d.** CCl_4

8.7 In a solution of KF, only the ions of K^+ and F^- are present in the solvent. In an HF solution, there are a few ions of H^+ and F^- present, but mostly dissolved HF molecules.

8.9 **a.** $KCl(s) \xrightarrow{H_2O} K^+(aq) + Cl^-(aq)$

    b. $CaCl_2(s) \xrightarrow{H_2O} Ca^{2+}(aq) + 2Cl^-(aq)$

    c. $K_3PO_4(s) \xrightarrow{H_2O} 3K^+(aq) + PO_4^{3-}(aq)$

    d. $Fe(NO_3)_3(s) \xrightarrow{H_2O} Fe^{3+}(aq) + 3NO_3^-(aq)$

8.11 **a.** mostly molecules and a few ions
    b. ions only
    c. molecules only

8.13 **a.** strong electrolyte
    b. weak electrolyte
    c. nonelectrolyte

8.15 **a.** 1 Eq   **b.** 2 Eq   **c.** 2 Eq   **d.** 6 Eq

8.17 0.154 mole of Na^+, 0.154 mole of Cl^-

8.19 55 mEq/L

8.21 **a.** saturated   **b.** unsaturated

8.23 **a.** unsaturated   **b.** unsaturated   **c.** saturated

8.25 **a.** 68 g of KCl   **b.** 12 g of KCl

8.27 **a.** The solubility of solid solutes typically increases as temperature increases.
    b. The solubility of a gas is less at a higher temperature.
    c. Gas solubility is less at a higher temperature and the CO_2 pressure in the can is increased.

8.29 **a.** soluble   **b.** insoluble   **c.** insoluble
     d. soluble   **e.** soluble

8.31 **a.** No solid forms.

     b. $2Ag^+(aq) + 2\cancel{NO_3^-}(aq) + 2\cancel{K^+}(aq) + S^{2-}(aq) \longrightarrow$
$$Ag_2S(s) + 2\cancel{NO_3^-}(aq) + 2\cancel{K^+}(aq)$$
$$2Ag^+(aq) + S^{2-}(aq) \longrightarrow Ag_2S(s)$$

     c. $Ca^{2+}(aq) + 2\cancel{Cl^-}(aq) + 2\cancel{Na^+}(aq) + SO_4^{2-}(aq) \longrightarrow$
$$CaSO_4(s) + 2\cancel{Cl^-}(aq) + 2\cancel{Na^+}(aq)$$
$$Ca^{2+}(aq) + SO_4^{2-}(aq) \longrightarrow CaSO_4(s)$$

     d. $3Cu^{2+}(aq) + 6\cancel{Cl^-}(aq) + 6\cancel{Li^+}(aq) + 2PO_4^{3-}(aq) \longrightarrow$
$$Cu_3(PO_4)_2(s) + 6\cancel{Cl^-}(aq) + 6\cancel{Li^+}(aq)$$
$$3Cu^{2+}(aq) + 2PO_4^{3-}(aq) \longrightarrow Cu_3(PO_4)_2(s)$$

8.33 5% (m/m) is 5 g of glucose in 100 g of solution, whereas 5% (m/v) is 5 g of glucose in 100 mL of solution.

8.35 **a.** 17% (m/m)   **b.** 5.3% (m/m)

8.37 **a.** 30.% (m/v)   **b.** 11% (m/v)

8.39 **a.** 2.5 g of KCl   **b.** 50. g of NH_4Cl

8.41 79.9 mL of alcohol

8.43 **a.** 20. g of mannitol
     b. 300 g of mannitol

8.45 2 L

8.47 **a.** 0.50 M glucose solution
     b. 0.036 M KOH solution
     c. 0.250 M NaCl solution

8.49 **a.** 3.0 moles of NaCl
     b. 0.40 mole of KBr
     c. 0.25 mole of $MgCl_2$

8.51 **a.** 120 g of NaOH
     b. 60. g of KCl
     c. 5.5 g of HCl

8.53 **a.** 1.5 L   **b.** 10. L   **c.** 62.5 mL

8.55 **a.** 2.0 M HCl solution
     b. 2.0 M NaOH solution
     c. 2.5% (m/v) KOH solution
     d. 3.0% (m/v) H_2SO_4 solution

8.57 **a.** 0.60 L   **b.** 250 mL   **c.** 6.0 L   **d.** 180 mL

8.59 **a.** 10.4 g of $PbCl_2$
     b. 18.8 mL of $Pb(NO_3)_2$ solution

8.61 **a.** 206 mL of HCl solution
     b. 0.500 mole of H_2 gas

8.63 **a.** solution   **b.** suspension

8.65 **a.** 0.060 mole of NaCl (0.12 mole of particles)
     b. 0.030 mole of K_3PO_4 (0.12 mole of particles)

8.67 **a.** starch
     b. from pure water into the starch
     c. starch

8.69 **a.** B 10% (m/v) starch
     b. B 8% (m/v) albumin
     c. B 10% (m/v) sucrose

8.71 **a.** hypotonic   **b.** hypotonic
     c. isotonic   **d.** isotonic

8.73 **a.** NaCl   **b.** alanine   **c.** NaCl   **d.** urea

8.75 **a.** 3   **b.** 1   **c.** 2

8.77 The skin of the cucumber acts like a semipermeable membrane and the more dilute solution inside flows into the brine solution.

8.79 **a.** 2   **b.** 3

8.81 **a.** beaker 3
     b. $Na^+(aq) + Cl^-(aq) + Ag^+(aq) + NO_3^-(aq) \longrightarrow$
$$AgCl(s) + Na^+(aq) + NO_3^-(aq)$$
     c. $Ag^+(aq) + Cl^-(aq) \longrightarrow AgCl(s)$

8.83 **a.** 2   **b.** 1   **c.** 3   **d.** 2

8.85 Because iodine is a nonpolar molecule, it will dissolve in hexane, a nonpolar solvent. Iodine does not dissolve in water, because water is a polar solvent.

8.87 222 g of water

8.89 **a.** unsaturated solution
     b. saturated solution
     c. saturated solution

8.91 17.0% (m/m)

8.93 **a.** 60 g of amino acids, 380 g of glucose, and 100 g of lipids
     b. 2700 kcal

8.95 38 mL of solution

8.97 To make a 2.00 M KCl solution, weigh out 37.3 g of KCl (0.500 mole) and place in a volumetric flask. Add water to dissolve the KCl and give a final volume of 0.250 liter.

8.99 **a.** 35.0% (m/m) HNO_3
     b. 165 mL
     c. 42.4% (m/v) HNO_3
     d. 6.73 M

8.101 **a.** 1600 g of $Al(NO_3)_3$
     b. 6.8 g of $C_6H_{12}O_6$

8.103 When solutions of $NaNO_3$ and KCl are mixed, no insoluble products are formed. All the combinations of salts are soluble. When KCl and $Pb(NO_3)_2$ solutions are mixed, the insoluble salt $PbCl_2$ forms.

8.105 **a.** $Ag^+(aq) + Cl^-(aq) \longrightarrow AgCl(s)$
     b. none
     c. $Ba^{2+}(aq) + SO_4^{2-}(aq) \longrightarrow BaSO_4(s)$

8.107 **a.** 0.100 M NaBr solution
     b. 0.450 M K_2SO_4 solution
     c. 1.76 M NaOH solution

8.109 **a.** 50.0 mL of HCl solution
     b. 125 mL of HCl solution
     c. 250. mL of HCl solution

8.111 30.0 mL of HCl solution

8.113 The solution will dehydrate the flowers because water will flow out of the cells of the flowers into the more concentrated salt solution.

8.115 Drinking seawater will cause water to flow out of the body cells and further dehydrate a person.

8.117 2.40 g of NO

8.119 **a.** Na^+ salts are soluble.
     b. The halide salts containing Pb^{2+} are insoluble.
     c. K^+ salts are soluble.
     d. Salts containing NH_4^+ ions are soluble.
     e. Salts containing CO_3^{2-} are usually insoluble.
     f. Salts containing PO_4^{3-} and Fe^{3+} are insoluble.

8.121 **a.** 11.6% (m/m)   **b.** 2.39 M   **c.** 0.383 M

8.123 **a.** 15.7% (m/m) NaOH
     b. 122 mL
     c. 4.51 M

8.125 11.6 g of NaBr

9 Chemical Equilibrium

"I use radioactive isotopes to understand the cycling of elements like carbon and phosphorus in the ocean," explains Claudia Benitez-Nelson, a chemical oceanographer and Associate Professor of Geological Sciences at the University of South Carolina. "For example, I use thorium-234 to trace how and when particles are formed and transported to the bottom of the ocean. I also examine the biological consumption of the nutrient phosphorus by measuring fluctuations over time in the levels of the naturally occurring radioactive isotopes of phosphorus. My knowledge of chemistry is essential for understanding nutrient biogeochemistry and carbon sequestration in the oceans."

Oceanographers study the oceans and the plants and animals that live there. They study marine life, the chemical compounds in the ocean, the shape and composition of the ocean floor, and the effects of waves and tides.

Mastering**CHEMISTRY**™

Visit **www.masteringchemistry.com** for self-study materials and instructor-assigned homework.

arlier we looked at chemical reactions and determined the amounts of substances that react and the products that form. Now we are interested in how fast a reaction goes. If we know how fast a medication acts on the body, we can adjust the time over which the medication is taken. In construction, substances are added to cement to make it dry faster so work can continue. Some reactions such as explosions or the formation of precipitates in a solution are very fast. We know that when we roast a turkey or bake a cake that the reaction is slower. Some reactions such as the tarnishing of silver and the aging of the body are even slower. (See Figure 9.1.) We will see that some reactions need energy to keep running, whereas other reactions produce energy. We burn gasoline in our automobile engines to produce energy to make our cars move. We will also look at the effect of changing the concentrations of reactants or products on the rate of reaction.

Up to now, we have considered a reaction as proceeding in a forward direction from reactants to products. However, in many reactions a reverse reaction also takes place as products collide to reform reactants. When the forward and reverse reactions take place at the same rates the amounts of reactants and products stay the same. When this balance in forward and reverse rate is reached, we say that the reaction has reached *equilibrium*. At equilibrium, both reactants and products are present, though some reaction mixtures contain mostly reactants and form only a few products, while others contain mostly products and few reactants.

Reaction rate
increases

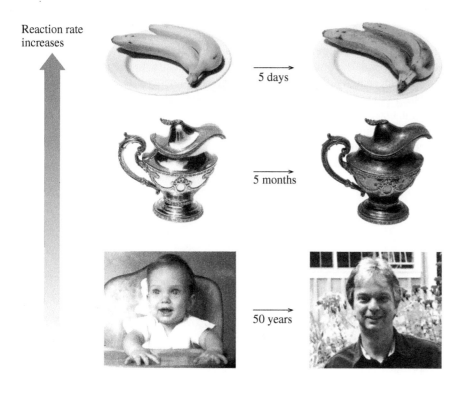

FIGURE 9.1 Reaction rates vary greatly for everyday processes. A banana ripens in a few days, silver tarnishes in a few months, while the aging process of humans takes many years.

Q How would you compare the rates of the reaction that forms sugars in plants by photosynthesis with the reactions that digest sugars in the body?

5 days

5 months

50 years

9.1 Rates of Reactions

For a chemical reaction to take place, the molecules of the reactants must come in contact with each other. The **collision theory** indicates that a reaction takes place only when molecules collide with the proper orientation and with sufficient energy. Many collisions can occur, but only a few actually lead to the formation of product. For example, consider the reaction of nitrogen (N_2) and oxygen (O_2) molecules. (See Figure 9.2.) To form the nitrogen oxide (NO) product, the collisions between the N_2 and the O_2 molecules must place the atoms in the proper alignment. If the molecules are not aligned properly, no reaction takes place.

LEARNING GOAL

Describe how temperature, concentration, and catalysts affect the rate of a reaction.

FIGURE 9.2 Reacting molecules must collide, have a minimum amount of energy, and the proper orientation to form products.

Q What happens when reacting molecules collide with the minimum energy but do not have the proper orientation?

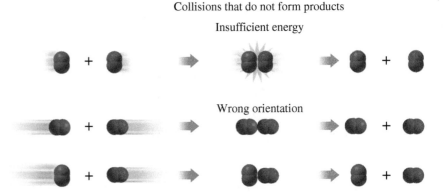

Activation Energy

Even when a collision has the proper orientation, there still must be sufficient energy to break the bonds between the atoms of the reactants. The **activation energy** is the amount of energy required to break the bonds between atoms of reactants. In Figure 9.3, activation energy appears as an energy hill. The concept of activation energy is analogous to climbing a hill. To reach a destination on the other side, we must have the energy needed to climb to the top of the hill. Once we are at the top, we can run down the other side. The energy needed to get us from our starting point to the top of the hill would be our activation energy.

In the same way, a collision must provide enough energy to push the reactants to the top of the energy hill. Then the reactants may be converted to products. If the energy provided

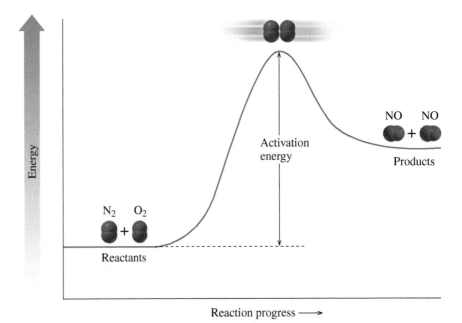

FIGURE 9.3 The activation energy is the energy needed to convert the colliding molecules into product.

Q What happens in a collision of reacting molecules that have the proper orientation but not the energy of activation?

by the collision is less than the activation energy, the molecules simply bounce apart, and no reaction occurs. The features that lead to a successful reaction are summarized as follows:

Three Conditions Required for a Reaction to Occur

1. **Collision**   The reactants must collide.
2. **Orientation**   The reactants must align properly to break and form bonds.
3. **Energy**   The collision must provide the energy of activation.

Reaction Rates

The **rate** (or speed) **of reaction** is determined by measuring the amount of a reactant used up, or the amount of a product formed, in a certain period of time:

$$\text{Rate of reaction} = \frac{\text{change in concentration}}{\text{change in time}}$$

Perhaps we can describe the rate of reaction by the analogy of eating a pizza. When we start to eat, we have a whole pizza. As time goes by, there are fewer slices of pizza left. If we know how long it took to eat the pizza, we could determine the rate at which the pizza was consumed. Let's assume 4 slices are eaten every 8 minutes. That gives a rate of $\frac{1}{2}$ slice per minute. After 16 minutes, all 8 slices are gone.

Rate at which pizza slices are eaten

Slices eaten	0	4 slices	6 slices	8 slices
Time (min)	0	8 min	12 min	16 min

$$\text{Rate} = \frac{4 \text{ slices}}{8 \text{ min}} = \frac{1 \text{ slice}}{2 \text{ min}} = \frac{\frac{1}{2} \text{ slice}}{1 \text{ min}}$$

 **TUTORIAL**
Factors That Affect Rate

Factors That Affect the Rate of a Reaction

Some reactions go very fast, while others are very slow. For any reaction, the rate is affected by changes in temperature, changes in the concentration of the reactants, and the addition of catalysts.

   Temperature At higher temperatures, the increase in kinetic energy makes the reacting molecules move faster. As a result, more collisions occur, and more colliding molecules have sufficient energy to react and form products. If we want food to cook faster, we use more heat to raise the temperature. When body temperature rises, there is an increase in the pulse rate, rate of breathing, and metabolic rate. On the other hand, we slow down reactions by lowering the temperature. We refrigerate perishable foods to retard spoilage and make them last longer. For some injuries, we apply ice to lessen the bruising process.

   Concentrations of Reactants For virtually all reactions, the rate of a reaction increases when the concentrations of the reactants increases. When there are more reacting molecules, more collisions can occur, and the reaction goes faster. (See Figure 9.4.) For example, a person having difficulty breathing may be given oxygen. The increase in the number of oxygen molecules in the lungs increases the rate at which oxygen combines with hemoglobin and helps the patient breathe more easily.

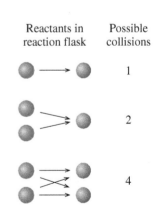

Reactants in reaction flask	Possible collisions
	1
	2
	4

FIGURE 9.4 Increasing the concentration of a reactant increases the number of collisions that are possible.

Q How many collisions are possible if one more red reactant is added?

Catalysts Another way to speed up a reaction is to lower the activation energy. We saw that the activation energy is the energy needed to break apart the bonds of the reacting molecules. If a collision provides less energy than the activation energy, the bonds do not break apart and the molecules bounce apart. A **catalyst** speeds up a reaction by providing a different way for the reaction to proceed that has a lower activation energy. When activation energy is lowered, more collisions provide sufficient energy for reactants to form product. During a reaction, a catalyst is not changed or consumed.

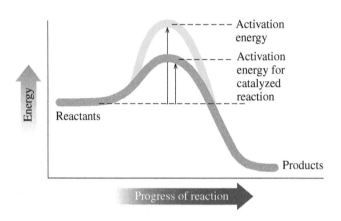

TABLE 9.1 Factors That Increase Reaction Rate

Factor	Reason
More reactants	More collisions
Higher temperature	More collisions, more collisions with energy of activation
Adding a catalyst	Lowers energy of activation

Catalysts have many uses in industry. In the manufacturing of margarine, hydrogen (H_2) is added to vegetable oils. Normally, the reaction is very slow because it has a high activation energy. However, when platinum (Pt) is used as a catalyst, the reaction occurs rapidly. In the body, biocatalysts called enzymes make most metabolic reactions proceed at rates necessary for proper cellular activity. A summary of the factors affecting reaction rates is given in Table 9.1.

CONCEPT CHECK 9.1

■ **Rate of Reactions**

Describe how decreasing the concentration of a reactant would change the rate of a reaction.

ANSWER

If the concentration of a reactant is decreased, there will be fewer collisions of the reactant molecules, which would slow the rate of reaction.

SAMPLE PROBLEM   9.1

■ **Factors That Affect the Rate of Reaction**

Indicate whether the following changes will increase, decrease, or have no effect upon the rate of reaction:

a. increase in temperature
b. increase in the number of reactant molecules
c. adding a catalyst

SOLUTION

a. increase   **b.** increase   **c.** increase

STUDY CHECK

How does the lowering of temperature affect the rate of reaction?

ENVIRONMENTAL NOTE

Catalytic Converters

For over 20 years, manufacturers have been required to include catalytic converters on gasoline automobile engines. When gasoline burns, the products found in the exhaust of a car contain high levels of pollutants. These include carbon monoxide (CO) from incomplete combustion, hydrocarbons such as C_8H_{18} (octane) from unburned fuel, and nitrogen oxide (NO) from the reaction of N_2 and O_2 at the high temperatures reached within the engine. Carbon monoxide is toxic, and nitrogen oxide is involved in the formation of smog and acid rain.

The purpose of a catalytic converter is to lower the activation energy for reactions that convert each of these pollutants into substances such as CO_2, N_2, O_2, and H_2O, which are already present in the atmosphere.

$$2CO(g) + O_2(g) \longrightarrow 2CO_2(g)$$
$$2C_8H_{18}(g) + 25O_2(g) \longrightarrow 16CO_2(g) + 18H_2O(g)$$
$$2NO(g) \longrightarrow N_2(g) + O_2(g)$$

A catalytic converter consists of solid-particle catalysts, such as platinum (Pt) and palladium (Pd), on a ceramic honeycomb that provides a large surface area and facilitates contact with pollutants. As the pollutants pass through the converter, they react with the catalysts. Today, we all use unleaded gasoline because lead interferes with the ability of the Pt and Pd catalysts in the converter to react with the pollutants.

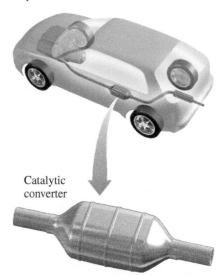

Catalytic converter

$2NO(g) \longrightarrow N_2(g) + O_2(g)$

NO absorbed on catalyst   NO dissociates

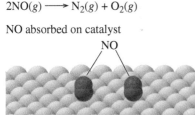

Surface of metal (Pt, Pd) catalyst

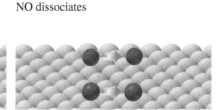

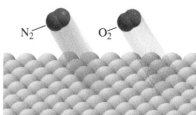

$2CO(g) + O_2(g) \longrightarrow 2CO_2(g)$

CO and O_2 absorbed on catalyst O_2 dissociates

Surface of metal (Pt, Pd) catalyst

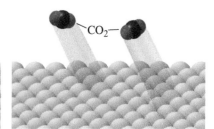

QUESTIONS AND PROBLEMS

Rates of Reactions

9.1 a. What is meant by the rate of a reaction?
  b. Why does bread grow mold more quickly at room temperature than in the refrigerator?

9.2 a. How does a catalyst affect the activation energy?
  b. Why is pure oxygen used in cases of respiratory distress?

9.3 In the following reaction, what happens to the number of collisions when more Br_2 molecules are added?

$$H_2(g) + Br_2(g) \longrightarrow 2HBr(g)$$

9.4 In the following reaction, what happens to the number of collisions when the temperature of the reaction is decreased?

$$H_2(g) + Br_2(g) \longrightarrow 2HBr(g)$$

9.5 How would each of the following change the rate of the reaction shown here?

$$2SO_2(g) + O_2(g) \longrightarrow 2SO_3(g)$$

a. adding SO_2 **b.** raising the temperature

c. adding a catalyst   **d.** removing some SO_2

9.6 How would each of the following change the rate of the reaction shown here?

$$2NO(g) + 2H_2(g) \longrightarrow N_2(g) + 2H_2O(g)$$

a. adding more NO   **b.** lowering the temperature

c. removing some H_2 **d.** adding a catalyst

9.2 Chemical Equilibrium

LEARNING GOAL

Use the concept of reversible reactions to explain chemical equilibrium.

TUTORIAL
Chemical Equilibrium

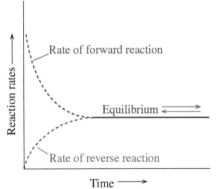

SELF STUDY ACTIVITY
Equilibrium

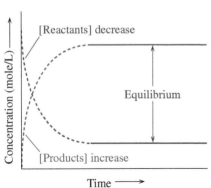

In earlier chapters, we considered the *forward reaction* in an equation and assumed that all of the reactants were converted to products. However, most of the time reactants are not completely converted to products, because a *reverse reaction* takes place in which products come together and form the reactants. When a reaction proceeds in both a forward and reverse direction, it is said to be reversible. We have looked at other reversible processes. For example, the melting of solids to form liquids and the freezing of liquids into solids is a reversible physical change. Even in our daily life we have reversible events. We go from home to school, and we return from school to home. We go up an escalator and come back down. We put money in our bank account and take money out.

An analogy for a forward and reverse reaction can be found in the phrase "We are going to the grocery store." Although we mention our trip in one direction, we know that we will also return home from the grocery store. Because our trip has both a forward and reverse direction, we can say the trip is reversible. It is not very likely that we would stay at the grocery store forever.

A trip to the grocery store can be used to illustrate another aspect of reversible reactions. Perhaps the grocery store is nearby and we usually walk. However, we can change our rate. Suppose that one day we drive to the store, which increases our rate and gets us to the store faster. Correspondingly, a car also increases the rate at which we return home.

Reversible Reactions

A **reversible reaction** proceeds in both the forward and reverse directions. That means there are two reaction rates: the rate of the forward reaction and the rate of the reverse reaction. When molecules begin to react, the rate of the forward reaction is faster than the rate of the reverse reaction. As reactants are consumed and products accumulate, the rate of the forward reaction decreases and the rate of the reverse reaction increases.

Equilibrium

Eventually, the rates of the forward and reverse reactions are equal; the reactants form products as often as products form reactants. A reaction reaches **chemical equilibrium** when there is no further change in the concentrations of the reactants and products.

> **At equilibrium:**
>
> The rate of the forward reaction is equal to the rate of the reverse reaction.
>
> No further changes occur in the concentrations of reactants and products, even though the two reactions continue at equal but opposite rates.

Let us look at the process as the reaction of H_2 and I_2 proceeds to equilibrium. (See Figure 9.5.) Initially, only H_2 and I_2 are present. Soon, a few molecules of HI are produced by the forward reaction. With more time, additional HI molecules are produced. As the concentration of HI increases, more HI molecules collide and react in the reverse direction.

Forward reaction: $H_2(g) + I_2(g) \longrightarrow 2HI(g)$

Reverse reaction: $2HI(g) \longrightarrow H_2(g) + I_2(g)$

As HI product builds up, the rate of the reverse reaction increases, while the rate of the forward reaction decreases. Eventually the rates become equal, which means the reaction

$$H_2(g) + I_2(g) \rightleftharpoons 2HI(g)$$

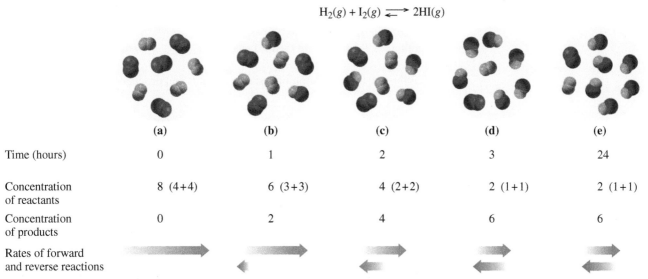

	(a)	(b)	(c)	(d)	(e)
Time (hours)	0	1	2	3	24
Concentration of reactants	8 (4+4)	6 (3+3)	4 (2+2)	2 (1+1)	2 (1+1)
Concentration of products	0	2	4	6	6
Rates of forward and reverse reactions					

FIGURE 9.5 **(a)** Initially, the reaction flask contains only the reactants H_2 and I_2. **(b)** The forward reaction between H_2 and I_2 begins to produce 2HI. **(c)** As the reaction proceeds, there are fewer molecules of H_2 and I_2 and more molecules of HI, which increases the rate of the reverse reaction. **(d)** At equilibrium, the concentrations of reactants H_2 and I_2 and product HI are constant. **(e)** The reaction continues with the rate of the forward reaction equal to the rate of the reverse reaction.
Q How do the rates of the forward and reverse reactions compare once a chemical reaction reaches equilibrium?

has reached equilibrium. Even though the concentrations remain constant at equilibrium, the forward and reverse reactions continue to occur. The forward and reverse reactions are usually shown together in a single equation by using a double arrow. A reversible reaction is two opposing reactions that occur at the same time.

$$H_2(g) + I_2(g) \underset{\text{Reverse reaction}}{\overset{\text{Forward reaction}}{\rightleftharpoons}} 2HI(g)$$

SAMPLE PROBLEM   9.2

■ **Reversible Reactions**

Write the forward and reverse reactions for each of the following:

a. $N_2(g) + 3H_2(g) \rightleftharpoons 2NH_3(g)$ **b.** $2CO(g) + O_2 \rightleftharpoons 2CO_2(g)$

SOLUTION

The equations are separated into forward and reverse reactions.

a. Forward reaction: $N_2(g) + 3H_2(g) \longrightarrow 2NH_3(g)$
   Reverse reaction: $2NH_3(g) \longrightarrow N_2(g) + 3H_2(g)$
b. Forward reaction: $2CO(g) + O_2(g) \longrightarrow 2CO_2(g)$
   Reverse reaction: $2CO_2(g) \longrightarrow 2CO(g) + O_2(g)$

STUDY CHECK

Write the equation for the equilibrium reaction that contains the following reverse reaction:

   $2HBr(g) \longrightarrow H_2(g) + Br_2(g)$

CONCEPT CHECK 9.2

■ **Reaction Rates and Equilibrium**

Complete each of the following with equal or not equal, faster or slower, change or do not change:

a. Before equilibrium is reached, the concentrations of the reactants and products _____.

b. Initially, reactants placed in a container have a _____ rate of reaction than the rate of reaction of the products.

c. At equilibrium, the rate of the forward reaction is _____ to the rate of the reverse reaction.

d. At equilibrium, the concentrations of the reactants and products _____.

ANSWER

a. Until the rates of the forward and reverse reactions become equal, the concentrations of the reactants and products will *change*.

b. When there are only reactants in the container, the rate of the forward reaction will be *faster* than the rate of the reverse reaction.

c. Equilibrium is reached when the rates of the forward and reverse reactions become *equal*.

d. At equilibrium, when the rates of the forward and reverse reactions become equal, the concentrations of the reactants and products *do not change*.

QUESTIONS AND PROBLEMS

Chemical Equilibrium

9.7 What is meant by the term "reversible reaction"?

9.8 When does a reversible reaction reach equilibrium?

9.9 Which of the following processes are reversible?
  a. breaking a glass   **b.** melting snow   **c.** heating a pan

9.10 Which of the following processes are at equilibrium?
  a. Opposing rates of reaction are equal.
  b. Concentrations of reactants and products are equal.
  c. Concentrations of reactants and products do not change.

9.3 Equilibrium Constants

At equilibrium, reactions occur in opposite directions at the same rate, which means the concentrations of the reactants and products remain constant. We can use a ski lift as an analogy. Early in the morning, skiers at the bottom of the mountain begin to ride the ski lift up to the slopes. As skiers reach the top of the mountain, they ski down. Eventually, the number of people riding up the ski lift becomes equal to the number of people skiing down the mountain. There is no further change in the number of skiers on the slopes; the system is at equilibrium.

Equilibrium Constant Expression

TUTORIAL
Equilibrium Constant

Because the concentrations in a reaction at equilibrium no longer change, they can be used to set up a relationship between the products and the reactants. Suppose we write a general equation for reactants A and B that form products C and D. The small italic letters are the coefficients in the balanced equation.

$$a\text{A} + b\text{B} \rightleftharpoons c\text{C} + d\text{D}$$

An **equilibrium constant expression** for the reaction multiplies the concentrations of the products together and divides by the concentrations of the reactants. Each concentration is raised to a power that is its coefficient in the balanced chemical reaction. The square bracket around each substance indicates the concentration is expressed in moles per liter (M). The **equilibrium constant**, K_c, is the numerical value obtained by substituting molar concentrations at equilibrium into the expression. For our general reaction, the equilibrium constant expression is

Equilibrium constant

Equilibrium constant expression

$$K_c = \frac{\text{Products}}{\text{Reactants}} = \frac{[\text{C}]^c\,[\text{D}]^d}{[\text{A}]^a\,[\text{B}]^b} \quad \text{Coefficients}$$

For the reaction of H_2 and I_2 to form HI, we use the following steps to write the equilibrium constant expression:

STEP 1   Write the balanced equilibrium equation:

$$H_2(g) + I_2(g) \rightleftharpoons 2HI(g)$$

STEP 2   Write the concentrations of the products as the numerator and reactants as the denominator:

$$\frac{\text{Products} \longrightarrow}{\text{Reactants} \longrightarrow} \frac{[HI]}{[H_2][I_2]}$$

STEP 3   Write the coefficient of each substance as an exponent:

$$K_c = \frac{[HI]^2}{[H_2][I_2]}$$

CONCEPT CHECK 9.3

■ **Equilibrium Constant Expression**

Select the correctly written equilibrium constant expression for the following reaction, and explain your choice:

$$CH_4(g) + H_2O(g) \rightleftharpoons CO(g) + 3H_2(g)$$

a. $K_c = \dfrac{[CO]]3H_2]}{[CH_4]]H_2O]}$ **b.** $K_c = \dfrac{[CO][H_2]^3}{[CH_4][H_2O]}$

c. $K_c = \dfrac{[CH_4][H_2O]}{[CO][H_2]^3}$ **d.** $K_c = \dfrac{[CO][H_2]}{[CH_4][H_2O]}$

ANSWER
The correct equilibrium constant expression is **b.** The products are written in the numerator and the reactants are in the denominator. Because H_2 has a coefficient of 3 in the balanced equation, an exponent of 3 is used with the concentration of H_2.

SAMPLE PROBLEM   9.3

■ **Writing Equilibrium Constant Expressions**

Write the equilibrium constant expression for the following:

$$2SO_2(g) + O_2(g) \rightleftharpoons 2SO_3(g)$$

SOLUTION

STEP 1   Write the balanced equilibrium equation:

$$2SO_2(g) + O_2(g) \rightleftharpoons 2SO_3(g)$$

STEP 2   Write the concentrations of the products as the numerator and reactants as the denominator:

$$\frac{\text{Products} \longrightarrow}{\text{Reactants} \longrightarrow} \frac{[SO_3]}{[SO_2][O_2]}$$

STEP 3   Write the coefficient of each substance as an exponent:

$$K_c = \frac{[SO_3]^2}{[SO_2]^2[O_2]}$$

Guide to Writing the K_c Expression

STEP 1
Write the balanced equilibrium equation.

STEP 2
Write the concentrations of the products as the numerator and reactants as the denominator.

STEP 3
Write the coefficient of each substance in the equation as an exponent.

$$CaCO_3(s) \rightleftharpoons CaO(s) + CO_2(g)$$

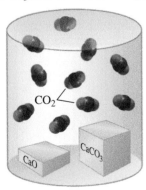

$T = 800\ °C$

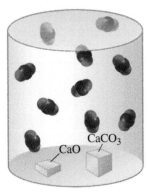

$T = 800\ °C$

FIGURE 9.6 At equilibrium at constant temperature, the concentration of CO_2 is the same regardless of the amounts of $CaCO_3(s)$ and $CaO(s)$ in the container.

Q Why are the concentrations of $CaO(s)$ and $CaCO_3(s)$ not included in K_c for the decomposition of $CaCO_3$?

STUDY CHECK

Write the balanced chemical equation that would give the following equilibrium constant expression:

$$K_c = \frac{[NO_2]^2}{[NO]^2[O_2]}$$

Heterogeneous Equilibrium

Up to now, our examples have been reactions that involve only gases. A reaction in which all the reactants and products are in the same physical state is a **homogenous equilibrium**. When the reactants and products are in two or more physical states, the equilibrium is termed a **heterogeneous equilibrium**. In the following example, solid calcium carbonate reaches equilibrium with solid calcium oxide and carbon dioxide gas; this is a heterogeneous equilibrium. (See Figure 9.6.)

$$CaCO_3(s) \rightleftharpoons CaO(s) + CO_2(g)$$

In contrast to gases, the concentrations of pure solids and pure liquids in a heterogeneous equilibrium are constant; they do not change. Therefore, pure solids and liquids are not included in the equilibrium constant expression. For this heterogeneous equilibrium, the K_c expression does not include the concentration of $CaCO_3(s)$ or $CaO(s)$. It is written as $K_c = [CO_2]$.

SAMPLE PROBLEM 9.4

■ **Heterogeneous Equilibrium Constant Expression**

Write the equilibrium constant expression for the following reaction at equilibrium:

$$4HCl(g) + O_2(g) \rightleftharpoons 2H_2O(l) + 2Cl_2(g)$$

SOLUTION

STEP 1   **Write the balanced equilibrium equation:**

$$4HCl(g) + O_2(g) \rightleftharpoons 2H_2O(l) + 2Cl_2(g)$$

STEP 2   **Write the concentrations of the products as the numerator and reactants as the denominator:**

$$\frac{Products \longrightarrow}{Reactants \longrightarrow} \frac{[Cl_2]}{[HCl][O_2]}$$

In the equilibrium constant expression for a heterogeneous reaction, the concentration of the liquid H_2O is not included.

STEP 3   **Write the coefficient of each substance as an exponent:**

$$K_c = \frac{[Cl_2]^2}{[HCl]^4[O_2]}$$

STUDY CHECK

Solid iron(II) oxide and carbon monoxide gas are in equilibrium with solid iron and carbon dioxide gas. Write the equation and the equilibrium constant expression for this reaction.

Calculating Equilibrium Constants

The numerical value of the equilibrium constant is calculated from the equilibrium constant expression by substituting experimentally measured concentrations of the reactants and products at equilibrium into the expression. For example, the equilibrium constant expression for the reaction of H_2 and I_2 is written

$$H_2(g) + I_2(g) \rightleftharpoons 2HI(g) \qquad K_c = \frac{[HI]^2}{[H_2][I_2]}$$

In the first experiment, the molar concentrations for the reactants and products at equilibrium are found to be $[H_2] = 0.10$ M, $[I_2] = 0.20$ M, and $[HI] = 1.04$ M. When we substitute these values into the equilibrium constant expression, we obtain the numerical value of the equilibrium constant:

Reactants   **Products**

$[H_2] = 0.10$ M $[HI] = 1.04$ M
$[I_2]\ \ = 0.20$ M

$$K_c = \frac{[HI]^2}{[H_2][I_2]} = \frac{[1.04]^2}{[0.10][0.20]} = 54$$

In experiments 2 and 3, we look at different equilibrium concentrations of reactants and products for the H_2, I_2, and HI system at the same temperature. When the concentrations of reactants and products are measured in each equilibrium sample and used to calculate the K_c for the reaction, the same value of K_c is obtained for each. (See Table 9.2.) Thus, a reaction at a specific temperature can have only one value for the equilibrium constant.

TABLE 9.2 Equilibrium Constant for $H_2(g) + I_2(g) \rightleftharpoons 2HI(g)$ at 427 °C

Experiment	$[H_2]$	$[I_2]$	$[HI]$	$K_c = \dfrac{[HI]^2}{[H_2][I_2]}$
1	0.10 M	0.20 M	1.04 M	54
2	0.20 M	0.20 M	1.47 M	54
3	0.30 M	0.17 M	1.66 M	54

The units of K_c depend on the specific equation. In the example of $[H_2]$, $[I_2]$, and $[HI]$, K_c has the units of $[M]^2/[M]^2$, which results in a value with no units. However, in the following example, the [M] units would not cancel, because $[M]^2/[M]^4 = 1/[M]^2 = [M]^{-2}$. Usually K_c is given without units. At 500 K, the value of K_c for the following reaction is 1.7×10^2. (In this text, we will give K_c without units.)

$$N_2(g) + 3H_2(g) \rightleftharpoons 2NH_3(g)$$

$$K_c = \frac{[NH_3]^2}{[N_2][H_2]^3} = 1.7 \times 10^2$$

SAMPLE PROBLEM 9.5

■ Calculating an Equilibrium Constant

The decomposition of dinitrogen tetroxide forms nitrogen dioxide:

$$N_2O_4(g) \rightleftharpoons 2NO_2(g)$$

What is the value of K_c at 100 °C if a reaction mixture at equilibrium contains $[N_2O_4] = 0.45$ M and $[NO_2] = 0.31$ M?

Guide to Calculating the K_c Value

STEP 1
Write the K_c expression for the equilibrium.

STEP 2
Substitute equilibrium (molar) concentrations and calculate K_c.

SOLUTION

Given   reactant: $[N_2O_2] = 0.45$ M   product: $[NO_2] = 0.31$ M

Need K_c value

STEP 1   **The equilibrium expression is written using the coefficients in the balanced equation as exponents of the molar concentrations:**

$$K_c = \frac{[NO_2]^2}{[N_2O_4]}$$

STEP 2   **Substitute the molar concentrations given for the equilibrium mixture into the equilibrium constant expression and calculate the K_c value:**

$$K_c = \frac{[0.31]^2}{[0.45]} = 0.21$$

STUDY CHECK

Ammonia decomposes when heated to give nitrogen and hydrogen:

$$2NH_3(g) \rightleftharpoons 3H_2(g) + N_2(g)$$

Calculate the equilibrium constant if an equilibrium mixture contains $[NH_3] = 0.040$ M, $[N_2] = 0.20$ M, and $[H_2] = 0.60$ M.

QUESTIONS AND PROBLEMS

Equilibrium Constants

9.11 Write the equilibrium constant expression, K_c, for each of the following reactions:
  a. $CH_4(g) + 2H_2S(g) \rightleftharpoons CS_2(g) + 4H_2(g)$
  b. $2NO(g) \rightleftharpoons N_2(g) + O_2(g)$
  c. $2SO_3(g) + CO_2(g) \rightleftharpoons CS_2(g) + 4O_2(g)$

9.12 Write the equilibrium constant expression, K_c, for each of the following reactions:
  a. $2HBr(g) \rightleftharpoons H_2(g) + Br_2(g)$
  b. $CO(g) + 2H_2(g) \rightleftharpoons CH_3OH(g)$
  c. $CH_4(g) + Cl_2(g) \rightleftharpoons CH_3Cl(g) + HCl(g)$

9.13 Identify each of the following as a homogeneous or heterogeneous equilibrium:
  a. $2O_3(g) \rightleftharpoons 3O_2(g)$
  b. $2NaHCO_3(s) \rightleftharpoons Na_2CO_3(s) + CO_2(g) + H_2O(g)$
  c. $CH_4(g) + H_2O(g) \rightleftharpoons 3H_2(g) + CO(g)$
  d. $4HCl(g) + O_2(g) \rightleftharpoons 2H_2O(l) + 2Cl_2(g)$

9.14 Identify each of the following as a homogeneous or heterogeneous equilibrium:
  a. $CO(g) + H_2(g) \rightleftharpoons C(s) + H_2O(g)$
  b. $CO(g) + 2H_2(g) \rightleftharpoons CH_3OH(l)$

  c. $CS_2(g) + 4H_2(g) \rightleftharpoons CH_4(g) + 2H_2S(g)$
  d. $Br_2(g) + Cl_2(g) \rightleftharpoons 2BrCl(g)$

9.15 Write the equilibrium constant expression for each of the reactions in problem 9.13.

9.16 Write the equilibrium constant expression for each of the reactions in problem 9.14.

9.17 What is the K_c for the following reaction at equilibrium if $[NO_2] = 0.21$ M and $[N_2O_4] = 0.030$ M?
$$N_2O_4(g) \rightleftharpoons 2NO_2(g)$$

9.18 What is the K_c for the following reaction at equilibrium if $[CO] = 0.20$ M, $[H_2O] = 0.30$ M, $[CO_2] = 0.30$ M, and $[H_2] = 0.033$ M?
$$CO_2(g) + H_2(g) \rightleftharpoons CO(g) + H_2O(g)$$

9.19 What is the K_c for the following reaction at equilibrium at 1000 °C if $[H_2] = 0.30$ M, $[CO] = 0.50$ M, $[CH_4] = 1.8$ M, and $[H_2O] = 2.0$ M?
$$CO(g) + 3H_2(g) \rightleftharpoons CH_4(g) + H_2O(g)$$

9.20 What is the K_c for the following reaction at equilibrium at 500 °C if $[H_2] = 0.40$ M, $[N_2] = 0.44$ M, and $[NH_3] = 2.2$ M?
$$N_2(g) + 3H_2(g) \rightleftharpoons 2NH_3(g)$$

9.4 Using Equilibrium Constants

We have seen that the values of K_c can be large or small. We can now look at the K_c values to predict how far the reaction proceeds to products at equilibrium. When a K_c is large, the numerator (products) is greater than the concentrations of the reactants in the denominator:

$$\frac{\textbf{[Products]}}{\text{[Reactants]}} = \textbf{Large } K_c$$

LEARNING GOAL

Use an equilibrium constant to predict the extent of reaction and to calculate equilibrium concentrations.

When a K_c is small, the numerator is smaller than the denominator, which means that the reaction favors the reactants:

$$\frac{\text{[Products]}}{\textbf{[Reactants]}} = \text{Small } K_c$$

Using a general reaction and its equilibrium constant expression, we can look at the relative concentrations of reactant A and product B:

$$A(g) \rightleftharpoons B(g) \quad K_c = \frac{[B]}{[A]}$$

For a large K_c, [B] is greater than [A]. For example, if the K_c is 1×10^3, or 1000, [B] would be 1000 times greater than [A] at equilibrium:

$$K_c = \frac{[B]}{[A]} = 1000 \quad \text{or rearranged} \quad [B] = 1000[A]$$

For a small K_c, [A] is greater than [B]. For example, if the K_c is 1×10^{-2}, [A] is 100 times greater than [B] at equilibrium:

$$K_c = \frac{[B]}{[A]} = \frac{1}{100} \quad \text{or rearranged} \quad [A] = 100[B]$$

Equilibrium mixtures with different values of K_c are illustrated in Figure 9.7.

Equilibrium with a Large K_c

A reaction with a large K_c forms a substantial amount of product by the time equilibrium is established. The greater the value of K_c, the more the equilibrium favors the products. A reaction with a very large K_c essentially goes to completion to give mostly products. Consider the reaction of SO_2 and O_2, which has a large K_c. At equilibrium, the reaction mixture contains mostly products and very little reactants:

$$2SO_2(g) + O_2(g) \rightleftharpoons 2SO_3(g)$$

$$K_c = \frac{[SO_3]^2}{[SO_2]^2\,[O_2]} \frac{\text{Mostly products}}{\text{Few reactants}} = 3.4 \times 10^2 \qquad \text{Reaction favors products}$$

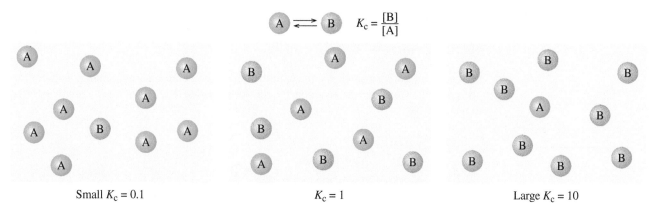

Small $K_c = 0.1$ $K_c = 1$ Large $K_c = 10$

FIGURE 9.7 A reaction with $K_c < 1$ contains a higher concentration of reactant [A] than product [B]. A reaction with K_c of about 1.0 has about the same concentrations of product [B] as reactant [A]. A reaction with $K_c > 1$ has a higher concentration of product [B] than reactant [A].

Q Does a reaction in which [A] = 100[B] at equilibrium have a K_c greater than, about equal to, or less than 1?

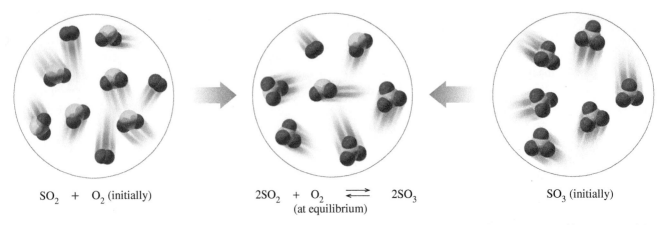

SO_2 + O_2 (initially) $2SO_2$ + O_2 $\rightleftharpoons$ $2SO_3$ SO_3 (initially)
(at equilibrium)

FIGURE 9.8 One sample initially contains SO_2 and O_2, while another sample contains only SO_3. At equilibrium, mostly SO_3 and only small amounts of SO_2 and O_2 are present in the equilibrium mixture.

Q Why is the same equilibrium mixture obtained from reactants as from products?

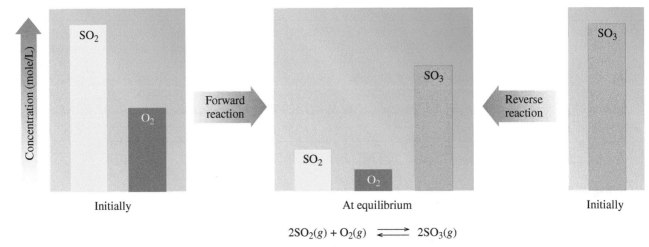

$$2SO_2(g) + O_2(g) \rightleftharpoons 2SO_3(g)$$

FIGURE 9.9 In the reaction of SO_2 and O_2, the equilibrium favors the formation of product SO_3, which results in a large K_c.

Q Why is an equilibrium mixture obtained after starting with pure SO_3?

We can start the reaction with only the reactants SO_2 and O_2, or we can start the reaction with just the product SO_3. (See Figure 9.8.) In one reaction, SO_2 and O_2 form SO_3; in the other, SO_3 reacts to form SO_2 and O_2. However, in both equilibrium mixtures, the concentration of SO_3 is much higher than the concentrations of SO_2 and O_2. (See Figure 9.9.) Because there is more product than reactant at equilibrium, the energy of activation for the forward reaction must be lower than the energy of activation for the reverse reaction.

Equilibrium with a Small K_c

For a reaction with a small K_c, the equilibrium mixture contains very small concentrations of products. Consider the reaction for the formation of NO, which has a small K_c. (See Figure 9.10.)

$$N_2(g) + O_2(g) \rightleftharpoons 2NO(g)$$

$$K_c = \frac{[NO]^2}{[N_2][O_2]} \frac{\text{Few products}}{\text{Mostly reactants}} = 2 \times 10^{-9} \qquad \text{Reaction favors reactants}$$

Whether the reaction begins with only the reactants, N_2 and O_2, or with the product, NO, the equilibrium mixture contains mostly reactants and very little product. The energy of activation for the forward reaction is much greater than the energy of activation for the reverse reaction. Reactions with very small K_c produce essentially no products.

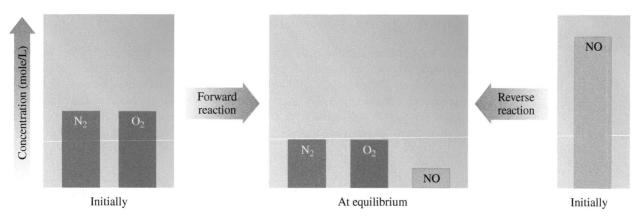

$$N_2(g) + O_2(g) \rightleftharpoons 2NO(g)$$

FIGURE 9.10 At equilibrium, the reaction $N_2 + O_2 \rightleftharpoons 2NO$ favors the reactants and the reaction mixture at equilibrium contains mostly N_2 and O_2, which results in a small K_c.

Q Starting with only NO in a closed container, how do the forward and reverse reactions change as equilibrium is reached?

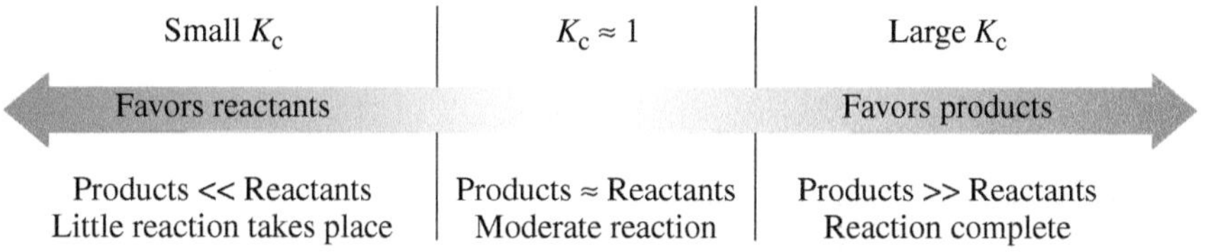

Small K_c	$K_c \approx 1$	Large K_c
Favors reactants		Favors products
Products << Reactants	Products ≈ Reactants	Products >> Reactants
Little reaction takes place	Moderate reaction	Reaction complete

FIGURE 9.11 The equilibrium constant, K_c, indicates how far a reaction goes to products. A reaction with a large K_c contains mostly products; a reaction with a small K_c contains mostly reactants.

Q Does a reaction with a $K_c = 1.2 \times 10^{15}$ contain mostly reactants or products at equilibrium?

Reactions with equilibrium constants close to 1 have about the same concentrations of reactants and products. (See Figure 9.11.) Table 9.3 lists some equilibrium constants and the extent of their reaction.

TABLE 9.3 Examples of Reactions with Large and Small K_c Values

Reactants	Products	K_c	Equilibrium Favors
$2CO(g) + O_2(g) \rightleftharpoons 2CO_2(g)$		2×10^{11}	Products
$2H_2(g) + S_2(g) \rightleftharpoons 2H_2S(g)$		1.1×10^7	Products
$N_2(g) + 3H_2(g) \rightleftharpoons 2NH_3(g)$		1.6×10^2	Products
$PCl_5(g) \rightleftharpoons PCl_3(g) + Cl_2(g)$		1.2×10^{-2}	Reactants
$N_2(g) + O_2(g) \rightleftharpoons 2NO(g)$		2×10^{-9}	Reactants

---

CONCEPT CHECK 9.4

■ **Extent of Reaction**

Predict whether the equilibrium favors the reactants or products for each of the following reactions:

a. $2H_2(g) + O_2(g) \rightleftharpoons 2H_2O(g)$ $K_c = 2.9 \times 10^{82}$ at 25 °C
b. $PCl_5(g) \rightleftharpoons PCl_3(g) + Cl_2(g)$ $K_c = 1.2 \times 10^{-2}$ at 225 °C

ANSWER
a. When a K_c has a large value, it indicates that there are high concentrations of products in the numerator and low concentrations of reactants in the denominator. Thus, this equilibrium favors the products.
b. When a K_c has a small value, it indicates that there are low concentrations of products in the numerator and high concentrations of reactants in the denominator. Thus, this equilibrium favors the reactants.

TUTORIAL
Calculations Using the
Equililbrium Constant

Calculating Concentrations at Equilibrium

When a reaction goes essentially all to products, we can use the mole-mole factors we studied earlier to calculate the quantity of a product. However, many reactions reach equilibrium without using up all the reactants. If this is the case, then we need to use the equilibrium constant to calculate the amounts of products that can be formed in the reaction. For example, if we know the equilibrium constant for a reaction and all the concentrations except one, we can calculate the unknown concentration using the equilibrium constant expression.

SAMPLE PROBLEM   9.6

■ Calculating Concentration Using an Equilibrium Constant

Phosgene ($COCl_2$) is a toxic substance that is produced by the reaction of carbon monoxide and chlorine; the K_c for the reaction is 5.0.

$$CO(g) + Cl_2(g) \rightleftharpoons COCl_2(g)$$

If the equilibrium concentrations for the reaction are $[Cl_2] = 0.25$ M and $[COCl_2] = 0.80$ M, what is the equilibrium concentration of $CO(g)$?

SOLUTION

Given $[Cl_2] = 0.25$ M, $[COCl_2] = 0.80$ M, $K_c = 5.0$
Need $[CO]$

Guide to Using the K_c Value

STEP 1
Write the K_c expression for the equilibrium equation.

STEP 2
Solve the K_c expression for the unknown concentration.

STEP 3
Substitute the known values into the rearranged K_c expression.

STEP 4
Check answer by using calculated concentration in the K_c expression.

STEP 1   **Write the K_c expression for the equilibrium.**   Using the balanced chemical equation, the equilibrium constant expression is written as

$$K_c = \frac{[COCl_2]}{[CO][Cl_2]}$$

STEP 2   **Solve the K_c expression for the unknown concentration.**   To rearrange the expression for $[CO]$, we multiply both sides by $[CO]$, which cancels the $[CO]$ on the right side:

$$K_c[CO] = \frac{[COCl_2] \times \cancel{[CO]}}{\cancel{[CO]}[Cl_2]}$$

$$K_c[CO] = \frac{[COCl_2]}{[Cl_2]}$$

To solve for $[CO]$, we divide both sides by K_c and cancel:

$$\frac{\cancel{K_c}[CO]}{\cancel{K_c}} = \frac{[COCl_2]}{K_c[Cl_2]}$$

$$[CO] = \frac{[COCl_2]}{K_c[Cl_2]}$$

STEP 3   **Substitute the known values into the rearranged K_c expression.**   Substituting the concentrations for the equilibrium mixture and the K_c value into the equilibrium constant expression gives the CO concentration:

$$[CO] = \frac{[COCl_2]}{K_c[Cl_2]}$$

$$[CO] = \frac{[0.80]}{5.0 \times [0.25]} = 0.64 \text{ M}$$

STEP 4   **Check the answer.**   We check the answer by substituting the calculated concentration into the K_c expression:

$$K_c = \frac{[COCl_2]}{[CO][Cl_2]}$$

$$K_c = \frac{[0.80]}{[0.64][0.25]} = 5.0$$

↗ Calculated

STUDY CHECK

Ethanol can be produced by reacting ethylene (C_2H_4) with water vapor. At 327 °C, the K_c is 9×10^3:

$$C_2H_4(g) + H_2O(g) \rightleftharpoons C_2H_5OH(g)$$

If an equilibrium mixture has concentrations of $[C_2H_4] = 0.020$ M and $[H_2O] = 0.015$ M, what is the equilibrium concentration of C_2H_5OH?

QUESTIONS AND PROBLEMS

Using Equilibrium Constants

9.21 Indicate whether each of the following equilibrium mixtures contain mostly products, mostly reactants, or both reactants and products:

    a. $Cl_2(g) + 2NO(g) \rightleftharpoons 2NOCl(g)$ $K_c = 3.7 \times 10^8$
    b. $H_2O(g) + CH_4(g) \rightleftharpoons CO(g) + 3H_2(g)$ $K_c = 4.7$
    c. $3O_2(g) \rightleftharpoons 2O_3(g)$ $K_c = 1.7 \times 10^{-56}$

9.22 Indicate whether each of the following equilibrium mixtures contain mostly products, mostly reactants, or both reactants and products:

    a. $CO(g) + Cl_2(g) \rightleftharpoons COCl_2(g)$ $K_c = 5.0$
    b. $2HF(g) \rightleftharpoons H_2(g) + F_2(g)$ $K_c = 1.0 \times 10^{-95}$
    c. $2NO(g) + O_2(g) \rightleftharpoons 2NO_2(g)$ $K_c = 6.0 \times 10^{13}$

9.23 The equilibrium constant, K_c, for the equilibrium

    $H_2(g) + I_2(g) \rightleftharpoons 2HI(g)$

is 54 at 425 °C. If the equilibrium mixture contains 0.030 M HI and 0.015 M I_2, what is the equilibrium concentration of H_2?

9.24 The equilibrium constant, K_c, for the equilibrium

    $N_2O_4(g) \rightleftharpoons 2NO_2(g)$

is 4.6×10^{-3}. If the equilibrium mixture contains 0.050 M NO_2, what is the concentration of N_2O_4?

9.25 The K_c at 100 °C is 2.0 for the reaction

    $2NOBr(g) \rightleftharpoons 2NO(g) + Br_2(g)$

If the system at equilibrium contains $[NO] = 2.0$ M and $[Br_2] = 1.0$ M, what is the [NOBr]?

9.26 An equilibrium mixture at 225 °C contains 0.14 M NH_3 and 0.18 M H_2 for the reaction

    $3H_2(g) + N_2(g) \rightleftharpoons 2NH_3(g)$

If the K_c at this temperature is 1.7×10^2, what is the equilibrium concentration of N_2?

9.5 Changing Equilibrium Conditions: Le Châtelier's Principle

We have seen that when a reaction reaches equilibrium, the rates of the forward and reverse reactions are equal, and the concentrations remain constant. Now we will look at what happens to a system at equilibrium when changes occur in reaction conditions such as changes in temperature, concentration, and pressure.

Le Châtelier's Principle

In the previous section, we saw that in a system at equilibrium, the forward and reverse reactions occur at equal rates. Thus, at equilibrium, the concentrations of the substances do not change. However, any changes in the reaction conditions will disturb the equilibrium. Removing one of the substances or adding more of one of the substances can change the

LEARNING GOAL

Use Le Châtelier's principle to describe the changes made in equilibrium concentrations when reaction conditions change.

TUTORIAL
Le Châtelier's Principle

concentration. The volume (pressure) can change or there may be a change in temperature. When we alter any of the conditions of a system at equilibrium, the rates of the forward and reverse reactions will no longer be equal. We say that a *stress* is placed on the equilibrium. We use **Le Châtelier's principle** to determine the direction that the equilibrium must shift to relieve that stress and reestablish equilibrium.

> **Le Châtelier's Principle**
> When a stress (change in conditions) is placed on a reaction at equilibrium, the equilibrium shifts in the direction that relieves the stress.

Effect of Concentration Changes

We will use the equilibrium for the reaction of PCl_5 to illustrate the stress caused by a change in concentration and to show how the system reacts to the stress. Consider the following reaction, which has a K_c of 0.042 at 250 °C:

$$PCl_5(g) \rightleftharpoons PCl_3(g) + Cl_2(g)$$

For a reaction at a given temperature, there is only one equilibrium constant. Even if there are changes in the concentrations of the components, the K_c value does not change. What will change are the concentrations of the other components in the reaction to relieve the stress. For example, we can see that an equilibrium mixture that contains 1.20 M PCl_5, 0.20 M PCl_3, and 0.25 M Cl_2 has a K_c of 0.042:

$$K_c = \frac{[PCl_3][Cl_2]}{[PCl_5]} = \frac{[0.20][0.25]}{[1.20]} = 0.042$$

Suppose that now we add PCl_5 to the equilibrium mixture to increase $[PCl_5]$ to 2.00 M. If we substitute the concentrations into the equilibrium expression at this point, the ratio of products to reactants is 0.025, which is smaller than the K_c of 0.042.

$$\frac{\text{Products}}{\text{Reactants (added)}} \quad \frac{[PCl_3][Cl_2]}{[PCl_5]} = \frac{[0.20][0.25]}{[2.00]} = 0.025 < K_c$$

Because a K_c cannot change for a reaction at a given temperature, adding more PCl_5 places a stress on the system. (See Figure 9.12.) Forming more of the products can relieve this stress. According to Le Châtelier's principle, adding reactants causes the equilibrium to *shift* toward the products.

Add PCl_5
$$PCl_5(g) \rightleftharpoons PCl_3(g) + Cl_2(g)$$

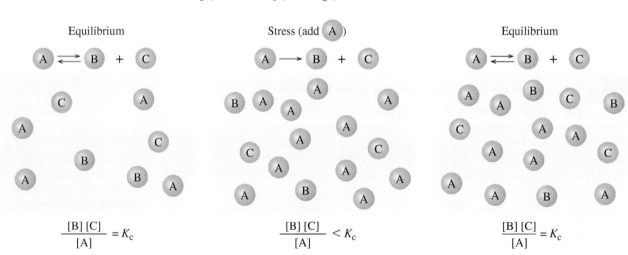

FIGURE 9.12 The addition of A places stress on the equilibrium of A $\rightleftharpoons$ B + C. To relieve the stress, the forward reaction converts some A to B + C and the equilibrium is reestablished.
Q When C is added, does the equilibrium shift to products or reactants? Why?

In our experiment, equilibrium is reestablished with new concentrations of $[PCl_5] = 1.94$ M, $[PCl_3] = 0.26$, and $[Cl_2] = 0.31$ M. The resulting equilibrium mixture now contains more reactants and products, but their new concentrations in the equilibrium expression are once again equal to the K_c.

$$K_c = \frac{[PCl_3][Cl_2]}{[PCl_5]} = \frac{[0.26][0.31]}{[1.94]} = 0.042 = K_c \quad \text{New higher concentrations}$$

Suppose that in another experiment some PCl_5 is removed from the original equilibrium mixture, which lowers the $[PCl_5]$ to 0.76 M. Now the ratio of the products to the reactants is greater than the K_c value of 0.042. The removal of some of the reactant has placed a stress on the equilibrium:

$$\frac{\text{Products}}{\text{Reactants (removed)}} = \frac{[PCl_3][Cl_2]}{[PCl_5]} = \frac{[0.20][0.25]}{[0.76]} = 0.066 > K_c$$

In this case, the stress is relieved as the reverse reaction converts some products to reactants. Using Le Châtelier's principle, we see that removing some reactant *shifts* the equilibrium toward the reactants.

Remove PCl_5

$$PCl_5(g) \rightleftharpoons PCl_3(g) + Cl_2(g)$$

In this experiment, equilibrium is reestablished with new concentrations of $[PCl_5] = 0.80$ M, $[PCl_3] = 0.16$ M, and $[Cl_2] = 0.21$ M. The resulting equilibrium mixture now contains lower concentrations of reactants and products, but their new concentrations in the equilibrium expression once again are equal to the K_c.

$$K_c = \frac{[PCl_3][Cl_2]}{[PCl_5]} = \frac{[0.16][0.21]}{[0.80]} = 0.042 = K_c \quad \text{New lower concentrations}$$

There can also be changes in the concentrations of other components in this reaction. We could increase or decrease the amount of one of the products in this reaction. Suppose the $[Cl_2]$ is doubled, which makes the product/reactant ratio greater than K_c:

$$\frac{[PCl_3][Cl_2]}{[PCl_5]} = \frac{[0.20][0.50]}{[1.20]} = 0.083 > K_c$$

With an increase in the concentration of Cl_2, the rate of the reverse reaction increases and converts some of the products to reactants. Using Le Châtelier's principle, we see that the addition of a product causes a *shift* toward the reactants.

Add Cl_2

$$PCl_5(g) \rightleftharpoons PCl_3(g) + Cl_2(g)$$

On the other hand, we could remove some Cl_2, which would decrease $[Cl_2]$ and *shift* the equilibrium toward the products.

Remove Cl_2

$$PCl_5(g) \rightleftharpoons PCl_3(g) + Cl_2(g)$$

In summary, Le Châtelier's principle indicates that a stress caused by adding a substance at equilibrium is relieved by shifting the reaction away from that substance. When some of a substance is removed, the equilibrium shifts toward that substance. These features of Le Châtelier's principle are summarized in Table 9.4.

Catalysts

Sometimes a catalyst is added to a reaction. Earlier we showed that a catalyst speeds up a reaction by lowering the activation energy. As a result, the rates of the forward and reverse reactions both increase. The time required to reach equilibrium is shorter, but the same ratios of products and reactants are attained. Therefore, a catalyst speeds up the forward and reverse reactions, but it has no effect on the equilibrium constant.

TABLE 9.4 Effect of Concentration Changes on Equilibrium
$PCl_5(g) \rightleftharpoons PCl_3(g) + Cl_2(g)$

Stress	Shift	Equilibrium Changes		
		$PCl_5(g)$	$PCl_3(g)$	$Cl_2(g)$
Increase PCl_5	Toward products	Added	More	More
Decrease PCl_5	Toward reactants	Removed	Less	Less
Increase PCl_3	Toward reactants	More	Added	Less
Decrease PCl_3	Toward products	Less	Removed	More
Increase Cl_2	Toward reactants	More	Less	Added
Decrease Cl_2	Toward products	Less	More	Removed

CONCEPT CHECK 9.5

■ **Effect of Changes in Concentrations**

Describe the effect of each of the following changes on the following reaction at equilibrium:

$$CO(g) + H_2O(g) \rightleftharpoons CO_2(g) + H_2(g)$$

a. increasing [CO]   **b.** increasing [H_2]   **c.** decreasing [H_2O]
d. decreasing [CO_2]   **e.** adding a catalyst

ANSWER

According to Le Châtelier's principle, when stress is applied to a reaction at equilibrium, the equilibrium will shift to relieve the stress.

a. When the reactant [CO] is increased, the rate of the forward reaction increases to shift the equilibrium to the products.

b. When the product [H_2] is increased, the rate of the reverse reaction increases to shift the equilibrium to the reactants.

c. When the reactant [H_2O] is decreased, the rate of the forward reaction decreases to shift the equilibrium to the reactants.

d. When the product [CO_2] is decreased, the rate of the reverse reaction decreases to shift the equilibrium to the products.

e. When a catalyst is added, it changes the rates of the forward and reverse reactions equally, which does not cause a shift in the equilibrium.

Effect of Volume (Pressure) Changes on Equilibrium

Reactions that involve gases exert pressure. Although the volume and therefore pressure can change, the value of the equilibrium constant does not change at a given temperature. Using the gas laws, we know that increasing the volume of the container decreases the pressure, while decreasing the volume increases the pressure.

According to Le Châtelier's principle, decreasing the number of moles of gas relieves the stress of increased pressure. This means that the reaction shifts toward the fewer number of moles. Let's look at the effect of decreasing the volume of the equilibrium mixture that originally contained 1.20 M PCl_5, 0.20 M PCl_3, and 0.25 M Cl_2 with a K_c of 0.042:

$$PCl_5(g) \rightleftharpoons PCl_3(g) + Cl_2(g)$$

$$K_c = \frac{[PCl_3][Cl_2]}{[PCl_5]} = \frac{[0.20][0.25]}{[1.20]} = 0.042$$

If we decrease the volume by half, all the molar concentrations are doubled. In the equation there are more moles of products than reactants, so there is an increase in the product/reactant ratio.

$$\frac{[PCl_3][Cl_2]}{[PCl_5]} = \frac{[0.40][0.50]}{[2.40]} = 0.083 > K_c$$

To relieve the stress, the equilibrium shifts toward the reactants, which reduces the concentrations of the products and increases the concentrations of the reactant. (See Figure 9.13.)

Decrease V

$$PCl_5(g) \rightleftharpoons PCl_3(g) + Cl_2(g)$$
1 mole   2 moles

HEALTH NOTE

Oxygen-Hemoglobin Equilibrium and Hypoxia

The transport of oxygen involves an equilibrium between hemoglobin (Hb), oxygen, and oxyhemoglobin (HbO_2):

$$Hb + O_2 \rightleftharpoons HbO_2$$

When the O_2 level is high in the alveoli of the lung, the reaction favors the product HbO_2. In the tissues where O_2 concentration is low, the reverse reaction releases the oxygen from the hemoglobin. The equilibrium expression is written

$$K_c = \frac{[HbO_2]}{[Hb][O_2]}$$

At normal atmospheric pressure, oxygen diffuses into the blood because the partial pressure of oxygen in the alveoli is higher than that in the blood. At altitudes above 8000 ft, the decrease in the amount of oxygen in the air results in a significant reduction of oxygen to the blood and body tissues. At an altitude of 18 000 feet, a person will obtain 29% less oxygen. When oxygen levels are lowered, a person may experience hypoxia, which has symptoms that include increased respiratory rate, headache, decreased mental acuteness, fatigue, decreased physical coordination, nausea, vomiting, and cyanosis. A similar problem occurs in persons with a history of lung disease that impairs

gas diffusion in the alveoli or in persons who have a reduced number of red blood cells, which occurs in smokers.

From the equilibrium expression, we see that a decrease in oxygen will shift the equilibrium to the reactants. Such a shift depletes the concentration of HbO_2 and causes the hypoxia condition:

$$Hb + O_2 \longleftarrow HbO_2$$

Immediate treatment of altitude sickness includes hydration, rest, and if necessary, descending to a lower altitude. The adaptation to lowered oxygen levels requires about 10 days. During this time, the bone marrow increases red blood cell production providing hemoglobin. A person living at a high altitude can have 50% more red blood cells than someone at sea level. This increase in hemoglobin causes a shift in the equilibrium back toward HbO_2 product. Eventually, the higher concentration of HbO_2 will provide more oxygen to the tissues and the symptoms of hypoxia will lessen:

$$Hb + O_2 \longrightarrow HbO_2$$

For some who climb high mountains, it is important to stop and acclimatize for several days at increasing altitudes. At very high altitudes, it may be necessary to use an oxygen tank.

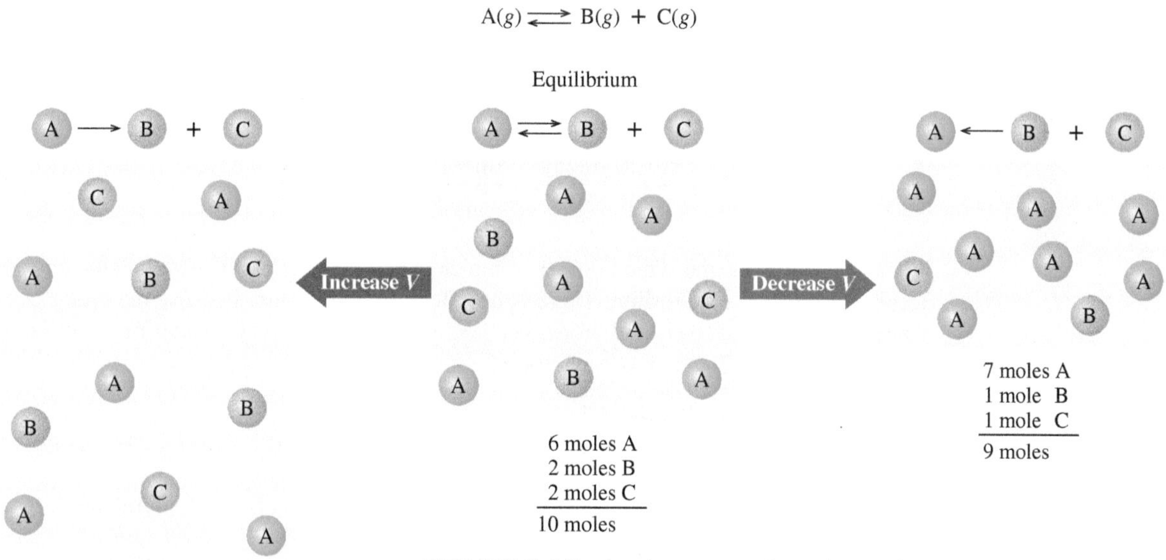

$$A(g) \rightleftharpoons B(g) + C(g)$$

Equilibrium

A $\longrightarrow$ B + C

←Increase V

A $\rightleftharpoons$ B + C

Decrease V→

A $\longleftarrow$ B + C

5 moles A
3 moles B
3 moles C
―――――
11 moles

6 moles A
2 moles B
2 moles C
―――――
10 moles

7 moles A
1 mole B
1 mole C
―――――
9 moles

FIGURE 9.13 The decrease in the volume of the container places stress on the equilibrium: $A(g) \rightleftharpoons B(g) + C(g)$. To relieve the stress, the reverse reaction converts some products to reactants, which gives a smaller number of moles of gas, reduces pressure, and reestablishes the equilibrium. When the volume increases, the forward reaction converts reactants to products to increase the moles of gas and relieve the stress.

Q If you want to increase the products, would you increase or decrease the volume of the reaction container?

When equilibrium is reestablished, the new concentrations are $[PCl_5]$ = 2.52 M, $[PCl_3]$ = 0.28 M, and $[Cl_2]$ = 0.38 M. The resulting equilibrium mixture contains new concentrations of reactants and products that are now equal to the K_c value, as the following shows:

At volume (1)

$[PCl_3]$ = 0.20 M

$[Cl_2]$ = 0.25 M

$[PCl_5]$ = 1.20 M

At volume (2)

0.28 M

0.38 M

2.52 M

$$K_c = \frac{[PCl_3][Cl_2]}{[PCl_5]} = \frac{[0.20][0.25]}{[1.20]} = \frac{[0.28][0.38]}{[2.52]} = 0.042$$

On the other hand, when volume increases and pressure decreases, the reaction shifts toward the greater number of moles. Suppose that the volume is doubled. Then the molar concentrations of all the gases decrease by half. Because there are more moles of products than reactants, there is a decrease in the product/reactant ratio as follows:

$$\frac{[PCl_3][Cl_2]}{[PCl_5]} = \frac{[0.10][0.13]}{[0.60]} = 0.022 < K_c$$

Now the equilibrium has to shift toward the products to relieve the stress, increasing the molar concentrations of the products.

Increase V

$$PCl_5(g) \xrightleftharpoons{} PCl_3(g) + Cl_2(g)$$

1 mole   2 moles

When equilibrium is reestablished, the new concentrations are $[PCl_5]$ = 0.56 M, $[PCl_3]$ = 0.14 M, and $[Cl_2]$ = 0.17 M. The resulting equilibrium mixture contains new concentrations of reactants and products that are now equal to the K_c value:

At volume (1)

$[PCl_3]$ = 0.20 M

$[Cl_2]$ = 0.25 M

$[PCl_5]$ = 1.20 M

At volume (2)

0.14 M

0.17 M

0.56 M

$$K_c = \frac{[PCl_3][Cl_2]}{[PCl_5]} = \frac{[0.20][0.25]}{[1.20]} = \frac{[0.14][0.17]}{[0.56]} = 0.042$$

When a reaction has the same number of moles of reactants as products, a volume change does not affect the equilibrium. There is no effect on equilibrium because the molar concentrations of the reactants and products change in the same way. Consider the reaction of H_2 and I_2 to form HI, which has a K_c of 54:

$$H_2(g) + I_2(g) \xrightleftharpoons{} 2HI(g)$$

2 moles of gas   2 moles of gas

Suppose we start with $[H_2]$ = 0.060 M, $[I_2]$ = 0.015 M, $[HI]$ = 0.22 M, giving us

$$\frac{[HI]^2}{[H_2][I_2]} = \frac{[0.22]^2}{[0.060][0.015]} = 54$$

If the volume is decreased by half, the pressure will double, and all the molar concentrations double. However, the equation has the same number of moles of products as reactants, so there is no effect on the equilibrium. The product/reactant ratio stays the same. We can see this by substituting the increased concentrations into the equilibrium constant expression, as follows:

At volume (1)   **At volume (2)**

$[HI] = 0.22$ M 0.44 M

$[H_2] = 0.060$ M 0.120 M

$[I_2] = 0.015$ M 0.030 M

$$K_c = \frac{[HI]^2}{[H_2][I_2]} = \frac{[0.22]^2}{[0.060][0.015]} = \frac{[0.44]^2}{[0.120][0.030]} = 54$$

SAMPLE PROBLEM   9.7

■ Effect of Changes in Volume

Indicate whether the effect of decreasing the volume for each of the following equilibria causes the number of moles of product to increase or decrease:

a. $C_2H_2(g) + 2H_2(g) \rightleftharpoons C_2H_6(g)$

b. $2NO_2(g) \rightleftharpoons 2NO(g) + O_2(g)$

c. $CO(g) + H_2O(g) \rightleftharpoons CO_2(g) + H_2(g)$

SOLUTION

To relieve the stress of decreasing the volume, the equilibrium shifts toward the side with the fewer moles of gaseous components.

a. The equilibrium shifts to C_2H_6 (product) to reduce the number of moles of gas. The number of moles of product is increased.

$$\underset{\text{3 moles of gas}}{C_2H_2(g) + 2H_2(g)} \longrightarrow \underset{\text{1 mole of gas}}{C_2H_6(g)}$$

b. The equilibrium shifts to NO_2 (reactant) to reduce the number of moles of gas. The number of moles of product is decreased.

$$\underset{\text{2 moles of gas}}{2NO_2(g)} \longleftarrow \underset{\text{3 moles of gas}}{2NO(g) + O_2(g)}$$

c. There is no shift in equilibrium because there is no change in the number of moles; the moles of reactant are equal to the moles of product. The number of moles of product does not change.

$$\underset{\text{2 moles of gas}}{CO(g) + H_2O(g)} \rightleftharpoons \underset{\text{2 moles of gas}}{CO_2(g) + H_2(g)}$$

STUDY CHECK

Suppose you want to increase the yield of product in the following reaction. Would you increase or decrease the volume of the reaction container?

$$CO(g) + 2H_2(g) \rightleftharpoons CH_3OH(g)$$

Effect of a Change in Temperature on Equilibrium

In the effects of changes on equilibrium, we have seen that shifts in equilibrium occur to reestablish the same value of the equilibrium constant. However, if we change the temperature of a system at equilibrium, we change the value of K_c. When the temperature of an equilibrium system increases, the favored reaction is the one that removes the heat. When heat is added to an endothermic reaction, the equilibrium shifts to the products to use up

TABLE 9.5 Equilibrium Shifts for Temperature Changes in an Endothermic Reaction

K_c	Temperature Change	Equilibrium Shift	Change in K_c Value
$\dfrac{[NO]^2}{[N_2][O_2]}$	⬆ Increase	More product $\dfrac{[NO]^2}{[N_2][O_2]}$ Less reactant	⬆ Increases
$\dfrac{[NO]^2}{[N_2][O_2]}$	⬇ Decrease	Less product $\dfrac{[NO]^2}{[N_2][O_2]}$ More reactant	⬇ Decreases

heat. The value of K_c increases because the shift increases the product concentration and decreases the reactant concentration.

$$\text{Increase } T; \text{ increase } K_c$$

$$N_2(g) + O_2(g) + \text{heat} \rightleftharpoons 2NO(g)$$

If the temperature is lowered, the equilibrium shifts to increase the concentrations of the reactants, and the value of K_c decreases. (See Table 9.5.)

$$\text{Decrease } T; \text{ decrease } K_c$$

$$N_2(g) + O_2(g) + \text{heat} \rightleftharpoons 2NO(g)$$

For an exothermic reaction, the addition of heat favors the reverse reaction, which uses up heat. The value of K_c for an exothermic reaction decreases when the temperature increases.

$$\text{Increase } T; \text{ decrease } K_c$$

$$2SO_2(g) + O_2(g) \rightleftharpoons 2SO_3(g) + \text{heat}$$

If heat is removed, the equilibrium of an exothermic reaction favors the products, which provides heat. (See Table 9.6.)

$$\text{Decrease } T; \text{ increase } K_c$$

$$2SO_2(g) + O_2(g) \rightleftharpoons 2SO_3(g) + \text{heat}$$

TABLE 9.6 Equilibrium Shifts for Temperature Changes in an Exothermic Reaction

K_c	Temperature Change	Equilibrium Shift	Change in K_c Value
$\dfrac{[SO_3]^2}{[SO_2]^2[O_2]}$	⬆ Increase	Less product $\dfrac{[SO_3]^2}{[SO_2]^2[O_2]}$ More reactant	⬇ Decreases
$\dfrac{[SO_3]^2}{[SO_2]^2[O_2]}$	⬇ Decrease	More product $\dfrac{[SO_3]^2}{[SO_2]^2[O_2]}$ Less reactant	⬆ Increases

SAMPLE PROBLEM 9.8

■ Effect of Temperature Change on Equilibrium

Indicate the change in the concentration of products and the change in K_c when the temperature of each of the following reactions at equilibrium is increased:

a. $N_2(g) + 3H_2(g) \rightleftharpoons 2NH_3(g) + 92 \text{ kJ}$

b. $N_2(g) + O_2(g) + 180 \text{ kJ} \rightleftharpoons 2NO(g)$

SOLUTION

a. The addition of heat shifts an exothermic reaction to reactants, which decreases the concentration of the products. The K_c will decrease.

b. The addition of heat shifts an endothermic reaction to products, which increases the concentration of the products. The K_c will increase.

STUDY CHECK

Indicate the change in the concentration of reactants and the K_c when there is a decrease in the temperature of each of the reactions at equilibrium in Sample Problem 9.8.

Table 9.7 summarizes the ways we can use Le Châtelier's principle to determine the shift in equilibrium that relieves a stress caused by change in a condition.

TABLE 9.7 Effects of Condition Changes on Equilibrium

Condition	Change (Stress)	Reaction to Remove Stress
Concentration	Add reactant	Forward
	Remove reactant	Reverse
	Add product	Reverse
	Remove product	Forward
Volume (container)	Decrease	Toward fewer moles in the gas phase
	Increase	Toward more moles in the gas phase
Temperature	**Endothermic reaction**	
	Raise T	Forward, new value for K_c
	Lower T	Reverse, new value for K_c
	Exothermic reaction	
	Raise T	Reverse, new value for K_c
	Lower T	Forward, new value for K_c
Catalyst	Increases rates equally	No effect

QUESTIONS AND PROBLEMS

Changing Equilibrium Conditions: Le Châtelier's Principle

9.27 a. Does the addition of reactant to an equilibrium mixture cause the product/reactant ratio to be higher or lower than the K_c?

  b. According to Le Châtelier's principle, how is equilibrium in part **a** established?

9.28 a. What is the effect on the K_c when the temperature of an exothermic reaction is lowered?

  b. According to Le Châtelier's principle, how is equilibrium in part **a** established?

9.29 In the lower atmosphere, oxygen is converted to ozone (O_3) by the energy provided from lightning:

$$3O_2(g) + \text{heat} \rightleftharpoons 2O_3(g)$$

For each of the following changes at equilibrium, indicate whether the equilibrium shifts to products, reactants, or does not shift:

a. adding $O_2(g)$

b. adding $O_3(g)$

c. raising the temperature

d. decreasing the volume of the container

e. adding a catalyst

9.30 Ammonia is produced by reacting nitrogen gas and hydrogen gas:

$$N_2(g) + 3H_2(g) \rightleftharpoons 2NH_3(g) + 92 \text{ kJ}$$

For each of the following changes at equilibrium, indicate whether the equilibrium shifts to products, reactants, or does not shift:

a. removing $N_2(g)$
b. lowering the temperature
c. adding $NH_3(g)$
d. adding $H_2(g)$
e. increasing the volume of the container

9.31 Hydrogen chloride can be made by reacting hydrogen gas and chlorine gas:

$$H_2(g) + Cl_2(g) + \text{heat} \rightleftharpoons 2HCl(g)$$

For each of the following changes at equilibrium, indicate whether the equilibrium shifts to products, reactants, or does not shift:

a. adding $H_2(g)$
b. increasing the temperature
c. removing $HCl(g)$
d. adding a catalyst
e. removing $Cl_2(g)$

9.32 When heated, carbon reacts with water to produce carbon monoxide and hydrogen:

$$C(s) + H_2O(g) + \text{heat} \rightleftharpoons CO(g) + H_2(g)$$

For each of the following changes at equilibrium, indicate whether the equilibrium shifts to products, reactants, or does not shift:

a. increasing the temperature
b. adding $C(s)$
c. removing $CO(g)$ as it forms
d. adding $H_2O(g)$
e. decreasing the volume of the container

HEALTH NOTE

Homeostasis: Regulation of Body Temperature

In a physiological system of equilibrium called *homeostasis*, changes in our environment are balanced by changes in our bodies. It is crucial to our survival that we balance heat gain with heat loss. If we do not lose enough heat, our body temperature rises. At high temperatures, the body can no longer regulate our metabolic reactions. If we lose too much heat, body temperature drops. At low temperatures, essential functions proceed too slowly.

The skin plays an important role in the maintenance of body temperature. When the outside temperature rises, receptors in the skin send signals to the brain. The temperature-regulating part of the brain stimulates the sweat glands to produce perspiration. As perspiration evaporates from the skin, heat is removed, and the body temperature is lowered.

In cold temperatures, epinephrine is released, causing an increase in metabolic rate, which increases the production of heat. Receptors on the skin signal the brain to contract the blood vessels. Less blood flows through the skin, and heat is conserved. The production of perspiration stops to lessen the heat lost by evaporation.

Blood vessels dilate
• sweat production increases
• sweat evaporates
• skin cools

Blood vessels constrict and epinephrine is released
• metabolic activity increases
• muscular activity increases
• shivering occurs
• sweat production stops

9.6 Equilibrium in Saturated Solutions

LEARNING GOAL

Write the solubility product expression for a slightly soluble salt and calculate its K_{sp}. Use the K_{sp} to determine the solubility of a slightly soluble salt.

Until now, we have looked primarily at equilibrium in the context of gases. However, there are also equilibrium systems that involve aqueous solutions, some of which are saturated solutions or contain insoluble salts. Everyday examples of solubility equilibrium in solution are found in tooth decay and kidney stones. When bacteria in the mouth react with sugars in food, acids are produced that dissolve the enamel of a tooth, which is made of a mineral called hydroxyapatite, $Ca_5(PO_4)_3OH$. Kidney stones are composed of calcium salts such as calcium oxalate, CaC_2O_4, and calcium phosphate, $Ca_3(PO_4)_2$, which are rather insoluble. When Ca^{2+} ions and oxalate $C_2O_4^{2-}$ ions exceed their solubility in the kidneys, they will precipitate, forming solid CaC_2O_4:

$$Ca^{2+}(aq) + C_2O_4^{2-}(aq) \rightleftharpoons CaC_2O_4(s)$$

$$3Ca^{2+}(aq) + 2PO_4^{3-}(aq) \rightleftharpoons Ca_3(PO_4)_2(s)$$

To understand the role of solubility in biology and the environment, we can look at the equilibrium that occurs in saturated solutions.

Solubility Product Constant

In Chapter 8, we learned that a saturated solution contains some undissolved solute in contact with the maximum amount of dissolved solute. A saturated solution is a dynamic system in which the rate of dissolution for a solute has become equal to the rate of solute recrystallization out of solution. As long as the temperature remains constant, the concentration of the ions in the saturated solution is constant. Let us look at the equilibrium equation for the dissolution of CaC_2O_4, which is written with the solid solute on the left and the ions in solution on the right:

$$CaC_2O_4(s) \rightleftharpoons Ca^{2+}(aq) + C_2O_4^{2-}(aq)$$

At equilibrium, the concentrations of the Ca^{2+} and $C_2O_4^{2-}$ are constant. We can represent the solubility of CaC_2O_4 by an equilibrium expression called the **solubility product constant**, K_{sp}. As in other heterogeneous equilibria (section 9.3), the concentration of the solid is constant and not included in the K_{sp}:

$$K_{sp} = [Ca^{2+}][C_2O_4^{2-}]$$

In another example, we consider the equilibrium of solid calcium fluoride and its ions Ca^{2+} and F^-:

$$CaF_2(s) \rightleftharpoons Ca^{2+}(aq) + 2F^-(aq)$$

At equilibrium, the rate of dissolving for CaF_2 is equal to the rate of its recrystallization, which means the concentrations of the ions remain constant. The solubility product for this solubility is written as the product of the ion concentrations. As with other equilibrium expressions, the $[F^-]$ is raised to the power of 2 because there is a coefficient of 2 in the equilibrium equation:

$$K_{sp} = [Ca^{2+}][F^-]^2$$

CONCEPT CHECK 9.6

■ **Writing the Solubility Product Expression**

For each of the following slightly soluble salts, write the equilibrium equation and the solubility product expression:
a. AgBr   **b.** Li_2CO_3

ANSWER

a. In the equation, the solid salt is written on the left in equilibrium with the ions Ag^+ and Br^- in aqueous solution; the solubility product expression, K_{sp}, gives the product of the molar concentrations of the ions:

$$AgBr(s) \rightleftharpoons Ag^+(aq) + Br^-(aq) \qquad K_{sp} = [Ag^+][Br^-]$$

b. In the equation, the solid salt is written on the left in equilibrium with the ions $2Li^+$ and CO_3^{2-} in aqueous solution; the solubility product expression, K_{sp}, gives the molar concentrations of the ions with $[Li^+]$ with an exponent of 2, which is its coefficient in the balanced equation:

$$Li_2CO_3(s) \rightleftharpoons 2Li^+(aq) + CO_3^{2-}(aq) \qquad K_{sp} = [Li^+]^2[CO_3^{2-}]$$

TABLE 9.8 Solubility Product Constants (K_{sp}) for Selected Ionic Compounds (25 °C)

Formula	K_{sp}
AgCl	1.8×10^{-10}
Ag_2SO_4	1.2×10^{-5}
$BaCO_3$	2.0×10^{-9}
$BaSO_4$	1.1×10^{-10}
CaF_2	3.2×10^{-11}
$Ca(OH)_2$	6.5×10^{-6}
$CaSO_4$	2.4×10^{-5}
$PbCl_2$	1.5×10^{-6}
$PbCO_3$	7.4×10^{-14}

Calculating the Solubility Product Constant

Experiments in the lab can measure the concentrations of ions in a saturated solution. For example, we can make a saturated solution of $CaCO_3$ by adding solid $CaCO_3$ to water and stirring until equilibrium is reached. Then we would measure the concentrations of Ca^{2+} and CO_3^{2-} in solution. Suppose that a saturated solution of $CaCO_3$ has $[Ca^{2+}] = 7.1 \times 10^{-5}$ M and $[CO_3^{2-}] = 7.1 \times 10^{-5}$ M.

STEP 1   Write the equilibrium equation for solubility:

$$CaCO_3(s) \rightleftharpoons Ca^{2+}(aq) + CO_3^{2-}(aq)$$

STEP 2   Write the solubility product expression (K_{sp}):

$$K_{sp} = [Ca^{2+}][CO_3^{2-}]$$

STEP 3   Substitute the molar concentrations of the ions into the K_{sp} expression:

$$K_{sp} = [7.1 \times 10^{-5}][7.1 \times 10^{-5}] = 5.0 \times 10^{-9}$$

Table 9.8 gives values of K_{sp} for a selected group of ionic compounds at 25 °C.

SAMPLE PROBLEM   9.9

■ Calculating a Solubility Product Constant

A saturated solution of strontium fluoride, SrF_2, has $[Sr^{2+}] = 8.7 \times 10^{-4}$ M and $[F^-] = 1.7 \times 10^{-3}$ M. What is the value of K_{sp} for SrF_2?

SOLUTION

STEP 1   Write the equilibrium equation for solubility:

$$SrF_2(s) \rightleftharpoons Sr^{2+}(aq) + 2F^-(aq)$$

STEP 2   Write the solubility product expression, K_{sp}:

$$K_{sp} = [Sr^{2+}][F^-]^2$$

STEP 3   Substitute the molar concentrations of the ions into the K_{sp} expression:

$$K_{sp} = [8.7 \times 10^{-4}][1.7 \times 10^{-3}]^2 = 2.5 \times 10^{-9}$$

STUDY CHECK

What is the K_{sp} of silver iodide, AgI, if a saturated solution has $[Ag^+] = 9.2 \times 10^{-9}$ M and $[I^-] = 9.2 \times 10^{-9}$ M?

Guide to Calculating K_{sp}

STEP 1
Write the equilibrium equation for the dissociation of the ionic compound.

STEP 2
Write the K_{sp} expression with the molarity of each ion raised to a power equal to its coefficient.

STEP 3
Substitute the molarity of each ion into the K_{sp} and calculate.

Solubility (S) and K_{sp}

The *solubility* (S) of a slightly soluble salt is the number of moles of solute that dissolve in 1 liter of solution. For example, the solubility of CdS is found experimentally to be 1×10^{-12} M. This means that 1×10^{-12} mole of CdS in 1 liter dissociates into Cd^{2+} and S^{2-} ions: $[Cd^{2+}] = 1 \times 10^{-12}$ M and $[S^{2-}] = 1 \times 10^{-12}$ M.

$$CdS(s) \rightleftharpoons Cd^{2+}(aq) + S^{2-}(aq)$$

$$S = 1 \times 10^{-12} \text{ mole/L}$$

If we know the K_{sp} of a salt, we can calculate the molarity of each ion and determine the solubility of a slightly soluble salt as shown in Sample Problem 9.10.

■ **Calculating the Solubility of a Slightly Soluble Salt**

Calculate the solubility (S) of $PbSO_4$ if the K_{sp} is 1.6×10^{-8}.

SOLUTION

STEP 1   Write the equilibrium equation for solubility:

$$PbSO_4(s) \rightleftarrows Pb^{2+}(aq) + SO_4{}^{2-}(aq)$$

STEP 2   Write the solubility product expression, K_{sp}:

$$K_{sp} = [Pb^{2+}][SO_4{}^{2-}]$$

STEP 3   Show the molarity of the ions as S in the equation with the known value of K_{sp}:

$$K_{sp} = [S][S] = 1.6 \times 10^{-8}$$

STEP 4   Solve for the solubility S:

$$S \times S = S^2 = 1.6 \times 10^{-8}$$
$$S = \sqrt{1.6 \times 10^{-8}} = 1.3 \times 10^{-4} \text{ mole/L}$$

Guide to Calculating Solubility from K_{sp}

STEP 1
Write the equilibrium equation for the dissociation of the ionic compound.

STEP 2
Write the K_{sp} expression.

STEP 3
Substitute S for the molarity of each ion into the K_{sp}.

STEP 4
Calculate the solubility (S).

STUDY CHECK

Calculate the solubility (S) of NiS if NiS has a K_{sp} of 4×10^{-20}.

Earlier we described kidney stones as crystals composed of calcium salts, such as calcium oxalate, CaC_2O_4. Kidney stones form when the ion product $[Ca^{2+}][C_2O_4{}^{2-}]$ is equal to or greater than the solubility product K_{sp}. Normally, the urine contains substances such as magnesium and citrate ions that prevent the formation of kidney stones. Some of the factors that contribute to the formation of kidney stones are drinking too little water, limited activity, consuming foods with high levels of oxalate, and some metabolic diseases. Prevention includes drinking large quantities of water and decreasing consumption of foods high in oxalate, such as spinach, rhubarb, and soybean products.

QUESTIONS AND PROBLEMS

Equilibrium in Saturated Solutions

9.33 For each of the following slightly soluble salts, write the equilibrium equation and the solubility product expression:
  a. $MgCO_3$
  b. PbI_2
  c. Ag_3PO_4

9.34 For each of the following slightly soluble salts, write the equilibrium equation and the solubility product expression:
  a. $PbSO_4$
  b. $Al(OH)_3$
  c. BaF_2

9.35 A saturated solution of barium sulfate, $BaSO_4$, has $[Ba^{2+}] = 1 \times 10^{-5}$ M and $[SO_4{}^{2-}] = 1 \times 10^{-5}$ M. What is the value of K_{sp} for $BaSO_4$?

9.36 A saturated solution of silver bromide, $AgBr$, has $[Ag^+] = 7.1 \times 10^{-7}$ M and $[Br^-] = 7.1 \times 10^{-7}$ M. What is the value of K_{sp} for $AgBr$?

9.37 A saturated solution of silver carbonate, Ag_2CO_3, has $[Ag^+] = 2.6 \times 10^{-4}$ M and $[CO_3{}^{2-}] = 1.3 \times 10^{-4}$ M. What is the value of K_{sp} for Ag_2CO_3?

9.38 A saturated solution of barium fluoride, BaF_2, has $[Ba^{2+}] = 3.6 \times 10^{-3}$ M and $[F^-] = 7.2 \times 10^{-3}$ M. What is the value of K_{sp} for BaF_2?

9.39 What are $[Cu^+]$ and $[I^-]$ in a saturated CuI solution if the K_{sp} of CuI is 1×10^{-12}?

9.40 What are $[Sn^{2+}]$ and $[S^{2-}]$ in a saturated SnS solution if the K_{sp} of SnS is 1×10^{-26}?

CONCEPT MAP

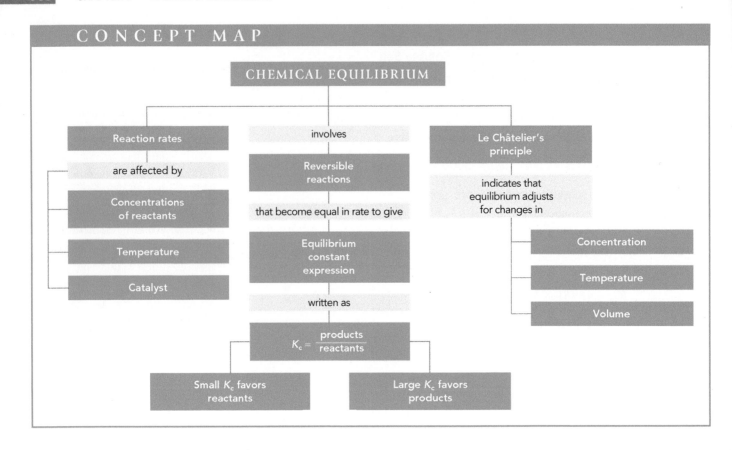

CHAPTER REVIEW

9.1 Rates of Reactions

LEARNING GOAL: *Describe how temperature, concentration, and catalysts affect the rate of a reaction.*

The rate of a reaction is the speed at which the reactants are converted to products. Increasing the concentrations of reactants, raising the temperature, or adding a catalyst can increase the rate of a reaction.

9.2 Chemical Equilibrium

LEARNING GOAL: *Use the concept of reversible reactions to explain chemical equilibrium.*

Chemical equilibrium occurs in a reversible reaction when the rate of the forward reaction becomes equal to the rate of the reverse reaction. At equilibrium, no further change occurs in the concentrations of the reactants and products as the forward and reverse reactions continue.

9.3 Equilibrium Constants

LEARNING GOAL: *Calculate the equilibrium constant for a reversible reaction given the concentrations of reactants and products at equilibrium.*

An equilibrium constant, K_c, is the ratio of the concentrations of the products to the concentrations of the reactants with each concentration raised to a power equal to its coefficient in the chemical equation. For heterogeneous reactions, only gases are placed in the equilibrium expression.

9.4 Using Equilibrium Constants

LEARNING GOAL: *Use an equilibrium constant to predict the extent of reaction and to calculate equilibrium concentrations.*

A large value of K_c indicates the equilibrium favors the products and could go nearly to completion, whereas a small value of K_c shows that the equilibrium favors the reactants. Equilibrium constants can be used to calculate the concentration of a component in the equilibrium mixture.

9.5 Changing Equilibrium Conditions: Le Châtelier's Principle

LEARNING GOAL: *Use Le Châtelier's principle to describe the changes made in equilibrium concentrations when reaction conditions change.*

The addition of reactants or removal of products favors the forward reaction. Removal of reactants or addition of products favors the reverse reaction. A decrease in the volume of a reaction container changes the pressure of gases at equilibrium causing a shift to the side with the fewer number of moles. Raising or lowering the temperature for exothermic and endothermic reactions changes the value of K_c and shifts the equilibrium for a reaction.

9.6 Equilibrium in Saturated Solutions

LEARNING GOAL: *Write the solubility product expression for a slightly soluble salt and calculate its K_{sp}. Use the K_{sp} to determine the solubility of a slightly soluble salt.*

In a saturated solution of a slightly soluble salt, the rate of dissolving the solute is equal to the rate of recrystallization. In a saturated solution, the concentrations of the ions from the solute are constant and can be used to calculate the solubility product constant (K_{sp}) for the salt. If the K_{sp} is known, the solubility of the salt can be calculated.

KEY TERMS

activation energy The energy required to break apart the bonds of the reacting molecules.

catalyst A substance that increases the rate of reaction by lowering the activation energy.

chemical equilibrium The point at which the forward and reverse reactions take place at the same rate so that there is no further change in concentrations of reactants and products.

collision theory A model for a chemical reaction that states that molecules must collide with sufficient energy in order to form products.

equilibrium constant expression The ratio of the concentrations of products to the concentrations of reactants with each component raised to an exponent equal to the coefficient of that compound in the chemical equation.

equilibrium constant, K_c The numerical value obtained by substituting the equilibrium concentrations of the components into the equilibrium constant expression.

heterogeneous equilibrium An equilibrium system in which the components are in different states.

homogenous equilibrium An equilibrium system in which all components are in the same state.

Le Châtelier's principle When a stress is placed on a system at equilibrium, the equilibrium shifts to relieve that stress.

rate of reaction The speed at which reactants are used to form product(s).

reversible reaction A reaction in which a forward reaction occurs from reactants to products, and a reverse reaction occurs from products back to reactants.

solubility product constant, K_{sp} The product of the concentrations of the ions in a saturated solution of a slightly soluble salt with each concentration raised to a power equal to its coefficient in the equilibrium equation.

UNDERSTANDING THE CONCEPTS

9.41 Would the reaction shown in the diagrams have a large or small equilibrium constant?

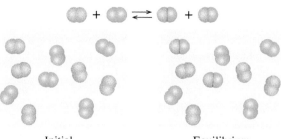

Initial	Equilibrium

9.42 Would the reaction shown in the diagrams have a large or small equilibrium constant?

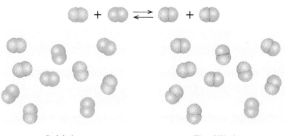

Initial	Equilibrium

9.43 **a.** Would T_2 be higher or lower than T_1 for the reaction shown in the diagrams?
b. Would K_c for T_2 be larger or smaller than the K_c for T_1?

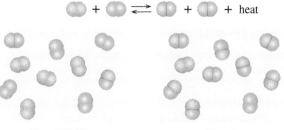

$T_1 = 300\ °C$	$T_2 = ?$

9.44 **a.** Would the reaction shown in the diagrams be exothermic or endothermic?
b. To increase K_c for this reaction, would you raise or lower the temperature?

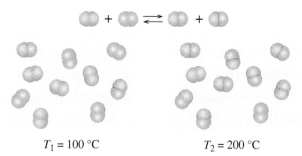

$T_1 = 100\ °C$	$T_2 = 200\ °C$

9.45 Consider the following reaction at equilibrium:

$$C_2H_4(g) + Cl_2(g) \rightleftharpoons C_2H_4Cl_2(g) + \text{heat}$$

Indicate how each of the following will shift the equilibrium:
a. raising the temperature of the reaction
b. decreasing the volume of the reaction container
c. adding a catalyst
d. adding Cl_2

9.46 Consider the following reaction at equilibrium:

$$N_2(g) + O_2(g) + \text{heat} \rightleftharpoons 2NO(g)$$

Indicate how each of the following will shift the equilibrium:
a. raising the temperature of the reaction
b. decreasing the volume of the reaction container
c. adding a catalyst
d. adding N_2

9.47 If a salt has the solubility product expression $K_{sp} = [Fe^{3+}][OH^-]^3$, what is the equilibrium equation for the solubility?

9.48 If a salt has the solubility product expression $K_{sp} = [Bi^{3+}]^2[S^{2-}]^3$, what is the equilibrium equation for the solubility?

ADDITIONAL QUESTIONS AND PROBLEMS

For instructor-assigned homework, go to www.masteringchemistry.com.

9.49 Write the equilibrium constant expression for each of the following reactions:

a. $CH_4(g) + 2O_2(g) \rightleftharpoons CO_2(g) + 2H_2O(g)$

b. $4NH_3(g) + 3O_2(g) \rightleftharpoons 2N_2(g) + 6H_2O(g)$

c. $C(s) + 2H_2(g) \rightleftharpoons CH_4(g)$

9.50 Write the equilibrium constant expression for each of the following reactions:

a. $2C_2H_6(g) + 7O_2(g) \rightleftharpoons 4CO_2(g) + 6H_2O(g)$

b. $2NaHCO_3(s) \rightleftharpoons Na_2CO_3(s) + CO_2(g) + H_2O(g)$

c. $4NH_3(g) + 5O_2(g) \rightleftharpoons 4NO(g) + 6H_2O(g)$

9.51 For each of the following reactions at equilibrium, indicate if the equilibrium mixture contains mostly products, mostly reactants, or both products and reactants:

a. $H_2(g) + Cl_2(g) \rightleftharpoons 2HCl(g)$ $\quad K_c = 1.3 \times 10^{34}$

b. $2NOBr(g) \rightleftharpoons 2NO(g) + Br_2(g)$ $\quad K_c = 2.0$

c. $2NOCl(g) \rightleftharpoons Cl_2(g) + 2NO(g)$ $\quad K_c = 2.7 \times 10^{-9}$

9.52 For each of the following reactions at equilibrium, indicate if the equilibrium mixture contains mostly products, mostly reactants, or both products and reactants:

a. $2H_2O(g) \rightleftharpoons 2H_2(g) + O_2(g)$ $\quad K_c = 4 \times 10^{-48}$

b. $N_2(g) + 3H_2(g) \rightleftharpoons 2NH_3(g)$ $\quad K_c = 0.30$

c. $2SO_2(g) + O_2(g) \rightleftharpoons 2SO_3(g)$ $\quad K_c = 1.2 \times 10^9$

9.53 Write the equation for each of the following equilibrium constant expressions:

a. $K_c = \dfrac{[SO_2][Cl_2]}{[SO_2Cl_2]}$

b. $K_c = \dfrac{[BrCl]^2}{[Br_2][Cl_2]}$

c. $K_c = \dfrac{[CH_4][H_2O]}{[CO][H_2]^3}$

d. $K_c = \dfrac{[N_2O][H_2O]^3}{[O_2]^2[NH_3]^2}$

9.54 Write the equation for each of the following equilibrium constant expressions:

a. $K_c = \dfrac{[CO_2][H_2]}{[CO][H_2O]}$

b. $K_c = \dfrac{[H_2][F_2]}{[HF]^2}$

c. $K_c = \dfrac{[O_2][HCl]^4}{[Cl_2]^2[H_2O]^2}$

d. $K_c = \dfrac{[CS_2][H_2]^4}{[CH_4][H_2S]^2}$

9.55 Consider the reaction

$$2NH_3(g) \rightleftharpoons N_2(g) + 3H_2(g)$$

a. Write the equilibrium constant expression for K_c.

b. What is the K_c for the reaction if at equilibrium the concentrations are [NH_3] = 0.20 M, [H_2] = 0.50 M, and [N_2] = 3.0 M?

9.56 Consider the reaction

$$2SO_2(g) + O_2(g) \rightleftharpoons 2SO_3(g)$$

a. Write the equilibrium constant expression for K_c.

b. What is the K_c for the reaction if at equilibrium the concentrations are [SO_2] = 0.10 M, [O_2] = 0.12 M, and [SO_3] = 0.60 M?

9.57 The equilibrium constant for the following reaction is 5.0 at 100 °C. If an equilibrium mixture contains [NO_2] = 0.50 M, what is the [N_2O_4]?

$$2NO_2(g) \rightleftharpoons N_2O_4(g)$$

9.58 The equilibrium constant for the following reaction is 0.20 at 1000 °C. If an equilibrium mixture contains solid carbon, [H_2O] = 0.40 M, and [CO] = 0.40 M, what is the [H_2]?

$$C(s) + H_2O(g) \rightleftharpoons CO(g) + H_2(g)$$

9.59 According to Le Châtelier's principle, does the equilibrium shift to products or reactants when O_2 is added to the equilibrium mixture of each of the following reactions?

a. $3O_2(g) \rightleftharpoons 2O_3(g)$

b. $2CO_2(g) \rightleftharpoons 2CO(g) + O_2(g)$

c. $P_4(g) + 5O_2(g) \rightleftharpoons P_4O_{10}(s)$

d. $2SO_2(g) + 2H_2O(g) \rightleftharpoons 2H_2S(g) + 3O_2(g)$

9.60 According to Le Châtelier's principle, what is the effect on the products when N_2 is added to the equilibrium mixture of each of the following reactions?

a. $2NH_3(g) \rightleftharpoons 3H_2(g) + N_2(g)$

b. $N_2(g) + O_2(g) \rightleftharpoons 2NO(g)$

c. $2NO_2(g) \rightleftharpoons N_2(g) + 2O_2(g)$

d. $4NH_3(g) + 3O_2(g) \rightleftharpoons 2N_2(g) + 6H_2O(g)$

9.61 Would decreasing the volume of the equilibrium mixture of each of the following reactions cause the equilibrium to shift, and if so, will the shift be toward products or reactants?

a. $3O_2(g) \rightleftharpoons 2O_3(g)$

b. $2CO_2(g) \rightleftharpoons 2CO(g) + O_2(g)$

c. $P_4(g) + 5O_2(g) \rightleftharpoons P_4O_{10}(s)$

d. $2SO_2(g) + 2H_2O(g) \rightleftharpoons 2H_2S(g) + 3O_2(g)$

9.62 Would increasing the volume of the equilibrium mixture of each of the following reactions cause the equilibrium to shift, and if so, will the shift be toward products or reactants?

a. $2NH_3(g) \rightleftharpoons 3H_2(g) + N_2(g)$

b. $N_2(g) + O_2(g) \rightleftharpoons 2NO(g)$

c. $2NO_2(g) \rightleftharpoons N_2(g) + 2O_2(g)$

d. $4NH_3(g) + 3O_2(g) \rightleftharpoons 2N_2(g) + 6H_2O(g)$

9.63 For each of the following K_c values, indicate whether the equilibrium mixture contains mostly reactants, mostly products, or similar amounts of reactants and products:

a. $N_2(g) + O_2(g) \rightleftharpoons 2NO(g)$ $\quad K_c = 1 \times 10^{-30}$

b. $H_2(g) + Br(g) \rightleftharpoons 2HBr(g)$ $\quad K_c = 2.0 \times 10^{19}$

9.64 Indicate if you would increase or decrease the volume of the container to *increase* the yield of the products in each of the following:

a. $2C(s) + O_2(g) \rightleftharpoons 2CO(g)$

b. $2CH_4(g) \rightleftharpoons C_2H_2(g) + 3H_2(g)$

c. $2H_2(g) + O_2(g) \rightleftharpoons 2H_2O(g)$

9.65 For each of the following slightly soluble salts, write the equilibrium equation and the solubility product expression:
a. $CuCO_3$ b. PbF_2 c. $Fe(OH)_3$

9.66 For each of the following slightly soluble salts, write the equilibrium equation and the solubility product expression:
a. CuS b. Ag_2SO_4 c. $Zn(OH)_2$

9.67 A saturated solution of iron(II) sulfide, FeS, has $[Fe^{2+}] = 7.7 \times 10^{-10}$ M and $[S^{2-}] = 7.7 \times 10^{-10}$ M. What is the value of K_{sp} for FeS?

9.68 A saturated solution of copper(I) chloride, CuCl, has $[Cu^+] = 1.1 \times 10^{-3}$ M and $[Cl^-] = 1.1 \times 10^{-3}$ M. What is the value of K_{sp} for CuCl?

9.69 A saturated solution of manganese(II) hydroxide, $Mn(OH)_2$, has $[Mn^{2+}] = 3.7 \times 10^{-5}$ M and $[OH^-] = 7.4 \times 10^{-5}$ M. What is the value of K_{sp} for $Mn(OH)_2$?

9.70 A saturated solution of silver chromate, Ag_2CrO_4, has $[Ag^+] = 1.3 \times 10^{-4}$ M and $[CrO_4^{2-}] = 6.5 \times 10^{-5}$ M. What is the value of K_{sp} for Ag_2CrO_4?

9.71 What are $[Cd^{2+}]$ and $[S^{2-}]$ in a saturated CdS solution if the K_{sp} of CdS is 1.0×10^{-24}?

9.72 What are $[Cu^{2+}]$ and $[CO_3^{2-}]$ in a saturated $CuCO_3$ solution if the K_{sp} of $CuCO_3$ is 1×10^{-26}?

CHALLENGE QUESTIONS

9.73 You mix 0.10 mole of PCl_5 with 0.050 mole of PCl_3 and 0.050 mole of Cl_2 in a 1.0 L flask.

$$PCl_5(g) \rightleftharpoons PCl_3(g) + Cl_2(g) \quad K_c = 4.2 \times 10^{-2}$$

a. Is the reaction at equilibrium?
b. If not, will the reaction proceed in the forward or reverse direction?

9.74 You mix 0.10 mole of NO, 0.10 mole of NOBr, and 0.10 mole of Br_2 in a 1.0 L container.

$$2NOBr(g) \rightleftharpoons 2NO(g) + Br_2(g) \quad K_c = 2.0 \text{ at } 100 \text{ °C}$$

a. Is the reaction at equilibrium?
b. If not, will the reaction proceed in the forward or reverse direction?

9.75 Consider the following reaction:

$$PCl_5(g) \rightleftharpoons PCl_3(g) + Cl_2(g)$$

a. Write the equilibrium constant expression.
b. Initially 0.60 mole of PCl_5 is placed in 1.00 L flask. At equilibrium, there is 0.16 mole of PCl_3 in the flask. What are the equilibrium concentrations of the PCl_5 and Cl_2?
c. What is the equilibrium constant for the reaction?
d. If 0.20 mole of Cl_2 is added to the equilibrium mixture, will $[PCl_5]$ increase or decrease?

9.76 The K_c at 100 °C is 2.0 for the reaction

$$2NOBr(g) \rightleftharpoons 2NO(g) + Br_2(g)$$

In an experiment, 1.0 mole of NO, 1.0 mole of NOBr, and 1.0 mole of Br_2 was placed in a 1.0 L container.
a. What is the equilibrium constant expression for the reaction?
b. Is the system at equilibrium?

c. If not, will the rate of the forward or reverse reaction initially speed up?
d. Which concentration(s) will be greater than 1.0 mole/L at equilibrium, and which will be less than 1.0 mole/L?

9.77 For the reaction

$$C(s) + CO_2(g) \rightleftharpoons 2CO(g)$$

the equilibrium mixture contains solid carbon, [CO] = 0.030 M, and $[CO_2]$ = 0.060 M.
a. What is the value of K_c for the reaction at this temperature?
b. What is the effect of adding more CO_2 to the equilibrium mixture?
c. What is the effect of decreasing the volume of the container?

9.78 Indicate how each of the following will affect the equilibrium concentration of CO in the following reaction:

$$C(s) + H_2O(g) + 31 \text{ kcal} \rightleftharpoons CO(g) + H_2(g)$$

a. add H_2
b. increase the temperature of the reaction
c. increase the volume of the container
d. add $C(s)$
e. decrease the volume of the container
f. add a catalyst
g. decrease the temperature of the reaction
h. remove H_2O

9.79 The antacid milk of magnesia, which contains $Mg(OH)_2$, is used to neutralize excess stomach acid. If the solubility of $Mg(OH)_2$ in water is 9.7×10^{-3} g/L, what is the K_{sp}?

9.80 In a saturated solution of CaF_2, the $[F^-] = 2.2 \times 10^{-3}$ M. What is $[Ca^{2+}]$?

ANSWERS

ANSWERS TO STUDY CHECKS

9.1 Lowering the temperature will decrease the rate of reaction.

9.2 $H_2(g) + Br_2(g) \rightleftharpoons 2HBr(g)$

9.3 $2NO(g) + O_2(g) \rightleftharpoons 2NO_2(g)$

9.4 $FeO(s) + CO(g) \rightleftharpoons Fe(s) + CO_2(g)$

$$K_c = \frac{[CO_2]}{[CO]}$$

9.5 $K_c = 27$

9.6 $[C_2H_5OH] = 2.7$ M

9.7 Decreasing the volume will increase the yield of product.

9.8 a. A decrease in temperature will decrease the concentration of reactants and increase the K_c value.
b. A decrease in temperature will increase the concentration of reactants and decrease the K_c value.

9.9 $K_{sp} = 8.5 \times 10^{-17}$

9.10 The solubility of NiS is 2×10^{-10} M.

ANSWER TO SELECTED QUESTIONS AND PROBLEMS

9.1 a. The rate of the reaction indicates how fast the products form.
b. Reactions go faster at higher temperatures.

9.3   The number of collisions will increase when the number of Br_2 molecules is increased.

9.5   **a.** increase   **b.** increase
         c. increase   **d.** decrease

9.7   A reversible reaction is one in which a forward reaction converts reactants to products, while a reverse reaction converts products to reactants.

9.9   **a.** not reversible   **b.** reversible   **c.** reversible

9.11 **a.** $K_c = \dfrac{[CS_2][H_2]^4}{[CH_4][H_2S]^2}$ **b.** $K_c = \dfrac{[N_2][O_2]}{[NO]^2}$

         c. $K_c = \dfrac{[CS_2][O_2]^4}{[SO_3]^2[CO_2]}$

9.13 **a.** homogeneous equilibrium
         b. heterogeneous equilibrium
         c. homogeneous equilibrium
         d. heterogeneous equilibrium

9.15 **a.** $K_c = \dfrac{[O_2]^3}{[O_3]^2}$ **b.** $K_c = [CO_2][H_2O]$

         c. $K_c = \dfrac{[H_2]^3[CO]}{[CH_4][H_2O]}$ **d.** $K_c = \dfrac{[Cl_2]^2}{[HCl]^4[O_2]}$

9.17 $K_c = 1.5$

9.19 $K_c = 260$

9.21 **a.** mostly products
         b. both reactants and products
         c. mostly reactants

9.23 $[H_2] = 1.1 \times 10^{-3}$ M

9.25 $[NOBr] = 1.4$ M

9.27 **a.** When more reactant is added to an equilibrium mixture, the product/reactant ratio is initially less than K_c.
         b. According to Le Châtelier's principle, equilibrium is reestablished when the forward reaction forms more products to make the product/reactant ratio equal the K_c again.

9.29 **a.** Equilibrium shifts to products.
         b. Equilibrium shifts to reactants.
         c. Equilibrium shifts to products.
         d. Equilibrium shifts to products.
         e. No shift in equilibrium occurs.

9.31 **a.** Equilibrium shifts to products.
         b. Equilibrium shifts to products.
         c. Equilibrium shifts to products.
         d. No shift in equilibrium occurs.
         e. Equilibrium shifts to reactants.

9.33 **a.** $MgCO_3(s) \rightleftharpoons Mg^{2+}(aq) + CO_3^{2-}(aq)$;
$$K_{sp} = [Mg^{2+}][CO_3^{2-}]$$
         b. $PbI_2(s) \rightleftharpoons Pb^{2+}(aq) + 2I^-(aq)$; $K_{sp} = [Pb^{2+}][I^-]^2$
         c. $Ag_3PO_4(s) \rightleftharpoons 3Ag^+(aq) + PO_4^{3-}(aq)$;
$$K_{sp} = [Ag^+]^3[PO_4^{3-}]$$

9.35 $K_{sp} = 1 \times 10^{-10}$

9.37 $K_{sp} = 8.8 \times 10^{-12}$

9.39 $[Cu^+] = 1 \times 10^{-6}$ M; $[I^-] = 1 \times 10^{-6}$ M

9.41 The reaction would have a small equilibrium constant.

9.43 **a.** T_2 is lower than T_1.
         b. K_c for T_2 is larger than K_c for T_1.

9.45 **a.** shift toward reactants
         b. shift toward products

c. no change
d. shift toward products

9.47 $Fe(OH)_3(s) \rightleftharpoons Fe^{3+}(aq) + 3OH^-(aq)$

9.49 **a.** $K_c = \dfrac{[CO_2][H_2O]^2}{[CH_4][O_2]^2}$ **b.** $K_c = \dfrac{[N_2]^2[H_2O]^6}{[NH_3]^4[O_2]^3}$

         c. $K_c = \dfrac{[CH_4]}{[H_2]^2}$

9.51 **a.** mostly products
         b. both products and reactants
         c. mostly reactants

9.53 **a.** $SO_2Cl_2(g) \rightleftharpoons SO_2(g) + Cl_2(g)$
         b. $Br_2(g) + Cl_2(g) \rightleftharpoons 2BrCl(g)$
         c. $CO(g) + 3H_2(g) \rightleftharpoons CH_4(g) + H_2O(g)$
         d. $2O_2(g) + 2NH_3(g) \rightleftharpoons N_2O(g) + 3H_2O(g)$

9.55 **a.** $K_c = \dfrac{[N_2][H_2]^3}{[NH_3]^2}$ **b.** $K_c = 9.4$

9.57 $[N_2O_4] = 1.3$ M

9.59 **a.** Equilibrium shifts to products.
         b. Equilibrium shifts to reactants.
         c. Equilibrium shifts to products.
         d. Equilibrium shifts to reactants.

9.61 **a.** Equilibrium shifts to products.
         b. Equilibrium shifts to reactants.
         c. Equilibrium shifts to products.
         d. Equilibrium shifts to reactants.

9.63 **a.** A small K_c indicates that the equilibrium mixture contains mostly reactants.
         b. A large K_c indicates that the equilibrium mixture contains mostly products.

9.65 **a.** $CuCO_3(s) \rightleftharpoons Cu^{2+}(aq) + CO_3^{2-}(aq)$;
$$K_{sp} = [Cu^{2+}][CO_3^{2-}]$$
         b. $PbF_2(s) \rightleftharpoons Pb^{2+}(aq) + 2F^-(aq)$; $K_{sp} = [Pb^{2+}][F^-]^2$
         c. $Fe(OH)_3(s) \rightleftharpoons Fe^{3+}(aq) + 3OH^-(aq)$;
$$K_{sp} = [Fe^{3+}][OH^-]^3$$

9.67 $K_{sp} = 5.9 \times 10^{-19}$

9.69 $K_{sp} = 2.0 \times 10^{-13}$

9.71 $[Cd^{2+}] = 1.0 \times 10^{-12}$ M; $[S^{2-}] = 1.0 \times 10^{-12}$ M

9.73 **a.** The reaction is not at equilibrium.
         b. The reaction will proceed in the forward direction.

9.75 **a.** $K_c = \dfrac{[PCl_3][Cl_2]}{[PCl_5]}$

         b. At equilibrium, the concentrations are $[Cl_2] = 0.16$ M, $[PCl_5] = 0.84$ M.
         c. $K_c = 0.058$
         d. $[PCl_5]$ will increase.

9.77 **a.** $K_c = 0.015$
         b. If more CO_2 is added, the equilibrium will shift to the products.
         c. If the container volume is decreased, the equilibrium will shift to the reactants.

9.79 $K_{sp} = 2.0 \times 10^{-11}$

Acids and Bases

10

"In a stat lab, we are sent blood samples of patients in emergency situations," says Audrey Trautwein, clinical laboratory technician, Stat Lab, Santa Clara Valley Medical Center. *"We may need to assess the status of a trauma patient in ER or a patient who is in surgery. For example, an acidic blood pH diminishes cardiac function and affects the actions of certain drugs. In a stat situation, it is critical that we obtain our results fast. This is done using a blood gas analyzer. As I put a blood sample into the analyzer, a small probe draws out a measured volume, which is tested simultaneously for pH, P_{O_2}, and P_{CO_2}, as well as for electrolytes, glucose, and hemoglobin. In about one minute we have our test results, which are sent to the doctor's computer."*

Lemons, grapefruit, and vinegar taste sour because they contain acids. We have acid in our stomach that helps us digest food. We produce lactic acid in our muscles when we exercise. Acid from bacteria turns milk sour to make cottage cheese or yogurt. Bases are solutions that neutralize acids. Sometimes we take antacids such as milk of magnesia to offset the effects of too much stomach acid.

The pH of a solution describes its acidity. The lungs and the kidneys are the primary organs that regulate the pH of body fluids, including blood and urine. Major changes in the pH of the body fluids can severely affect biological activities within the cells. Buffers are present to prevent large fluctuations in pH.

In the environment, the pH of rain, water, and soil can have significant effects. When rain becomes too acidic, it can dissolve marble statues and accelerate the corrosion of metals. In lakes and ponds, the acidity of water can affect the ability of fish to survive. The acidity of the soil around plants affects their growth. If the soil pH is too acidic or too basic, the roots of the plant cannot take up some nutrients. Most plants thrive in soil with a nearly neutral pH, although certain plants such as orchids, camellias, and blueberries require a more acidic soil.

10.1 Acids and Bases

LEARNING GOAL

Describe and name Arrhenius and Brønsted–Lowry acids and bases; identify conjugate acid–base pairs.

The term *acid* comes from the Latin word *acidus*, which means "sour." We are familiar with the sour tastes of vinegar, lemons, and other common acidic foods.

In 1887, the Swedish chemist Svante Arrhenius was the first to describe **acids** as substances that produce hydrogen ions (H^+) when they dissolve in water. For example, hydrogen chloride ionizes in water to give hydrogen ions, H^+, and chloride ions, Cl^-. The hydrogen ions, H^+, give acids a sour taste, change blue litmus indicator to red, and corrode some metals.

$$HCl(g) \xrightarrow{\text{H}_2\text{O}} H^+(aq) + Cl^-(aq)$$

Polar covalent   Ionization   Hydrogen ion
compound   in water

Naming Acids

Acids dissolve in water to produce hydrogen ions along with a negative ion that may be a simple nonmetal anion or a polyatomic ion.

When an acid dissolves in water to produce a hydrogen ion and a simple nonmetal anion, the prefix *hydro* is used before the name of the nonmetal, and its *ide* ending is changed to *ic acid*. For example, hydrogen chloride (HCl) dissolves in water to form HCl(*aq*), which is named hydrochloric acid. An exception is hydrogen cyanide (HCN), which as an acid is named hydrocyanic acid, HCN(*aq*). When an acid contains an oxygen-containing polyatomic ion, the name of the acid comes from the name of the polyatomic ion. The *ate* in the name is replaced with *ic acid*. If the acid contains a polyatomic ion with an *ite* ending, its name ends with *ous acid*. The names of some common acids and their anions are listed in Table 10.1.

CONCEPT CHECK 10.1

■ **Naming Acids**

a. If H_2SO_4 is named sulfuric acid, what is the name of H_2SO_3? Why?

b. In part **a**, why is the prefix *hydro* not used at the beginning of either name?

ANSWER

a. H_2SO_3 is named sulfurous acid. The acid of a polyatomic anion that ends in *ate* replaces the *ate* ending with *ic acid*. The acid of the polyatomic anion that ends in *ite* replaces the *ite* ending with *ous acid*.

b. The prefix *hydro* is used only when the anion is a simple nonmetal anion or CN^-, and not with an acid that includes a polyatomic anion.

TABLE 10.1 Naming Common Acids

Acid	Name of Acid	Anion	Name of Anion
HCl	**Hydro**chloric acid	Cl^-	Chlor**ide**
HBr	**Hydro**bromic acid	Br^-	Brom**ide**
HCN	**Hydro**cyanic acid	CN^-	Cyan**ide**
HNO_3	Nitr**ic** acid	NO_3^-	Nitr**ate**
HNO_2	Nitr**ous** acid	NO_2^-	Nitr**ite**
H_2SO_4	Sulfur**ic** acid	SO_4^{2-}	Sulf**ate**
H_2SO_3	Sulfur**ous** acid	SO_3^{2-}	Sulf**ite**
H_2CO_3	Carbon**ic** acid	CO_3^{2-}	Carbon**ate**
H_3PO_4	Phosphor**ic** acid	PO_4^{3-}	Phosph**ate**
$HClO_4$	**Per**chlor**ic** acid	ClO_4^-	**Per**chlor**ate**
$HClO_3$	Chlor**ic** acid	ClO_3^-	Chlor**ate**
$HClO_2$	Chlor**ous** acid	ClO_2^-	Chlor**ite**
HClO	**Hypo**chlor**ous** acid	ClO^-	**Hypo**chlor**ite**
$HC_2H_3O_2$	Acet**ic** acid	$C_2H_3O_2^-$	Acet**ate**

Bases

You may be familiar with some bases such as antacids, ammonia, drain openers, and oven cleaners. According to the Arrhenius theory, **bases** are ionic compounds that dissociate into cations and hydroxide ions (OH^-) when they dissolve in water. For example, sodium hydroxide is an Arrhenius base that dissociates in water to give sodium ions, Na^+, and hydroxide ions, OH^-.

Most Arrhenius bases are formed from Groups 1A (1) and 2A (2) metals, such as NaOH, KOH, LiOH, and $Ca(OH)_2$. Bases such as $Al(OH)_3$ and $Fe(OH)_3$ are strong, but they are fairly insoluble. The hydroxide ions (OH^-) give Arrhenius bases common characteristics such as a bitter taste and a slippery feel. A base turns litmus indicator blue and phenolphthalein indicator pink.

Naming Bases

Typical Arrhenius bases are named as *hydroxides*.

Bases	Name
NaOH	Sodium **hydroxide**
KOH	Potassium **hydroxide**
$Ca(OH)_2$	Calcium **hydroxide**
$Al(OH)_3$	Aluminum **hydroxide**

NaOH(s)

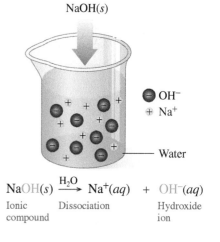

● OH^-
⊕ Na^+

Water

$$NaOH(s) \xrightarrow{H_2O} Na^+(aq) + OH^-(aq)$$

Ionic compound   Dissociation   Hydroxide ion

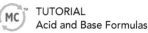

TUTORIAL
Acid and Base Formulas

TUTORIAL
Naming Acids and Bases

CONCEPT CHECK 10.2

■ Dissociation of an Arrhenius Base

Write an equation for the dissociation of calcium hydroxide in water.

ANSWER

When calcium hydroxide, $Ca(OH)_2$, dissolves in water, the solution contains calcium ions (Ca^{2+}) and twice as many hydroxide ions (OH^-). The equation is written as

$$Ca(OH)_2(s) \xrightarrow{H_2O} Ca^{2+}(aq) + 2OH^-(aq)$$

SAMPLE PROBLEM 10.1

■ **Names and Formulas of Acids and Bases**

a. Name each of the following as an acid or base:
    1. H_3PO_4 **2.** NaOH
b. Write the formula of each of the following acids:
    1. nitrous acid   **2.** hydrobromic acid

SOLUTION

a. 1. phosphoric acid   **2.** sodium hydroxide
b. 1. HNO_2 **2.** HBr

STUDY CHECK

a. Give the name for $HClO_3$.
b. Write the formula of iron(III) hydroxide.

Brønsted–Lowry Acids and Bases

In 1923, J. N. Brønsted in Denmark and T. M. Lowry in Great Britain expanded the definition of acids and bases. A **Brønsted–Lowry acid** donates a proton (hydrogen ion, H^+) to another substance, and a **Brønsted–Lowry base** accepts a proton.

> A Brønsted–Lowry acid is a proton (H^+) donor.
> A Brønsted–Lowry base is a proton (H^+) acceptor.

A free, dissociated proton (H^+) does not actually exist in water. Its attraction to polar water molecules is so strong that the proton bonds to the water molecule and forms a **hydronium ion, H_3O^+**.

$$H\!-\!\overset{..}{\underset{|}{O}}\!:\; +\; H^+ \longrightarrow \left[H\!-\!\overset{..}{\underset{|}{O}}\!-\!H \right]^+$$

Water   Proton   Hydronium ion

We can write the formation of a hydrochloric acid solution as a transfer of a proton from hydrogen chloride to water. By accepting a proton in the reaction, water is acting as a base according to the Brønsted–Lowry concept.

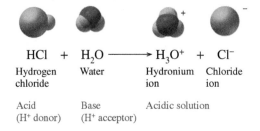

$$HCl \;+\; H_2O \longrightarrow H_3O^+ \;+\; Cl^-$$

Hydrogen   Water   Hydronium   Chloride
chloride   ion   ion

Acid   Base   Acidic solution
(H^+ donor)   (H^+ acceptor)

In another reaction, ammonia (NH_3) reacts with water. Because the nitrogen atom of NH_3 has a stronger attraction for a proton, water acts as an acid by donating a proton.

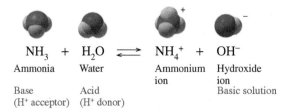

$$NH_3 \;+\; H_2O \rightleftharpoons NH_4^+ \;+\; OH^-$$

Ammonia   Water   Ammonium   Hydroxide
                            ion   ion

Base   Acid   Basic solution
(H^+ acceptor)   (H^+ donor)

Table 10.2 compares some characteristics of acids and bases.

TABLE 10.2 Some Characteristics of Acids and Bases

Characteristic	Acids	Bases
Reaction: Arrhenius	Produce H^+	Produce OH^-
Reaction: Brønsted–Lowry	Donate H^+	Accept H^+
Electrolytes	Yes	Yes
Taste	Sour	Bitter, chalky
Feel	May sting	Slippery
Litmus	Red	Blue
Phenolphthalein	Colorless	Pink
Neutralization	Neutralize bases	Neutralize acids

SAMPLE PROBLEM 10.2

■ Acids and Bases

In each of the following equations, identify the reactant that is a Brønsted–Lowry acid and the reactant that is a Brønsted–Lowry base:

a. $HBr(aq) + H_2O(l) \longrightarrow H_3O^+(aq) + Br^-(aq)$
b. $H_2O(l) + CN^-(aq) \rightleftharpoons HCN(aq) + OH^-(aq)$

SOLUTION

a. HBr, Brønsted–Lowry acid; H_2O, Brønsted–Lowry base

b. H_2O, Brønsted–Lowry acid; CN^-, Brønsted–Lowry base

STUDY CHECK

When HNO_3 reacts with water, water acts as a Brønsted–Lowry base. Write the equation for the reaction.

Conjugate Acid–Base Pairs

According to the Brønsted–Lowry theory, a **conjugate acid–base pair** consists of molecules or ions related by the loss or gain of one H^+. Every acid–base reaction contains two conjugate acid–base pairs because protons are transferred in both the forward and reverse reactions. When the acid HA donates H^+, the conjugate base A^- forms. When the base B accepts the H^+, it forms the conjugate acid BH^+. We can write a general equation for a Brønsted–Lowry acid–base reaction as follows:

Conjugate acid–base pair

$$\text{HA} \quad + \quad \text{B} \quad \rightleftharpoons \quad \text{A}^- \quad + \quad \text{BH}^+$$

| **Acid 1** | **Base 2** | **Base 1** | **Acid 2** |
| H^+ donor | H^+ acceptor | H^+ acceptor | H^+ donor |

Conjugate acid–base pair

TUTORIAL

Identifying Conjugate
Acid–Base Pairs

Conjugate acid–base pair

HF   F⁻

Conjugate acid–base pair

H_2O H_3O^+

Now we can identify the conjugate acid–base pairs in a reaction such as hydrofluoric acid and water. Because the reaction is reversible, the conjugate acid H_3O^+ can transfer a proton to the conjugate base F^- and re-form the acid HF. Using the relationship of loss and gain of one H^+, we identify the conjugate acid–base pairs as HF and F^- along with H_3O^+ and H_2O.

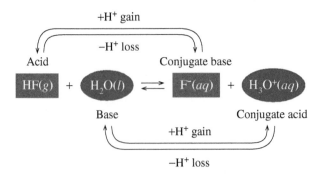

In another proton-transfer reaction, ammonia, NH_3, accepts H^+ from H_2O to form the conjugate acid NH_4^+ and conjugate base OH^-. Each of these conjugate acid–base pairs, NH_3 and NH_4^+ as well as H_2O and OH^-, are related by the loss and gain of one H^+.

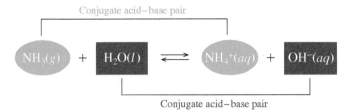

In these two examples, we see that water can act as an acid when it donates H^+ or a base when it accepts H^+. Substances that can act as both acids and bases are **amphoteric**. For water, the most common amphoteric substance, the acidic or basic behavior depends on the other reactant. Water donates H^+ when it reacts with a stronger base and accepts H^+ when it reacts with a stronger acid. Another example of an amphoteric substance is bicarbonate, HCO_3^-. With a stronger base, HCO_3^- donates H^+ to give CO_3^{2-}. But when HCO_3^- reacts with a stronger acid, it accepts a proton to form H_2CO_3.

SAMPLE PROBLEM 10.3

■ **Conjugate Acid–Base Pairs**

Write the formula of the conjugate base of each of the following Brønsted–Lowry acids:

a. $HClO_3$ **b.** H_2CO_3

SOLUTION

The conjugate base forms when the acid donates a proton.

a. ClO_3^- is the conjugate base that forms when $HClO_3$ donates H^+.
b. HCO_3^- is the conjugate base that forms when H_2CO_3 donates H^+.

STUDY CHECK

Write the conjugate acid of each of the following Brønsted–Lowry bases:
a. HS^- **b.** NO_2^-

SAMPLE PROBLEM 10.4

■ **Identifying Conjugate Acid–Base Pairs**

Identify the conjugate acid–base pairs in the following equation:

$$HBr(aq) + NH_3(aq) \longrightarrow Br^-(aq) + NH_4^+(aq)$$

SOLUTION

Acting as a Brønsted–Lowry acid, HBr donates H^+ to form Br^- as its conjugate base. The NH_3, acting as a Brønsted–Lowry base, accepts H^+ to form its conjugate acid NH_4^+. One conjugate acid–base pair is HBr and Br^-, and the other is NH_4^+ and NH_3.

STUDY CHECK

In the following reaction, identify the conjugate acid–base pairs:

$$HCN(aq) + SO_4^{2-}(aq) \rightleftharpoons CN^-(aq) + HSO_4^-(aq)$$

QUESTIONS AND PROBLEMS

Acids and Bases

10.1 Indicate whether each of the following statements is characteristic of an acid or a base:
  a. has a sour taste
  b. neutralizes bases
  c. produces H^+ ions in water
  d. is named potassium hydroxide

10.2 Indicate whether each of the following statements is characteristic of an acid or a base:
  a. neutralizes acids   **b.** produces OH^- in water
  c. has a slippery feel   **d.** turns litmus red

10.3 Name each of the following acids and bases:
  a. HCl   **b.** $Ca(OH)_2$ **c.** H_2CO_3
  d. HNO_3 **e.** H_2SO_3 **f.** $Fe(OH)_2$

10.4 Name each of the following acids and bases:
  a. $Al(OH)_3$ **b.** HBr   **c.** H_2SO_4
  d. KOH   **e.** HNO_2 **f.** $HClO_3$

10.5 Write formulas for the following acids and bases:
  a. magnesium hydroxide **b.** hydrofluoric acid
  c. phosphoric acid   **d.** lithium hydroxide
  e. copper(II) hydroxide

10.6 Write formulas for the following acids and bases:
  a. barium hydroxide   **b.** hydroiodic acid
  c. nitric acid   **d.** iron(III) hydroxide
  e. sodium hydroxide

10.7 In each of the following, identify the Brønsted–Lowry acid and Brønsted–Lowry base:
  a. $HI(aq) + H_2O(l) \longrightarrow H_3O^+(aq) + I^-(aq)$
  b. $F^-(aq) + H_2O(l) \rightleftharpoons HF(aq) + OH^-(aq)$

10.8 In each of the following, identify the Brønsted–Lowry acid and the Brønsted–Lowry base:
  a. $CO_3^{2-}(aq) + H_2O(l) \rightleftharpoons HCO_3^-(aq) + OH^-(aq)$
  b. $H_2SO_4(aq) + H_2O(l) \longrightarrow H_3O^+(aq) + HSO_4^-(aq)$

10.9 Write the formula and name of the conjugate base for each of the following acids:
  a. HF   **b.** H_2O **c.** H_2CO_3 **d.** HSO_4^-

10.10 Write the formula and name of the conjugate base for each of the following acids:
  a. HCO_3^- **b.** H_3O^+ **c.** HPO_4^{2-} **d.** HNO_2

10.11 Write the formula and name of the conjugate acid for each of the following bases:
  a. CO_3^{2-} **b.** H_2O **c.** $H_2PO_4^-$ **d.** Br^-

10.12 Write the formula and name of the conjugate acid for each of the following bases:
  a. SO_4^{2-} **b.** CN^-
  c. OH^- **d.** ClO_2^-, chlorite ion

10.13 Identify the Brønsted–Lowry acid–base pairs in the following equations:
  a. $H_2CO_3(aq) + H_2O(l) \rightleftharpoons H_3O^+(aq) + HCO_3^-(aq)$
  b. $NH_4^+(aq) + H_2O(l) \rightleftharpoons H_3O^+(aq) + NH_3(aq)$
  c. $HCN(aq) + NO_2^-(aq) \rightleftharpoons CN^-(aq) + HNO_2(aq)$

10.14 Identify the Brønsted–Lowry acid–base pairs in the following equations:
  a. $H_3PO_4(aq) + H_2O(l) \rightleftharpoons H_3O^+(aq) + H_2PO_4^-(aq)$
  b. $CO_3^{2-}(aq) + H_2O(l) \rightleftharpoons OH^-(aq) + HCO_3^-(aq)$
  c. $H_3PO_4(aq) + NH_3(aq) \rightleftharpoons NH_4^+(aq) + H_2PO_4^-(aq)$

10.2   Strengths of Acids and Bases

The *strength* of acids is determined by the moles of H_3O^+ that are produced for each mole of acid that dissolves. The *strength* of bases is determined by the moles of OH^- that are produced for each mole of base that dissolves. In the process called **dissociation**, an acid or base separates into ions in water. Acids and bases vary greatly in their ability to produce H_3O^+ or OH^-. Strong acids and strong bases dissociate completely. In water, weak acids and weak bases dissociate only slightly, leaving most of the initial acid or base undissociated.

LEARNING GOAL

Write equations for the dissociation of strong and weak acids; write the equilibrium expression for a weak acid.

TABLE 10.3 Some Conjugate Acid–Base Pairs

Increasing acid strength

Acid			Conjugate Base
Strong acids			
Perchloric acid	$HClO_4$	ClO_4^-	Perchlorate ion
Sulfuric acid	H_2SO_4	HSO_4^-	Hydrogen sulfate ion
Hydroiodic acid	HI	I^-	Iodide ion
Hydrobromic acid	HBr	Br^-	Bromide ion
Hydrochloric acid	HCl	Cl^-	Chloride ion
Nitric acid	HNO_3	NO_3^-	Nitrate ion
Weak acids			
Hydronium ion	H_3O^+	H_2O	Water
Hydrogen sulfate ion	HSO_4^-	SO_4^{2-}	Sulfate ion
Phosphoric acid	H_3PO_4	$H_2PO_4^-$	Dihydrogen phosphate ion
Nitrous acid	HNO_2	NO_2^-	Nitrite ion
Hydrofluoric acid	HF	F^-	Fluoride ion
Acetic acid	$HC_2H_3O_2$	$C_2H_3O_2^-$	Acetate ion
Carbonic acid	H_2CO_3	HCO_3^-	Bicarbonate ion
Hydrosulfuric acid	H_2S	HS^-	Hydrogen sulfide ion
Ammonium ion	NH_4^+	NH_3	Ammonia
Hydrocyanic acid	HCN	CN^-	Cyanide ion
Bicarbonate ion	HCO_3^-	CO_3^{2-}	Carbonate ion
Hydrogen sulfide ion	HS^-	S^{2-}	Sulfide ion
Water	H_2O	OH^-	Hydroxide ion

Increasing base strength

Strong and Weak Acids

Strong acids are examples of strong electrolytes because they donate protons so easily that their dissociation in water is virtually complete. For example, when the strong acid HCl dissociates in water, H^+ is transferred to H_2O, and the resulting solution contains essentially only the ions H_3O^+ and Cl^-. We consider the reaction of HCl in H_2O as going nearly 100% to products. Therefore, the equation for a strong acid such as HCl is written with a single arrow to the products:

$$HCl(g) + H_2O(l) \longrightarrow H_3O^+(aq) + Cl^-(aq)$$

There are only a handful of strong acids. All other acids are weak acids. Table 10.3 lists the strong acids along with some common weak acids, from strongest to weakest acid.

Weak acids are weak electrolytes. **Weak acids** dissociate slightly in water, which means that only a small percentage of the weak acid donates H^+ to H_2O. Thus, a weak acid reacts with water to form only a small amount of H_3O^+ ions. Even at high concentrations, weak acids produce low concentrations of H_3O^+ ions. (See Figure 10.1.) Many of the products you drink or use at home contain weak acids. In carbonated soft drinks, for example, CO_2 dissolves in water to form carbonic acid, H_2CO_3. A weak acid such as H_2CO_3 reaches equilibrium between the mostly undissociated H_2CO_3 molecules and the ions H_3O^+ and HCO_3^-. Such a reaction is written with a double arrow. A longer reverse arrow may be used to indicate that the equilibrium favors the undissociated reactants:

$$H_2CO_3(aq) + H_2O(l) \xleftarrow{\hspace{1em}} \rightleftharpoons H_3O^+(aq) + HCO_3^-(aq)$$

Carbonic acid   Bicarbonate ion

Citric acid is a weak acid found in fruits and fruit juices such as lemons, oranges, and grapefruit. Vinegar contains another weak acid known as acetic acid, $HC_2H_3O_2$. In the vinegar used in salad dressings, acetic acid is present typically as a 5% (m/v) acetic acid solution:

$$HC_2H_3O_2(l) + H_2O(l) \xleftarrow{\hspace{1em}} \rightleftharpoons H_3O^+(aq) + C_2H_3O_2^-(aq)$$

Acetic acid   Acetate ion

FIGURE 10.1 A strong acid such as HCl is completely dissociated (≈100%) in solution, whereas a solution of a weak acid such as $HC_2H_3O_2$ contains mostly molecules and a few ions.

Q What is the difference between a strong acid and a weak acid?

In summary, if HA is a strong acid in water, the solution consists of the ions H_3O^+ and A^-. However, if HA is a weak acid, the aqueous solution consists mostly of undissociated HA and only a few H_3O^+ and A^- ions. (See Figure 10.2.)

Strong acid: $HA(aq) + H_2O(l) \longrightarrow H_3O^+(aq) + A^-(aq)$ (100% dissociated)

Weak acid: $HA(aq) + H_2O(l) \rightleftharpoons H_3O^+(aq) + A^-(aq)$ (small % dissociated)

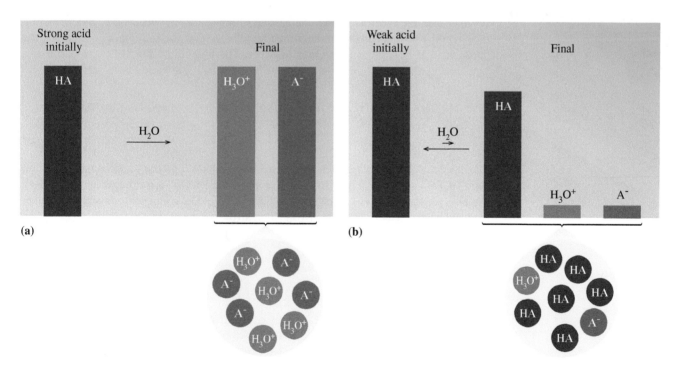

FIGURE 10.2 **(a)** A strong acid dissociates in water to give H_3O^+ and A^- ions. **(b)** A weak acid in water dissociates only slightly to form a solution containing only a few H_3O^+ and A^- ions and mostly undissociated HA molecules.

Q How does the height of the H_3O^+ and A^- in the bar diagram change for a strong acid compared to a weak acid?

Strong and Weak Bases

As strong electrolytes, **strong bases** dissociate completely in water. Because these strong bases are ionic compounds, they dissociate in water to give an aqueous solution of a metal ion and hydroxide ion. The Group 1A (1) hydroxides are very soluble in water, which can give high concentrations of OH^- ions. The other strong bases are much less soluble in water, but they dissolve completely as ions. For example, when KOH, a strong base, dissociates in water, the solution consists only of the ions K^+ and OH^-:

$$KOH(s) \xrightarrow{H_2O} K^+(aq) + OH^-(aq)$$

The Arrhenius bases of Groups 1A (1) and 2A (2), such as LiOH, KOH, NaOH, and $Ba(OH)_2$, are strong bases. Sodium hydroxide, NaOH (also known as lye), is used in household products to remove grease in ovens and to clean drains. Because high concentrations of hydroxide ions cause severe damage to the skin and eyes, directions must be followed carefully when such products are used in the home, and use in the chemistry laboratory should be carefully supervised. If you spill an acid or a base on your skin or get some in your eyes, be sure to flood the area immediately with water for at least 10 minutes and seek medical attention. **Weak bases** are weak electrolytes, which are poor acceptors of protons and produce very few ions in solution. A typical weak base, ammonia, NH_3, is found in window cleaners. In an aqueous solution, a few ammonia molecules accept protons to form NH_4^+ and OH^-:

$$NH_3(g) + H_2O(l) \rightleftharpoons NH_4^+(aq) + OH^-(aq)$$
Ammonia   Ammonium hydroxide

Direction of Reaction

There is a relationship between the components in each conjugate acid–base pair. The strong acids that donate protons easily have weak conjugate bases that do not readily accept protons. This conjugate base is a very weak base. As the strength of the acid decreases, the strength of its conjugate base increases.

In any acid–base reaction, there are two acids and two bases. However, one acid is stronger than the other acid, and one base is stronger than the other base. By comparing their relative strengths, we can determine the direction of the reaction. For example, the strong acid H_2SO_4 gives up protons to water. The hydronium ion H_3O^+ produced is a weaker acid than H_2SO_4, and the conjugate base HSO_4^- is a weaker base than water:

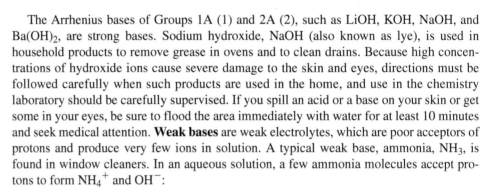

$$H_2SO_4(aq) + H_2O(l) \longrightarrow H_3O^+(aq) + HSO_4^-(aq) \quad \text{Strongly favors products}$$
Stronger   Stronger   Weaker   Weaker
acid   base   acid   base

Let's look at another reaction in which water donates a proton to carbonate CO_3^{2-} to form HCO_3^- and OH^-. From Table 10.3, we see that HCO_3^- is a stronger acid than H_2O. We also see that OH^- is a stronger base than CO_3^{2-}. The equilibrium favors the weaker acid and base reactants, as shown by the long arrow for the reverse reaction:

$$CO_3^{2-}(aq) + H_2O(l) \underset{\longleftarrow}{\rightleftharpoons} HCO_3^-(aq) + OH^-(aq) \quad \text{Strongly favors reactants}$$
Weaker   Weaker   Stronger   Stronger
base   acid   acid   base

SAMPLE PROBLEM 10.5

■ **Direction of Reaction**

Does equilibrium favor the reactants or products in the following reaction?

$$HF(aq) + H_2O(l) \rightleftharpoons H_3O^+(aq) + F^-(aq)$$

SOLUTION

From Table 10.3, we see that HF is a weaker acid than H_3O^+ and that H_2O is a weaker base than F^-. Equilibrium favors the reverse direction and therefore the reactants:

$$HF(aq) + H_2O(l) \mathrel{\mathop{\rightleftarrows}} H_3O^+(aq) + F^-(aq)$$
Weaker acid Weaker base   Stronger acid   Stronger base

STUDY CHECK

Does the reaction of nitric acid and water favor the reactants or the products?

Dissociation Constants for Weak Acids

We have seen that reactions of weak acids in water reach equilibrium. If HA is a weak acid, the concentrations of H_3O^+ and A^- are small, which means that the equilibrium favors the reactants:

$$HA(aq) + H_2O(l) \mathrel{\mathop{\rightleftarrows}} H_3O^+(aq) + A^-(aq)$$

As we have seen, acids have different strengths depending on how much they dissociate in water. Because the dissociation of strong acids in water is essentially complete, the reaction is not considered to be an equilibrium situation. However, because weak acids in water dissociate only slightly, the ion products reach equilibrium with the undissociated weak acid molecules. Thus, an equilibrium expression can be written for weak acids that gives the ratio of the concentrations of products to the weak acid reactants. As with other equilibrium constants, the molar concentration of the products is divided by the molar concentration of the reactants:

$$\frac{[H_3O^+][A^-]}{[HA][H_2O]}$$

Because water is a pure liquid, its concentration, which is constant, is omitted from the equilibrium constant, called the **acid dissociation constant**, K_a (or acid ionization constant). Thus for a weak acid HA, the K_a is written

$$K_a = \frac{[H_3O^+][A^-]}{[HA]} \quad \text{Acid dissociation constant}$$

Let's consider the equilibrium of carbonic acid, which dissociates in water to form bicarbonate and hydronium ions:

$$H_2CO_3(aq) + H_2O(l) \mathrel{\mathop{\rightleftarrows}} HCO_3^-(aq) + H_3O^+(aq)$$

The K_a expression for carbonic acid at 25 °C is

$$K_a = \frac{[H_3O^+][HCO_3^-]}{[H_2CO_3]} = 4.3 \times 10^{-7}$$

The K_a measured for carbonic acid is small, which confirms that the equilibrium of carbonic acid in water favors the reactants. (Recall that the concentration units are omitted in the values given for equilibrium constants.)

We can conclude that weak acids will have small K_a values because their equilibria favor the reactants. The smaller the K_a value, the weaker the acid. On the other hand, strong acids, which are essentially 100% dissociated, have large K_a values, although these values are not usually measured. Table 10.4 gives some K_a values for selected weak acids.

TUTORIAL
Using Dissociation Constants

TABLE 10.4 K_a Values for Selected Weak Acids

Name	Formula	K_a
Phosphoric acid	H_3PO_4	7.5×10^{-3}
Hydrofluoric acid	HF	7.2×10^{-4}
Nitrous acid	HNO_2	4.5×10^{-4}
Formic acid	$HCHO_2$	1.8×10^{-4}
Acetic acid	$HC_2H_3O_2$	1.8×10^{-5}
Carbonic acid	H_2CO_3	4.3×10^{-7}
Dihydrogen phosphate	$H_2PO_4^-$	6.2×10^{-8}
Hydrocyanic acid	HCN	4.9×10^{-10}
Bicarbonate	HCO_3^-	5.6×10^{-11}
Hydrogen phosphate	HPO_4^{2-}	2.2×10^{-13}

We have described strong and weak acids in several ways. Table 10.5 summarizes the characteristics of acids in terms of strength and equilibrium position.

TABLE 10.5 Characteristics of Acids

Characteristic	Strong Acids	Weak Acids
Equilibrium position	Toward ionized products	Toward unionized reactants
K_a	Large	Small
$[H_3O^+]$ and $[A^-]$	100% of initial [HA]	Small percent of initial [HA]
Conjugate bases	Weak	Strong

CONCEPT CHECK 10.3

■ Acid Dissociation Constants

Acid HX has a K_a of 4.0×10^{-4}, and acid HY has K_a of 8.0×10^{-6}. If each acid has a 0.10 M concentration, which solution has the higher concentration of H_3O^+?

ANSWER

Acid HX has a larger K_a value than acid HY. When acid HX dissolves in water, there is more dissociation of HX, which gives a higher concentration of H_3O^+ and X^- ions in solution.

SAMPLE PROBLEM 10.6

■ Writing Acid Dissociation Constants

Write the expression for the acid dissociation constant for nitrous acid.

SOLUTION

The equation for the dissociation of nitrous acid is written

$$HNO_2(aq) + H_2O(l) \rightleftharpoons H_3O^+(aq) + NO_2^-(aq)$$

The acid dissociation constant is written as the concentrations of the products divided by the concentration of the undissociated weak acid:

$$K_a = \frac{[H_3O^+][NO_2^-]}{[HNO_2]}$$

STUDY CHECK

Which is the stronger acid, nitrous acid or carbonic acid? Why?

QUESTIONS AND PROBLEMS

Strengths of Acids and Bases

10.15 What is meant by the phrase, "A strong acid has a weak conjugate base"?

10.16 What is meant by the phrase, "A weak acid has a strong conjugate base"?

10.17 Identify the stronger acid in each pair:
  a. HBr or HNO_2
  b. H_3PO_4 or HSO_4^-
  c. HCN or H_2CO_3

10.18 Identify the stronger acid in each pair:
  a. NH_4^+ or H_3O^+
  b. H_2SO_4 or HCN
  c. H_2O or H_2CO_3

10.19 Identify the weaker acid in each pair:
  a. HCl or HSO_4^-
  b. HNO_2 or HF
  c. HCO_3^- or NH_4^+

10.20 Identify the weaker acid in each pair:
  a. HNO_3 or HCO_3^-
  b. HSO_4^- or H_2O
  c. H_2SO_4 or H_2CO_3

10.21 Predict whether the equilibrium for each of the following reactions favors the reactants or the products:
  a. $H_2CO_3(aq) + H_2O(l) \rightleftharpoons H_3O^+(aq) + HCO_3^-(aq)$
  b. $NH_4^+(aq) + H_2O(l) \rightleftharpoons H_3O^+(aq) + NH_3(aq)$
  c. $HCl(aq) + NH_3(aq) \rightleftharpoons Cl^-(aq) + NH_4^+(aq)$

10.22 Predict whether the equilibrium for each of the following reactions favors the reactants or the products:
  a. $H_3PO_4(aq) + H_2O(l) \rightleftharpoons H_3O^+(aq) + H_2PO_4^-(aq)$
  b. $CO_3^{2-}(aq) + H_2O(l) \rightleftharpoons OH^-(aq) + HCO_3^-(aq)$
  c. $HS^-(aq) + H_2O(l) \rightleftharpoons H_3O^+(aq) + S^{2-}(aq)$

10.23 Write an equation for the acid–base reaction between ammonium ion and sulfate ion. Why does the equilibrium favor the reactants?

10.24 Write an equation for the acid–base reaction between nitrous acid and sulfate ion. Why does the equilibrium favor the reactants?

10.25 Consider the following acids and their dissociation constants:

$$H_2SO_3(aq) + H_2O(l) \rightleftharpoons H_3O^+(aq) + HSO_3^-(aq)$$
$$K_a = 1.2 \times 10^{-2}$$
$$HS^-(aq) + H_2O(l) \rightleftharpoons H_3O^+(aq) + S^{2-}(aq)$$
$$K_a = 1.3 \times 10^{-19}$$

  a. Which is the stronger acid, H_2SO_3 or HS^-?
  b. What is the conjugate base of H_2SO_3?
  c. Which acid has the weaker conjugate base?
  d. Which acid has the stronger conjugate base?
  e. Which acid produces more ions?

10.26 Consider the following acids and their dissociation constants:

$$HPO_4^{2-}(aq) + H_2O(l) \rightleftharpoons H_3O^+(aq) + PO_4^{3-}(aq)$$
$$K_a = 2.2 \times 10^{-13}$$
$$HCHO_2(aq) + H_2O(l) \rightleftharpoons H_3O^+(aq) + CHO_2^-(aq)$$
$$K_a = 1.8 \times 10^{-4}$$

  a. Which is the weaker acid, HPO_4^{2-} or $HCHO_2$?
  b. What is the conjugate base of HPO_4^{2-}?
  c. Which acid has the weaker conjugate base?
  d. Which acid has the stronger conjugate base?
  e. Which acid produces more ions?

10.27 Phosphoric acid reacts with water to form dihydrogen phosphate and hydronium ion. Write the equation and equilibrium expression for the dissociation of the acid.

10.28 Carbonic acid, a weak acid, reacts with water to form bicarbonate and hydronium ion. Write the equation and equilibrium expression for the dissociation of the acid.

10.3 Ionization of Water

We have seen that in acid–base reactions water is amphoteric; it can act either as an acid or as a base. Does this observation mean that water can be both an acid and a base? Yes, this is exactly what happens with water molecules in pure water. Let's see how this happens. One water molecule acts as an acid by donating a H^+ to another water molecule, which acts as a base. The products are the conjugate acid H_3O^+ and the conjugate base OH^-. Let's take a look at the conjugate acid–base pairs of water:

LEARNING GOAL

Use the ion-product constant of water to calculate the $[H_3O^+]$ and $[OH^-]$ in an aqueous solution.

TUTORIAL
Ionization of Water

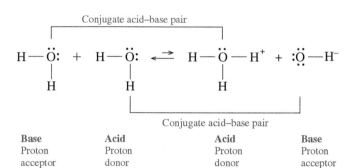

| Base | Acid | Acid | Base |
| Proton acceptor | Proton donor | Proton donor | Proton acceptor |

FIGURE 10.3 In a neutral solution, $[H_3O^+]$ and $[OH^-]$ are equal. In acidic solutions, the $[H_3O^+]$ is greater than the $[OH^-]$. In basic solutions, the $[OH^-]$ is greater than the $[H_3O^+]$.

Q Is a solution that has $[H_3O^+] = 1.0 \times 10^{-3}$ M acidic, basic, or neutral?

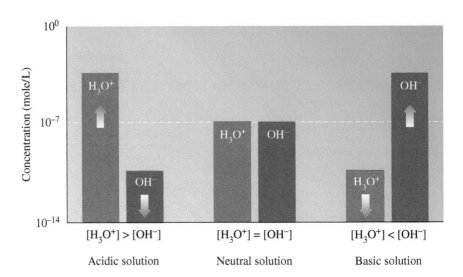

In the ionization of water, there is both a forward and a reverse reaction:

$$H_2O(l) + H_2O(l) \rightleftharpoons H_3O^+(aq) + OH^-(aq)$$

Every time a H^+ is transferred between two water molecules, the products are one H_3O^+ and one OH^-. Experiments have determined that in pure water the concentrations of H_3O^+ and OH^- at 25 °C are each 1.0×10^{-7} M. Square brackets around the symbols indicate their concentrations in moles per liter (M):

Pure water $[H_3O^+] = [OH^-] = 1.0 \times 10^{-7}$ M

When we multiply these concentrations, it forms the **ion-product constant of water**, K_w, which is 1.0×10^{-14} at 25 °C. The concentration units are omitted in the K_w value.

$$K_w = [H_3O^+] \times [OH^-]$$
$$= (1.0 \times 10^{-7}\,M)(1.0 \times 10^{-7}\,M) = 1.0 \times 10^{-14}$$

The K_w value of 1.0×10^{-14} is important because it applies to any aqueous solution at 25 °C: all aqueous solutions have H_3O^+ and OH^-.

When the $[H_3O^+]$ and $[OH^-]$ in a solution are equal, the solution is **neutral**. However, most solutions are not neutral and have different concentrations of $[H_3O^+]$ and $[OH^-]$. If acid is added to water, there is an increase in $[H_3O^+]$ and a decrease in $[OH^-]$, which makes an acidic solution. If base is added, $[OH^-]$ increases and $[H_3O^+]$ decreases, which makes a basic solution. (See Figure 10.3.) However, for any aqueous solution, whether it is neutral, acidic, or basic, the product $[H_3O^+] \times [OH^-]$ is equal to K_w (1.0×10^{-14}) at 25 °C. Therefore, if the $[H_3O^+]$ is given, K_w can be used to calculate the $[OH^-]$. Or if the $[OH^-]$ is given, K_w can be used to calculate the $[H_3O^+]$. (See Table 10.6.)

$$K_w = [H_3O^+] \times [OH^-]$$

$$[OH^-] = \frac{K_w}{[H_3O^+]} \qquad\qquad [H_3O^+] = \frac{K_w}{[OH^-]}$$

TABLE 10.6 Examples of $[H_3O^+]$ and $[OH^-]$ in Neutral, Acidic, and Basic Solutions

Type of Solution	$[H_3O^+]$	$[OH^-]$	K_w (25 °C)
Neutral	1.0×10^{-7} M	1.0×10^{-7} M	1.0×10^{-14}
Acidic	1.0×10^{-2} M	1.0×10^{-12} M	1.0×10^{-14}
Acidic	2.5×10^{-5} M	4.0×10^{-10} M	1.0×10^{-14}
Basic	1.0×10^{-8} M	1.0×10^{-6} M	1.0×10^{-14}
Basic	5.0×10^{-11} M	2.0×10^{-4} M	1.0×10^{-14}

To illustrate these calculations, let's determine the $[H_3O^+]$ for a solution that has an $[OH^-] = 1.0 \times 10^{-6}$ M.

STEP 1   **Write the K_w for water:**

$$K_w = [H_3O^+][OH^-] = 1.0 \times 10^{-14}$$

STEP 2   **Rearrange the K_w to solve for the unknown.**   Dividing through by the $[OH^-]$ gives

$$\frac{K_w}{[OH^-]} = \frac{[H_3O^+] \times [\cancel{OH^-}]}{[\cancel{OH^-}]}$$

$$[H_3O^+] = \frac{1.0 \times 10^{-14}}{[OH^-]}$$

STEP 3   **Substitute the $[OH^-]$ and calculate the $[H_3O^+]$:**

$$[H_3O^+] = \frac{1.0 \times 10^{-14}}{[1.0 \times 10^{-6}]} = 1.0 \times 10^{-8} \text{ M}$$

Because the $[OH^-]$ of 1.0×10^{-6} M is larger than the $[H_3O^+]$ of 1.0×10^{-8} M, the solution is basic.

SAMPLE PROBLEM   10.7

■ Calculating $[H_3O^+]$ and $[OH^-]$ in Solution

A vinegar solution has a $[H_3O^+] = 2.0 \times 10^{-3}$ M at 25 °C. What is the $[OH^-]$ of the vinegar solution? Is the solution acidic, basic, or neutral?

SOLUTION

STEP 1   **Write the K_w for water:**

$$K_w = [H_3O^+] \times [OH^-] = 1.0 \times 10^{-14}$$

STEP 2   **Arrange the K_w to solve for the unknown.**   Rearranging the K_w for OH^- gives

$$\frac{K_w}{[H_3O^+]} = \frac{[\cancel{H_3O^+}] \times [OH^-]}{[\cancel{H_3O^+}]}$$

$$[OH^-] = \frac{1.0 \times 10^{-14}}{[H_3O^+]}$$

STEP 3   **Substitute the known $[H_3O^+]$ and calculate:**

$$[OH^-] = \frac{1.0 \times 10^{-14}}{[2.0 \times 10^{-3}]} = 5.0 \times 10^{-12} \text{ M}$$

Because the $[H_3O^+]$ of 2.0×10^{-3} M is much larger than the $[OH^-]$ of 5.0×10^{-12} M, the solution is acidic.

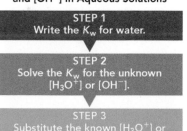

Guide to Calculating $[H_3O^+]$ and $[OH^-]$ in Aqueous Solutions

STEP 1
Write the K_w for water.

STEP 2
Solve the K_w for the unknown $[H_3O^+]$ or $[OH^-]$.

STEP 3
Substitute the known $[H_3O^+]$ or $[OH^-]$ and calculate.

STUDY CHECK

What is the $[H_3O^+]$ of an ammonia cleaning solution with an $[OH^-] = 4.0 \times 10^{-4}$ M? Is the solution acidic, basic, or neutral?

QUESTIONS AND PROBLEMS

Ionization of Water

10.29 Why are the concentrations of H_3O^+ and OH^- equal in pure water?

10.30 What is the meaning and value of K_w?

10.31 In an acidic solution, how does the concentration of H_3O^+ compare to the concentration of OH^-?

10.32 If a base is added to pure water, why does the $[H_3O^+]$ decrease?

10.33 Indicate whether the following are acidic, basic, or neutral solutions at 25 °C:
  a. $[H_3O^+] = 2.0 \times 10^{-5}$ M
  b. $[H_3O^+] = 1.4 \times 10^{-9}$ M
  c. $[OH^-] = 8.0 \times 10^{-3}$ M
  d. $[OH^-] = 3.5 \times 10^{-10}$ M

10.34 Indicate whether the following are acidic, basic, or neutral solutions at 25 °C:
  a. $[H_3O^+] = 6.0 \times 10^{-12}$ M
  b. $[H_3O^+] = 1.4 \times 10^{-4}$ M
  c. $[OH^-] = 5.0 \times 10^{-12}$ M
  d. $[OH^-] = 4.5 \times 10^{-2}$ M

10.35 Calculate the $[H_3O^+]$ of each aqueous solution with the following $[OH^-]$ at 25 °C:

  a. coffee, 1.0×10^{-9} M
  b. soap, 1.0×10^{-6} M
  c. cleanser, 2.0×10^{-5} M
  d. lemon juice, 4.0×10^{-13} M

10.36 Calculate the $[H_3O^+]$ of each aqueous solution with the following $[OH^-]$ at 25 °C:
  a. NaOH, 1.0×10^{-2} M
  b. aspirin, 1.8×10^{-11} M
  c. milk of magnesia, 1.0×10^{-5} M
  d. sea water, 2.5×10^{-6} M

10.37 Calculate the $[OH^-]$ of each aqueous solution with the following $[H_3O^+]$ at 25 °C:
  a. vinegar, 1.0×10^{-3} M
  b. urine, 5.0×10^{-6} M
  c. ammonia, 1.8×10^{-12} M
  d. NaOH, 4.0×10^{-13} M

10.38 Calculate the $[OH^-]$ of each aqueous solution with the following $[H_3O^+]$ at 25 °C:
  a. baking soda, 1.0×10^{-8} M
  b. orange juice, 2.0×10^{-4} M
  c. milk, 5.0×10^{-7} M
  d. bleach, 4.8×10^{-12} M

10.4 The pH Scale

LEARNING GOAL

Calculate pH from $[H_3O^+]$; given the pH, calculate the $[H_3O^+]$ and $[OH^-]$ of a solution.

 CASE STUDY
Hyperventilation and Blood pH

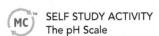 **SELF STUDY ACTIVITY**
The pH Scale

Many kinds of careers such as respiratory therapy, food processing, medicine, agriculture, spa and pool maintenance, and soap manufacturing require personnel to measure the $[H_3O^+]$ and $[OH^-]$ of solutions. The proper levels of acidity are necessary for soil to support plant growth, and to prevent algae in swimming pool water. Measuring the acidity levels of blood and urine checks the function of the kidneys.

On the pH scale, a number between 0 and 14 represents the H_3O^+ concentration for most solutions. A neutral solution has a pH of 7.0 at 25 °C. An acidic solution has a pH value less than 7. A basic solution has a pH value greater than 7. (See Figure 10.4.)

Acidic solution	pH < 7	$[H_3O^+] > 1.0 \times 10^{-7}$ M
Neutral solution	pH = 7	$[H_3O^+] = 1.0 \times 10^{-7}$ M
Basic solution	pH > 7	$[H_3O^+] < 1.0 \times 10^{-7}$ M

In the laboratory, a pH meter is commonly used to determine the pH of a solution. There are also various indicators and pH papers that turn specific colors when placed in solutions of different pH values. The pH is found by comparing the colors to a color chart. (See Figure 10.5.)

CONCEPT CHECK 10.4

■ pH of Solutions

Consider the pH of the following items:

Item	pH
Rootbeer	5.8
Kitchen cleaner	10.9
Pickles	3.5
Glass cleaner	7.6
Cranberry juice	2.9

a. Place the pH values of the preceding items in order of most acidic to most basic.
b. Which item has the highest $[H_3O^+]$?
c. Which item has the highest $[OH^-]$?

ANSWER

a. The most acidic item is the one with the lowest pH, and the most basic is the item with the highest pH: cranberry juice (2.9), pickles (3.5), rootbeer (5.8), glass cleaner (7.6), kitchen cleaner (10.9).
b. The item with the highest $[H_3O^+]$ would have the lowest pH value, which is cranberry juice.
c. The item with the highest $[OH^-]$ would have the highest pH value, which is kitchen cleaner.

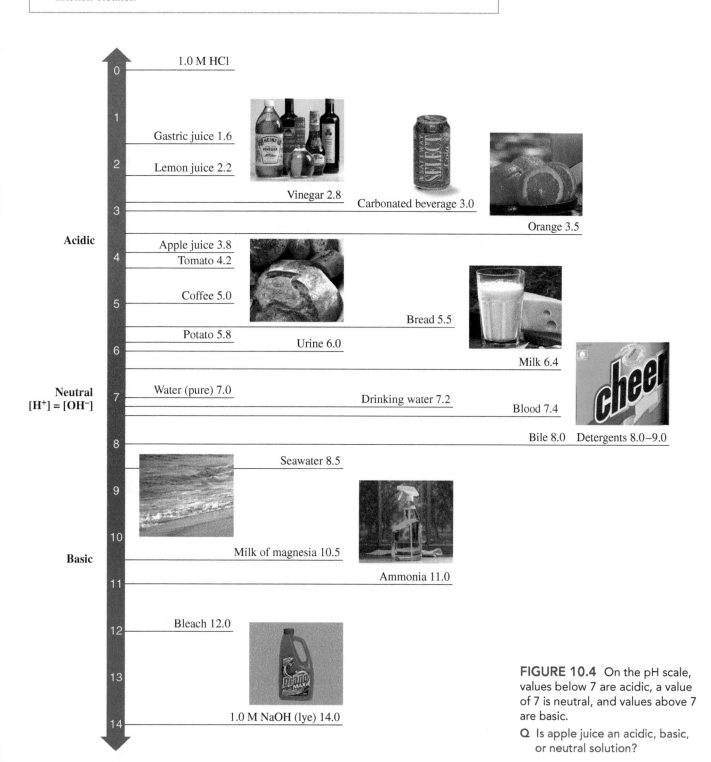

FIGURE 10.4 On the pH scale, values below 7 are acidic, a value of 7 is neutral, and values above 7 are basic.

Q Is apple juice an acidic, basic, or neutral solution?

(a)

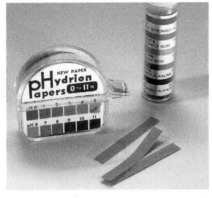
(b)

(c)

FIGURE 10.5 The pH of a solution can be determined using **(a)** a pH meter, **(b)** pH paper, and **(c)** indicators that turn different colors corresponding to different pH values.

Q If a pH meter reads 4.00, is the solution acidic, basic, or neutral?

Calculating the pH of Solutions

MC **TUTORIAL**
Logarithms

MC **TUTORIAL**
The pH Scale

The pH scale is a log scale that corresponds to the hydrogen-ion concentrations of aqueous solutions. Mathematically, **pH** is the negative logarithm (base 10) of the H_3O^+ concentration:

$$pH = -\log[H_3O^+]$$

Essentially, the negative powers of 10 in the molar concentrations are converted to positive numbers. For example, a lemon juice solution with $[H_3O^+] = 1.0 \times 10^{-2}$ M has a pH of 2.00. This can be calculated using the pH equation:

$$pH = -\log[1.0 \times 10^{-2}]$$

$$pH = -(-2.00)$$

$$= 2.00$$

The number of *decimal places* in the pH value is the same as the number of significant figures in the $[H_3O^+]$.

$$[H_3O^+] = \mathbf{1.0} \times 10^{-2} \qquad pH = \mathbf{2.00}$$

Two significant figures   Two decimal places

HEALTH NOTE

Stomach Acid, HCl

When a person sees, smells, thinks about, or tastes food, the gastric glands in the stomach begin to secrete a strongly acidic solution of HCl. In a single day, a person may secrete as much as 2000 mL of gastric juice.

The HCl in the gastric juice activates a digestive enzyme called *pepsin* that breaks down proteins in food entering the stomach. The secretion of HCl continues until the stomach has a pH of about 2, which is the optimum pH for activating the digestive enzymes without ulcerating the stomach lining. Normally, large quantities of viscous mucus are secreted within the stomach to protect its lining from acid and enzyme damage.

CONCEPT CHECK 10.5

■ Calculating pH

Indicate if the pH values given for the following are correct or incorrect, and state why:

a. $[H_3O^+] = 1 \times 10^{-6}$ pH = −6.0
b. $[OH^-] = 1.0 \times 10^{-10}$ pH = 10.00
c. $[H_3O^+] = 1.0 \times 10^{-6}$ pH = 6.00
d. $[OH^-] = 1 \times 10^{-2}$ pH = 12.0

ANSWER

a. Incorrect. The pH of this solution is 6.0, which has a positive value, not negative.
b. Incorrect. The pH is calculated from the $[H_3O^+]$, not $[OH^-]$. This solution has a $[H_3O^+]$ of 1.0×10^{-4}, for a pH of 4.00. There are two zeros after the decimal point to match the two significant figures in the coefficient of 1.0.
c. Correct. The pH has two zeros after the decimal point to match the two significant figures in the coefficient of 1.0.
d. Correct. The pH is calculated from the $[H_3O^+] = 1 \times 10^{-12}$ with one zero after the decimal point to match the one significant figure in the coefficient.

Steps for a pH Calculation

The pH of a solution is determined using the *log* key and *changing the sign*. For example, to calculate the pH of a vinegar solution with $[H_3O^+] = 2.4 \times 10^{-3}$ M, you can use the following steps:

Display Shows

STEP 1 **Enter the $[H_3O^+]$ value.** Enter 2.4 and press $\boxed{\text{EE or EXP}}$. $2.4^{\,00}$ or $2.4\,00$ or $2.4\,E00$

Enter 3 and press $\boxed{+/-}$ to change the power $2.4^{\,-03}$ or $2.4-03$ or $2.4\,E-03$

to −3. (For calculators without a change sign key, consult the instructions for the calculator.)

STEP 2 **Press the $\boxed{\text{log}}$ key.** -2.619789

Change the sign. 2.619789

The steps can be combined to give the calculator sequence as follows:

$$pH = -\log[2.4 \times 10^{-3}] = 2.4 \; \boxed{\text{EE or EXP}} \; 3 \; \boxed{+/-} \; \boxed{\text{log}} \; \boxed{+/-}$$
$$= 2.619789$$

Be sure to check the instructions for your calculator. On some calculators, the numbers are entered as they appear in the pH expression as follows:

$$-2.4 \; \boxed{\text{log}} \; \boxed{\text{EE}} \; -03$$

STEP 3 **Adjust significant figures.** In a pH value, the number to the *left* of the decimal point is an *exact* number derived from the power of ten. The number of digits to the *right* of the decimal point is equal to the number of significant figures in the coefficient:

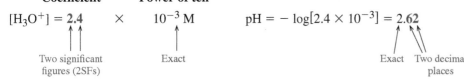

Coefficient   Power of ten

$[H_3O^+] = \mathbf{2.4} \quad \times \quad 10^{-3} \text{ M} \qquad pH = -\log[2.4 \times 10^{-3}] = \mathbf{2.62}$

Two significant   Exact   Exact   Two decimal
figures (2SFs)   places

Because pH is a log scale, a change of one pH unit corresponds to a ten-fold change in $[H_3O^+]$. It is important to note that the pH decreases as the $[H_3O^+]$ increases. For example, a solution with a pH of 2.00 has a $[H_3O^+]$ 10 times higher than a solution with a pH of 3.00, and 100 times higher than a solution with a pH of 4.00.

SAMPLE PROBLEM 10.8

■ Calculating pH

Determine the pH for the following solutions:

a. $[H_3O^+] = 1.0 \times 10^{-5}$ M **b.** $[H_3O^+] = 5 \times 10^{-8}$ M

SOLUTION

a. STEP 1 **Enter the $[H_3O^+]$:**

Display

$1.0 \; \boxed{\text{EE or EXP}} \; 5 \; \boxed{+/-}$ $1.0^{\,-05}$ or $1.0-05$ or $1.0\,E-05$

STEP 2 **Press the *log* key and the *change sign* key:**

$\boxed{\text{log}} \quad \boxed{+/-}$ 5

STEP 3 **Adjust the number of digits to the *right* of the decimal point to equal the number of significant figures in the coefficient:**

1.0×10^{-5} M pH = 5.00

2 SFs $\longrightarrow$ 2 digits to the *right* of the decimal point

b. STEP 1 **Enter the $[H_3O^+]$:**

Display

5 (EE or EXP) 8 (+/−)　　　5^{-08} or $5-08$ or $5E-08$

STEP 2 **Press the *log* key and the *change sign* key:**

(log) (+/−)　　　　　　　　7.301029

STEP 3 **Adjust the number of digits to the *right* of the decimal point to equal the significant figures in the coefficient:**

5×10^{-8} M　　pH = 7.3

1 SF ────────→ 1 digit to the *right* of the decimal point

STUDY CHECK

What is the pH of bleach with $[H_3O^+] = 4.2 \times 10^{-12}$ M?

SAMPLE PROBLEM　10.9

■ **Calculating pH from $[OH^-]$**

What is the pH of an ammonia solution at 25 °C with $[OH^-] = 3.7 \times 10^{-3}$ M?

SOLUTION

STEP 1 **Enter the $[H_3O^+]$.** Because $[OH^-]$ is given for the ammonia solution, we have to calculate $[H_3O^+]$ using the ion-product constant of water, K_w. Dividing through by $[OH^-]$ gives $[H_3O^+]$.

$$\frac{K_w}{[OH^-]} = \frac{[H_3O^+]\,[\cancel{OH^-}]}{[\cancel{OH^-}]}$$

$$[H_3O^+] = \frac{1.0 \times 10^{-14}}{[3.7 \times 10^{-3}]} = 2.7 \times 10^{-12} \text{ M}$$

Display

2.7 (EE or EXP) 12 (+/−) = 2.7^{-12} or $2.7-12$ or $2.7\,E-12$

STEP 2 **Press the *log* key, and then the *change sign* key:**

(log)　(+/−)　　　　　　　11.56863

STEP 3 **Adjust the number of digits to the *right* of the decimal point to equal the SFs in the coefficient:**

2.7×10^{-12} M　　pH = 11.57

2 SFs ────────→ 2 digits *after* the decimal point

STUDY CHECK

Calculate the pH of a sample of acid rain that has $[OH^-] = 2 \times 10^{-10}$ M.

Calculating $[H_3O^+]$ from pH

In another calculation, we are given the pH of a solution and asked to determine the $[H_3O^+]$. This is a reverse of the pH calculation:

$[H_3O^+] = 10^{-pH}$

For pH values that are not whole numbers, the calculation requires the use of the *10^x* key, which is usually a 2nd function key. On some calculators, this operation is done using the *inverse* key and the *log* key.

SAMPLE PROBLEM 10.10

■ **Calculating [H₃O⁺] from pH**

Calculate $[H_3O^+]$ for each of the following solutions:

a. coffee, pH of 5.0
b. baking soda, pH of 8.25

SOLUTION

a. coffee, pH of 5.0

STEP 1 **Enter the pH value and press the *change sign* key:**

                                                        Display

        5.0 (+/−)   −5.0

STEP 2 **Convert −pH to concentration.** Press the *2nd function* key and then the *10ˣ* key:

        (2nd) (10ˣ)   0.00001 or $1.^{-05}$ or $1 − 05$

Or press the *inverse* key and then the *log* key:

        (inv) (log)   0.00001 or $1.^{-05}$ or $1 − 05$

On some calculators, the numbers are entered as they appear:

        $10^x − 5.0$

Write the display in scientific notation with units of concentration: 1×10^{-5} M.

STEP 3 **Adjust the significant figures in the coefficient.** The pH value of 5.0 has only one digit to the *right* of the decimal point, which means the $[H_3O^+]$ is written with only one significant figure:

        $[H_3O^+] = 1 \times 10^{-5}$ M

b. baking soda, pH of 8.25

STEP 1 **Enter the pH value and press the *change sign* key:**

                                                        Display

        8.25 (+/−)   −8.25

STEP 2 **Convert −pH to concentration.** Press the *2nd function* key and then the *10ˣ* key.

        (2nd) (10ˣ) 5.62341^{-09} or $5.62341 − 09$ or 5.62341 E-09

Or press the *inverse* key and then the *log* key.

        (inv) (log) 5.62341^{-09} or $5.62341 − 09$ or 5.62341 E-09

Write the display in scientific notation with units of concentration: 5.62341×10^{-9} M.

STEP 3 **Adjust the significant figures in the coefficient.** Because the pH value of 8.25 has two digits to the *right* of the decimal point, the $[H_3O^+]$ is written with two significant figures:

        $[H_3O^+] = 5.6 \times 10^{-9}$ M

STUDY CHECK

What is the $[H_3O^+]$ and $[OH^-]$ of a beer that has a pH of 4.50?

A comparison of $[H_3O^+]$, $[OH^-]$, and their corresponding pH values is given in Table 10.7.

TABLE 10.7 A Comparison of $[H_3O^+]$, $[OH^-]$, and Corresponding pH Values at 25 °C

$[H_3O^+]$	pH	$[OH^-]$	
10^0	0	10^{-14}	
10^{-1}	1	10^{-13}	
10^{-2}	2	10^{-12}	
10^{-3}	3	10^{-11}	Acidic
10^{-4}	4	10^{-10}	
10^{-5}	5	10^{-9}	
10^{-6}	6	10^{-8}	
10^{-7}	7	10^{-7}	Neutral
10^{-8}	8	10^{-6}	
10^{-9}	9	10^{-5}	
10^{-10}	10	10^{-4}	
10^{-11}	11	10^{-3}	Basic
10^{-12}	12	10^{-2}	
10^{-13}	13	10^{-1}	
10^{-14}	14	10^0	

QUESTIONS AND PROBLEMS

The pH Scale

10.39 Why does a neutral solution have a pH of 7.00 at 25 °C?

10.40 If you know the $[OH^-]$, how can you determine the pH of a solution?

10.41 State whether each of the following solutions is acidic, basic, or neutral:
  a. blood, pH 7.38   b. vinegar, pH 2.8
  c. drain cleaner, pH 11.2 d. coffee, pH 5.5
  e. tomatoes, pH 4.2   f. chocolate cake, pH 7.6

10.42 State whether each of the following solutions is acidic, basic, or neutral:
  a. soda, pH 3.2
  b. shampoo, pH 5.7
  c. laundry detergent, pH 9.4
  d. rain, pH 5.8
  e. honey, pH 3.9
  f. cheese, pH 7.4

10.43 Calculate the pH of each solution given the following $[H_3O^+]$ or $[OH^-]$ values:
  a. $[H_3O^+] = 1.0 \times 10^{-4}$ M
  b. $[H_3O^+] = 3.0 \times 10^{-9}$ M
  c. $[OH^-] = 1.0 \times 10^{-5}$ M
  d. $[OH^-] = 2.5 \times 10^{-11}$ M
  e. $[H_3O^+] = 6.7 \times 10^{-8}$ M
  f. $[OH^-] = 8.2 \times 10^{-4}$ M

10.44 Calculate the pH of each solution given the following $[H_3O^+]$ or $[OH^-]$ values:
  a. $[H_3O^+] = 1.0 \times 10^{-8}$ M

  b. $[H_3O^+] = 5.0 \times 10^{-6}$ M
  c. $[OH^-] = 4.0 \times 10^{-2}$ M
  d. $[OH^-] = 8.0 \times 10^{-3}$ M
  e. $[H_3O^+] = 4.7 \times 10^{-2}$ M
  f. $[OH^-] = 3.9 \times 10^{-6}$ M

10.45 Complete the following table:

$[H_3O^+]$	$[OH^-]$	pH	Acidic, Basic, or Neutral?
	1.0×10^{-6} M		
		3.00	
2.8×10^{-5} M			
		4.62	

10.46 Complete the following table:

$[H_3O^+]$	$[OH^-]$	pH	Acidic, Basic, or Neutral?
		10.00	
			Neutral
6.4×10^{-12} M			
		11.3	

EXPLORE YOUR WORLD

Using Vegetables and Flowers as pH Indicators

Many flowers and vegetables with strong color, especially reds and purples, contain compounds that change color with changes in pH. Some examples are red cabbage, cranberry juice, and cranberry drinks.

Materials Needed

Red cabbage, water, and a saucepan; or cranberry juice or drinks

Several glasses or small glass containers, and some tape and a pen or pencil to mark the containers

Several colorless household solutions such as vinegar, lemon juice, other fruit juices; baking soda; antacids; aspirin; window cleaners; soaps; shampoos; and detergents

Procedure

1. Obtain a bottle of cranberry juice or cranberry drink, or use red cabbage to prepare the red cabbage pH indicator as follows: Tear up several red cabbage leaves and place them in a saucepan and cover with water. Boil for about 5 minutes. Cool and collect the purple solution.

2. Place small amounts of each household solution into separate clear glass containers, and mark what each one is. If the sample is a solid or a thick liquid, add a small amount of water. Add some cranberry juice or some red cabbage indicator until you obtain a color.

3. Observe the colors of the various samples. The colors that indicate acidic solutions are the red and pink colors (pH 1–4) and the pink to lavender colors (pH 5–6). A neutral solution has about the same purple color as the indicator. Bases will give blue to green color (pH 8–11) or a yellow color (pH 12–13).

4. Arrange your samples by color and pH. Classify each of the solutions as acidic (pH 1–6), neutral (pH 7), or basic (pH 8–13).

5. Try to make an indicator using other colorful fruits or flowers.

QUESTIONS

1. Which products that tested acidic listed an acid on their labels?
2. Which products that tested basic listed a base on their labels?
3. How many products were neutral?
4. Which flowers or vegetables behaved as indicators?

10.5 Reactions of Acids and Bases

Typical reactions of acids and bases include the reactions of acids with metals, bases, and carbonate or bicarbonate ions. For example, when you drop an antacid tablet in water, the bicarbonate ion and citric acid in the tablet react to produce carbon dioxide bubbles, a salt, and water.

LEARNING GOAL

Write balanced equations for reactions of acids with metals, carbonates, and bases.

Acids and Metals

Acids react with certain metals to produce hydrogen gas (H_2) and a salt, which is an ionic compound that does not contain H^+ or OH^-. Metals that react with acids include potassium, sodium, calcium, magnesium, aluminum, zinc, iron, and tin. In these single replacement reactions, the metal ion replaces the hydrogen in the acid:

(MC) SELF STUDY ACTIVITY
Nature of Acids and Bases

$$Mg(s) + 2HCl(aq) \longrightarrow MgCl_2(aq) + H_2(g)$$
Metal   Acid   Salt   Hydrogen

$$Zn(s) + 2HCl(aq) \longrightarrow ZnCl_2(aq) + H_2(g)$$
Metal   Acid   Salt   Hydrogen

Acids and Carbonates

When an acid is added to a carbonate or bicarbonate (hydrogen carbonate), the products are carbon dioxide gas, water, and an ionic compound (salt). The acid reacts with CO_3^{2-} or HCO_3^- to produce carbonic acid, H_2CO_3, which breaks down rapidly to CO_2 and H_2O. The net ionic equation is written by omitting the metal ions and chloride ions that are not reacting:

$$2HCl(aq) + Na_2CO_3(aq) \longrightarrow CO_2(g) + H_2O(l) + 2NaCl(aq)$$
Acid   Carbonate   Carbon dioxide   Water   Salt

$$HCl(aq) + NaHCO_3(aq) \longrightarrow CO_2(g) + H_2O(l) + NaCl(aq)$$
Acid   Bicarbonate   Carbon dioxide   Water   Salt

GREEN CHEMISTRY NOTE

Acid Rain

Natural rain is slightly acidic, with a pH of 5.6. In the atmosphere, carbon dioxide combines with water to form carbonic acid, a weak acid, which dissociates to give hydronium ions and bicarbonate:

$$CO_2(g) + H_2O(l) \rightleftharpoons H_2CO_3(aq)$$

$$H_2CO_3(aq) + H_2O(l) \rightleftharpoons H_3O^+(aq) + HCO_3^-(aq)$$

However, in many parts of the world, rain has become considerably more acidic. *Acid rain* is a term given to precipitation such as rain, snow, hail, or fog in which the water has a pH that is less than 5.6. In the United States, pH values of rain have decreased to about 4–4.5. In some parts of the world, pH values have been reported as low as 2.6, which is about as acidic as lemon juice or vinegar. Because the calculation of pH involves powers of 10, a pH value of 2.6 would be 1000 times more acidic than natural rain.

Although natural sources such as volcanoes and forest fires release SO_2, the primary sources of acid rain today are from the burning of fossil fuels in automobiles and coal in industrial plants. When coal and oil are burned, the sulfur impurities combine with oxygen in the air to produce SO_2 and SO_3. The reaction of SO_3 with water forms sulfuric acid, H_2SO_4, a strong acid:

$$S(g) + O_2(g) \longrightarrow SO_2(g)$$

$$2SO_2(g) + O_2(g) \longrightarrow 2SO_3(g)$$

$$SO_3(g) + H_2O(l) \longrightarrow H_2SO_4(aq)$$

In an effort to decrease the formation of acid rain, legislation has required a reduction in SO_2 emissions. Coal-burning plants have installed equipment called "scrubbers" that absorb SO_2 before it is emitted. In a smokestack, "scrubbing" removes 95% of the SO_2 as the flue gases containing SO_2 pass through limestone ($CaCO_3$) and water. The end product, $CaSO_4$, also called "gypsum," is used in agriculture and to prepare cement products.

Nitrogen oxide forms at high temperatures in the engines of automobiles as air containing nitrogen and oxygen gases is burned. As nitrogen oxide is emitted into the air, it combines with more oxygen to form nitrogen dioxide, which is responsible for the brown color of smog. When nitrogen dioxide dissolves in water in the atmosphere, nitric acid, a strong acid, forms:

$$N_2(g) + O_2(g) \longrightarrow 2NO(g)$$

$$2NO(g) + O_2(g) \longrightarrow 2NO_2(g)$$

$$3NO_2(g) + H_2O(g) \longrightarrow 2HNO_3(aq) + NO(g)$$

Air currents in the atmosphere carry the sulfuric acid and nitric acid many thousands of kilometers before they precipitate in areas

1994

Marble statue in Washington Square Park

far away from the site of the initial contamination. The acids in acid rain have detrimental effects on marble and limestone structures, lakes, and forests. Throughout the world, monuments made of marble (a form of $CaCO_3$) are deteriorating as acid rain dissolves the marble:

$$CaCO_3(s) + H_2SO_4(aq) \longrightarrow CaSO_4(aq) + H_2O(l) + CO_2(g)$$

Acid rain is also changing the pH of many lakes and streams in parts of the United States and Europe. When the pH of a lake falls below 4.5–5, most fish and plant life cannot survive. As the soil near a lake becomes more acidic, aluminum becomes more soluble. Increased levels of aluminum ion in lakes are toxic to fish and other water animals.

Trees and forests are susceptible to acid rain, too. Acid rain breaks down the protective waxy coating on leaves and interferes with photosynthesis. Tree growth is impaired as nutrients and minerals in the soil dissolve and wash away. In Eastern Europe, acid rain is causing an environmental disaster. Nearly 70% of the forests in the Czech Republic have been severely damaged, and some parts of the land are so acidic that crops will not grow.

Acids and Bases

In a reaction called **neutralization**, acids react with bases to produce a salt and water. The H^+ of an acid and the OH^- of a strong base combine to form water as one product. The salt is the cation from the base and the anion from the acid. We can write the following equation for the neutralization reaction between HCl and NaOH:

$$HCl(aq) + NaOH(aq) \longrightarrow NaCl(aq) + H_2O(l)$$

Acid   Base   Salt   Water

If we write the strong acid HCl and the strong base NaOH as ions, we see that H^+ combines with OH^- to form water, leaving the ions Na^+ and Cl^- in solution:

$$H^+(aq) + Cl^-(aq) + Na^+(aq) + OH^-(aq) \longrightarrow$$
$$Na^+(aq) + Cl^-(aq) + H_2O(l) \qquad \text{Ionic equation}$$

Now we omit the ions that do not change during the reaction (spectator ions):

$$H^+(aq) + \cancel{Cl^-(aq)} + \cancel{Na^+(aq)} + OH^-(aq) \longrightarrow$$
$$\cancel{Na^+(aq)} + \cancel{Cl^-(aq)} + H_2O(l)$$

The *net ionic equation* for the neutralization is the reaction of H^+ and OH^- to form H_2O:

$$H^+(aq) + OH^-(aq) \longrightarrow H_2O(l) \qquad \text{Net ionic equation}$$

Balancing Neutralization Equations

In a neutralization reaction, one H^+ always combines with one OH^-. Therefore, coefficients are needed to balance H^+ in the acid with the OH^- in the base. We balance the neutralization of HCl and $Ba(OH)_2$ as follows:

STEP 1   Write the reactants and products:

$$HCl(aq) + Ba(OH)_2(s) \longrightarrow H_2O(l) + \text{salt}$$

STEP 2   Balance the H^+ in the acid with the OH^- in the base.   Placing a 2 in front of the HCl provides $2H^+$ for the $2OH^-$ in $Ba(OH)_2$:

$$2HCl(aq) + Ba(OH)_2(s) \longrightarrow H_2O(l) + \text{salt}$$

STEP 3   Balance the H_2O with the H^+ and OH^-.   Use a coefficient of 2 in front of H_2O to balance $2H^+$ and $2OH^-$.

$$2HCl(aq) + Ba(OH)_2(s) \longrightarrow \mathbf{2}H_2O(l) + \text{salt}$$

STEP 4   Write the salt from the remaining ions in the acid and base.   The ions Ba^{2+} and $2Cl^-$ are used to write the formula of the salt as $BaCl_2$:

$$\mathbf{2HCl}(aq) + \mathbf{Ba(OH)_2}(s) \longrightarrow \mathbf{2H_2O}(l) + \mathbf{BaCl_2}(aq)$$

SAMPLE PROBLEM 10.11

■ Reactions of Acids

Write a balanced equation for the reaction of HCl(*aq*) with each of the following:

a. Al(*s*)   **b.** K_2CO_3(*s*)   **c.** $Mg(OH)_2$(*s*)

SOLUTION

a. Al

STEP 1   Write the reactants and products.   When a metal reacts with an acid, the products are H_2 gas and a salt:

$$Al(s) + HCl(aq) \longrightarrow H_2(g) + \text{salt}$$

STEP 2   Determine the formula of the salt.   When Al(*s*) dissolves, it forms Al^{3+}, which is balanced by $3Cl^-$ from HCl:

$$\mathbf{Al}(s) + HCl(aq) \longrightarrow H_2(g) + \mathbf{AlCl_3}(aq)$$

STEP 3   Balance the equation:

$$\mathbf{2}Al(s) + \mathbf{6}HCl(aq) \longrightarrow \mathbf{3}H_2(g) + \mathbf{2}AlCl_3(aq)$$

b. K_2CO_3

STEP 1 **Write the reactants and products.** When a carbonate reacts with an acid, the products are $CO_2(g)$, $H_2O(l)$, and a salt:

$$K_2CO_3(s) + HCl(aq) \longrightarrow CO_2(g) + H_2O(l) + \text{salt}$$

STEP 2 **Determine the formula of the salt.** When $K_2CO_3(s)$ dissolves, it forms K^+, which is balanced by $1Cl^-$ from HCl:

$$\mathbf{K_2CO_3}(s) + HCl(aq) \longrightarrow CO_2(g) + H_2O(l) + \mathbf{KCl}(aq)$$

STEP 3 **Balance the equation.** A coefficient of 2 in front of KCl balances the 2K in K_2CO_3, and a coefficient of 2 in front of HCl balances the 2 Cl in 2KCl:

$$K_2CO_3(s) + \mathbf{2}HCl(aq) \longrightarrow CO_2(g) + H_2O(l) + \mathbf{2}KCl(aq)$$

c. $Mg(OH)_2$

STEP 1 **Write the reactants and products.** When a base reacts with an acid, the products are $H_2O(l)$ and a salt:

$$Mg(OH)_2(s) + HCl(aq) \longrightarrow H_2O(l) + \text{salt}$$

STEP 2 **Balance the H^+ in the acid with the OH^- in the base.** Placing a 2 in front of the HCl provides $2H^+$ for $2OH^-$ in $Mg(OH)_2$:

$$Mg(OH)_2(s) + \mathbf{2}HCl(aq) \longrightarrow H_2O(l) + \text{salt}$$

STEP 3 **Balance the H_2O with the H^+ and OH^-:**

$$Mg(OH)_2(s) + \mathbf{2}HCl(aq) \longrightarrow \mathbf{2}H_2O(l) + \text{salt}$$

STEP 4 **Write the salt from the remaining ions in the acid and base:**

$$\mathbf{Mg(OH)_2}(s) + \mathbf{2}HCl(aq) \longrightarrow 2H_2O(l) + \mathbf{MgCl_2}(aq)$$

STUDY CHECK

Write the balanced equation for the reaction between H_2SO_4 and $NaHCO_3$.

Guide to Balancing an Equation for Neutralization

> **STEP 1**
> Write the reactants and products.

> **STEP 2**
> Balance the H^+ in the acid with the OH^- in the base.

> **STEP 3**
> Balance the H_2O with the H^+ and the OH^-.

> **STEP 4**
> Write the salt from the remaining ions.

Acid–Base Titration

Suppose we need to find the molarity of an HCl solution of unknown concentration. We can do this by a laboratory procedure called **titration** in which we neutralize an acid sample with a known amount of base. In our titration, we first place a measured volume of the acid in a flask and add a few drops of an *indicator* such as phenolphthalein. An indicator is a compound that dramatically changes color when the pH of the solution changes. In an acidic solution, phenolphthalein is colorless. Then we fill a buret with a NaOH solution of known molarity and carefully add NaOH to the acid in the flask, as shown in Figure 10.6.

In the titration, we neutralize the acid by adding a volume of base that contains a matching number of moles of OH^-. We know that neutralization has taken place when the

FIGURE 10.6 The titration of an acid. A known volume of an acid is placed in a flask with an indicator and titrated with a measured volume of NaOH to the neutralization point.

Q What data is needed to determine the molarity of the acid in the flask?

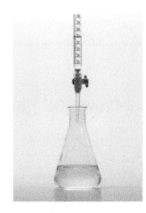

HEALTH NOTE

Antacids

Antacids are substances used to neutralize excess stomach acid (HCl). Some antacids are mixtures of aluminum hydroxide and magnesium hydroxide. These hydroxides are not very soluble in water, so the levels of available OH^- are not damaging to the intestinal tract. However, aluminum hydroxide has the side effects of producing constipation and binding phosphate in the intestinal tract, which may cause weakness and loss of appetite. Magnesium hydroxide has a laxative effect. These side effects are less likely when a combination of the antacids is used.

$$Al(OH)_3(aq) + 3HCl(aq) \longrightarrow AlCl_3(aq) + 3H_2O(l)$$

$$Mg(OH)_2(s) + 2HCl(aq) \longrightarrow MgCl_2(aq) + 2H_2O(l)$$

Some antacids use calcium carbonate to neutralize excess stomach acid. About 10% of the calcium is absorbed into the bloodstream, where it elevates the levels of serum calcium. Calcium carbonate is not recommended for patients who have peptic ulcers or a tendency to form kidney stones.

$$CaCO_3(s) + 2HCl(aq) \longrightarrow H_2O(l) + CO_2(g) + CaCl_2(aq)$$

Still other antacids contain sodium bicarbonate. This type of antacid has a tendency to increase blood pH and elevate sodium levels in the body fluids. It also is not recommended in the treatment of peptic ulcers.

$$NaHCO_3(s) + HCl(aq) \longrightarrow NaCl(aq) + CO_2(g) + H_2O(l)$$

The neutralizing substances in some antacid preparations are given in Table 10.8.

TABLE 10.8 Basic Compounds in Some Antacids

Antacid	Base(s)
Amphojel	$Al(OH)_3$
Milk of magnesia	$Mg(OH)_2$
Mylanta, Maalox, Di-Gel, Gelusil, Riopan	$Mg(OH)_2$, $Al(OH)_3$
Bisodol, Rolaids	$CaCO_3$, $Mg(OH)_2$
Titralac, Tums, Pepto-Bismol	$CaCO_3$
Alka-Seltzer	$NaHCO_3$, $KHCO_3$

phenolphthalein in the solution changes from colorless to pink. This is called the neutralization *endpoint*. From the volume added and molarity of the NaOH, we can calculate the number of moles of NaOH and then the concentration of the acid.

SAMPLE PROBLEM 10.12

■ Titration of an Acid

A 25.0-mL sample of an HCl solution is placed in a flask with a few drops of phenolphthalein (indicator). If 32.6 mL of a 0.185 M NaOH solution is needed to reach the endpoint, what is the concentration (M) of the HCl solution?

$$NaOH(aq) + HCl(aq) \longrightarrow NaCl(aq) + H_2O(l)$$

SOLUTION

STEP 1 Given   32.6 mL of 0.185 M NaOH; 25.0 mL of HCl = 0.0250 L of HCl
          Need   molarity of HCl

STEP 2 Plan

mL of NaOH solution → Metric factor → L → Molarity factor → moles of NaOH → Mole-mole factor → moles of HCl → Divide by liters → M HCl solution

STEP 3 Equalities/Conversion Factors

1 L of NaOH = 1000 mL of NaOH   1 L of NaOH = 0.185 mole of NaOH

$$\frac{1\ L}{1000\ mL} \text{ and } \frac{1000\ mL}{1\ L} \qquad \frac{1\ L}{0.185\ mole\ NaOH} \text{ and } \frac{0.185\ mole\ NaOH}{1\ L}$$

1 mole of HCl = 1 mole of NaOH

$$\frac{1\ mole\ HCl}{1\ mole\ NaOH} \text{ and } \frac{1\ mole\ NaOH}{1\ mole\ HCl}$$

STEP 4   Set Up Problem

$$32.6 \text{ mL NaOH solution} \times \frac{1 \text{ L NaOH}}{1000 \text{ mL NaOH}} \times \frac{0.185 \text{ mole NaOH}}{1 \text{ L NaOH}} \times \frac{1 \text{ mole HCl}}{1 \text{ mole NaOH}}$$

**Guide to Calculations
for an Acid–Base Titration**

STEP 1
State the given and needed
quantities and concentrations.

STEP 2
Write a plan to calculate
molarity or volume.

STEP 3
State equalities and conversion
factors, including concentration.

STEP 4
Set up problem to
calculate needed quantity.

$$= 0.00603 \text{ mole of HCl solution}$$

$$\text{Molarity HCl} = \frac{0.00603 \text{ mole HCl}}{0.0250 \text{ L HCl}} = 0.241 \text{ M HCl solution}$$

STUDY CHECK

What is the molarity of an HCl solution if 28.6 mL of a 0.175 M NaOH solution is needed to neutralize a 25.0-mL sample of the HCl solution?

QUESTIONS AND PROBLEMS

Reactions of Acids and Bases

10.47 Complete and balance the equation for each of the following reactions:
  a. $ZnCO_3(s) + HBr(aq) \longrightarrow$
  b. $Zn(s) + HCl(aq) \longrightarrow$
  c. $HCl(aq) + NaHCO_3(s) \longrightarrow$
  d. $H_2SO_4(aq) + Mg(OH)_2(s) \longrightarrow$

10.48 Complete and balance the equations for each of the following reactions:
  a. $KHCO_3(s) + HCl(aq) \longrightarrow$
  b. $Ca(s) + H_2SO_4(aq) \longrightarrow$
  c. $HNO_3(aq) + Al(OH)_3(s) \longrightarrow$
  d. $Na_2CO_3(s) + H_2SO_4(aq)$

10.49 Balance each of the following neutralization reactions:
  a. $HCl(aq) + Mg(OH)_2(s) \longrightarrow MgCl_2(aq) + H_2O(l)$
  b. $H_3PO_4(aq) + LiOH(aq) \longrightarrow Li_3PO_4(aq) + H_2O(l)$

10.50 Balance each of the following neutralization reactions:
  a. $HNO_3(aq) + Ba(OH)_2(s) \longrightarrow Ba(NO_3)_2(aq) + H_2O(l)$
  b. $H_2SO_4(aq) + Al(OH)_3(s) \longrightarrow Al_2(SO_4)_3(aq) + H_2O(l)$

10.51 Write a balanced equation for the neutralization of each of the following:
  a. $H_2SO_4(aq)$ and $NaOH(aq)$
  b. $HCl(aq)$ and $Fe(OH)_3(s)$
  c. $H_2CO_3(aq)$ and $Mg(OH)_2(s)$

10.52 Write a balanced equation for the neutralization of each of the following:
  a. $H_3PO_4(aq)$ and $NaOH(aq)$
  b. $HI(aq)$ and $LiOH(aq)$
  c. $HNO_3(aq)$ and $Ca(OH)_2(s)$

10.53 What is the molarity of an HCl solution if 5.00 mL of a HCl solution is titrated with 28.6 mL of a 0.145 M NaOH solution?

$$HCl(aq) + NaOH(aq) \longrightarrow NaCl(aq) + H_2O(l)$$

10.54 If 29.7 mL of 0.205 M KOH is required to completely neutralize 25.0 mL of a $HC_2H_3O_2$ solution, what is the molarity of the acetic acid solution?

$$HC_2H_3O_2(aq) + KOH(aq) \longrightarrow KC_2H_3O_2(aq) + H_2O(l)$$

10.55 If 38.2 mL of 0.163 M KOH is required to neutralize completely 25.0 mL of a H_2SO_4 solution, what is the molarity of the acid solution?

$$H_2SO_4(aq) + 2KOH(aq) \longrightarrow K_2SO_4(aq) + 2H_2O(l)$$

10.56 A solution of 0.162 M NaOH is used to neutralize 25.0 mL of a H_2SO_4 solution. If 32.8 mL of a NaOH solution is required to reach the endpoint, what is the molarity of the H_2SO_4 solution?

$$H_2SO_4(aq) + 2NaOH(aq) \longrightarrow Na_2SO_4(aq) + 2H_2O(l)$$

10.57 A solution of 0.204 M NaOH is used to neutralize 50.0 mL of a H_3PO_4 solution. If 16.4 mL of a NaOH solution is required to reach the endpoint, what is the molarity of the H_3PO_4 solution?

$$H_3PO_4(aq) + 3NaOH(aq) \longrightarrow Na_3PO_4(aq) + 3H_2O(l)$$

10.58 A solution of 0.312 M KOH is used to neutralize 15.0 mL of a H_3PO_4 solution. If 28.3 mL of a KOH solution is required to reach the endpoint, what is the molarity of the H_3PO_4 solution?

$$H_3PO_4(aq) + 3KOH(aq) \longrightarrow K_3PO_4(aq) + 3H_2O(l)$$

10.6 Acid–Base Properties of Salt Solutions

LEARNING GOAL

Predict whether a salt will form an acidic, basic, or neutral solution.

When a salt dissolves in water, it dissociates into cations and anions. Solutions of salts can be acidic, basic, or neutral. Anions and cations from strong acids and bases do not affect pH; however, anions from weak acids and cations from weak bases change the pH of an aqueous solution.

Salts That Form Neutral Solutions

A solution of a salt containing a cation from a strong base and an anion from a strong acid will be neutral. For example, a salt such as $NaNO_3$ forms a neutral solution:

$$NaNO_3(s) \xrightarrow{H_2O} \underset{\substack{\text{Does not} \\ \text{change } H^+}}{Na^+(aq)} + \underset{\substack{\text{Does not attract} \\ H^+ \text{ from water}}}{NO_3^-(aq)} \qquad \substack{\text{Neutral solution} \\ (pH = 7.0)}$$

The cation, Na^+, from the strong base NaOH does not change the H^+ concentration and the anion, NO_3^-, from the strong acid HNO_3 does not attract H^+ from water. Thus, there is no effect on the pH of water; the solution is neutral, with a pH of 7.0. Salts such as NaCl, KCl, KNO_3, and KBr contain cations from strong bases and anions from strong acids and form neutral solutions.

Some Components of Neutral Salt Solutions

Cations of strong bases: Group 1A (1): Li^+, Na^+, K^+
Group 2A (2): Ca^{2+}, Mg^{2+}, Sr^{2+}, Ba^{2+}
Anions of strong acids: Cl^-, Br^-, I^-, NO_3^-, ClO_4^-

Salts That Form Basic Solutions

A salt solution containing the cation from a strong base and the anion from a weak acid produces a basic solution. Suppose we have a solution of the salt NaF, which contains Na^+ and F^- ions:

$$NaF(s) \xrightarrow{H_2O} \underset{\substack{\text{Does not} \\ \text{change } H^+}}{Na^+(aq)} + \underset{\substack{\text{Attracts } H^+ \\ \text{from water}}}{F^-(aq)}$$

The metal ion Na^+ has no effect on the pH of the solution. However, F^- is the conjugate base of the weak acid HF. Thus, F^- will attract a proton from water and form OH^- in solution, which makes it basic:

$$F^-(aq) + H_2O(l) \rightleftharpoons HF(aq) + OH^-(aq) \qquad \text{Basic solution (pH > 7.0)}$$

Other salts with anions from weak acids such as NaCN, KNO_2, and Na_2SO_4 also produce basic solutions.

Some Components of Basic Salt Solutions

Cations of strong bases: Group 1A (1): Li^+, Na^+, K^+
Group 2A (2): Ca^{2+}, Mg^{2+}, Sr^{2+}, Ba^{2+}
Anions of weak acids: F^-, NO_2^-, CN^-, CO_3^{2-}, SO_4^{2-}, $C_2H_3O_2^-$, S^{2-}, PO_4^{3-}

Salts That Form Acidic Solutions

A salt solution containing a cation from a weak base and an anion from a strong acid produces an acidic solution. Suppose we have a solution of the salt NH_4Cl, which contains NH_4^+ and Cl^- ions:

TUTORIAL
Salts of Weak Acids and Bases

$$NH_4Cl(s) \xrightarrow{H_2O} \underset{\substack{\text{Donates } H^+ \\ \text{to water}}}{NH_4^+(aq)} + \underset{\substack{\text{Does not attract} \\ H^+ \text{ from water}}}{Cl^-(aq)}$$

TABLE 10.9 Cations and Anions of Salts in Neutral, Basic, and Acidic Salt Solutions

Type of Solution	Cations	Anions	pH
Neutral	From strong bases: Group 1A (1): Li^+, Na^+, K^+ Group 2A (2): Ca^{2+}, Mg^{2+}, Sr^{2+}, Ba^{2+} (but not Be^{2+})	From strong acids: Cl^-, Br^-, I^-, NO_3^-, ClO_4^-	7.0
Basic	From strong bases: Group 1A (1): Li^+, Na^+, K^+ Group 2A (2): Ca^{2+}, Mg^{2+}, Sr^{2+}, Ba^{2+} (but not Be^{2+})	From weak acids: F^-, NO_2^-, CN^-, CO_3^{2-}, SO_4^{2-}, $C_2H_3O_2^-$, S^{2-}, PO_4^{3-}	>7.0
Acidic	From weak bases: NH_4^+ and Be^{2+}, Al^{3+}, Zn^{2+}, Cr^{3+}, Fe^{3+} (small, highly charged metal ions)	From strong acids: Cl^-, Br^-, I^-, NO_3^-, ClO_4^-	<7.0

The anion Cl^- has no effect on the pH of the solution. However, as a weak acid, the cation NH_4^+ donates a proton to water, which produces H_3O^+:

$$NH_4^+(aq) + H_2O(l) \rightleftharpoons NH_3(aq) + H_3O^+(aq) \qquad \text{Acidic solution (pH < 7.0)}$$

Some Components of Acidic Salt Solutions

Cations of weak bases: NH_4^+ and Be^{2+}, Al^{3+}, Zn^{2+}, Cr^{3+}, Fe^{3+}
            (small, highly charged metal ions)

Anions of strong acids: Cl^-, Br^-, I^-, NO_3^-, ClO_4^-

Table 10.9 summarizes the cations and anions of salts that form neutral, basic, and acidic solutions. Table 10.10 summarizes the acid–base properties of some typical salts in water.

Sometimes a salt contains the cation of a weak base and the anion of a weak acid. For example, when NH_4F dissociates in water, it produces NH_4^+ and F^-. We have seen that NH_4^+ forms an acidic solution and F^- forms a basic solution. The ion that reacts to a greater extent with water determines whether the solution is acidic or basic. The salt solution will be neutral only if the ions react with water to the same extent. The determination of these reactions is complex and will not be considered in this text.

TABLE 10.10 Acid–Base Properties of Some Salt Solutions

Typical Salts	Types of Ions	pH	Solution
$NaCl$, $MgBr_2$, KNO_3	Cation from a strong base Anion from a strong acid	7.0	Neutral
NaF, $MgCO_3$, KNO_2	Cation from a strong base Anion from a weak acid	>7.0	Basic
NH_4Cl, $FeBr_3$, $Al(NO_3)_3$	Cation from a weak base Anion from a strong acid	<7.0	Acidic

SAMPLE PROBLEM   10.13

■ **Predicting the Acid–Base Properties of Salt Solutions**

Predict whether solutions of each of the following salts would be acidic, basic, or neutral:

a. KCN   **b.** NH_4Br **c.** $NaNO_3$

SOLUTION

a. KCN

There are only six strong acids; all other acids are weak. Bases with cations from Groups 1A (1) and 2A (2) are strong; all other bases are weak. For the salt

KCN, the cation is from a strong base (KOH), but the anion is from a weak acid (HCN):

$$KCN(s) \xrightarrow{H_2O} K^+(aq) + CN^-(aq)$$

The cation K^+ has no effect on pH. However, the anion CN^- will attract protons from water to produce a basic solution:

$$CN^-(aq) + H_2O(l) \rightleftharpoons HCN(aq) + OH^-(aq)$$

b. NH_4Br

In the salt NH_4Br, the cation is from a weak base, NH_3, but the anion is from a strong acid, HBr:

$$NH_4Br(s) \xrightarrow{H_2O} NH_4^+(aq) + Br^-(aq)$$

The anion Br^- has no effect on pH because it is from HBr, a strong acid. However, the cation NH_4^+ will donate protons to water to produce an acidic solution:

$$NH_4^+(aq) + H_2O(l) \rightleftharpoons NH_3(aq) + H_3O^+(aq)$$

c. $NaNO_3$

The salt $NaNO_3$ contains a cation from a strong base (NaOH) and an anion from a strong acid (HNO_3). Thus, there is no change of pH; the salt solution is neutral:

$$NaNO_3(s) \xrightarrow{H_2O} Na^+(aq) + NO_3^-(aq)$$

STUDY CHECK

Would a solution of Na_3PO_4 be acidic, basic, or neutral?

QUESTIONS AND PROBLEMS

Acid–Base Properties of Salt Solutions

10.59 Why does a salt containing a cation from a strong base and an anion from a weak acid form a basic solution?

10.60 Why does a salt containing a cation from a weak base and an anion from a strong acid form an acidic solution?

10.61 Predict whether each of the following salts will form an acidic, basic, or neutral solution. For acidic and basic solutions, write an equation for the reaction that takes place.
  a. $MgCl_2$ **b.** NH_4NO_3 **c.** Na_2CO_3 **d.** K_2S

10.62 Predict whether each of the following salts will form an acidic, basic, or neutral solution. For acidic and basic solutions, write an equation for the reaction that takes place.
  a. Na_2SO_4 **b.** KBr   **c.** $BaCl_2$ **d.** NH_4I

10.7 Buffers

The pH of water and most solutions changes drastically when a small amount of acid or base is added. However, if a solution is buffered, there is little change in pH. A **buffer solution** is a solution that maintains pH by neutralizing added acid or base. For example, blood contains buffers that maintain a consistent pH of about 7.4. If the pH of the blood goes slightly above or below 7.4, changes in our oxygen levels and our metabolic processess can be drastic enough to cause death. Even though we obtain acids and bases from foods and cellular reactions, the buffers in the body absorb those compounds so effectively that the pH of the blood remains essentially unchanged. (See Figure 10.7.)

In a buffer, an acid must be present to react with any OH^- that is added, and a base must be available to react with any added H_3O^+. However, that acid and base must not neutralize each other. Therefore, a combination of an acid–base conjugate pair is used in buffers.

LEARNING GOAL

Describe the role of buffers in maintaining the pH of a solution.

SELF STUDY ACTIVITY
pH and Buffers

FIGURE 10.7 Adding an acid or a base to water changes the pH drastically, but a buffer resists pH change when small amounts of acid or base are added.

Q Why does the pH change several pH units when acid is added to water but not when acid is added to a buffer?

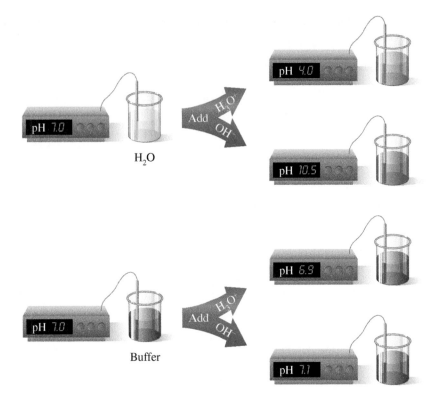

TUTORIAL
Preparing Buffer Solutions

Most buffer solutions consist of nearly equal concentrations of a weak acid and a salt containing its conjugate base. (See Figure 10.8.) Buffers may also contain a weak base and the salt of the weak base, which contains its conjugate acid.

For example, a buffer can be made from the weak acid acetic acid ($HC_2H_3O_2$), and its salt, sodium acetate ($NaC_2H_3O_2$). As a weak acid, acetic acid dissociates slightly in water to form H_3O^+ and a very small amount of $C_2H_3O_2^-$. The presence of sodium acetate provides a much larger concentration of acetate ion ($C_2H_3O_2^-$), which is necessary for its buffering capability:

$$HC_2H_3O_2(aq) + H_2O(l) \rightleftharpoons H_3O^+(aq) + C_2H_3O_2^-(aq)$$

Large amount   Large amount

Let's see how this buffer solution maintains the H_3O^+ concentration. When a small amount of acid is added, it will combine with the acetate ion (anion) as the equilibrium shifts to the reactant acetic acid. There will be a small decrease in the $[C_2H_3O_2^-]$ and a small increase in $[HC_2H_3O_2]$, but the $[H_3O^+]$ will not change very much:

$$HC_2H_3O_2(aq) + H_2O(l) \longleftarrow H_3O^+(aq) + C_2H_3O_2^-(aq)$$

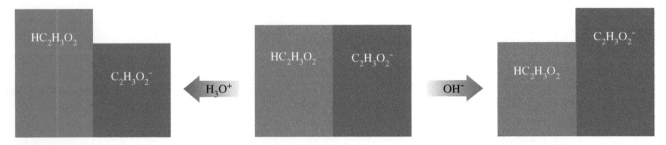

FIGURE 10.8 The buffer described here consists of about equal concentrations of acetic acid ($HC_2H_3O_2$) and its conjugate base acetate ion ($C_2H_3O_2^-$). Adding H_3O^+ to the buffer uses up some $C_2H_3O_2^-$, whereas adding OH^- neutralizes some $HC_2H_3O_2$. The pH of the solution is maintained as long as the added amounts of acid or base are small compared to the concentrations of the buffer components.

Q How does this acetic acid/acetate ion buffer maintain pH?

If a small amount of base is added to this buffer solution, it is neutralized by the acetic acid, and acetate and water are produced. The $[HC_2H_3O_2]$ decreases slightly, and the $[C_2H_3O_2^-]$ increases slightly, but again the $[H_3O^+]$ does not change very much:

$$HC_2H_3O_2(aq) + OH^-(aq) \longrightarrow H_2O(l) + C_2H_3O_2^-(aq)$$

CONCEPT CHECK 10.6

■ Identifying Buffer Solutions

Indicate whether each of the following would make a buffer solution:

a. HCl (a strong acid) and NaCl
b. H_3PO_4 (a weak acid)
c. HF (a weak acid) and NaF

ANSWER
a. No. A buffer requires a weak acid, not a strong acid, and a salt containing its conjugate base.
b. No. A weak acid is part of a buffer, but the salt containing the conjugate base of the weak acid is also needed.
c. Yes. This mixture would be a buffer because it contains a weak acid and a salt containing its conjugate base F^-.

Calculating the pH of a Buffer

By rearranging the K_a expression to give $[H_3O^+]$, we can obtain the ratio of the acetic acid/acetate buffer:

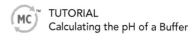
MC™ TUTORIAL
Calculating the pH of a Buffer

$$K_a = \frac{[H_3O^+][C_2H_3O_2^-]}{[HC_2H_3O_2]}$$

Solving for $[H_3O^+]$ gives

$$[H_3O^+] = K_a \times \frac{[HC_2H_3O_2]}{[C_2H_3O_2^-]}$$

Because K_a is a constant, the $[H_3O^+]$ is determined by the $[HC_2H_3O_2]/[C_2H_3O_2^-]$ ratio. As long as the addition of small amounts of either acid or base changes the ratio of $[HC_2H_3O_2]/[C_2H_3O_2^-]$ only slightly, the changes in $[H_3O^+]$ will be small and the pH will be maintained. It is important to note that the amount of acid or base that is added must be small compared to the supply of the buffer components $HC_2H_3O_2$ and $C_2H_3O_2^-$. If a large amount of acid or base is added, the buffering capacity of the system may be exceeded.

Other buffers can be prepared from conjugate acid–base pairs such as $H_2PO_4^-/HPO_4^{2-}$, HPO_4^{2-}/PO_4^{3-}, HCO_3^-/CO_3^{2-}, or NH_4^+/NH_3. The pH of the buffer solution will depend on the acid–base pair chosen.

SAMPLE PROBLEM 10.14

■ pH of a Buffer

The K_a for acetic acid, $HC_2H_3O_2$, is 1.8×10^{-5}. What is the pH of a buffer prepared with 1.0 M $HC_2H_3O_2$ and 1.0 M $C_2H_3O_2^-$?

SOLUTION

$$HC_2H_3O_2(aq) + H_2O(l) \rightleftharpoons H_3O^+(aq) + C_2H_3O_2^-(aq)$$

Guide to Calculating pH of a Buffer

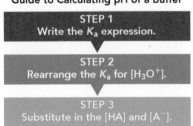

STEP 1
Write the K_a expression.

STEP 2
Rearrange the K_a for [H$_3$O$^+$].

STEP 3
Substitute in the [HA] and [A$^-$].

STEP 4
Use [H$_3$O$^+$] to calculate pH.

STEP 1   Write the K_a expression:

$$K_a = \frac{[H_3O^+][C_2H_3O_2^-]}{[HC_2H_3O_2]}$$

STEP 2   Rearrange K_a for [H$_3$O$^+$]:

$$[H_3O^+] = K_a \times \frac{[HC_2H_3O_2]}{[C_2H_3O_2^-]}$$

STEP 3   Substitute [HA] and [A$^-$]. Substituting these values in the expression for [H$_3$O$^+$] gives

$$[H_3O^+] = 1.8 \times 10^{-5} \times \frac{[1.0]}{[1.0]}$$

$$[H_3O^+] = 1.8 \times 10^{-5}\,M$$

STEP 4   Use [H$_3$O$^+$] to calculate pH. Using the concentration of [H$_3$O$^+$] in the pH expression gives the pH of the buffer:

$$pH = -\log[1.8 \times 10^{-5}] = 4.74$$

STUDY CHECK

The acid-base pair in a buffer is $H_2PO_4^-$/HPO_4^{2-}, which has a K_a of 6.2×10^{-8}. What is the pH of a buffer that is 0.10 M $H_2PO_4^-$ and 0.50 M HPO_4^{2-}?

QUESTIONS AND PROBLEMS

Buffers

10.63 Consider the following: (a) NaOH and NaCl, (b) H_2CO_3 and $NaHCO_3$, (c) HF and KF, (d) KCl and NaCl. Which of these represent a buffer system? Explain.

10.64 Consider the following: (a) H_3PO_4, (b) $NaNO_3$, (c) $HC_2H_3O_2$ and $NaC_2H_3O_2$, and (d) HCl and NaOH. Which of these represent a buffer system? Explain.

10.65 Consider the buffer system of hydrofluoric acid, HF, and its salt, NaF:

$$HF(aq) + H_2O(l) \rightleftharpoons H_3O^+(aq) + F^-(aq)$$

a. What is the purpose of the buffer system?
b. Why does a buffer require a salt that contains the same conjugate base as the acid?
c. How does the buffer react when some H_3O^+ is added?
d. How does the buffer react when some OH^- is added?

10.66 Consider the buffer system of nitrous acid, HNO_2, and its salt, $NaNO_2$:

$$HNO_2(aq) + H_2O(l) \rightleftharpoons H_3O^+(aq) + NO_2^-(aq)$$

a. What is the purpose of a buffer system?
b. What is the purpose of $NaNO_2$ in the buffer?
c. How does the buffer react when some H_3O^+ is added?
d. How does the buffer react when some OH^- is added?

10.67 Nitrous acid has a K_a of 4.5×10^{-4}. What is the pH of a buffer solution containing 0.10 M HNO_2 and 0.10 M NO_2^-?

10.68 Acetic acid has a K_a of 1.8×10^{-5}. What is the pH of a buffer solution containing 0.15 M $HC_2H_3O_2$ (acetic acid) and 0.15 M $C_2H_3O_2^-$?

10.69 Compare the pH of a HF buffer that contains 0.10 M HF and 0.10 M NaF with another HF buffer that contains 0.060 M HF and 0.120 M NaF. (See Table 10.4.)

10.70 Compare the pH of a H_2CO_3 buffer that contains 0.10 M H_2CO_3 and 0.10 M $NaHCO_3$ with another H_2CO_3 buffer that contains 0.15 M H_2CO_3 and 0.050 M $NaHCO_3$. (See Table 10.4.)

HEALTH NOTE

Buffers in the Blood

The arterial blood has a normal pH of 7.35–7.45. If changes in H_3O^+ lower the pH below 6.8 or raise it above 8.0, cells cannot function properly and death may result. In our cells, CO_2 is continually produced as an end product of cellular metabolism. Some CO_2 is carried to the lungs for elimination, and the rest dissolves in body fluids such as plasma and saliva, forming carbonic acid. As a weak acid, carbonic acid dissociates to give bicarbonate and H_3O^+. More of the anion HCO_3^- is supplied by the kidneys to give an important buffer system in the body fluid, the H_2CO_3/HCO_3^- buffer:

$$CO_2 + H_2O \rightleftharpoons H_2CO_3 \rightleftharpoons H_3O^+ + HCO_3^-$$

Excess H_3O^+ entering the body fluids reacts with HCO_3^-, and excess OH^- reacts with the carbonic acid:

$$H_2CO_3(aq) + H_2O(l) \longleftarrow H_3O^+(aq) + HCO_3^-(aq)$$
Equilibrium shifts left

$$H_2CO_3(aq) + OH^-(aq) \longrightarrow H_2O(l) + HCO_3^-(aq)$$
Equilibrium shifts right

For the carbonic acid, we can write the equilibrium expression as

$$K_a = \frac{[H_3O^+][HCO_3^-]}{[H_2CO_3]}$$

To maintain the normal blood pH (7.35–7.45), the ratio of H_2CO_3/HCO_3^- needs to be about 1 to 10, which is obtained by typical concentrations in the blood of 0.0024 M H_2CO_3 and 0.024 M HCO_3^-:

$$[H_3O^+] = K_a \times \frac{[H_2CO_3]}{[HCO_3^-]}$$

$$= 4.3 \times 10^{-7} \times \frac{[0.0024]}{[0.024]} = 4.3 \times 10^{-7} \times 0.10 = 4.3 \times 10^{-8}\,M$$

$$pH = -\log(4.3 \times 10^{-8}) = 7.37$$

In the body, the concentration of carbonic acid is closely associated with the partial pressure of CO_2. Table 10.11 lists the normal values for arterial blood. If the CO_2 level rises, producing more H_2CO_3, the equilibrium produces more H_3O^+, which lowers the pH. This condition is called acidosis. Difficulty with ventilation or gas diffusion can lead to respiratory acidosis, which can happen in emphysema or when an accident or depressive drugs affect the medulla of the brain.

A lowering of the CO_2 level leads to a high blood pH, a condition called alkalosis. Excitement, trauma, or a high temperature may cause a person to hyperventilate, which expels large amounts of CO_2. As the partial pressure of CO_2 in the blood falls below normal, the equilibrium shifts from H_2CO_3 to CO_2 and H_2O. This shift decreases the $[H_3O^+]$ and raises the pH. Table 10.12 lists some of the conditions that lead to changes in the blood pH and some possible treatments. The kidneys also regulate H_3O^+ and HCO_3^- components, but they do so more slowly than the adjustment made by the lungs through ventilation.

TABLE 10.11 Normal Values for Blood Buffer in Arterial Blood

P_{CO_2}	40 mm Hg
H_2CO_3	2.4 mmoles/L of plasma
HCO_3^-	24 mmoles/L of plasma
pH	7.35–7.45

TABLE 10.12 Acidosis and Alkalosis: Symptoms, Causes, and Treatments

Respiratory Acidosis: CO_2 ↑ pH ↓	
Symptoms:	Failure to ventilate, suppression of breathing, disorientation, weakness, coma
Causes:	Lung disease blocking gas diffusion (e.g., emphysema, pneumonia, bronchitis, and asthma); depression of respiratory center by drugs, cardiopulmonary arrest, stroke, poliomyelitis, or nervous system disorders
Treatment:	Correction of disorder, infusion of bicarbonate

Metabolic Acidosis: H^+ ↑ pH ↓	
Symptoms:	Increased ventilation, fatigue, confusion
Causes:	Renal disease, including hepatitis and cirrhosis; increased acid production in diabetes mellitus, hyperthyroidism, alcoholism, and starvation; loss of alkali in diarrhea; acid retention in renal failure
Treatment:	Sodium bicarbonate given orally, dialysis for renal failure, insulin treatment for diabetic ketosis

Respiratory Alkalosis: CO_2 ↓ pH ↑	
Symptoms:	Increased rate and depth of breathing, numbness, light-headedness, tetany
Causes:	Hyperventilation due to anxiety, hysteria, fever, exercise; reaction to drugs such as salicylate, quinine, and antihistamines; conditions causing hypoxia (e.g., pneumonia, pulmonary edema, and heart disease)
Treatment:	Elimination of anxiety-producing state, rebreathing into a paper bag

Metabolic Alkalosis: H^+ ↓ pH ↑	
Symptoms:	Depressed breathing, apathy, confusion
Causes:	Vomiting, diseases of the adrenal glands, ingestion of excess alkali
Treatment:	Infusion of saline solution, treatment of underlying diseases

CONCEPT MAP

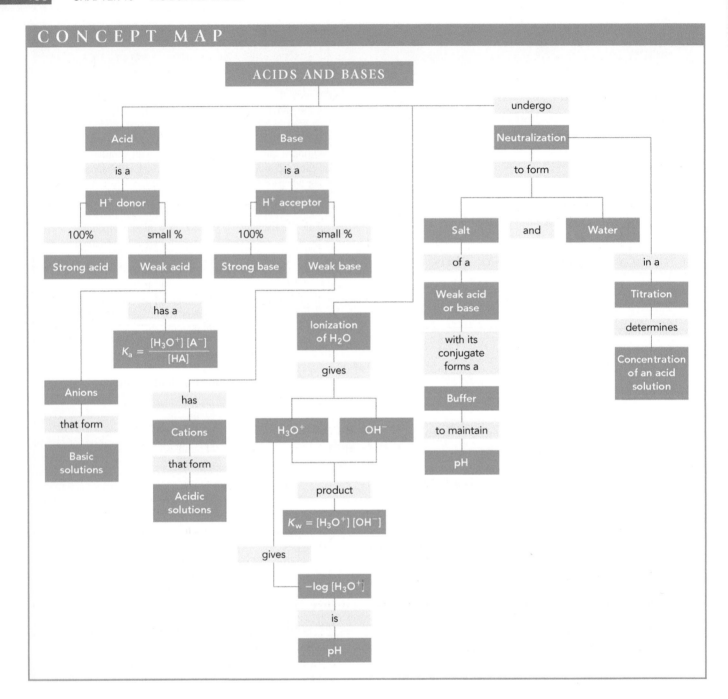

CHAPTER REVIEW

10.1 Acids and Bases

LEARNING GOAL: *Describe and name Arrhenius and Brønsted–Lowry acids and bases; identify conjugate acid–base pairs.*

An Arrhenius acid produces H^+ and an Arrhenius base produces OH^- in aqueous solutions. Acids taste sour, may sting, and neutralize bases. Bases taste bitter, feel slippery, and neutralize acids.

According to the Brønsted–Lowry theory, acids are proton (H^+) donors and bases are proton acceptors. Two conjugate acid–base pairs are present in an acid–base reaction. Each acid–base pair is related by the loss or gain of one H^+. For example, when the aqueous acid HF donates H^+, the F^- it forms is its conjugate base because F^- is capable of accepting H^+. The other acid–base pair would be H_2O and H_3O^+:

$$HF(aq) + H_2O(l) \rightleftharpoons H_3O^+(aq) + F^-(aq)$$

10.2 Strengths of Acids and Bases

LEARNING GOAL: *Write equations for the dissociation of strong and weak acids; write the equilibrium expression for a weak acid.*

In strong acids, all the H^+ in the acid is donated to H_2O; in a weak acid, only a small percentage of acid molecules produce H_3O^+. Strong bases are hydroxides of Groups 1A (1) and 2A (2) that dissociate completely in water. An important weak base is ammonia, NH_3. In water, weak acids and weak bases produce only a few ions when equilibrium is reached. The reaction for a weak acid can be written as $HA + H_2O \rightleftharpoons H_3O^+ + A^-$. The acid dissociation expression is written as $K_a = \dfrac{[H_3O^+][A^-]}{[HA]}$.

10.3 Ionization of Water

LEARNING GOAL: *Use the ion-product constant of water to calculate the $[H_3O^+]$ and $[OH^-]$ in an aqueous solution.*

In pure water, a few molecules transfer protons to other water molecules, producing small but equal amounts of $[H_3O^+]$ and $[OH^-]$, such that each has a concentration of 1×10^{-7} mole/L. The ion-product constant, K_w, $= [H_3O^+] \times [OH^-] = 1 \times 10^{-14}$ at 25 °C, applies to all aqueous solutions. In acidic solutions, the $[H_3O^+]$ is greater than the $[OH^-]$. In basic solutions, the $[OH^-]$ is greater than the $[H_3O^+]$.

10.4 The pH Scale

LEARNING GOAL: *Calculate pH from $[H_3O^+]$; given the pH, calculate the $[H_3O^+]$ and $[OH^-]$ of a solution.*

The pH scale is a range of numbers, typically from 0 to 14, which relates to the $[H_3O^+]$ of the solution. A neutral solution has a pH of 7. In acidic solutions, the pH is below 7; in basic solutions, the pH is above 7. Mathematically, pH is the negative logarithm of the hydronium ion concentration ($-\log[H_3O^+]$).

10.5 Reactions of Acids and Bases

LEARNING GOAL: *Write balanced equations for reactions of acids with metals, carbonates, and bases.*

When an acid reacts with a metal, hydrogen gas and a salt are produced. The reaction of an acid with a carbonate or bicarbonate produces carbon dioxide, a salt, and water. In neutralization, an acid reacts with a base to produce a salt and water. In titration, an acid sample is neutralized with a known amount of a base. From the volume and molarity of the base, the concentration of the acid is calculated.

10.6 Acid–Base Properties of Salt Solutions

LEARNING GOAL: *Predict whether a salt will form an acidic, basic, or neutral solution.*

A salt of a weak acid contains an anion that removes protons from water and makes the solution basic. A salt of a weak base contains an ion that donates a proton to water, producing an acidic solution. Salts of strong acids and bases give neutral solutions because they contain ions that do not affect the pH.

10.7 Buffers

LEARNING GOAL: *Describe the role of buffers in maintaining the pH of a solution.*

A buffer solution resists changes in pH when small amounts of acid or base are added. A buffer contains either a weak acid and its salt or a weak base and its salt. The weak acid reacts with added OH^-, and the anion of the salt reacts with added H^+. Buffers are important in maintaining the pH of the blood.

■ KEY TERMS

acid A substance that dissolves in water and produces hydrogen ions (H^+), according to the Arrhenius theory. All acids are proton donors, according to the Brønsted–Lowry theory.

acid dissociation constant (K_a) The product of the concentrations of the ions from the dissociation of a weak acid divided by the concentration of the weak acid.

amphoteric Substances that can act as either an acid or a base in water.

base A substance that dissolves in water and produces hydroxide ions (OH^-), according to the Arrhenius theory. All bases are proton acceptors, according to the Brønsted–Lowry theory.

Brønsted–Lowry acids and bases An acid is a proton donor; a base is a proton acceptor.

buffer solution A solution of a weak acid and its conjugate base or a weak base and its conjugate acid that maintains the pH by neutralizing added acid or base.

conjugate acid–base pair An acid and base that differ by one H^+. When an acid donates a proton, the product is its conjugate base, which is capable of accepting a proton in the reverse reaction.

dissociation The separation of an acid or base into ions in water.

hydronium ion, H_3O^+ The ion formed by the attraction of a proton (H^+) to a H_2O molecule.

ion-product constant of water, K_w The product of $[H_3O^+]$ and $[OH^-]$ in solution; $K_w = [H_3O^+][OH^-]$.

neutral The term that describes a solution with equal concentrations of H_3O^+ and OH^-.

neutralization A reaction between an acid and a base to form a salt and water.

pH A measure of the $[H_3O^+]$ in a solution; pH $= -\log[H_3O^+]$.

strong acid An acid that completely ionizes in water.

strong base A base that completely ionizes in water.

titration The addition of base to an acid sample to determine the concentration of the acid.

weak acid An acid that is a poor donor of H^+ and dissociates only slightly in water.

weak base A base that is a poor acceptor of H^+ and produces a small number of ions in water.

■ UNDERSTANDING THE CONCEPTS

10.71 In each of the following diagrams of acid solutions, determine if each diagram represents a strong acid or a weak acid. The acid has the formula HX.

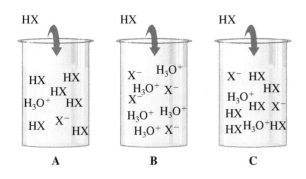

10.72 Adding a few drops of a strong acid to water will lower the pH appreciably. However, adding the same number of drops to a buffer does not appreciably alter the pH. Why?

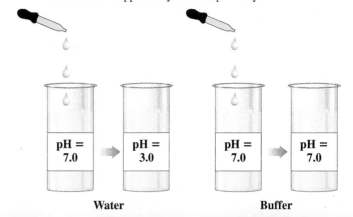

10.73 Sometimes, during stress or trauma, a person can start to hyperventilate. Then the person might breathe into a paper bag to avoid fainting.

a. What changes occur in the blood pH during hyperventilation?
b. How does breathing into a paper bag help return blood pH to normal?

10.74 In the blood plasma, pH is maintained by the carbonic acid–bicarbonate buffer system.
a. How is pH maintained when acid is added to the buffer system?
b. How is pH maintained when base is added to the buffer system?

ADDITIONAL QUESTIONS AND PROBLEMS

For instructor-assigned homework, go to www.masteringchemistry.com.

10.75 Identify each of the following as an acid, base, or salt, and give its name:
a. LiOH   **b.** $Ca(NO_3)_2$ **c.** HBr
d. $Ba(OH)_2$ **e.** H_2CO_3 **f.** $HClO_2$

10.76 Identify each of the following as an acid, base, or salt, and give its name:
a. H_3PO_4 **b.** $MgBr_2$ **c.** NH_3
d. H_2SO_4 **e.** NaCl   **f.** KOH

10.77 Are each of the following examples acidic, basic, or neutral?
a. rain, pH 5.2   **b.** tears, pH 7.5   **c.** tea, pH 3.8
d. cola, pH 2.5   **e.** photo developer, pH 12.0

10.78 Are each of the following examples acidic, basic, or neutral?
a. saliva, pH 6.8   **b.** urine, pH 5.9
c. pancreatic juice, pH 8.0
d. bile, pH 8.4   **e.** blood, pH 7.45

10.79 One ingredient in some antacids is $Mg(OH)_2$.
a. If the base is not very soluble in water, why is it considered a strong base?
b. What is the neutralization reaction of $Mg(OH)_2$ with stomach acid, HCl?

10.80 Acetic acid, $HC_2H_3O_2$, found in vinegar, is a weak acid. Why?

10.81 Using Table 10.3, identify the stronger acid in each of the following pairs:
a. HF or HCN   **b.** H_3O^+ or NH_4^+
c. HNO_2 or $HC_2H_3O_2$ **d.** H_2O or HCO_3^-

10.82 Using Table 10.3, identify the stronger base in each of the following pairs:
a. H_2O or Cl^- **b.** OH^- or NH_3
c. SO_4^{2-} or NO_2^- **d.** CO_3^{2-} or H_2O

10.83 Determine the pH for the following solutions:
a. $[H_3O^+] = 2.0 \times 10^{-8}$ M   **b.** $[H_3O^+] = 5.0 \times 10^{-2}$ M
c. $[OH^-] = 3.5 \times 10^{-4}$ M   **d.** $[OH^-] = 0.0054$ M

10.84 Determine the pH for the following solutions:
a. $[OH^-] = 1.0 \times 10^{-7}$ M
b. $[H_3O^+] = 4.2 \times 10^{-3}$ M
c. $[H_3O^+] = 0.0001$ M
d. $[OH^-] = 8.5 \times 10^{-9}$ M

10.85 Are the solutions in Problem 10.83 acidic, basic, or neutral?

10.86 Are the solutions in Problem 10.84 acidic, basic, or neutral?

10.87 What are the $[H_3O^+]$ and $[OH^-]$ for a solution with the following pH values?
a. 3.00   **b.** 6.48   **c.** 8.85
d. 11.00   **e.** 9.20

10.88 What are the $[H_3O^+]$ and $[OH^-]$ for a solution with the following pH values?
a. 10.0   **b.** 5.0   **c.** 7.00
d. 6.5   **e.** 1.82

10.89 Solution A has a pH of 4.5, and solution B has a pH of 6.7.
a. Which solution is more acidic?
b. What is the $[H_3O^+]$ in each?
c. What is the $[OH^-]$ in each?

10.90 Solution X has a pH of 9.5, and solution Y has a pH of 7.5.
a. Which solution is more acidic?
b. What is the $[H_3O^+]$ in each?
c. What is the $[OH^-]$ in each?

10.91 What is the $[OH^-]$ in a solution that contains 0.225 g of NaOH in 0.250 L of solution?

10.92 What is the $[H_3O^+]$ in a solution that contains 1.54 g of HNO_3 in 0.500 L of solution?

10.93 What is the pH of a solution prepared by dissolving 2.5 g of HCl in water to make 425 mL of solution?

10.94 What is the pH of a solution prepared by dissolving 1.00 g of $Ca(OH)_2$ in water to make 875 mL of solution?

10.95 Calculate the volume (mL) of a 0.150 M NaOH solution that will completely neutralize the following:
a. 25.0 mL of a 0.288 M HCl solution
b. 10.0 mL of a 0.560 M H_2SO_4 solution

10.96 How many milliliters of 0.215 M NaOH solution are needed to completely neutralize 2.50 mL of 0.825 M H_2SO_4 solution?

10.97 A solution of 0.205 M NaOH is used to neutralize 20.0 mL of H_2SO_4. If 45.6 mL of NaOH is required to reach the endpoint, what is the molarity of the H_2SO_4 solution?

$$H_2SO_4(aq) + 2NaOH(aq) \longrightarrow Na_2SO_4(aq) + 2H_2O(l)$$

10.98 A 10.0-mL sample of vinegar, which is an aqueous solution of acetic acid, $HC_2H_3O_2$, requires 16.5 mL of 0.500 M NaOH to reach the endpoint in a titration. What is the molarity of the acetic acid solution?

$$HC_2H_3O_2(aq) + NaOH(aq) \longrightarrow NaC_2H_3O_2(aq) + H_2O(l)$$

10.99 Will solutions of the following salts be acidic, basic, or neutral?
  a. KF **b.** NaCN **c.** NH_4NO_3 **d.** NaBr

10.100 Will solutions of the following salts be acidic, basic, or neutral?
  a. K_2SO_4 **b.** KNO_2 **c.** $MgCl_2$ **d.** NH_4Cl

10.101 A buffer is made by dissolving H_3PO_4 and NaH_2PO_4 in water.
  a. Write an equation that shows how this buffer neutralizes added acid.
  b. Write an equation that shows how this buffer neutralizes added base.

c. Calculate the pH of this buffer if it is 0.10 M H_3PO_4 and 0.10 M $H_2PO_4^-$; the K_a for H_3PO_4 is 7.5×10^{-3}.
d. Calculate the pH of this buffer if it is 0.50 M H_3PO_4 and 0.20 M $H_2PO_4^-$; the K_a for H_3PO_4 is 7.5×10^{-3}.

10.102 A buffer is made by dissolving $HC_2H_3O_2$ and $NaC_2H_3O_2$ in water.
  a. Write an equation that shows how this buffer neutralizes added acid.
  b. Write an equation that shows how this buffer neutralizes added base.
  c. Calculate the pH of this buffer if it is 0.10 M $HC_2H_3O_2$ and 0.10 M $C_2H_3O_2^-$; the K_a for $HC_2H_3O_2$ is 1.8×10^{-5}.
  d. Calculate the pH of this buffer if it is 0.20 M $HC_2H_3O_2$ and 0.40 M $C_2H_3O_2^-$; the K_a for $HC_2H_3O_2$ is 1.8×10^{-5}.

CHALLENGE QUESTIONS

10.103 Complete the following table:

Acid	Conjugate base
H_2O	
	CN^-
HNO_2	
	$H_2PO_4^-$

10.104 Complete the following table:

Base	Conjugate acid
	HS^-
	H_3O^+
NH_3	
HCO_3^-	

10.105 Consider the following:
  1. H_2S 2. H_3PO_4 3. HCO_3^-
  a. For each, write the formula of the conjugate base.
  b. For each, write the K_a expression.
  c. Write the formula of the weakest acid.
  d. Write the formula of the strongest acid.

10.106 Identify the conjugate acid–base pairs in each of the following equations and state whether the equilibrium mixture contains mostly products or mostly reactants:
  a. $NH_3(aq) + HNO_3(aq) \rightleftarrows NH_4^+(aq) + NO_3^-(aq)$
  b. $H_2O(l) + HBr(aq) \rightleftarrows H_3O^+(aq) + Br^-(aq)$
  c. $HNO_2(aq) + HS^-(aq) \rightleftarrows H_2S(g) + NO_2^-(aq)$
  d. $Cl^-(aq) + H_2O(l) \rightleftarrows OH^-(aq) + HCl(aq)$

10.107 Complete and balance each of the following:
  a. $ZnCO_3(s) + H_2SO_4(aq) \longrightarrow$
  b. $Al(s) + HNO_3(aq) \longrightarrow$
  c. $H_3PO_4(aq) + Ca(OH)_2(aq) \longrightarrow$
  d. $KHCO_3(s) + HNO_3(aq) \longrightarrow$

10.108 Predict whether a solution of each of the following salts is acidic, basic, or neutral. For salts that form acidic or basic solutions, write a balanced equation for the reaction.
  a. NH_4Br **b.** KNO_2 **c.** $Mg(NO_3)_2$
  d. BaF_2 **e.** K_2S

10.109 Determine each of the following for a 0.050 M KOH solution:
  a. $[H_3O^+]$ **b.** pH

c. products when reacted with H_3PO_4
d. milliliters required to neutralize 40.0 mL of 0.035 M H_2SO_4

10.110 Consider the reaction of KOH and HNO_2.
  a. Write the balanced chemical equation.
  b. Calculate the milliliters of 0.122 M KOH required to neutralize 36.0 mL of 0.250 M HNO_2.
  c. Determine whether the final solution would be acidic, basic, or neutral.

10.111 One of the most acidic lakes in the United States is Little Echo Pond in the Adirondacks in New York. Recently, this lake had a pH of 4.2, well below the recommended pH of 6.5.

a. What is the $[H_3O^+]$ and $[OH^-]$ of Little Echo Pond?
b. What is the $[H_3O^+]$ and $[OH^-]$ of a lake that has a pH of 6.5?
c. One way to raise the pH of an acidic lake (and restore aquatic life) is to add limestone ($CaCO_3$). How many grams of $CaCO_3$ are needed to neutralize 1.0 kL of the acidic water from Little Echo Pond if the acid is written as HA?

$$2HA + CaCO_3(s) \longrightarrow CaA_2 + CO_2(g) + H_2O(l)$$

10.112 The daily output of stomach acid (gastric juice) is 1000 mL to 2000 mL. Prior to a meal, stomach acid (HCl) typically has a pH of 1.42.
  a. What is the $[H_3O^+]$ of stomach acid?
  b. The antacid Maalox contains 200. mg of $Al(OH)_3$ per tablet. Write the neutralization equation and calculate the milliliters of stomach acid neutralized by two tablets of Maalox.
  c. The antacid milk of magnesia contains 400. mg of $Mg(OH)_2$ per teaspoon. Write the neutralization equation and calculate the milliliters of stomach acid that are neutralized by 1 tablespoon of milk of magnesia (1 tablespoon = 3 teaspoons).

ANSWERS

ANSWERS TO STUDY CHECKS

10.1 a. chloric acid   **b.** $Fe(OH)_3$

10.2 $HNO_3(aq) + H_2O(l) \longrightarrow H_3O^+(aq) + NO_3^-(aq)$

10.3 A base accepts a proton to form its conjugate acid.
   a. H_2S **b.** HNO_2

10.4 The conjugate acid–base pairs are HCN/CN^- and SO_4^{2-}/HSO_4^-.

10.5 $HNO_3 + H_2O \rightleftharpoons H_3O^+ + NO_3^-$
The products are favored because HNO_3 is a stronger acid than H_3O^+.

10.6 Nitrous acid has a larger K_a than carbonic acid; it dissociates more in H_2O, forms more $[H_3O^+]$, and is a stronger acid.

10.7 $[H_3O^+] = 2.5 \times 10^{-11}$ M, basic

10.8 11.38

10.9 4.3

10.10 $[H_3O^+] = 3.2 \times 10^{-5}$ M, $[OH^-] = 3.1 \times 10^{-10}$ M

10.11 $H_2SO_4(aq) + 2NaHCO_3(s) \longrightarrow$
$Na_2SO_4(aq) + 2CO_2(g) + 2H_2O(l)$

10.12 0.200 M HCl

10.13 The anion PO_4^{3-} reacts with H_2O forming the weak acid HPO_4^{2-} and OH^-, which makes the solution basic.

10.14 pH = 7.91

ANSWERS TO SELECTED QUESTIONS AND PROBLEMS

10.1 a. acid   **b.** acid   **c.** acid   **d.** base

10.3 a. hydrochloric acid   **b.** calcium hydroxide
   c. carbonic acid   **d.** nitric acid
   e. sulfurous acid   **f.** iron(II) hydroxide

10.5 a. $Mg(OH)_2$ **b.** HF   **c.** H_3PO_4
   d. LiOH   **e.** $Cu(OH)_2$

10.7 a. HI is the acid (proton donor) and H_2O is the base (proton acceptor).
   b. H_2O is the acid (proton donor) and F^- is the base (proton acceptor)

10.9 a. F^-, fluoride ion
   b. OH^-, hydroxide ion
   c. HCO_3^-, bicarbonate ion *or* hydrogen carbonate ion
   d. SO_4^{2-}, sulfate ion

10.11 a. HCO_3^-, bicarbonate ion *or* hydrogen carbonate ion
   b. H_3O^+, hydronium ion
   c. H_3PO_4, phosphoric acid
   d. HBr, hydrobromic acid

10.13 a. acid H_2CO_3, conjugate base HCO_3^-
   base H_2O, conjugate acid H_3O^+
   b. acid NH_4^+, conjugate base NH_3
   base H_2O, conjugate acid H_3O^+
   c. acid HCN, conjugate base CN^-
   base NO_2^-, conjugate acid HNO_2

10.15 A strong acid is a good proton donor, whereas its conjugate base is a poor proton acceptor.

10.17 a. HBr   **b.** HSO_4^- **c.** H_2CO_3

10.19 a. HSO_4^- **b.** HNO_2 **c.** HSO_3^-

10.21 a. reactants   **b.** reactants   **c.** products

10.23 The reactants are favored because NH_4^+ is a weaker acid than HSO_4^-:

$$NH_4^+(aq) + SO_4^{2-}(aq) \rightleftharpoons NH_3(aq) + HSO_4^-(aq)$$

10.25 a. H_2SO_3 **b.** HSO_3^- **c.** H_2SO_3
   d. HS^- **e.** H_2SO_3

10.27 $H_3PO_4(aq) + H_2O(l) \rightleftharpoons H_3O^+(aq) + H_2PO_4^-(aq)$

$$K_a = \frac{[H_3O^+][H_2PO_4^-]}{[H_3PO_4]}$$

10.29 In pure water, $[H_3O^+] = [OH^-]$ because one of each is produced every time a proton transfers from one water molecule to another.

10.31 In an acidic solution, the $[H_3O^+]$ is greater than the $[OH^-]$.

10.33 a. acidic   **b.** basic   **c.** basic   **d.** acidic

10.35 a. 1.0×10^{-5} M   **b.** 1.0×10^{-8} M
   c. 5.0×10^{-10} M   **d.** 2.5×10^{-2} M

10.37 a. 1.0×10^{-11} M   **b.** 2.0×10^{-9} M
   c. 5.6×10^{-3} M   **d.** 2.5×10^{-2} M

10.39 In a neutral solution, the $[H_3O^+]$ is 1.0×10^{-7} M and the pH is 7.00, which is the negative value of the power of 10.

10.41 a. basic   **b.** acidic   **c.** basic
   d. acidic   **e.** acidic   **f.** basic

10.43 a. 4.00   **b.** 8.52   **c.** 9.00
   d. 3.40   **e.** 7.17·   **f.** 10.92

10.45

$[H_3O^+]$	$[OH^-]$	pH	Acidic, Basic, or Neutral?
1.0×10^{-8} M	1.0×10^{-6} M	8.00	Basic
1.0×10^{-3} M	1.0×10^{-11} M	3.00	Acidic
2.8×10^{-5} M	3.6×10^{-10} M	4.55	Acidic
2.4×10^{-5} M	4.2×10^{-10} M	4.62	Acidic

10.47 a. $ZnCO_3(s) + 2HBr(aq) \longrightarrow ZnBr_2(aq) + CO_2(g) + H_2O(l)$
   b. $Zn(s) + 2HCl(aq) \longrightarrow ZnCl_2(aq) + H_2(g)$
   c. $HCl(aq) + NaHCO_3(s) \longrightarrow NaCl(aq) + H_2O(l) + CO_2(g)$
   d. $H_2SO_4(aq) + Mg(OH)_2(s) \longrightarrow MgSO_4(aq) + 2H_2O(l)$

10.49 a. $2HCl(aq) + Mg(OH)_2(s) \longrightarrow MgCl_2(aq) + 2H_2O(l)$
   b. $H_3PO_4(aq) + 3LiOH(aq) \longrightarrow Li_3PO_4(aq) + 3H_2O(l)$

10.51 a. $H_2SO_4(aq) + 2NaOH(aq) \longrightarrow Na_2SO_4(aq) + 2H_2O(l)$
   b. $3HCl(aq) + Fe(OH)_3(s) \longrightarrow FeCl_3(aq) + 3H_2O(l)$
   c. $H_2CO_3(aq) + Mg(OH)_2(s) \longrightarrow MgCO_3(s) + 2H_2O(l)$

10.53 0.829 M HCl

10.55 0.125 M H_2SO_4

10.57 0.0223 M H_3PO_4

10.59 The anion from the weak acid removes a proton from H_2O to make a basic solution.

10.61 a. neutral
   b. acidic, $NH_4^+(aq) + H_2O(l) \rightleftharpoons NH_3(aq) + H_3O^+(aq)$
   c. basic, $CO_3^{2-}(aq) + H_2O(l) \rightleftharpoons HCO_3^-(aq) + OH^-(aq)$
   d. basic, $S^{2-}(aq) + H_2O(l) \rightleftharpoons HS^-(aq) + OH^-(aq)$

10.63 (b) and (c) are buffer systems. (b) contains the weak acid H_2CO_3 and its salt $NaHCO_3$. (c) contains HF, a weak acid, and its salt KF.

10.65 a. A buffer system keeps the pH constant.
   b. The conjugate base neutralizes any H_3O^+ added.
   c. The added H_3O^+ reacts with F^- from NaF.
   d. The added OH^- is neutralized by the HF.

10.67 pH = 3.35

10.69 The pH of the 0.10 M HF/0.10 M NaF buffer is 3.14. The pH of the 0.060 M HF/0.120 M NaF buffer is 3.44.

10.71 A. weak acid   **B.** strong acid   **C.** weak acid

10.73 a. Hyperventilation will lower the CO_2 level in the blood, which lowers the H_2CO_3 concentration, which decreases the H_3O^+ and increases the blood pH.
   b. Breathing into a bag will increase the CO_2 level, increase the H_2CO_3, increase H_3O^+, and lower the blood pH.

10.75 a. base, lithium hydroxide   **b.** salt, calcium nitrate
   c. acid, hydrobromic acid   **d.** base, barium hydroxide
   e. acid, carbonic acid   **f.** acid, chlorous acid

10.77 a. acidic   **b.** basic   **c.** acidic   **d.** acidic   **e.** basic

10.79 a. The $Mg(OH)_2$ that dissolves is completely dissociated, making it a strong base.
   b. $Mg(OH)_2(aq) + 2HCl(aq) \longrightarrow MgCl_2(aq) + 2H_2O(l)$

10.81 a. HF   **b.** H_3O^+ **c.** HNO_2 **d.** HCO_3^-

10.83 a. pH 7.70   **b.** pH 1.30   **c.** pH 10.54   **d.** pH 11.73

10.85 a. basic   **b.** acidic   **c.** basic   **d.** basic

10.87 a. $[H_3O^+] = 1.0 \times 10^{-3}$ M; $[OH^-] = 1.0 \times 10^{-11}$ M
   b. $[H_3O^+] = 3.3 \times 10^{-7}$ M; $[OH^-] = 3.0 \times 10^{-8}$ M
   c. $[H_3O^+] = 1.4 \times 10^{-9}$ M; $[OH^-] = 7.1 \times 10^{-6}$ M
   d. $[H_3O^+] = 1.0 \times 10^{-11}$ M; $[OH^-] = 1.0 \times 10^{-3}$ M
   e. $[H_3O^+] = 6.3 \times 10^{-10}$ M; $[OH^-] = 1.6 \times 10^{-5}$ M

10.89 a. A
   b. A, $[H_3O^+] = 3 \times 10^{-5}$ M   B, $[H_3O^+] = 2 \times 10^{-7}$ M
   c. A, $[OH^-] = 3 \times 10^{-10}$ M   B, $[OH^-] = 5 \times 10^{-8}$ M

10.91 $[OH^-] = 0.0225$ M

10.93 pH = 0.80

10.95 a. 48.0 mL of NaOH solution
   b. 74.7 mL of NaOH solution

10.97 0.234 M H_2SO_4

10.99 a. basic   **b.** basic   **c.** acidic   **d.** neutral

10.101 a. $H_2PO_4^-(aq) + H_3O^+(aq) \longrightarrow H_3PO_4(aq) + H_2O(l)$
   b. $H_3PO_4(aq) + OH^-(aq) \longrightarrow H_2PO_4^-(aq) + H_2O(l)$
   c. pH = 2.12   **d.** pH = 1.72

10.103

Acid	Conjugate base
H_2O	OH^-
HCN	CN^-
HNO_2	NO_2^-
H_3PO_4	$H_2PO_4^-$

10.105 a. 1. HS^- 2. $H_2PO_4^-$ 3. CO_3^{2-}
   b. 1. $\dfrac{[H_3O^+][HS^-]}{[H_2S]}$ 2. $\dfrac{[H_3O^+][H_2PO_4^-]}{[H_3PO_4]}$
   3. $\dfrac{[CO_3^{2-}][H_3O^+]}{[HCO_3^-]}$
   c. HCO_3^- **d.** H_3PO_4

10.107 a. $ZnCO_3(s) + H_2SO_4(aq) \longrightarrow$
              $ZnSO_4(aq) + CO_2(g) + H_2O(l)$
   b. $2Al(s) + 6HNO_3(aq) \longrightarrow 2Al(NO_3)_3(aq) + 3H_2(g)$
   c. $2H_3PO_4(aq) + 3Ca(OH)_2(aq) \longrightarrow$
              $Ca_3(PO_4)_2(s) + 6H_2O(l)$
   d. $KHCO_3(s) + HNO_3(aq) \longrightarrow$
              $KNO_3(aq) + CO_2(g) + H_2O(l)$

10.109 a. $[H_3O^+] = 2.0 \times 10^{-13}$ M
   b. pH = 12.70
   c. $3KOH(aq) + H_3PO_4(aq) \longrightarrow K_3PO_4(aq) + 3H_2O(l)$
   d. 56 mL of KOH solution

10.111 a. $[H_3O^+] = 6 \times 10^{-5}$ M; $[OH^-] = 2 \times 10^{-10}$ M
   b. $[H_3O^+] = 3 \times 10^{-7}$ M; $[OH^-] = 3 \times 10^{-8}$ M
   c. 3 g of $CaCO_3$

CI.17 Methane is a major component of purified natural gas used for heating and cooking. When 1 mole of methane gas burns with oxygen to produce carbon dioxide and water vapor, 883 kJ of heat is produced. Methane gas has a density of 0.715 g/L at STP. For transport, the volume of natural gas is decreased by cooling it to −163 °C, which gives liquefied natural gas (LNG) with a density of 0.45 g/mL. A tank on a ship can hold 7.0 million gallons of LNG.

a. Write the electron-dot formula and the molecular formula of methane if it consists of one carbon atom bonded to four hydrogen atoms.
b. What is the mass, in kilograms, of LNG (assume that LNG is all methane) transported in one tank on a ship?
c. What is the volume, in liters, of methane gas when the LNG in one tank is converted to gas at STP?
d. Write the balanced equation for the reaction of methane and oxygen in a gas burner.

e. How many kilograms of oxygen are needed to react with all of the methane provided by one tank of LNG?
f. How much heat, in kilojoules, is released from burning all of the methane in one tank of LNG?

CI.18 Automobile exhaust is a major cause of air pollution. The pollutants formed from gasoline include nitrogen oxide, which is produced at high temperatures in an automobile engine from nitrogen and oxygen gases in the air. Once emitted into the air, nitrogen oxide reacts with oxygen to produce nitrogen dioxide, a reddish-brown gas with a sharp, pungent odor that makes up smog. A component of gasoline is octane, C_8H_{18}, which has a

density of 0.803 g/cm^3. In 1 year, a typical automobile uses 550 gal of gasoline and produces 41 lb of nitrogen oxide.

a. Write balanced equations for the production of nitrogen oxide and nitrogen dioxide.
b. If all the nitrogen oxide emitted by one automobile is converted to nitrogen dioxide in the atmosphere, how many kilograms of nitrogen dioxide are produced in 1 year by a single automobile?
c. Write a balanced equation for the reaction of octane with oxygen gas to give carbon dioxide and water vapor.
d. How many moles of C_8H_{18} are present in 15.2 gal of octane?
e. How many liters of carbon dioxide (at STP) would this car produce in 1 year? (Assume complete reaction of octane.)

CI.19 A piece of magnesium with a mass of 0.121 g is added to 50.0 mL of 1.00 M HCl at a temperature of 22.0 °C. When the magnesium dissolves, the solution reaches a temperature of 33.0 °C:

$$Mg(s) + 2HCl(aq) \longrightarrow MgCl_2(aq) + H_2(g)$$

a. What is the limiting reactant?
b. What volume of hydrogen gas would be produced if the pressure is 750. mm Hg and the temperature 33 °C?

c. How many joules were released by the reaction of the magnesium? Assume the density of HCl solution is 1.00 g/mL and the specific heat of HCl solution is the same as for water.

d. What is the heat of reaction for Mg in J/g? In kJ/mole?

CI.20 In wine making, sugar ($C_6H_{12}O_6$) from grapes undergoes fermentation in the absence of oxygen to produce ethanol and carbon dioxide. A bottle of vintage port wine has a volume of 750 mL and contains 135 mL of ethanol (C_2H_6O). Ethanol has a density of 0.789 g/mL. In 1.5 lb of grapes, there are 26 g of grape sugar.

a. Calculate the percent concentration of ethanol by volume (v/v).

b. What is the molarity (M) of ethanol in the port wine?

c. Write the balanced equation for the fermentation reaction of grape sugar.

d. How many grams of sugar from grapes are required to produce one bottle of port wine?

e. How many bottles of port wine can be produced from 1.0 ton of grapes? (1 ton = 2000 lb)

CI.21 Consider the following reaction at equilibrium:

$$2H_2(g) + S_2(g) \rightleftharpoons 2H_2S(g) + \text{heat}$$

In a 10.0-L container, an equilibrium mixture contains 2.0 g of H_2, 10. g of S_2, and 68 g of H_2S.

a. What is the K_c value for this equilibrium mixture?

b. If H_2 is added to the mixture, how will the equilibrium shift?

c. How will the equilibrium shift if the mixture is placed in a 5.00-L container with no change in temperature?

d. If a 5.00-L container has an equilibrium mixture of 0.30 mole of H_2 and 2.5 moles of H_2S, what is the equilibrium concentration of S_2 if temperature is the same?

e. Will an increase in temperature increase or decrease the K_c value?

CI.22 A mixture of 25.0 g of CS_2 gas and 30.0 g of O_2 gas is placed in 10.0-L closed container and heated to 125 °C. The products of complete reaction are carbon dioxide gas and sulfur dioxide gas.

a. Write a balanced equation for the reaction.

b. How many grams of CO_2 are produced?

c. What is the partial pressure of the remaining reactant?

d. What is the final pressure in the container?

CI.23 A metal completely reacts with 34.8 mL of 0.520 M HCl.

a. Write a balanced equation for the reaction of the metal M and HCl(aq) to form $MCl_3(aq)$ and H_2 gas.

b. What volume, in milliliters, of H_2 at STP is produced?

c. How many moles of metal M reacted?

d. If the metal has a mass of 0.420 g, use your results from part **c** to determine the molar mass of the metal M.

e. What is the name and symbol of metal M in part **d**?

f. Write the balanced equation for the reaction using the symbol of the metal from part **e**.

CI.24 In a teaspoon (5.0 mL) of a common liquid antacid, there are 200. mg of $Ca(OH)_2$ and 200. mg of $Al(OH)_3$. A 0.080 M HCl solution, which is similar to stomach acid, is used to neutralize 5.0 mL of the liquid antacid.

a. Write the equation for the neutralization of HCl and $Ca(OH)_2$.
b. Write the equation for the neutralization of HCl and $Al(OH)_3$.
c. What is the pH of the HCl solution?

d. How many milliliters of the HCl solution is needed to neutralize the $Ca(OH)_2$?
e. How many milliliters of the HCl solution is needed to neutralize the $Al(OH)_3$?

■ ANSWERS

CI.17 **a.**
$$H-\overset{\displaystyle H}{\underset{\displaystyle H}{\overset{|}{\underset{|}{C}}}}-H \quad CH_4$$

b. 1.2×10^7 kg of LNG (methane)
c. 1.7×10^{10} L of methane at STP
d. $CH_4(g) + 2O_2(g) \longrightarrow CO_2(g) + 2H_2O(g)$
e. 4.8×10^7 kg of O_2
f. 6.6×10^{11} kJ

CI.19 **a.** Mg is the limiting reactant.
b. 0.127 L of H_2
c. 2.30×10^3 J
d. 1.90×10^4 J/g, 462 kJ/mole

CI.21 **a.** $K_c = 250$
b. If H_2 is added, the equilibrium will shift toward the products.
c. If the volume decreases, the equilibrium shifts toward the products.
d. $[S_2] = 0.28$ mole/L
e. An increase in temperature will decrease the value of K_c.

CI.23 **a.** $2M(s) + 6HCl(aq) \longrightarrow 2MCl_3(aq) + 3H_2(g)$
b. 203 mL of H_2
c. 6.03×10^{-3} mole of M
d. 69.7 g/mole
e. Gallium, Ga
f. $2Ga(s) + 6HCl(aq) \longrightarrow 2GaCl_3(aq) + 3H_2(g)$

CREDITS

p. ii — Foodcollection\Getty Images, Inc - Foodcollection Royalty Free

Prologue

p. 1 — San Francisco Museum of Art
p. 2 — *top:* Pearson Education/Pearson Science
p. 2 — *bottom:* Pearson Education/Pearson Science
p. 3 — *top:* Robert Mathena\Fundamental Photographs, NYC
p. 3 — *bottom:* Photodisc/Getty Images
p. 4 — Thomas Hollyman\Photo Researchers, Inc.
p. 5 — Bill Bachmann\Photo Researchers, Inc.
p. 6 — *left:* The Alchimist's Workshop, 1570, Jan van der Straet (Jannes Stradanus), Palazzo Vecchio, Florence, Italy/Bridgeman Art Library
p. 6 — *right:* Erich Lessing\Art Resource, N.Y.
p. 8 — [Photographer]/Stone/Getty Images
p. 12 — H. Armstrong Roberts\Corbis -

Chapter 1

p. 14 — Pearson Education/Pearson Science
p. 16 — *top:* Pearson Education/Pearson Science
p. 16 — *bottom:* Pearson Education/Pearson Science
p. 17 — *top:* Pearson Education/Pearson Science
p. 17 — *bottom:* Pearson Education/Pearson Science
p. 18 — *left:* Photolibrary.com
p. 18 — *right:* Anatomy/University "la Sapienza". Rome/Science Photo Library
p. 20 — Texas Instruments Incorporated
p. 24 — Pearson Education/Pearson Science
p. 29 — Shutterstock
p. 30 — *top:* Pearson Education/Pearson Science
p. 30 — *center:* istockphoto.com
p. 30 — *bottom:* Pearson Education/Pearson Science
p. 32 — Pearson Education/Pearson Science
p. 33 — *top:* Pearson Education/Pearson Science
p. 33 — *bottom:* Pearson Education/Pearson Science
p. 35 — *top:* Pearson Education/Pearson Science
p. 35 — *bottom:* Pearson Science
p. 36 — istockphoto.com
p. 39 — Getty Images/Digital Vision
p. 41 — Christopher Cormack\Corbis
p. 43 — Pearson Education/Pearson Science

p. 45 — *top, left:* Pearson Education/Pearson Science
p. 45 — *top, right:* Pearson Education/Pearson Science
p. 45 — *bottom:* istockphoto.com
p. 46 — *top, left:* Prof. P. La Motta, Dept. Anatomy, University La Sapienza, Rome\Photo Researchers, Inc.
p. 46 — *top, right:* Phanie\Photo Researchers, Inc.
p. 46 — *bottom:* Pearson Education/Pearson Science
p. 47 — Michael R. Wrigth
p. 48 — Joav Levy\Alamy Images

Chapter 2

p. 55 — Pearson Education/Pearson Science
p. 56 — istockphoto.com
p. 57 — *top:* istockphoto.com
p. 57 — *center:* Pearson Education/Pearson Science
p. 57 — *bottom:* Pearson Education/Pearson Science
p. 58 — Jack Star\Getty Images/Digital Vision
p. 65 — istockphoto.com
p. 71 — Getty Images - Photodisc
p. 72 — *top:* Pearson Education/Pearson Science
p. 72 — *bottom, left:* Richard Megna\Fundamental Photographs, NYC
p. 72 — *bottom, right:* Pearson Education/Pearson Science
p. 73 — *left, middle:* Pearson Education/Pearson Science
p. 73 — *right:* Pearson Education/Pearson Science
p. 73 — *left:* istockphoto.com
p. 73 — *right, middle:* Shutterstock
p. 73 — *bottom, left:* Dave King © Dorling Kindersley
p. 73 — *bottom, right:* David Murray and Jules Selmes © Dorling Kindersley
p. 74 — Pearson Education/Pearson Science
p. 75 — *top:* Siede Preis\Getty Images, Inc.- Photodisc.
p. 75 — *center, left:* Pearson Education/Pearson Science
p. 75 — *bottom, right:* Pearson Education/Pearson Science
p. 76 — *top, right:* Pearson Education/Pearson Science
p. 76 — *top, left:* Pearson Education/Pearson Science
p. 76 — *bottom:* Shutterstock
p. 77 — Pearson Education/Pearson Science
p. 79 — Pearson Education/Pearson Science
p. 81 — Pearson Education/Pearson Science
p. 82 — *right:* istockphoto.com
p. 82 — *middle:* Helene Canada\istockphoto.com

p. 82 — *left:* Pearson Education/Pearson Science
p. 83 — Comstock Complete
p. 89 — *top:* istockphoto.com
p. 89 — *bottom:* istockphoto.com
p. 90 — *top, left:* Pearson Education/Pearson Science
p. 90 — *top, middle:* Masterfile Royalty Free Division
p. 90 — *top, right:* Spencer Jones\Getty Images, Inc.- Photodisc.
p. 90 — *center:* Jonathan Wood\Getty Images - BC
p. 90 — *bottom:* Mark Dahners\AP Wide World Photos

Chapter 3

p. 93 — *top, left:* Photolibrary\Photolibrary.com - Royalty Free
p. 93 — *bottom, left:* Plush Studios\Getty Images/Royalty Free
p. 93 — *bottom, right:* Pearson Education/Pearson Science
p. 94 — *left:* Photolibrary\Photolibrary.com - Royalty Free
p. 94 — *right:* Masterfile Royalty Free Division;
p. 95 — Getty Images/Digital Vision
p. 97(A) — Pearson Education/Pearson Science
p. 97(B) — Pearson Education/Pearson Science
p. 97(C) — Pearson Education/Pearson Science
p. 97(D) — Pearson Education/Pearson Science
p. 97(E) — Pearson Education/Pearson Science
p. 98 — Mary Ann Sullivan
p. 101 — *left:* Pearson Education/Pearson Science
p. 101 — *middle:* Pearson Education/Pearson Science
p. 101 — *right:* Pearson Education/Pearson Science
p. 102 — Pearson Education/Pearson Science
p. 103 — Pearson Education/Pearson Science
p. 105 — Lawrence Berkeley National Laboratory
p. 106 — Pearson Education/Pearson Science
p. 108 — *left:* Pearson Education/Pearson Science
p. 108 — *right:* Pearson Education/Pearson Science
p. 109 — Pearson Education/Pearson Science
p. 111 — Pearson Education/Pearson Science
p. 114 — istockphoto.com
p. 115 — *top:* Pearson Education/Pearson Science
p. 115 — *bottom:* Pearson Education/Pearson Science
p. 116 — Shutterstock
p. 117 — David Young Wolff\PhotoEdit Inc.
p. 126 — Pearson Education/Pearson Science

Design features

Tree in a lightbulb, Courtesy of www.istockphoto.com; Collection of Gerberas, Courtesy of www.istockphoto.com; Golden caduceus, Tom Grill\Getty Images Inc. RF; Close-up of a personal data assistant, Photodisc/Getty Images; Internet concept, Courtesy of www.istockphoto.com

GLOSSARY/INDEX

METRIC AND SI UNITS AND SOME USEFUL CONVERSION FACTORS

Length   SI unit meter (m)

1 meter (m) = 100 centimeters (cm)
1 meter (m) = 1000 millimeters (mm)
1 cm = 10 mm
1 kilometer (km) = 0.6214 mile (mi)
1 inch (in.) = 2.54 cm (exact)

Volume   SI unit cubic meter (m^3)

1 liter (L) = 1000 milliliters (mL)
1 mL = 1 cm^3
1 L = 1.06 quart (qt)
1 qt = 946 mL

Mass   SI unit kilogram (kg)

1 kilogram (kg) = 1000 grams (g)
1 g = 1000 milligrams (mg)
1 kg = 2.20 lb
1 lb = 454 g
1 mole = 6.02×10^{23} particles
Water
density = 1.00 g/mL

Temperature   SI unit kelvin (K)

$°F = 1.8(°C) + 32$

$°C = \dfrac{(°F - 32)}{1.8}$

$K = °C + 273$

Pressure   SI unit pascal (Pa)

1 atm = 760 mmHg
1 atm = 760 torr
1 mole (STP) = 22.4 L
$R = 0.0821$ L·atm/mole·K
$R = 62.4$ L·mmHg/mole·K

Energy   SI unit joule (J)

1 calorie (cal) = 4.184 J
1 kcal = 1000 cal
Water
Heat of fusion = 80. cal/g; 334 J/g
Heat of vaporization = 540 cal/g; 2260 J/g
Specific heat = 4.184 J/g°C; 1 cal/g°C

PREFIXES FOR METRIC (SI) UNITS

Prefix	Symbol	Power of Ten
Values greater than 1		
peta	P	10^{15}
tera	T	10^{12}
giga	G	10^{9}
mega	M	10^{6}
kilo	k	10^{3}
Values less than 1		
deci	d	10^{-1}
centi	c	10^{-2}
milli	m	10^{-3}
micro	μ	10^{-6}
nano	n	10^{-9}
pico	p	10^{-12}
femto	f	10^{-15}

FORMULAS AND MOLAR MASSES OF SOME TYPICAL COMPOUNDS

Name	Formula	Molar Mass (g/mole)	Name	Formula	Molar Mass (g/mole)
Ammonia	NH_3	17.0	Hydrogen chloride	HCl	36.5
Ammonium chloride	NH_4Cl	53.5	Iron(III) oxide	Fe_2O_3	159.8
Ammonium sulfate	$(NH_4)_2SO_4$	132.1	Magnesium oxide	MgO	40.3
Bromine	Br_2	159.8	Methane	CH_4	16.0
Butane	C_4H_{10}	58.0	Nitrogen	N_2	28.0
Calcium carbonate	$CaCO_3$	100.1	Oxygen	O_2	32.0
Calcium chloride	$CaCl_2$	111.1	Potassium carbonate	K_2CO_3	138.2
Calcium oxide	CaO	56.1	Propane	C_3H_8	44.0
Carbon dioxide	CO_2	44.0	Sodium chloride	NaCl	58.5
Chlorine	Cl_2	71.0	Sodium hydroxide	NaOH	40.0
Copper(II) sulfide	CuS	95.7	Sulfur dioxide	SO_2	64.1
Hydrogen	H_2	2.0	Water	H_2O	18.0